First cost $= n \, W(.2) + C(n+1)$

$$= \left[\frac{1500}{L} \cdot (10L^2 + 1000L - 50,000)(.2)\right] + \left[\left(\frac{1500}{L}+1\right)\right.$$
$$\left. \times (80,000 + 80L)\right]$$

33

Managerial and Engineering Economy

THIRD EDITION

Managerial and Engineering Economy

ECONOMIC DECISION-MAKING

THIRD EDITION

George A. Taylor

Thayer School of Engineering
Dartmouth College

Brooks/Cole Engineering Division
A Division of Wadsworth, Inc.

Printed in the United States of America

10   9   8   7   6   5   4   3

Library of Congress Cataloging in Publication Data: Library of Congress Catalog Card Number: 79-66276

ISBN 0-534-24866-7

Preface

MANAGERIAL AND ENGINEERING ECONOMY is designed to provide a
sound introduction to economic decision-making, that is, selecting the best
alternative according to economic criteria. The book is intended for students of
engineering, business administration, economics, accounting, and finance. Considering the breadth of the subject, the text also provides fundamentals for
students majoring in the sciences, social sciences, or humanities and, as a study
and reference tool, for executives in all functional areas. The only prerequisites
are basic algebra and the ability to think quantitatively.

The author has consistently aimed to show how this discipline establishes a
guide for every course of action in an industrial enterprise. Economic decision-
making also provides the basis of communication—the common ground—between
all sectors of the organization: engineering, planning, marketing, finance, production, and administration.

Several significant improvements have been made in the Third Edition. This
edition uses the Standard Functional Symbols in all examples and problems.
This format, which originated with an *ad hoc* committee of the Engineering
Economy Division of the American Society for Engineering Education, was
adopted by the Society and appeared in the *Engineering Economist,* Volume 14,
Number 2. This publication gives two sets of standards: mnemonic and functional. Because the mnemonic set that was adopted was not truly mnemonic
and opened the way for error, it has since been discarded. Meanwhile, the existence of a clearly understandable set of functional factors led most writers and
ANSI, the American National Standards Institute, to adopt the functional set.
The Third Edition uses the Functional Symbols as a universal language. Although writers may use functional symbols, it is still a universal practice to
describe the factors in the derivations, in the tables, and in the text by the traditional names, as for example: "single-payment compound-amount factor." (See
Section 3.12.)

Another improvement in the Third Edition concerns particularly instructors
teaching a basic, one-term course in Engineering Economy. The limited time
available for study, assignments, and class recitations requires the instructor to

decide what material to include in the course and what must be omitted from the text.

In this edition we continue to give a complete coverage of the subject, but here for the first time we indicate to instructors and other users how they can recognize the basic from the extended materials. Certain sections are marked with an asterisk to indicate "supplemental study." All of these supplemental sections occur in the body of the text because that is where they belong. The supplemental material is logically derived from the reasoning in the basic material. It is developed by an intellectual extension of the basic reasoning and does not break the continuity of the student's thinking. Instructors pressed for time in a one-term course can therefore omit the sections marked with an asterisk without loss of continuity, decrease in quality, or sacrifice in the competence they expect in the course. These sections are identified in the "Contents" for the convenient reference of instructors.

Even with the omission of these supplemental sections, instructors may find that they still have more material than they can cover. If time is severely limited, instructors may benefit from a list of the chapters that should be covered:

Chapters 1-8 inclusive, but entirely omitting Continuous Interest Sections 3.18-3.24 and Dual Rates Sections 8.14-8.20.

Chapter 11 except for Obsolescence Factors Sections 11.13-11.15.

Students who pass the course with a knowledge of these fundamentals can associate with either engineer or manager in this kind of decision-making. If more time is available, after having covered the foregoing basics, instructors may elect any of the other areas—with the possible omission of supplementary sections. They may want to cover part of Chapter 15 Taxes or Chapter 18 Public Economic or Chapter 10 Economic Life. Finally, there is an expanded discussion of the effects of inflation on economic decisions in Section 16.13.

A Solutions Manual for Instructors with solutions to the problems in the text and suggestions on how to use these problems to stimulate class discussions is available.

My sincere thanks go to the students and members of the executives programs who studied with me during the many years of developing this book and who gave constructive ideas and encouragment.

George A. Taylor

Contents

10 Economic Life   183

11 Replacement Economy   213

12 Economy of Variations in Operating Activities   242

13 Minimum Cost Points   271

Managerial and Engineering Economy

THIRD EDITION

1

Alternatives

1.1 DECISION-MAKING DEFINED

Economic Decision-Making expresses the primary objective of this book, and the expectation that the subject will be a dynamic and valuable tool to the person who learns to use it. We can demonstrate this immediately by noting the following definition of decision-making.

Competent decision-making is a two-part activity:

1. The generation of all the alternative courses of action that the situation demands.
2. The selection of the best course of action from these alternatives.

This definition disagrees with those definitions which merely limit decision-making to choosing between alternatives X and Y. The reason for our two-part definition is that no manager, given the authority of choosing a course of action, can defend a bad decision by pointing out that he made a mathematically correct choice between two very poor alternatives. It is the decision-maker's job to conceive, create, discover, and develop all possible courses of action that the given situation demands. A decision to approve expenditures for products X or Y always must imply that products Z, X_1, or Y_1 should not be approved. If X is selected, enormous—perhaps fatal—losses can result if Z subsequently proves to be the product that should have been selected.

The manager is called on to provide the "best" solution to a given problem, and thus he must innovate, simply because existing alternatives may be greatly inferior to those which he can create. This, of course, is a large responsibility, and unfortunately one for which few managers have been educated. But whether a manager knows how to innovate or not, he will be responsible as long as he is the designated decision-maker.

If the first phase of decision-making is innovation, then the second is economic discrimination, or (as it is called in this text) economic decision-making. The principles and techniques of this discipline are the subject of this book. Many decision-makers function without a knowledge of economic decision-making, and this lack invites unbelievable losses—as the reader will observe in the many examples in the text.

It may seem that limiting our subject to economic decision-making eliminates consideration of innovation. While innovation constitutes a different subject and a separate mode of thinking, an understanding of the economic criteria can develop an awareness of other courses of action that might exist or can be devised. This awareness often can put the decision-maker on the track of new alternatives of significant economic potential, and it will certainly make him cautious of merely choosing between two alternatives without considering that other, better choices might exist.

Knowing the criteria by which these alternatives will be selected or rejected is in itself an opeıational guide to identifying or discovering other courses of action. For example, if product Y is more trouble-free than X (a desirable feature, say, because competent repair service is unavailable) might we develop product Z which is even more reliable, or Y_1 which provides almost the same features as Y or Z at a lower price? This thinking will be guided by economic awareness. Practiced in this manner, the subject becomes a dynamic management tool.

This suggests that we might examine in more depth the responsibilities and great opportunities which exist in the decision-maker's role.

1.2 THE TWO ROLES OF THE EXECUTIVE

Every executive has basically two roles, and many executives perform only one of these.

His first role is to "maintain standards," that is, to see that activities are performed as planned, that costs do not exceed the preset standard cost, that labor performs the job by the preset standard method, that the required labor and material are on hand, that shipments occur on schedule in the right quantity, that planned quality of the product does not deteriorate, and so on. Maintaining present standards is a major task performed by many executives not only with "sleeves rolled up" but often after regular business hours. It is commonly understood that if something can go wrong it will, and so the executive seems continually to be repairing the breaches which develop in business operations. Even with strict adherence to the exception principle, the exceptions are enough to keep an executive busy. The executive's function in this role is like that of a servomechanism, because every dynamic system needs continuous readjustment to make it follow the standard. No one denies that this function demands great effort.

The second role of the executive is to improve the existing standards so that the company can maintain or improve its profits. In this role the executive must generate alternatives. Ideally, he challenges every standard and method in his sphere of responsibility, searches for alternative ones, and adopts them according to economic criteria. This role is vital because any company that is content only to maintain its existing standards will find itself failing because of competitive pressure. The company that successfully keeps its status quo, while other companies improve their methods and increase their profits, will eventually discover it cannot meet the prices established by its progressive competitors. Many executives, nevertheless, are unprepared to fill this challenging role, and too often their education in economic decision-making is badly neglected or totally lacking. George Terborgh[1] says, "When we consider the advanced techniques now employed in other areas of business management, we may well wonder if equipment policy is not, in general, the most backward sector of all. We are inclined to think it is." We suggest that this statement can be broadened to include the whole area of economic decision-making.

Regardless of how hard an executive works in his role of "maintaining standards," his company can fail and he can fail personally as a manager. Let us not overlook the fact that some executives have worked very diligently, faithfully, and successfully to maintain standards. Some executives indeed have been so preoccupied in this task that there has been no change in standards in their business in many years. (The most successful ones, in this respect, may be out of business.)

What we have said, therefore, is that every manager has two fundamental roles:

1. Maintain the existing standards
2. Create improved standards.

Reflection on the two roles of the manager will lead to the conclusion that everyone, whatever his level or area of authority, ought to function as a decision-maker. To perform these roles he must realize that for every existing course of action under his control there is an alternative course of action which can be economically superior and that it is his responsibility as the manager to search for and discover that alternative. He cannot claim a lack of education in the processes of decision-making as an excuse for his inability to accept and adequately perform that responsibility. On the other hand, the opportunities to perform as this kind of a decision-maker are unlimited and the rewards for competent performance are high.

1.3 THE MANAGER'S ROLE IN THE FUNCTIONAL AREAS OF THE COMPANY

Modern management principles make the operating managers and administrators responsible for identifying the areas that should be improved and for seeing that the improvement is made. This replaces the concept that the only function of the operating manager is to control his area (and very likely to resist changes, since changes disturb his control).

Modern management makes the staff departments responsible to the operating

[1]George Terborgh, *Dynamic Equipment Policy* (New York: McGraw-Hill, 1949), p. 216.

departments in creating improvements, and this reduces the resistance that the staff sometimes encounters from the operating departments.

The financial department—the focal point of the decision-making process—reviews projects submitted for the board of director's approval. Consequently, managers are often required to evaluate *all* proposals by the same competent techniques. Such standards should apply whether a lesser manager is judging a proposal or is passing it on for upper management or board approval.

The result in all cases is a demand for better knowledge of the decision-making process and the economic justification techniques presented in this text. This especially increases the need to know by the operating managers and the need to know *more* and to demonstrate competence by both staff and financial managers.

1.4 THE SEARCH FOR ALTERNATIVES

The executive's second role originates in his first role. Take the example of a foreman setting up a machine for a production run according to a standard previously established for the purpose. Whether or not the foreman has any difficulty maintaining this standard (and he may—with defective parts, missing fixtures, etc.), the standard itself can become the basis of a search for an economically better way of setting up a machine for production. By questioning the various facets of the present method, the responsible executive can generate alternatives. Such questions might be: Who should set up the machine—the foreman, the production worker, a special set-up man? How should the machine be set up? Can special tools be designed to do the job more efficiently? Can the method be automatized? What machine should be set up? Has the correct machine been selected? Can the present machine be improved? What piece should be produced? Is this the best design of the piece? Then, with full awareness of the economic criteria, the executive can determine which alternatives will result in lower costs, including considerations of waste, unreliability and poor quality.

Let us examine another situation. An executive has to authorize payment of next Friday's payroll of $50,000. Presumably he is satisfied that this sum has been computed in accordance with the standards for determining the compensation for work done. This acceptance of the present payroll involves a degree of decision-making. Greater decisions, however, are demanded in connection with his second role—creating better standards according to economic criteria. The fact is that this Friday's payroll is the result of economic decision-making which occurred years ago. Except for those decisions the payroll might be $45,000 today or even $65,000. By generating better methods of production today, the payroll on some future Friday can be less.

Out of every act performed in accordance with existing standards, the executive, if he is trained to think this way, can generate economic alternatives. This decision-making invades every executive area from sales to production and from finance to engineering.

An interesting exercise will result from selecting any business activity and applying this kind of economic decision-making. Consider the example of a company receiving a potential customer's request for a sales brochure. The standard practice is to mail him as promptly as possible a bulletin on the standard line of the product. There are many alternatives to this course of action, one of which might be sufficiently better, depending on criteria, to become a new standard. Another alternative is to send the sales manager with a salesman on the strength that this is a "hot lead." Another alternative is to phone the customer to find whether the lead seems genuine, whether the customer will be in, or whether the information requested is understood. A third alternative is to redesign the brochure to attract more sales; a fourth is to change the product to better meet the customer's needs, and so on.

In discussing the role of generating economic alternatives, we must not overlook the fact that many companies have appointed executives of their organization to supervise or actually perform the staff work of planning, designing, and engineering. The major function of these executives is to create change, but mere change alone is not economic decision-making.

Take the example of an engineer designing a forming machine to be used in manufacturing a new piece in the factory. This tool can be designed from drawings that have been in use for years merely by changing them to meet the size and shape of the new piece to be worked. This would be equivalent to maintaining the status quo or maintaining the standards of design. On the other hand, to fit the role we are discussing, the engineer should examine all the alternative designs for the machine as well as its component parts, and he should evaluate all these alternatives and select the most economic.

In another example, the executive responsible for planning a proposed business expansion should not plan merely to extend present production practices in his company but should examine all the possible alternative methods of production. Furthermore, he should consider alternative plant locations, variations in the design of the product, alternative methods of handling, storing, inspecting, packaging, and so on.

No engineering or design function is exempt from his mode of thinking. Consider the case of the civil engineer designing a bridge for a river crossing. Many economic alternatives are possible, not only concerning the exact place of crossing, but also the path of crossing (if it is a long bridge), the economic number of piers and abutments, alternative designs of piers and footings, alternative designs of superstructure. Almost every known design of bridge—truss, cantilever, arch, suspension, and girder—is combined in the Chesapeake Bay Bridge, as can be seen in Fig. 1.4. This bridge shows that the shortest distance between two points may not be the cheapest and illustrates the diverse designs of piers and superstructures in a single crossing. We expect that the particular path and the alternative designs were selected to meet economic criteria and not, as one student quipped, "because they had a lot of turnover of personnel in the design department."

Figure 1.4   The Chesapeake Bay Bridge incorporates many designs of footings and spans: a problem in economic decision-making

1.5 ECONOMIC DECISION-MAKING

Every dollar we spend, propose to spend or do not propose to spend becomes the basis for economic decision-making. If an executive decides to do nothing about his $50,000 payroll, he is nevertheless making an economic decision. A decision to do nothing is a decision to continue his present practice and to reject all alternatives, those he is aware of and those that he is not aware of because he has not searched for them.

Most executives would agree that the decision to approve $40,000 for the purchase of a new machine is a typical example of an economic decision. But it cannot be called a competent economic decision unless (1) all the alternatives have been examined, (2) all the cost and income elements have been included, and (3) the principles and techniques for evaluation are correct. The correct economic decision might be to reject spending $40,000 for a new machine and keep the old one, or to spend $25,000 for a different machine, or to spend $75,000 for a still different machine, or to spend $15,000 to improve the present one, and so on.

Every decision of an executive, then, involves economic decision-making.

Some years ago an executive attempted to prove to one of our students that no economic decision-making could pertain to the situation he was confronted with. At that time over twenty of our graduate students were conducting surveys of economic decision processes used in industry. To do this, each visited a business, collected the data used in the decision, and recorded the method of evaluation and the conclusion. As a courtesy for the information received, the students offered to present written commentaries using modern principles and the latest techniques. In one instance a student, after receiving the usual cordial reception and expression of great interest in the principles and techniques which he planned to apply to the data, was challenged by this divulgence as he was leaving: "Young man, I forgot to tell you that this new machine which I am going to buy will replace a machine which is 40 years old and beyond repair. If I don't replace this machine, my production will stop and I'll be out of business. Now please make your computation and tell me whether or not I should make the purchase."

This attitude demonstrates an almost complete disregard of the concept of economic decision-making. In the first place we note that this executive's decision began many years ago. Investigation revealed that he should have replaced the machine at least 25 years earlier and, by not doing so, rejected the savings that replacement would have brought. Furthermore, every year since then he has been making a wrong decision by not replacing it; for 25 years he has been rejecting the savings available to him. The present value of the savings, repeatedly rejected over this long period, was quite large. But that is not the full significance of the story, because even his present decision could be wrong if he did not consider all the alternatives presently available to him. Did he select the best machine to be used in the best process to make the right piece by the right person in the right place at the right time?

As we have noted, economic decision-making, in a complete sense, includes both generating and evaluating alternatives. Since the choice of some alternative is always the object of the decision, economic decision-making can proceed only if alternatives have been established. Without a knowledge of alternatives we are just continuing the status quo, maintaining the standards, and carrying out the decisions made in the past.

1.6 THE COST COMMITMENT OF A DECISION

Too many executives do not feel a true responsibility for the costs they create or the costs they protect by maintaining the status quo. It would seem that the representative executive, including the planning executive and engineer, assumes that spending money is the inevitable consequence of his job, the obvious privilege of his executive function. If he is a designer, may he take it for granted that he has the privilege of creating any cost that may result from his design? When an executive becomes accustomed to this attitude he feels that these costs are "the company's responsibility." If he reflects on this, however, he will

realize that these costs, in his sphere of management, are *his* responsibility, because he, not the company, selected the proposed design from all the possible
alternative designs.

The privilege or obligation of an executive to suggest alternatives is not performed without the responsibility to prove that his suggestion is less costly—or,
to state it more accurately, more profitable—than any other alternative. He
must face up to the costs resulting from his suggestion and he must realize that
his suggestion, if adopted, will commit his company to costs that they do not
now have. In the end, of course, he must show that it is better to incur these
costs than any other costs resulting from all alternative proposals, but in the beginning he must have an awareness of all the costs which will result from
his decision.

If an executive disregards the economic aspects of a decision, he is disregarding
the cost commitments that will result from his decision. Even the "cost-
conscious" executive who ignores economic decision-making can be unaware of
the full cost commitment of his decisions because he is too inclined to be
conscious of only the *present* costs. In many instances the future commitments
from a present decision far outweigh the present cost. For example, the recommendation to purchase a $10,000 machine tool is a commitment to pay all its
future costs, and this commitment may be far-reaching. The future costs will
include the power to run the machine, the labor to operate it, the setup and
put-away costs, the cost of material spoilage and labor wastage, extra supervision, the cost of lot sizes if any, maintenance and repair, inspection, insurance,
and taxes. Any special incomes such as salvage values should be included, and
the entire analysis should be made over the lifetime of the intended service. The
decision to buy the tool is a decision to pay all these operating disbursements.
Suppose these are estimated to be $8,000 a year for a predicted tool life of
8 years at the end of which the tool could be salvaged for $2,000. Then the
stream of costs could be displayed as follows:

```
                                        Salvage income = 2,000
10,000   8,000   8,000   8,000   8,000   8,000   8,000   8,000   8,000
  ├───────┼───────┼───────┼───────┼───────┼───────┼───────┼───────┤
  0       1       2       3       4       5       6       7       8
```

The out-of-pocket commitment is $10,000 + 8(8000) - 2000 = $72,000$, or about
7 times the first cost. This total commitment is the cost responsibility of the
engineer who designs or suggests it, the operating executive who recommends it,
the financial executive who passes it, and the top management and directors
who finally approve it.

The total commitment must be judged and approved by economic criteria
which we will develop and present in this book. At this point a preliminary test
of the proposed purchase of this machine tool is to compare its out-of-pocket
commitment of $72,000 with the commitment of each alternative way of doing
the same machining operation, such as use of more automatic or less automatic
tools, higher- or lower-speed tools, second-hand tools, and the incumbent tool—if

one exists.   If the total commitment of one of the alternatives is found to be $65,000, then it would appear from our preliminary test that we should not approve a machine having a total cost of $72,000.[1]

1.7 ENGINEERING EFFICIENCY VERSUS FINANCIAL EFFICIENCY

In 1923 O. B. Goldman[2] protested that the literature too often failed to prepare the engineer for economic decision-making. He said, "It seems peculiar and is indeed very unfortunate that so many authors in their engineering books give no, or very little, consideration to costs, in spite of the fact that the primary duty of the engineer is to consider costs in order to obtain real economy—to get the most power, for example, not from the least number of pounds of steam, but from the least possible number of dollars and cents: to get the best financial efficiency."

The goal of equipment selection, and for that matter the goal of all engineering and all managerial activity, is acceptable financial efficiency, not engineering efficiency. Example 1.7 illustrates this point.

EXAMPLE 1.7   A machine tool can be obtained for $10,000. Its annual operating disbursements for labor, fuel, maintenance, and so on, will be $8,000 over its predicted 8-year life period at the end of which its salvage value will be $2,000. An alternative tool can be obtained for the same job for $20,000. Its operating disbursements will be $6,000 a year over an 8-year economic life with $3,000 salvage value at that time.   Examine the out-of-pocket commitments for each.

A Salvage income = 2,000
  10,000   8,000   8,000   8,000   8,000   8,000   8,000   8,000   8,000
    0   1   2   3   4   5   6   7   8

B Salvage income = 3,000
  20,000   6,000   6,000   6,000   6,000   6,000   6,000   6,000   6,000
    0   1   2   3   4   5   6   7   8

SOLUTION.   The total out-of-pocket commitment for A is $72,000. The total out-of-pocket commitment for B is $65,000.

We note that B has the higher engineering efficiency, because although the machines have equal output, B's input, measured by its operating disbursements, is $6,000 a year compared to $8,000 for A. We expect this, because paying $10,000 more on the first cost for B should be a measure of the extra efficiencies built into the machine.

The financial efficiency is an entirely different measure than engineering efficiency. B will perform the same job as A, but with a smaller total number of

---

[1] As we will show in the next chapter, the mere summing of dollars is an insufficient comparison of alternatives—something additional must be performed.

[2] Otto B. Goldman, *Financial Engineering*, 2nd ed. (New York: Wiley, 1923), p. 84.

dollars. According to Goldman's statement, B has the higher financial efficiency. In this case B has higher engineering efficiency as well as higher financial efficiency. This is a mere coincidence.

1.8 SEARCHING FOR LOW ENGINEERING EFFICIENCY

If the choice between alternatives is based on financial efficiency alone, the search for alternatives must be conducted without regard to engineering efficiency. This means that the search for high financial efficiency is not necessarily a search for higher engineering efficiency. If that were so, the choice would be made solely on engineering efficiency. Therefore it may be helpful to point out that a vigorous search for low engineering efficiency can, in many cases, disclose the best economic decision, as the following example will attempt to show.

EXAMPLE 1.8   The machines in the previous example are being proposed for use in a plant where they are required to do much less work. With reduced utilization it is expected that the operating disbursements for labor, power, maintenance, and so on, for machine A will be only $2,000 a year and for machine B only $1,500, as displayed on the following time scales. Compare the engineering and financial efficiencies of the two machines.

A

10,000	2,000	2,000	2,000	2,000	2,000	2,000	2,000	2,000
0	1	2	3	4	5	6	7	8

Salvage income = 2,000

B

20,000	1,500	1,500	1,500	1,500	1,500	1,500	1,500	1,500
0	1	2	3	4	5	6	7	8

Salvage income = 3,000

SOLUTION.   The out-of-pocket cost commitment of A is $24,000. The out-of-pocket cost commitment of B is $29,000.

We see that machine B with the higher engineering efficiency has the lower financial efficiency.

This example illustrates a number of points. First, it proves that there is no shortcut formula for economic decision-making: the executive must have competence to work out each case on its own merits. The choice[1] of machine was switched from B in Example 1.6 to A in Example 1.7, from the machine with the higher engineering efficiency to the one with the lower engineering efficiency. The choice was affected by a change in the utilization of the equipment. It will also be affected by changes in the hourly labor rate, unit cost of energy, the value of floor space, the cost of reliability, or any other cost ingredient. The combined effect of these cost elements must be evaluated by the executive for each new situation based on a knowledge of the principles and techniques which we will attempt to present in the following chapters.

---

[1] As stated in Section 1.6, merely adding costs is insufficient. Observing which machine has the *higher* financial efficiency is also insufficient—it must be higher by a satisfactory margin, as we will show later.

The example also illustrates that the machine selected for one situation may be rejected in another. As we noted, the search for alternatives with low engineering efficiency is as necessary as the search for those with high engineering efficiency. A conclusion justified in one situation can be reversed by changes in utilization or unit costs. We conclude, therefore, that the alternatives can be legion, an observation which provides exciting opportunities for research, invention, and creative design.

The example also suggests that economic criteria provide the guide to all management action and to all management functions including engineering, planning, and designing. Because executives in these areas often propose most of the plans for spending money, they should recognize that economic decision-making provides the compass by which every engineer and every manager should steer his course. By it he will be able to guide and direct all his engineering and managerial activities.

The statement that the primary objective of engineering is to achieve satisfactory financial efficiency is not inconsistent with the other objectives of engineering—namely, accuracy, reliability, and safety. The engineer is still expected to design machines that will run and buildings that will not collapse and to employ all the previous competence of his art and his science. But as we will show later, even the questions of accuracy, reliability, and safety are decided by economic considerations. In many if not most instances, it is not economically feasible to design for absolute accuracy, one hundred percent reliability, or perfect safety. Economic criteria provide the engineer with a goal for his activities beyond satisfying the requirements of pounds and feet.

As expected, the objective of engineering is consistent with the objective of the business enterprise: the maximization of profit. Whether the alternative is an engineering alternative or an alternative in marketing, finance, office procedure, human relations, inventory, or production, the test of the decision is by the same criteria. These criteria give the men who propose suggestions and those who approve them a common test and a mutual aim. It provides the men of finance and those in engineering and production with a common language, possibly for the first time.

The costs generated by economic decisions can be divided into two general classes: (1) cost-reduction expenditures and (2) income-expansion expenditures.

1.9 COST-REDUCTION EXPENDITURES

Most suggestions relate to expenditures intended to reduce future costs, but relatively few pertain to expansion of the gross income. In a few instances, the expenditures may effect both an increase in income and a reduction of cost; for example, a suggestion can decrease the cost of production but also increase quality so that the product commands a higher price.

A characteristic of a cost-reduction expenditure is that the decision does not affect the gross income. Assume that a manufacturer of electric motors produces the shafts for these motors on semiautomatic lathes, but a cost-reduction proposal shows that it will be more economical to make the shafts on fully automatic lathes. Obviously the shaft itself is the same in both cases, and the decision will not affect the sales or the gross income. (A different situation results if a cost reduction is so great that it permits a price reduction. This could occur if the motor is completely redesigned to allow lower-cost production processes. The income will be expanded because presumably more sales will occur at the lower price level. This is an example of the combined cost-reduction income-expansion expenditures just mentioned.) To repeat, in the case of a cost-reduction expenditure the gross income is irrelevant. Frequently we do not know what it is, nor do we need to know. Example 1.7 illustrated this. Of course, we note that, although the gross income is unchanged, the reduced cost will increase the *net* profits which, after all, is the goal of the decision.

1.10 INCOME-EXPANSION EXPENDITURES

Where an expenditure increases the gross income, the decision is also governed by the increase in net profits.

In the first test of a proposed income-expansion expenditure, the total income must exceed the total cost commitment. In the second test, the resulting net profit must be *sufficiently* attractive for every dollar expended, to justify spending that dollar. For example, no one will approve an expenditure if the resulting gross income will just recover the total costs. In fact no one will approve an expenditure if the gross income will only slightly exceed the costs.[1] Then by how much must it exceed costs?

We can make a similar observation for cost-reduction expenditures: a mere difference in the total-cost commitments of the alternatives is not sufficient to justify a choice. In Example 1.7 the commitment for A was $72,000 and for B $65,000, an increase in net profits of $7,000. Inasmuch as just any increase is not enough, the question is how much must the net profits be increased to justify a choice? The answers to these questions is the purpose of this text and will be pursued in the next chapter.

1.11 THE SCOPE OF A DECISION: HUMAN ELEMENTS OF PROFITS

Every numerical profitability statement implies that the human relations affected by the proposal have been disregarded. Certainly some human consequences cannot be quantified, and thus cannot appear in the numerical evaluation, but even in such cases all of the irreducible and nonquantifiable effects of a proposal should be listed.

The first principle is that all factors that affect a decision must be identified and accounted for. In addition to economic and physical effects, there may be spiritual, moral, or humane considerations. Although these may be difficult to perceive because they are neither tangible nor quantifiable, whenever they may be discovered they will be credited to or charged against the innovator of the project and the persons who approved it.

[1] Disregarding favorable considerations that are intangible and therefore unquantifiable.

Human considerations, so easy to overlook, can prove to be most detrimental (or beneficial!) to the success of a proposal, even though the sponsors may think them insignificant. The human elements may prove to be the main reasons why the idea won't work, why the workers or the public refuse to accept it, why the machine doesn't deliver the expected output, and why the best technical design breeds trouble. The human elements can easily nullify the prospective high rate of return computed without them—whether the human elements were omitted by error or because the analyst found no way to quantify them.

As an example of the nullifying effect of neglecting consideration of the human element of a proposal consider that the predicted advantages of installing belt-line production can be unattainable if the workers show a strong enough aversion to the subdivision of tasks inherent in that method of production.[1] On the other hand, enlarging each worker's responsibility and setting up individual work benches may increase job satisfaction and the worker's performance.

The human considerations resulting from a proposal include effects on health from air and noise pollution; on enjoyment and recreation from waste pollution and ecological destruction; on safety from hazardous conditions; on job satisfaction from boredom; on self-respect, personal degradation, or loss of status from poor job design and company policy. The company pays in many ways for employee dissatisfaction which may cause low productivity, slowdowns, complaints, strikes, high employee turnover, poor company image, difficulty in hiring qualified employees, customer rejection, and so on.

1.12 CRITERIA FOR ADOPTION

The criteria for adoption of a proposal must anticipate all the variables that can be affected by the proposal. We have placed these criteria under the following headings:
1. Feasible
2. Easier to perform
3. Humane
4. Legal and Ethical
5. Profitable

While our procedures in this text will be quantitative, we must recognize the importance of all the factors which we cannot quantify. The first four criteria listed ahead are difficult—perhaps impossible—to evaluate numerically, yet the numbers are likely to be very large, whatever they may be. For example, the legal and ethical criteria warn us that no new product, regardless of the prospective high rate of return from its sale, can be justified if it can be sold only by deceiving the customer. Or another way of viewing it is that the rate of return so computed errs because of the vast effects of legal and ethical aberrations including: law suits, declining sales as the market awakes, the possibility of zero sales because of government action, declining sales of other products due to the

---

[1] See "Boredom Spells Trouble on the Assembly Line," *Life Magazine*, 1 September 1972, p. 30.

company's unattractive image, the effect of that image on the entire operation (such as, perhaps, its inability to attract desirable employees).

The feasibility criterion means: Will it work? As in the previous example predictions of costs or incomes are incorrect to the degree that the scheme won't work. The penalty for its violation may be the cost of recall, rework, damage suits, right up to the total loss from a product that won't work at all under field conditions. Feasibility may be affected by physical factors, as in the case of a machine or a production process, or by human factors in which the people cannot or will not perform the proposed operation as designed.

The criterion that the innovation be easier to perform will not be discussed here, but it relates to resistance of the users, whether the company's own employees or its customers, to accept and perform an operation that is harder than the one it replaces. Progress is generally identified with the reduction of physical effort, and buyers and users demand this in new products and processes except in unique circumstances.

In the Section 1.11 we discussed the human factors that must be satisfied in any proposal. In this section we have divided the human factors into various subsets. For example, a proposal may not be feasible because it violates certain rules of human acceptability, or a proposal may not be acceptable because it requires the users to work harder, not easier, or a proposal may be unacceptable because it violates legal or ethical restraints. But we also list here another human factor: The proposal must be humane. Again this is not entirely separate from the previous factors but it addresses itself to proposals which may result in degradation of the worker, discrimination against the worker, loss of employment, loss of status, and loss of job satisfaction due to boredom or enslaving operations. More and more a company discovers that its operations may not disregard societal responsibilities, whether humanitarian or environmental, ecological, ethical, legal.

As noted the criteria are not mutually exclusive. A proposal may prove unfeasible if it violates any of the stated human factors. And profitability cannot exist in violation of these factors either. Obviously there can be no profit if the product won't work, or buyers reject it, or the law prevents its sale regardless of the outstanding ability of the analyst to make numerical calculations.

PROBLEMS

1.1 Give some alternatives to fastening 2 pieces of metal with 6 bolts[a]; typing 6 letters to notify 6 department heads of a meeting; transporting small castings to the sandblast room on a hand-drawn dolly; heat-treating steel shafts in a gas-fired furnace; shipping electric motors by rail from the factory in Pennsylvania to the manufacturer's warehouse in San Francisco; selling insurance by visits from salesmen. [a]*Ans.:* Fasten with metal screws instead of bolts, make it one piece not two, use any other number of bolts, weld the pieces, use material other than metal, and so on.

1.2 Give the cost commitment of (a) a new car; (b) a general-purpose lathe in a

metalworking shop; (c) a new highway; (d) a lighting system in a manufacturing plant; (e) a pair of skis.

1.3 (a) Compare the cost pattern of a machine with low engineering efficiency
with one having a high engineering efficiency. Illustrate, giving comparative
first costs, operating disbursements, and salvage values over the economic
lives of the machines. (b) How does the proposed utilization of the
machines affect the choice between them? (c) Show how the less efficient
machine can be the better choice.

1.4 Show why the following alternatives can compete economically on a given
project. For example, a special turret lathe may be justified as an alternative
to a general-purpose lathe because, in spite of its higher first cost, it has a
lower future cost for operating labor.

Conveyors vs lift trucks in a foundry

Concrete warehouse vs all-metal warehouse

Machine tools direct-coupled to motors vs belted[b]

Fluorescent vs incandescent lighting

Gasoline engine vs diesel operating a lighting generator

Wood water pipe vs steel in a gravity aqueduct.

[b]Ans.: Direct-coupled motors have higher first cost because they are
slower speed, but they produce annual savings by eliminating the transmission losses of belting.

1.5 Repeat Problem 1.4 for the following alternatives: an automated or straight-
line vs a job-lot factory for producing the same quantity of a given product;
18-inch vs 21-inch pipeline for transmitting a given daily quantity of natural
gas; operating a given metal-cutting tool at high speed vs medium speed; a
20-story vs a 30-story office building on a given plot of land; rebuilding an
old machine vs buying a new one.

1.6 What is a distinguishing characteristic of a cost-reduction expenditure?
What is the final test of a cost-reduction expenditure?

1.7 A farmer can improve his crop yield by increasing the fertilization and
tillage of each acre. He presently spends $100 to cultivate each acre and
receives $150 gross income per acre. However, if he spends $120, he will
receive $180, and so on, as listed below. Which method should he adopt
for his 10-acre farm? Why?

Method	Cost	Income
a	$1,000	$1,500
b	1,200	1,800
c	1,400	2,000
d	1,600	2,150

1.8 Use the previous example to establish and illustrate the essential criteria for
deciding *between* alternative income-expansion investments.

1.9 A recommendation has been sent to you for the purchase of a certain piece
of equipment. It does not mention any of the following: (a) the method, if
any, being used to perform the job at present; (b) what alternatives were
considered, if any. If these considerations are important, show why.

2

Requiring a Rate of Return

2.1 THE PROFIT MOTIVE

In Chapter 1 we observed that income-expansion expenditures were approved only if the investor expected to receive something more than he expended. The motivation for such decisions is the expectation of profits. It follows that each *expenditure* that holds forth prospects of *profits* can be classified as an investment because spending money with the expectation of profits is the definition of an investment. We will see as we progress that the *investment principle* and the profit motive govern all spending decisions, both income-expansion and cost-reduction.

The profit motive can be explained as the inducement that causes man to forego satisfying his present desires based on the prospects of satisfying greater ones in the future. This motivation governs our personal investments. Where investments are governed by professional managers, as in industrial corporations, managers are being paid to satisfy the profit motive of the company's shareholders.

Profit may also be explained as the result of the productivity of capital. Money procures the methods, machines, men, and materials that can be coordinated to increase gross income or reduce costs. The resulting profit, caused by an expenditure of money, must be attributed to the productivity of capital.

2.2 COST OF CAPITAL

The user of capital must satisfy the profit motive of the supplier of capital. This obligation of the user must be reckoned as his cost for using capital. It is his capital use-rate, his cost of capital.

The use of capital is not gratuitous, any more than the use of land, machine tools, or houses is gratuitous. Every dollar of capital must satisfy the profit expected by the owner of the capital. The obligation to pay for the use of the

16

owner's funds may be a legal obligation, such as the contractual obligation to pay interest on borrowed funds. Or it may be a moral obligation, as in the case of using stockholders' money where the management is morally obligated to pay the shareholders' use-rate in the form of future dividends. Even with our own funds we have a common-sense obligation to recognize our own cost of capital by noting that the cost for a given expenditure is the income we lose by having to reject investment of the same funds elsewhere.

2.3 OPPORTUNITY COST

Every owner of capital has more than one opportunity to invest his money. Every time he accepts one of these opportunities he foregoes the opportunity of investing in another and, with it, he foregoes the profit that he could have made in that investment. This situation gives rise to the term *opportunity cost*. This concept holds that capital is never free, because selecting one use of capital implies the cost of foregoing the opportunity to earn a profit with it elsewhere.

Our personal finances provide a competent illustration of opportunity cost. Assume for simplicity we have only two opportunities to invest personal savings: one is to invest in bonds at 6% interest, and the other to invest in a house in which we propose to live. When we invest in the house we have given up the opportunity for a 6% annual profit.[1] We must recognize that this is the cost of capital for financing the purchase of our house with our own capital. Because of opportunity costs, not even our own money is free.

In industry, management has basically two opportunities for the investment of the firm's funds: one is to invest the money outside of the company, in the stocks and bonds of other organizations; the other is to invest within the company, in its own machines and processes. Management rarely invests company funds in enterprises outside of the company, for the simple reason that if the best investment opportunities for company funds lie outside of the company, the company perhaps should not continue in business. Opportunity costs based on a firm's investing funds outside of the company have little practical significance in establishing the company's cost of capital, but they certainly prove that money should never be invested in the fixed assets of the business without the expectation of profit.

We cannot mention opportunity cost without observing that it suggests a means of determining the cost of capital. We saw this to be true in regard to our personal finances, using our own funds. Of course, if we finance with borrowed funds, the rate we pay on the debt clearly establishes the cost of capital. With corporate finance the cost of borrowed money is similarly fixed by the cost of the loan. The cost of equity capital, however, including the capital generated by the plowback of earnings, is established not by the opportunities available to the corporation, but by the opportunities available to its stockholders. The cost of

---

[1] Neglecting the effects of inflation which could be favorable to purchasing real property as explained in Chapter 16.

equity capital is the shareholder's expectation of dividends. The dividend rate that he expects depends upon the other opportunities available to him. The cost of equity is an evaluation of the shareholder's expectations, and these expectations derive from the shareholder's opportunity costs. A detailed discussion of of this is given in Chapter 9.

2.4 ECONOMY ANALYSTS MUST ALLOW FOR THE COST OF CAPITAL

The expectations of lenders and shareholders alike to receive compensation for the use of their invested capital establishes the fact that it costs money to use money. If the cost of capital is figured at 10% per annum, the annual charge for capital for a machine costing $10,000 is $1,000; by this same reasoning you must allow for the cost of that money whether the $10,000 is employed to purchase machines or to purchase fuel, labor, maintenance, or repairs. In the final analysis the cost of capital is independent of its intended use, even if the user intends only to hold it in a safe in a reserve fund, hide it under the mattress, or establish inventory in his warehouse. There is no money on which the lender or owner does not expect a return, nor on which a user can avoid reckoning a cost. Money used to buy fuel could be used to buy machines; in fact such expenditures divert funds from the supply available for the purchase of machines. Every dollar must be treated as capital and be expected to earn money in order to meet the cost of capital.

2.5 TIME VALUE OF MONEY

The fundamental viewpoint in the previous section—that all money must earn at least the cost of capital—complicates computing the total lifetime cost as established so simply in Chapter 1.

The concept called the "time value of money" simplifies this viewpoint and provides a basis for visualizing the mathematics. This can be illustrated by considering a loan of $1,000 to be used over the next four years if the cost of capital is 10% a year. The amount owed at the end of the first year is the original sum of $1,000 plus the $100 cost of capital, or $1,100; at the end of the second year it is $1,100 plus the cost of capital for that year, $110, or a total of $1,210; at the end of the third year it is $1,210 plus a cost of $121, or $1331; and at the end of the fourth year it is $1,331 plus $133.10, or $1,464.10. This is the process of compounding, that is, the accumulation of interest on both the principal and the undistributed interest. By applying the concept of the time value of money to this example we observe that $1,000 today has a time value of $1,100 1 year hence, $1,210 2 years hence, $1,331 3 years hence, and $1,464.10 4 years hence. Conversely, the time value of $1,464.10 4 years hence is $1,000 today, and so on.

These are the time values at 10%. We recognize that the time value may not always be computed at 10%, but we should also recognize that it should never be zero. To prove this to yourself or to anyone else, ask yourself, "Will anybody lend me $1,000 today in return for $1,000 to be repaid (without fail) one year from now?" If they will not, then $1,000 next year is not the same as $1,000 today. If the minimum payment they will accept is $1,100, then $1,100 at the end of next year is the time value of $1,000 today, and, in that case, the time value of money is evaluated at 10% annually.

2.6 DISCOUNTING FUTURE INCOMES OR DISBURSEMENTS

The expression "discounting the future" also acknowledges the essential existence of a rate of return in all monetary transactions. Using the figures in the previous section, the borrower of $1,000 at 10% interest for 3 years will owe $1,331 at the end of the third year. The borrower and the lender are two parties to the same transaction so that the lender stands to receive an income of $1,331 3 years hence. The worth of that income today, however, is only $1,000. This fact may be described by saying that the future income of $1,331 *discounted* to the present is $1,000 at 10% interest. It is the reciprocal of the process of compounding.

But more important to our present discussion is the fact that discounting is merely an acknowledgment of the time value of money.

2.7 EXAMPLE OF THE TIME VALUE OF MONEY

In Chapter 1 we computed the total cost of a machine consisting of its first and future costs without including the cost of capital. At this point we should ask what is this total cost, taking into account the cost of capital?

EXAMPLE 2.7 The first cost of a machine is $1,000. Its operating cost for fuel and labor at the end of next year will be $1,100, and its operating cost for fuel, labor, and maintenance at the end of the second year will be $1,210. For simplicity assume that the machine will only be used for 2 years, and its salvage at that date will be zero. What is the total cost of the decision to use this machine if the cost of capital is 10%?

SOLUTION. The total cost is not $1,000 + $1,100 + $1,210 = $3,310. It is true that the owner will be "out-of-pocket" $3,310, but this is distributed over a 2-year period; the $3,310 is not a sum of money—it is a stream of money or a series of sums. To compute a single sum, or a total cost expressed at one point in time, we must adopt the viewpoint of the time value of money. The reader will note that the time values of these sums at 10% interest for 1-year and 2-year intervals were established in Section 2.5; therefore,

Time value today of $1,000 spent today   = $1,000
Time value today of $1,100 spent 1 year hence = 1,000
Time value today of $1,210 spent 2 years hence = 1,000
Total cost of machine = $3,000

In consideration of the time value of money, total cost must be computed at some point in time. In the foregoing example it was computed at the present point in time by employing the discounting procedures from Section 2.6 to give a *"present worth."* Alternatively, it would have been possible to compute the total cost at any point in time, as for example at the *end* of the two years.

2.8 INFLUENCE OF THE TIME VALUE OF MONEY ON A DECISION

The total cost of a machine including the cost of money is obviously not the same as its total cost excluding the cost of money. In comparing two alternative courses of action, it is natural to ask whether the cost of money should be a factor. The following example provides a simple illustration of two machines which have the same total cost if we disregard the time value of money and different total costs if we include it.

EXAMPLE 2.8   An automatic tool can be installed for $2,000 and is expected to have an annual operating cost of $100 at the end of each year of its 10-year life. A semiautomatic tool can be installed for $1,000 with annual operating costs of $200 over its 10-year life. Neglecting the cost of capital or the time value of money, we note that each has a total cost of $3,000 over its lifetime. If interest is 10%, how does this affect the choice?

SOLUTION.

AUTOMATIC TOOL

	Time Value Today
$2,000 to be spent today	$2,000.00
100 to be spent 1 yr hence	90.91
100 to be spent 2 yr hence	82.64
100 to be spent 3 yr hence	75.13
100 to be spent 4 yr hence	68.30
100 to be spent 5 yr hence	62.09
100 to be spent 6 yr hence	56.45
100 to be spent 7 yr hence	51.32
100 to be spent 8 yr hence	46.65
100 to be spent 9 yr hence	42.41
100 to be spent 10 yr hence	38.55
Zero time value, $3,000	10% time value, $2,614.45

SEMIAUTOMATIC TOOL

	Time Value Today
$1,000 to be spent today	$1,000.00
200 to be spent 1 yr hence	181.82
200 to be spent 2 yr hence	165.28
200 to be spent 3 yr hence	150.26
200 to be spent 4 yr hence	136.60
200 to be spent 5 yr hence	124.18
200 to be spent 6 yr hence	112.90
200 to be spent 7 yr hence	102.64
200 to be spent 8 yr hence	93.30
200 to be spent 9 yr hence	84.82
200 to be spent 10 yr hence	77.10
Zero time value, $3,000	10% time value, $2,228.90

If all future payments are converted to their present time value, we are in a position to make a valid comparison of the two machines. The tabulation shows a cost advantage at a 10% time value of money, in favor of the semiautomatic tool of $2,614.45 - $2,228.90 = $385.55. If the time value of money is zero, there is nothing to choose between the alternatives, but because the time value of money is never zero there will be an advantage of one over the other.

The cost advantage of the semiautomatic machine calls for its installation (all other things being the same) and the rejection of the fully automatic machine. The analysis, in this case, favors the less efficient machine having a first cost of only $1,000 and recommends investing the extra $1,000 not in the more efficient machine, but elsewhere in the business where it will bring a 10% rate of return (at least).

An entirely different approach leading to exactly the same conclusion is this: if $1,000 extra is spent today, the annual disbursements will be $100 less for 10 years. Is it advantageous to spend $1,000 today in order to save spending $100 a year for the next 10 years? Today's time value at 10% interest of these future savings is $614.45, as can be noted from the previous figures for the automatic tool. The saving is therefore less than the cost of $1,000 (by $385.55), and the disadvantage if the automatic tool is installed is $385.55. Conversely, this is also the advantage of installing the semiautomatic machine—just as we previously concluded.

2.9 PRODUCTIVITY OF CAPITAL AND MINIMUM REQUIRED RATE OF RETURN

We have noted that capital is productive, and its productivity earns a profit for the owner of capital. A closer look at this shows that the productivity of capital arises from the fact that money will purchase more efficient processes for making goods than the consumers could employ to make the goods themselves. Goods produced by these efficient methods can be offered to the consumers at prices which will be attractive even after paying profits to the manufacturer. It is therefore profitable for the owners of capital to invest their capital in these efficient enterprises by outright ownership, or on a shareholder basis, or by lending money.

The financial statements of the business—the profit and loss statement and the balance sheet—show the total profit earned on the owner's investment, but we should note that we can determine from these only the average productivity of the dollar. We should like to know how productive each dollar has been during the last period or even to know that each dollar was productive, but the accounting system is not designed to show this. Although the financial statements do not account for the profitability of each dollar over the *past* period, we can do a lot toward accounting for the profitability of each dollar in the *coming* periods. Before approving proposed investments of the owner's dollars, we should insist that *each* dollar give evidence (a) that it will earn a rate of return and (b) that this rate of return will not be less than an agreed minimum required rate. By re-

10% X

quiring each dollar to meet this minimum acceptable rate of return before its investment is approved, we anticipate the future day when we will look back and want to find a satisfactory profit. By examining the injection of new capital and the continuance of old capital by investment procedures, future profits can be reasonably assured.

How is this minimum required rate of return established? Although this will be explained in detail in Chapter 10, we must give some explanation now, since all the problems prior to Chapter 10 employ the concept of this minimum acceptable rate.

The minimum required rate of return arises out of a company's allotting its limited supply of funds to its greater demand for funds. For any year a company can predict the supply of money that will be available for the purchase of capital goods. The supply is largely from the plowback of earnings, some from the liquidation and depreciation of equipment, and it may include borrowed funds or new equity capital. The important fact at this instant is that the supply is limited and, compared to the demand, usually inadequate. The demand for funds, as we will see in more detail later, should arise almost entirely from the creativity of the organization in suggesting economic ways of spending money. To illustrate the problem, let us suppose the demand for funds for the coming year is predicted to be $1,250,000 but the supply of funds will be only $500,000. The objective of the management obviously should be to invest the $500,000 where it will earn the greatest return and to reject those propositions totalling $750,000 that promise the least return.

To do this properly, the management should be in a position to ladder each parcel of demand to show its prospective rate of return. If these are arrayed in descending order of their expected returns we would have the following table.

Parcel	Investment	Prospective return	Cumulative amount
A	$40,000	80% or more	$40,000
B	50,000	70 to 80%	90,000
C	65,000	60 to 70	155,000
D	85,000	50 to 60	240,000
E	120,000	40 to 50	360,000
F	140,000	30 to 40	500,000
G	175,000	20 to 30	675,000
H	215,000	10 to 20	890,000
I	360,000	up to 10	1,250,000

Then the $500,000 supply of funds should be allotted only to those projects that promise 30% rate of return or more. We interpret this to mean that the minimum required rate of return for the coming year is 30%.

Let us not overlook any of the implications of the minimum required rate of return. It means that any investment promising 30% should be approved and any project promising less than that should be denied. It also means that

$750,000 worth of good investments promising rates of return as high as 29 percent will be rejected. It is also very important to note that, if the predictions are correct, whenever an investment of 30% or more becomes available it must be accepted. The failure to accept a 30% investment would create a surplus in the budgeted funds which then could be invested only at a lower rate of return because the only remaining investment opportunities would be those below 30%.

The minimum required rate of return establishes the floor down to which we may invest but, more than that, as we have just described, it also dictates those investments that we must accept wherever we find them. Therefore it is also the *minimum acceptable rate of return*.

In any case where the management is unable to supply enough capital to intersect the cumulative demands for funds, the minimum required rate of return will exceed the cost of capital. The minimum required rate of return is not, in such cases, synonymous with the cost of capital. In these cases the cost of capital remains as a floor under the minimum required rate of return, but they converge as more funds are made available.

The previous illustration presumes that the parcels listed in the table are the only demands for funds that will be made. This assumption means that after selecting 30% as the minimum required rate of return based on the given data that, for example, one will not subsequently receive an unanticipated demand for a project promising 50%. It is not our intention at this time to consider how to anticipate or treat situations beyond the assumption made above. Our only objective at this time is to give a basic understanding of the philosophy of establishing a cutoff rate. The problems of practical budgeting and period planning are deferred for later consideration.

The minimum required rate of return is usually the required rate of return after taxes. However, until we introduce in Chapter 15 the computation of the cost of taxes, we will merely assume that the disbursement for taxes has in some way been included in the given disbursements.

2.10 THE ACCOUNTING VIEWPOINT

The accountant and the economy analyst perform entirely different functions. The accountant computes profit earned during past periods after incomes and expenses are known. He calculates the *results* of operations and determines what the return on capital *was*. The accountant subtracts expenses from revenue to to find the profit on the owner's investment. He does not add a required rate of return to his costs; on the contrary, his objective is to find what that rate of return might have been as a result of past operations.

The economy analyst, on the other hand, tests the profitability of a proposed operation. His procedure requires a minimum rate of return[1] to insure that a

---

[1] And obviously also allows for the cost of capital. How to determine this is explained in Section 9.11.

profit, hopefully a maximized profit, will be there when the day of accounting occurs.

Failure to recognize these differences in objectives and procedures has caused some basic misunderstanding of economy techniques, particularly by financial managers familiar with accounting procedures. The major misunderstanding develops from the fact that the accountant never adds the "cost of capital" to operations unless it is an actual disbursement such as interest on a bank loan or a mortgage, whereas the economy analyst charges *every* dollar with the responsibility of earning a cost of capital. Each, of course, is correct according to his own functions and objectives.

The accountant, furthermore, does not attempt to attribute a difference in profitability to each dollar of the total investment. The economy analyst can compute the profitability of each dollar in a prospective investment opportunity and, by auditing procedures, estimate the apparent profitability of each dollar after the investment has been made.

2.11 RATE OF RETURN, YIELD, AND INTEREST

The percentage earned by an investment goes by a number of different names such as rate of return, yield, profit, gain, interest. To some extent this usage takes advantage of the precise meaning of words. Interest, for example, generally refers to the payment on bank deposits or on debt capital rather than to the profit from a business investment. In the literature of engineering economy the term "interest" is used interchangeably with "rate of return," probably because the formulas used in computing the time value of money in economy analyses are the traditional "interest" formulas.

Whenever "interest" is used in its restricted sense, such as a disbursement for the use of debt capital, instead of with the broader meaning just defined, it will be clearly pointed out in the text. The term does, however, contribute to a misunderstanding of the objectives of the engineering economy analyst compared to those of the accountant.

2.12 YIELD IS AFTER RECOVERY OF CAPITAL

Every analysis of a spending decision must show a suitable rate of return—at least a minimum required rate of return—but we should remember that this return is, and can be, only after the recovery of the investment.

Some simple problems are deceiving if we do not keep this in mind. In a proposition to invest $1,000 and receive $50 a year we are inclined to say that interest is 5%. Actually, unless provisions are made for the definite recovery of capital or unless the income is guaranteed to continue forever, our prediction of 5% interest is unfounded. Depending on the future stream of earnings it could be that the prospects of recovering the investment, no less receiving a return on it, are unlikely. This is true in the analysis of a proposed investment or the audit of a past investment. An investor in stocks, bonds, or capital goods who spends his "profits" from a past investment can subsequently discover, when his investment fails to continue its predicted returns, that he has been spending his principal and that he never received a yield on his investment.

PROBLEMS

2.1 Explain the profit motive—synonymous with the investment principle—in connection with the following expenditures: a machine tool; a library; a space vehicles to explore the moon; a bridge at a new point on a river; an electric motor.

2.2 Show how the individual's opportunity cost affects the viewpoint that the corporation has a supply of cost-free capital for investment purposes.

2.3 Compute the time value of $1 today over the next 5 years if the charge for the use of money is 10%. Compare your answers with the column marked "/F/P/" in the 10% interest table at the end of the book.

2.4 Compute the time value of $1 5 years hence for each year down to the present time if capital costs 10%. Compare your "discounting" with the column marked "/P/F/" in the 10% table at the end of the book.

2.5 Based on the computations in Problem 2.4, what is the total "present" lump-sum cost of paying $100 at the end of every year through and including the end of year 5 if the time value of money is 10%?

2.6 Based on the computations in Problem 2.4, which machine should be selected if the time value of money is 10%: Machine A costs $10,000 installed and $3,000 a year to operate over its 5-year life. Machine B costs $5,000 installed and $4,000 a year to operate over its 5-year life.

2.7 A firm's minimum required rate of return is 25%. The company is considering a proposal to build a new chemical division which promises to earn a rate of return of 30% on an investment of $800,000. An alternative proposal is to enlarge the proposed new plant at an additional cost of $400,000. The prospective rate of return on this added increment of investment is 25%. Should the company put $800,000 or $1,200,000 into the new enterprise, all other things being equal?

2.8 Why does the economy analyst "charge" a minimum required rate of return in his analyses whereas the accountant does not make this charge (except for interest charges on contractual debts)?

3

Rate-of-Return Formulas and Derivations

3.1 TIME SCALE TECHNIQUE

Time scales are often indispensable for visualizing the predicted flow of cash resulting from a proposed investment.

A time scale is illustrated in Fig. 3.1. On this scale the units of time are interest periods, not months or years. For example, if interest is paid quarterly, a 10-year investment will show 40 time scale periods. Therefore only when the interest period is one year will the time scale units correspond to years. The number of the interest period, or the date of the interest period if we choose to use dates, is written below the time scale.

The dollar amounts are written above the line at the instant in time when they are predicted to occur. In instances where money will be expended throughout the year, it is customary to show it on the time scale as though the expenditure occurred entirely at the end of the year.[1] The sums on the time scales are taken to be disbursements unless otherwise indicated. Incomes, when they occur, will have to be clearly signaled on the time scale by the use of symbols or signs, as may be seen later in the text.

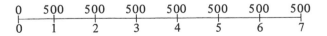

The time line above displays a uniform series of annual disbursements occurring at the end of each year for 7 years. We may note that the sum at point 1 is the disbursement occurring at the *end* of year 1, and the sum at point 2 is at

---

[1] An alternate convention is to assume continuous flow with continuous compounding. See Section 3.18.

26

the *end* of year 2, and so on (but also note that point 1 is the *beginning* of year 2 as well as the end of year 1).

We have found our method which treats all sums on the time scale as disbursements *unless marked to the contrary* to be entirely adequate.

One reason is that most problems concern the cost commitment of alternate *A* against the cost commitment of *B*. Most decisions are therefore between two or more different streams of cost outlays to achieve a given purpose. It is only when we consider the differences between these alternatives that we can display savings or cash flows or when we consider the less frequent cases of investing in new enterprises to expand gross incomes or cash flows. But these incomes, savings, or cash flows can be easily designated, when they occur, by whatever method best suits the display. Proper labeling as shown below achieves this differentiation as well as the best communication with the managers to whom the proposal is being made.

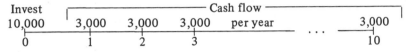

Invest 10,000 | 3,000 | 3,000 | 3,000 | Cash flow per year | ... | 3,000
0 | 1 | 2 | 3 | | | 10

Other methods are to use minus (or negative cost) to designate occasional disbursements, or a parenthesis for costs where incomes predominate, or symbols like *I* or *L* to designate incomes; but we strongly favor labeling because the time scale is the key to the solution.

As shown below, the analyst might also use arrows on the time scale: "down" to designate cost and "up" for income. He might proportion the length according to the value if that may serve his purpose, but our experience suggests that, as with any convention, labeling may be desirable to avoid confusion and misunderstanding.

10,000 | 3,000 | 3,000 | 3,000 | per year | ... | 3,000
0 | 1 | 2 | 3 | | | 10

3.2 SYMBOLS AND TERMS

The following symbols are used in the rate-of-return formulas:

P designates a present sum of money. On the time scale it occurs at point zero or at any other point *from* which we choose to measure time. *P*, as noted, is at the beginning of the initial period.

F designates a sum of money at a specified future date. On the time scale it occurs at point *n* or some future point *to* which we choose to go in time. *F* is at the *end* of the last period.

A designates a uniform series of end-of-period payments. To satisfy this definition they must be *equal* payments and they must occur at the *end* of *every* period. (The formulas are derived only for *P*, *F*, and *A* defined and located strictly as stated ahead.)

i designates the interest rate earned at the end of each period. "Interest" is used in its broadest sense and may mean "rate of return," "yield," "rate of profit," and so on.

n designates the number of interest periods.[1]

3.3 COMPOUND RATES OF RETURN

Interest, in banking, is the rate of return, or the return itself, paid to the depositor. If this interest is left on deposit, it is customary to pay interest on it. This reinvestment of interest and the payment of interest on interest as well as on the original investment constitute the process of compounding, designated by the term *compound interest*.

The operation of compound interest therefore means that at the end of the first "compounding period" the principal will have increased by the interest earned on it, and in the second period interest will be earned on this new sum of money. If compounding is quarterly this will occur four times a year.

The evaluation will depend on the interest per period and the number of periods. To determine the interest per period it is necessary in some cases to understand the following banking expressions which describe the frequency of compounding:

"Six percent compounded quarterly" means four interest periods a year paying 1.5% interest at the end of each 3-month period.

"Six percent compounded semiannually" means two interest periods a year paying 3% interest at the end of each 6-month period.

"Six percent interest" without any further qualification is taken to mean that the annual interest is 6%. The period is one year, with no compounding.

In the first two illustrations, 6% is the *nominal* interest, whereas the *effective* interest or actual annual interest is somewhat greater than 6%.[2] In the third illustration the nominal and effective interest are equal.

It will be observed that compounding reflects the concept inherent in the time value of money—namely, that *every* dollar "grows" with time. "Simple interest," on the other hand, does not reflect this time value of money because interest doesn't earn interest. Based on the concept of growth of every dollar, managerial and engineering alternatives will be evaluated by compound-interest mathematics.

3.4 SINGLE-PAYMENT COMPOUND-AMOUNT FACTOR

Given a present sum, *P*, what will be its future worth, *F*, at the end of *n* periods at compound interest, *i*?

---

[1] See Appendix re terms i, i_a, n, and N.
[2] See Section 3.15 for further discussion.

The time value of P will be:

at the end of the first period, $P + Pi = P(1 + i)$;

at the end of the second period, $P(1 + i) + P(1 + i)i = P(1 + i)^2$.

By induction, the sum F at the end of the nth period will be

$$F = P(1 + i)^n \qquad (3.4a)$$

The factor $(1 + i)^n$ is called the "single-payment compound-amount factor" and is represented by a mnemonic symbol (spcaf) or by the standard functional factor (F/P) so equation 3.4a may now be written,

$$F = P(\text{spcaf}) = P(F/P, i, n) \qquad (3.4b)$$
$$\quad\quad\;\; i\text{-}n$$

The following example illustrates the suggested technique for using the symbols.

EXAMPLE 3.4   How much will $1,000 become at 6% interest at the end of 10 years?

(1.06)

SOLUTION.

$$1.7908$$
$$F = P(F/P, .06, 10) = \$1,790.08$$

The term "single-payment compound-amount factor" is descriptive of the process it performs: it is the factor by which a single payment is multiplied to find its compound amount at a specified future date. The values of this and the functional factors are given in the appendix, beginning on page 489.

This factor in the literature of the subject is frequently referred to as the "compound-amount of $1."

3.5 SINGLE-PAYMENT PRESENT-WORTH FACTOR

Given a future sum F, find its value P today, n periods earlier. We realize this is the inverse of the process in Section 3.4, so

$$P = F \frac{1}{(1 + i)^n} \qquad (3.5a)$$

The factor $\dfrac{1}{(1 + i)^n}$ is called the "single-payment present-worth factor." The name describes its function: it is the factor by which a single (future) payment is multiplied to find its present worth. In terms of a mnemonic symbol or the standard functional factor we get

$$P = F(\text{sppwf}) = F(P/F, i, n)$$
$$\quad\quad\;\; i\text{-}n \qquad\qquad\qquad (3.5b)$$

This factor is also referred to as the "present worth of $1."

3.6 UNIFORM-SERIES COMPOUND-AMOUNT FACTOR

Given a uniform series of end-of-period payments A, what will "n" payments accumulate to at compound interest i? The problem is stated on the time scale:

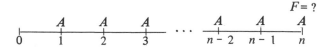

Each payment A is at compound interest for a different number of periods: the first is for $n - 1$ periods, the second for $n - 2$ periods, the next to the last for one period, and the last payment in year n draws no interest. The future sum F is the sum of the compound amounts computed by Eq. 3.4a:

$$F = A(1 + i)^{n-1} + A(1 + i)^{n-2} + A(1 + i)^{n-3} + \cdots + A(1 + i)^2 + A(1 + i) + A$$

$$(1)$$

Multiply Eq. (1) by $(1 + i)$

$$F(1 + i) = A(1 + i)^n + A(1 + i)^{n-1} + A(1 + i)^{n-2} + \cdots + A(1 + i)^3$$

$$+ A(1 + i)^2 + A(1 + i) \quad (2)$$

Subtract (1) from (2):

$$F(1 + i) - F = A(1 + i)^n - A$$

$$F = A\left[\frac{(1 + i)^n - 1}{i}\right] \qquad (3.6a)$$

The bracketed factor is called the "uniform-series compound-amount factor," the factor by which the uniform series A is multiplied to find its compound amount F. The equation written symbolically is

$$F = A \, (\text{uscaf}) = A \, (F/A, \, i, \, n) \qquad (3.6b)$$
$$\phantom{F = A \, (\text{uscaf})}{}_{i\text{-}n}$$

This factor is also referred to as the "compound amount of $1 per period."

3.7 SINKING-FUND DEPOSIT FACTOR

What uniform series of end-of-period deposits must be made for n periods at compound interest i to provide a required future sum F?

From Eq. 3.6a we can write

$$A = F\left[\frac{i}{(1 + i)^n - 1}\right] \qquad (3.7a)$$

The factor is called the "sinking-fund deposit factor," the factor by which a future sum F is multiplied to find the sinking-fund deposits that will accumulate it. The equation, written symbolically, is

$$A = F(\text{sfdf}) = F(A/F, i, n) \qquad \underset{i-n}{}$$

(3.7b)

This factor is also referred to as the "uniform series that amounts to $1."

3.8 CAPITAL-RECOVERY FACTOR

What is the future series of end-of-period payments that will just recover a present sum P over n periods with compound interest i, as illustrated below.

From prior developments,

$$A = F\left[\frac{i}{(1+i)^n - 1}\right] \text{ and } F = P(1+i)^n$$

Therefore

$$A = P\left[\frac{i(1+i)^n}{(1+i)^n - 1}\right]$$

(3.8a)

The factor is called the "capital-recovery factor." It is the factor by which a present capital sum P is multiplied to find the future series A that will exactly recover it with interest. Symbolically,

$$A = P(\text{crf}) = P(A/P, i, n) \qquad \underset{i-n}{}$$

(3.8b)

This factor is also referred to as the "uniform series that $1 will purchase."

3.9 UNIFORM-SERIES PRESENT-WORTH FACTOR

What is the present worth P of a uniform series of end-of-period payments A for n periods at compound interest i?
From Eq. 3.8a we can write

$$P = A\left[\frac{(1+i)^n - 1}{i(1+i)^n}\right]$$

(3.9a)

The factor is the "uniform-series present-worth factor." It is the factor by which the uniform series A is multiplied to find its present worth P. The equation, written symbolically, is

$$P = A(\text{uspwf}) = A(P/A, i, n) \qquad \underset{i-n}{}$$

(3.9b)

This factor is also referred to as "the present worth of $1 per period."

3.10 FORMULAS SUMMARIZED

single-payment compound-amount factor:

$$F = P(1 + i)^n = P(\text{spcaf}) = P(F/P, i, n) \atop {i-n}$$ (3.4)

single-payment present-worth factor:

$$P = F \frac{1}{(1 + i)^n} = F(\text{sppwf}) = F(P/F, i, n) \atop {i-n}$$ (3.5)

uniform-series compound-amount factor:

$$F = A \left[\frac{(1 + i)^n - 1}{i}\right] = A(\text{uscaf}) = A(F/A, i, n) \atop {i-n}$$ (3.6)

amt you have sinking-fund deposit factor:
to deposit to obtain
some future amt.

$$A = F \left[\frac{i}{(1 + i)^n - 1}\right] = F(\text{sfdf}) = F(A/F, i, n) \atop {i-n}$$ (3.7)

takes a   capital-recovery factor:
present amt. & changes
to uniform series.

$$A = P \left[\frac{i(1 + i)^n}{(1 + i)^n - 1}\right] = P(\text{crf}) = P(A/P, i, n) \atop {i-n}$$ (3.8)

uniform-series present-worth factor:

$$P = A \left[\frac{(1 + i)^n - 1}{i(1 + i)^n}\right] = A(\text{uspwf}) = A(P/A, i, n) \atop {i-n}$$ (3.9)

The above summarizes the six basic factors, but a knowledge of the two arithmetic-gradient factors in Section 3.17 will prove helpful in certain situations (especially tax computations).

3.11 FORMULAS VISUALIZED

With these six formulas the analyst can evaluate any alternatives, but the use of indiscriminate formulas can lead to serious errors. We recommend pausing to visualize the process which a formula is performing and observing whether this is the required process. This pause for reflection is good engineering and managerial practice.

In setting up an analysis, visualization of the necessary processes will be assisted by the use of time scales. Visualization of the function performed by each formula is promoted, as we have seen, by the symbols that have been assigned to the formulas.

EXAMPLE 3.11   A sum of $1,000 will be spent now, $500 a year will be spent at the end of each year for 6 years, and $800 will be spent at the beginning of the third and fifth years. What is the compound amount of these expenditures at the end of 6 years if interest is 10%?

SOLUTION.   The first step in visualizing the situation is to construct a time scale.

```
                    800           800
                     +             +
        1,000  500  500   500    500   500   500
          |     |    |     |      |     |     |
          0     1    2     3      4     5     6
```

The second step is to visualize the process for converting each sum or series to the required point in time. Visualizing the process assists in selecting the correct formulas. In the given case, we want the process for the compound amount of $1,000 after six periods, of $800 after four periods, of $800 after two periods, and the compound amount of the uniform end-of-year series of $500 for six periods. We visualize this as follows:

$$
\overset{1.772}{F = 1,000(F/P, .10, 6)} + \overset{1.464}{800(F/P, 4)} + \overset{1.210}{800(F/P, 2)} + \overset{7.716}{500(F/A, 6)}
$$

$$
= 1,772 + 1,171 + 968 + 3,858 = \$7,769
$$

Probably one of the most difficult processes for the beginner to visualize is the recovery of capital with interest, the (crf). Table 3.11 is intended to explain this process with capital of $10,000, 10% interest, and five end-of-year uniform payments for the recovery of capital. Then the series of repayments will be

$$
\overset{0.2638}{A = 10,000\ (A/P, .10, 5)} = \$2,638
$$

Table 3.11 shows that the money on deposit at the beginning of each period (column 1) earns interest during that period (column 2), and the payment at the end of the period (column 4) repays this interest plus some of the principal (column 6). For example, the unpaid principal at the beginning of year 2 is

Table 3.11   AN AID TO VISUALIZING THE CAPITAL RECOVERY FACTOR

Year	(1) Money owed at start of year	(2) Interest owed at end of year	(3) Principal and interest owed at end of year	(4) Repayment made at end of year	(5) Money owed at end of year after repayment	(6) Recovery of capital
1	$10,000	$1,000	$11,000	$2,638	$8,362	$1,638
2	8,362	836	9,198	2,638	6,560	1,802
3	6,560	656	7,216	2,638	4,578	1,982
4	4,578	458	5,036	2,638	2,398	2,180
5	2,398	240	2,638	2,638	0	2,398
					Total	$10,000

$8,362, the interest earned that year at 10% is $836, and the payment at the end of that year of $2,638 consists of the $836 in interest and $1,802 in principal. It will be noted that the proportion of interest and principal in each payment is not the same every year; the interest payments decrease while the repayments of principal increase. When the earned interest plus some of the principal is paid annually, the entire capital sum will eventually be repaid or recovered with interest. The money owed (columns 1, 3, and 5) therefore decreases until, at the end of year 5, all has been repaid.

3.12 HOW TO WRITE AND READ THE FORMULAS

Mnemonic symbols provide a simple vocabulary and language for reading the mathematical sentences which describe the operations performed on the numbers on the time scales. Mnemonic factors also seem to simplify visualizing these operations. However, to take maximum advantage of mnemonic factors they should be read in full and not by the letters. We should say "single-payment compound-amount factor" not "spcaf" or "CA" although we write it that way using the new standards. A full read-out reaffirms that "spcaf" is the factor by which we multiply a single payment in order to find its compound amount.

Some computer programmers have also felt that mnemonic symbols are more readily adaptable to writing mathematical sentences for the computer, as follows:

$$A = 10,000 \cdot CRF(10, 5)$$

The ASEE has published standardized formats for mnemonic symbols as well as functional symbols and, since the reader may find either of these in other literature, we have directed your attention to both formats and provided a minimum of necessary discussion to prepare you for encounters with the Mnemonic Format, although in this text we have employed the Standard Functional Format.

EXAMPLE 3.12 Write the mathematical statements of the following disbursements converted to a uniform series at a rate of return of 20% using mnemonic and functional formats.

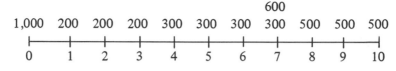

SOLUTIONS.

1. Full write-out of mnemonic symbols

$$A = [1,000 + 200(\text{uspwf}) + 300(\text{uspwf})(\text{sppwf}) + 500(\text{uspwf})(\text{sppwf})$$
$$\quad\quad\quad\quad\quad .20\text{-}3 \quad\quad\quad\quad 4 \quad\quad 3 \quad\quad\quad\quad 3 \quad\quad 7$$
$$\quad + 600(\text{sppwf})]\ (\text{crf})$$
$$\quad\quad\quad\quad 7 \quad\quad 10$$

This is a mnemonic sentence based on the first initials of factors which have been derived in Sections 3.4 through 3.9. These *names* of the factors are almost universally used by authors as titles for derivations or as headings in their interest tables. The sentence would be read using the full name, not the initials of the factor.

2. Standard Mnemonic Format

The same solution in the Standard Mnemonic Format would be written:

$$A = [1{,}000 + 200(\text{SPW}, .20, 3) + 300(\text{SPW}, 4)(\text{PW}, 3) + 500(\text{SPW}, 3)(\text{PW}, 7)$$

$$+ 600(\text{PW}, 7)](\text{CR}, 10)$$

and would be read Series Present-Worth factor, Present-Worth factor, and so on.

3. Standard Functional Format

Using the Standard Functional Format, the solution would be written:

$$A = [1{,}000 + 200(P/A, .20, 3) + 300(P/A, 4)(P/F, 3) + 500(P/A, 3)(P/F, 7)$$

$$+ 600(P/F, 7)](A/P, 10)$$

The Functional Format can be read in several modes. For example, $200(P/A, .20, 3)$ could be read "200 times the factor given A to find its present worth P if interest is 20% for 3 periods"; or simply "200 times the factor $(P/A, i, n)$"; and then again as noted in the headings of many published interest tables $200(P/A, .20, 3)$ might be read "200 times the uniform-series present-worth factor."

The point is whatever method one uses to write the symbols, one should visualize the function that the factor performs. This is the basis of all good engineering and management.

3.13 FORMULAS RELATED

The relationships between the formulas occasionally prove helpful. The following reciprocal relationships were previously noted:

$$\text{spcaf} = \frac{1}{\text{sppwf}} \quad \text{or} \quad (F/P) = \frac{1}{(P/F)}$$

$$\text{uscaf} = \frac{1}{\text{sfdf}} \quad \text{or} \quad (F/A) = \frac{1}{(A/F)}$$

$$\text{crf} = \frac{1}{\text{uspwf}} \quad \text{or} \quad (A/P) = \frac{1}{(P/A)}$$

Another helpful relationship results from the observation that

$$\text{crf} = \text{sfdf} + i \text{ whence } (A/P) = (A/F) + i \tag{3.13}$$

Equation 3.13 can be verified, with a little work, by proving an identity for the equation:

$$\frac{i(1 + i)^n}{(1 + i)^n - 1} = \frac{i}{(1 + i)^n - 1} + i$$

Another observation from the interest tables is

$$1 + (1 + i) + (1 + i)^2 + \cdots + (1 + i)^{n-2} + (1 + i)^{n-1} = \frac{(1 + i)^n - 1}{i}$$

or, stated symbolically,

$$1 + (F/P, 1) + (F/P, 2) + \cdots + (F/P, n - 2) + (F/P, n - 1) = (F/A, n)$$

This relationship was actually derived in Section 3.6, where it was shown that the compound amount of the series A equals $A(F/A, n)$.

The tables also show a somewhat similar relationship:

$$(1 + i)^{-1} + (1 + i)^{-2} + \cdots + (1 + i)^{1-n} + (1 + i)^{-n} = \frac{(1 + i)^n - 1}{i(1 + i)^n}$$

or, stated symbolically,

$$(P/F, 1) + (P/F, 2) + \cdots + (P/F, n - 1) + (P/F, n) = (P/A, n)$$

It can be noted that from these relationships a complete set of tables could be derived from a table of only single-payment compound-amount factors. These relationships will be useful when a complete set of tables is not available, they are helpful in some mathematical derivations and perhaps aid in visualization of the formulas.

3.14 ADDING AND SUBTRACTING ARE FORBIDDEN

Suppose we are given the annual sums shown on the time scale below and interest—the time value of money—is 10%.

	100	100	100	100	100	100	100	100	100	100
0	1	2	3	4	5	6	7	8	9	10

Each sum is worth $100 only at the point in time at which it is shown on the scale, and at any other point it is worth something else. For example, we cannot add $100 at the end of year 6 to $100 at the end of year 8. We must first find its time value at year 8, that is, we must convert it to year 8 before addition becomes meaningful. Since

$$\overset{1.210}{100 \, (F/P, .10, 2)} = \$121,$$

the sum of the two expenditures at year 8 is $121 + 100 = \$221$, not $200.

If we established a rule it would be this: *Amounts may be added or subtracted only if they occur at the same point in time.* Amounts occurring at different dates must first be converted to the same point in time, according to the time value of money, before they can be added or subtracted (or otherwise manipulated).

It is correct *to say* of this time scale that $1,000 will be paid in 10 equal year-end payments during the next 10 years. This is a correct *description* of the payments to be made; it is not, however, an evaluation of them.

3.15 NOMINAL AND EFFECTIVE RATES

Relative to the expression, "6% interest compounded quarterly," we observed in Section 3.3 that the nominal interest is 6% but that the effective, or actual, annual interest will be greater than 6%. Let us follow up by computing the effective interest.

Effective interest is the percentage increase in principal per annum. In this case there are four periods at 1.5% interest:

$$P \begin{array}{ccccc} | & | & | & | & F = ? \\ \hline 0 & 1 & 2 & 3 & 4 \end{array}$$

$$\text{Effective interest} = \left[\frac{F - P}{P}\right](100\%) = \left[\frac{P(F/P, .015, 4) - P}{P}\right](100\%)$$

$$= [(F/P, .015, 4) - 1]\ 100\% = 6.14\%$$
$$\overset{1.0614}{}$$

As noted above effective interest equals

$$[(F/P, i, n) - 1]\,100\%$$

where n is the number of interest periods per year and i is the interest per period.

Therefore, in this text i is the interest per interest period and obviously it is the effective interest of that period. In the above example 1.5% is the effective interest of each 3-month period. All the factors in the tables at the end of the text are computed for the effective interest for the stated periods.

3.16 SIMPLE RATES OF RETURN

With "simple" interest the practice is not to pay interest on interest. Illustrating the theory by a long-term loan, a present sum of $1,000 at 6% simple interest for 5 years would amount to $1,000 + (1,000)(5 \times 0.06) = $1,300$. In practice, simple interest is paid on short-term loans in which the time of the loan is measured in days.

The interest on a 60-day loan of $1,000 at 6% simple interest is

$$(1,000) \left(\frac{0.06}{365}\right)(60) = \$9.86$$

This possibly raises the question of how simple interest compares with compound interest on the same 60-day loan at 6% *compounded* daily.

$$\text{Interest} = (1{,}000)\left(1 + \frac{0.06}{365}\right)^{60} - 1{,}000 = \$9.91$$

(The operation is performed by calculator.)

The effective interest on this 60-day loan is only insignificantly higher (only one-half of 1%) than simple interest over the same period. The use of simple interest on short-term loans therefore seems justified from a practical standpoint.

3.17 COST AND INCOME GRADIENTS. THE ARITHMETIC-SERIES FACTOR

The disbursements for some equipment increase with the life of the equipment. If this increase is uniform, or assumed to be, useful formulas can be developed to reduce the labor of computation. For example, computing the "present worth" of the following series is a laborious process of over 20 computations unless a "gradient formula" is available.

0	4,000	4,100	4,200	4,300	...	increasing 100/yr	
0	1	2	3	4		19	20

If the series increases arithmetically, as shown above, we can represent the annual gradient of $100 a year by the symbol G and can convert the gradient-increases to a uniform series as follows (the annual uniform sum of $4,000 is already a series).[1]

0	0	G	$2G$	$3G$	...	$(n-2)G$	$(n-1)G$
0	1	2	3	4		$n-1$	n

$$F = G(F/P, i, n-2) + 2G(F/P, n-3) + \cdots + (n-2)G(F/P, 1) + (n-1)G \qquad (1)$$

multiply (1) by $(F/P, 1)$

$$F(F/P, 1) = G(F/P, n-1) + 2G(F/P, n-2) + \cdots + (n-2)G(F/P, 2)$$
$$+ (n-1)G(F/P, 1) \qquad (2)$$

Subtract (2) from (1):

$$F - F(F/P, 1) = -G(F/P, n-1) - G(F/P, n-2) - \cdots - G(F/P, 2) - G(F/P, 1)$$
$$+ (n-1)G \qquad (3)$$

---

[1] A geometric series is developed in Chapter 15 for a specific class of disbursements; however, the formula can also be used generally.

$$F(1 + i) - F = G\left[(F/P, n - 1) + (F/P, n - 2) + \cdots + (F/P, 2)\right.$$
$$\left. + (F/P, 1) + 1\right] - nG \tag{4}$$

but the bracketed set equals $(F/A, n)$ shown in Section 3.13, so $Fi = G(F/A, n) - nG$. Multiply (F) by $(A/F, n)$, the reciprocal of $(F/A, n)$:

$$Fi(A/F, n) = G - nG(A/F, n) \text{ but since } A = F(A/F, n)$$

$$A = \frac{G}{i} - \frac{nG}{i} \ (A/F, n) \tag{3.17a}$$

which may be written

$$A = G\left[\frac{1}{i} - \frac{n}{i} \ (A/F, n)\right] = G(\text{asf}) = G(A/G, n) \tag{3.17b}$$
$$\underset{i\text{-}n}{}$$

The bracketed term is called the "arithmetic-series factor." It is the factor by which the gradient G in an arithmetic series is multiplied to convert it to a uniform series A. The name is only partially descriptive because the process converts an arithmetic series to a uniform series and could be termed an "arithmetic-series uniform-series factor;" with some understanding, however, the double use of the word "series" can successfully be omitted.

In the given illustration, if i is 10%, the equivalent uniform series becomes

$$\overset{6.50807}{A = 4{,}000 + 100(A/G, .10, 20)}$$

The tables at the end of the text also give values for the "arithmetic-series present-worth factor" which is the present worth of the uniform gradient displayed on the foregoing time scale. Hence:

$$\text{aspwf} = (\text{asf})(\text{uspwf}) = (A/G)(P/A) = (P/G, i, n)$$

3.18 CONTINUOUS CASH FLOW AND CONTINUOUS COMPOUNDING

In the previous formulas all payments occurred discretely; they were lump sums at an instant in time. Also in the previous formulas, interest accumulated discretely at the end-of-period instant. Now we might ask whether discrete payments and discrete interest describe the actual events.

For the first part, actual payments may be lump sums often illustrated by first cost or salvage incomes, or they may flow more or less continuously through the year, typical of many operating disbursements. The cost of labor may be paid weekly; power, monthly; and materials at another interval. To assume that these costs flow without interruption, like water, is only an approximation, but it is probably closer to the real events than to assume that they all occur at the end of the year. We might add that the first cost P also may flow through the year, or years, as in the case of a large construction job.

In regard to continuous interest, this means continuous compounding or discounting. The concept of continuous interest arises from the view that earnings are created every day, hour, and minute of operation.

As a consequence, one school of thought assumes continuous cash flow and continuous interest instead of the discrete cash flow and discrete interest represented by the previous formulas. These are independent assumptions, because continuous interest can be applied either to lump sums or to continuous cash flows.

As noted, whether one assumes discrete or continuous cash flows for payments made throughout the year, the fact is that they are assumptions. The cash disbursements and incomes do not flow uniformly like a fluid; they flow intermittently in time and irregularly in amount. Both methods therefore give approximate results, but the objections to the shortcomings of either method are not great.

Evidence indicates that the discrete method is in greater use in industry and the colleges, in texts and in company manuals. Probably the most important reason for this is that industry, which determines the tools to be used, accepts the system which it is prepared to understand. The financial experience of most executives with discrete interest payments on bank deposits, bonds, mortgages, and other loans serves as the basis for comprehending "6% interest," for example. On the other hand, 6% continuous interest cannot, without adequate explanation, be related to the concept of interest with which the executive is familiar.

The previous concepts will be developed in the subsequent sections in terms of the following symbols and definitions:

n now designates years. (At continuous interest the number of *periods* in a year is an indefinitely large number.)

P, F, and A designate end-of-period lump-sum payments as before.

$\overline{P}$, $\overline{F}$, $\overline{A}$ designate the nominal or total annual amount computed at zero interest of the payments that flow continuously and uniformly throughout the year.

i designates the effective annual rate of continuous (or discrete) interest.

r designates the nominal annual rate of this continuous interest.

3.19 UNDERSTANDING CONTINUOUS INTEREST RATES

Continuous interest conceives of m interest periods a year, where m approaches infinity as a limit. Thus if r is the *nominal* annual interest, then the interest per period is r/m and (F/P) for m periods is $\left(1 + \dfrac{r}{m}\right)^m$.

Table 3.19 illustrates the effect of the number of compounding periods in a year. The table gives the value of F at the end of one year for P of $1, a range of m from 1 to infinity, and for two assumed values of nominal interest, $r = 20\%$

and 100%. In this case, $F = P(F/P)$, where the interest per period is r/m and the number of periods is m; therefore,

$$F = (1.00)\left(1 + \frac{r}{m}\right)^m$$

Table 3.19 demonstrates that we must understand whether the reference to "interest" is to nominal or effective interest. We must specify, for example, whether we mean 20% nominal continuous interest or 20% effective continuous interest. In discrete interest, the conventions define whether we are referring to effective or nominal interest; for example, an unqualified "6%" means 6% effective interest, but "6% compounded quarterly" means 6% nominal interest. In continuous interest we must define what we mean.

Since we must discriminate between nominal and effective rates, let us observe that it is more meaningful to specify the *effective* continuous interest, because that is the actual interest paid in a year. In the table, we note that the rates of

Table 3.19   COMPARISON OF NOMINAL AND EFFECTIVE
CONTINUOUS INTEREST

Number of periods per year, *m*	20% Nominal Interest		100% Nominal Interest	
	Amount of $1 at end of one year, F	*Effective interest (%)*	*Amount of $1 at end of one year, F*	*Effective interest (%)*
1	$1.2000	20.00	$2.0000	100.0
10	1.2190	21.90	2.5937	159.4
12	1.2194	21.94	2.6130	161.3
52	1.2209	22.09	2.6926	169.3
100	1.2211	22.11	2.7048	170.5
365	1.2213	22.13	2.7145	171.5
∞	1.2214	22.14	2.7183	171.8

22.14% or 171.8% specify the magnitude of interest paid, but the nominal rates of 20% and 100% give little idea of it.

It may also be helpful to observe that continuous interest is very nearly the same as interest compounded daily. In fact, increasing the periods from 365 to an infinitely large number raised the effective interest only insignificantly.

3.20 COMPARING CONTINUOUS AND CONVENTIONAL INTEREST

What is the value concept of 20% continuous interest compared to 20% discrete interest? If we hold to a rule of defining continuous interest in terms of its *effective* interest, the problem seems to disappear. If the discrete and continuous systems have equal *effective* interest, we know that each produces the same annual interest payment regardless of their differences in nominal interest. We are not concerned with nominal interest anyhow. In table 3.19 a discrete interest of 22.14%, for example, will be equal to an effective continuous interest of 22.14%.

The equation for the effective continuous interest will be shown to be $e^r - 1$, where r is the *nominal* continuous interest and e is 2.71828. Equating this to the effective discrete interest i, we get

$$i = e^r - 1 \tag{3.20}$$

If i is 22.14%, r, by solution of this equation, is 20% (as noted in Table 3.19). Or, if i is 20%, r is found to be 18.232%.

Following the proposed rule, therefore, the tables of continuous interest at the end of the text are indexed by effective interest, with the nominal interest indicated in parentheses. With the 20% table as an example, the effective interest $e^r - 1$ is 20%, but the nominal interest, r, is 18.232%.

The discrete tables are also indexed by effective interest, but in this instance the effective and nominal rates are equal because there is only one compounding period a year.

By using effective interest as the bench mark for both the continuous and the discrete systems, we maintain a single concept of the value of any specified interest rate.

3.21 DERIVATION OF FORMULAS FOR THE LUMP-SUM CASH FLOW OF P OR F AT CONTINUOUS INTEREST

As indicated in Section 3.18, continuous interest formulas fall into two categories: those for computing the time value of (a) instant or lump-sum payments and (b) those for computing the time value of continuous payments. In many cases the investment P and certain future sums F, such as the cost of overhaul or the income from salvage, or best represented as lump-sum payments. The formulas for computing the time value of these payments at continuous interest will be derived as follows.

The continuous single-payment compound amount factor can be derived from the discrete equation $F = P(1 + i)^n$, where n is the number of years and P and F are end-of-period lump-sum payments. The interest per period in the continuous factor will be r/m, where r is the nominal annual interest and m is the number of compounding periods (an indefinitely large number). Therefore,

$$F = P \left(1 + \frac{r}{m}\right)^{mn}$$

and this can be written

$$F = P \left(1 + \frac{r}{m}\right)^{(m/r)(nr)}$$

but $\quad \lim_{m \to \infty} \left(1 + \dfrac{r}{m}\right)^{m/r} = e,\ 2.71828$, the base of the natural or Napierian system of logarithms. So

$$F = P(e^{rn}) \tag{3.21a}$$

where the continuous factor $(F/P, r, n)$ is e^{rn}.

The effective annual interest is

$$\frac{F - P}{P} = \frac{P(e^r) - P}{P} = e^r - 1$$

If the effective discrete interest i equals the effective continuous interest $e^r - 1$, the discrete and continuous single-payment compound-amount factors will be equal, that is to say, $(1 + i)^n = e^{rn}$, where r, we must remember, is the nominal interest.

It should be noted again that F and P are lump-sum payments occurring at an instant in time.

The continuous single-payment present-worth factor is the reciprocal of the previous factor, so

$$P = F\left(\frac{1}{e^{rn}}\right)$$

where

$$(P/F, r, n) = \frac{1}{e^{rn}} \tag{3.21b}$$

If effective discrete and continuous interest are equal, the discrete and continuous single-payment compound-amount factors are equal. P and F are lump-sum instantaneous payments, as stated above.

3.22 DERIVATION OF FORMULAS FOR THE CONTINUOUS CASH FLOW OF $\overline{A}$ AT CONTINUOUS INTEREST

In many cases the annual payments A resulting from operating disbursements or income payments may be represented as flowing continuously through the year. The formulas for computing the time value of such payments at continuous interest are derived as follows:

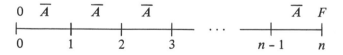

The continuous uniform-series compound-amount factor may be derived by starting with the discrete factor

$$F = A\left[\frac{(1 + i)^n - 1}{i}\right]$$

With continuous interest, r/m is the interest per period.

With continuous payments, A/m is each end-of-period payment made m times a year, where A is the total annual payment. So $\overline{A}$ designates the total annual amount of a series of payments flowing continuously through the year. A will continue to designate a series of discrete end-of-year payments. As before, m

approaches infinity. F, of course, is an instantaneous end-of-period payment. Therefore,

$$F = \frac{\bar{A}}{m} \left[\frac{\left(1 + \dfrac{r}{m}\right)^{(m/r)\,(nr)} - 1}{r/m} \right]$$

and

$$F = \bar{A}\left(\frac{e^{rn} - 1}{r}\right) = \bar{A}\,(\overline{\text{uscaf}}) = \bar{A}(F/\bar{A}, r, n) \underset{r-n}{} \qquad (3.22a)^1$$

From the preceding proof, the reader will realize that the discrete and continuous uniform-series compound-amount factors are not equal in this case. To indicate this fact, we will distinguish factors used with continuous interest and continuous cash flow $\bar{A}$ by a bar over the factor as shown.

The continuous sinking-fund factor and uniform-series compound-amount factors are reciprocals, so

$$\bar{A} = F\left(\frac{r}{e^{rn} - 1}\right) = F(\overline{\text{sfdf}}) = F(\bar{A}/F, r, n) \underset{r-n}{} \qquad (3.22b)$$

In this case, too, the discrete sinking-fund and continuous factors are not equal.

The continuous $(\overline{\text{crf}})$ is derived from

$$\bar{A} = F\left(\frac{r}{e^{rn} - 1}\right) \quad \text{and} \quad F = Pe^{rn}$$

whence

$$\bar{A} = P\left(\frac{re^{rn}}{e^{rn} - 1}\right) = P(\overline{\text{crf}}) = P(\bar{A}/P, r, n) \underset{r-n}{} \qquad (3.22c)$$

[1] A simpler derivation is

$$F = \bar{A}\int_0^n e^{rt}\, dt = \bar{A}\left(\frac{e^{rn} - 1}{r}\right).$$

We used the other derivation to show the relation between formulas.

We note that P is a lump-sum beginning of period payment. Here again, the discrete capital recovery factor and the continuous factor $(\overline{\text{crf}})$ are not equal.

The continuous uniform-series present-worth factor is the reciprocal of the capital recovery factor, so that

$$P = \overline{A}\left(\frac{e^{rn} - 1}{re^{rn}}\right) = \overline{A}\,\overline{(\text{uspwf})}_{r-n} = \overline{A}(P/\overline{A},\,r,\,n) \qquad (3.22d)$$

Here, of course, the discrete and continuous uniform-series present-worth factors are not equal. These factors would be the same if the effective interest rates are the same and if A was a lump sum. The difference is caused by the fact that $\overline{A}$ is a continuous payment.

$$F = P(e^{rn}) = P\overline{(\text{spcaf})}_{r-n} = (F/P,\,r,\,n)$$

$$P = F\left(\frac{1}{e^{rn}}\right) = F\overline{(\text{sppwf})}_{r-n} = F(P/F,\,r,\,n)$$

$$F = \overline{A}\left(\frac{e^{rn} - 1}{r}\right) = \overline{A}\,\overline{(\text{uscaf})}_{r-n} = \overline{A}(F/\overline{A},\,r,\,n)$$

$$\overline{A} = F\left(\frac{r}{e^{rn} - 1}\right) = F\overline{(\text{sfdf})}_{r-n} = F(\overline{A}/F,\,r,\,n)$$

$$\overline{A} = P\left(\frac{re^{rn}}{e^{rn} - 1}\right) \text{ or } P\left(\frac{r}{1 - e^{-rn}}\right) = P\overline{(\text{crf})}_{r-n} = P(\overline{A}/P,\,r,\,n)$$

$$P = \overline{A}\left(\frac{e^{rn} - 1}{re^{rn}}\right) \text{ or } \overline{A}\left(\frac{1 - e^{-rn}}{r}\right) = \overline{A}\,\overline{(\text{uspwf})}_{r-n} = \overline{A}(P/\overline{A},\,r,\,n)$$

where P is a first-of-year lump sum, F is an end-of-year lump sum, $\overline{A}$ is a series of continuous through-the-year payments, r is the nominal annual interest, and n is the number of years. Of course, the same formulas can be used for other calendar periods as well as years, but in that case P, F, A, r, and n must apply to the selected time period.

Formulas for the *lump-sum* cash flow of A at continuous interest are developed in Section 3.24. The factors developed in Section 3.24, however, are infrequently used. In the first place the factors are equal in value to the discrete factors (providing, of course, that the effective discrete interest equals the effective continuous interest). Furthermore, if continuous interest is adopted we might as well assume continuous flow of annual disbursements and incomes if these payments are not really lump sum.

3.23 DERIVATION OF FORMULAS FOR THE CONTINUOUS CASH FLOW OF $\overline{P}$ OR $\overline{F}$ AT CONTINUOUS INTEREST

The formulas derived in Section 3.21 were for use only with the lump-sum payments of P or F. But suppose these two payments, which we will now designate by $\overline{P}$ and $\overline{F}$, are made continuously throughout the year; then the compound amount of $\overline{P}$ at the end of n years is

$$F = \overline{P}(\underset{1}{\overline{\text{uscaf}}})(\underset{n-1}{\text{spcaf}}) = \overline{P}\left[\frac{e^{rn}(e^{rn}-1)}{re^r}\right] = \overline{P}(F/\overline{P}, r, n) \qquad (3.23a)$$

and the present worth at the beginning of n years is

$$P = \overline{F}(\underset{1}{\overline{\text{uscaf}}})(\underset{n-1}{\text{sppwf}}) = \overline{F}\left[\frac{e^r - 1}{re^{rn}}\right] = \overline{F}(P/\overline{F}, r, n) \qquad (3.23b)$$

The above formulas will cover those situations where the construction or the reconstruction of a project takes a year or more with the investment cost distributed over that period.

3.24 DERIVATION OF FORMULAS FOR THE LUMP-SUM CASH FLOW OF A AT CONTINUOUS INTEREST

These derivations promote a better understanding of the system of continuous interest and continuous cash flow versus instantaneous cash flow.

The first two formulas were developed earlier. They are repeated here because P and F are lump-sum payments:

(1) $$F = P(\underset{r-n}{\overline{\text{spcaf}}}) = Pe^{rn} = P(F/P, r, n) \qquad (3.24a)$$

As stated earlier, this factor is equal to the discrete single-payment compound-amount factor if effective discrete and continuous interest are equal.

(2)
$$P = F\left(\frac{1}{e^{rn}}\right) = F\overline{(\text{sppwf})}_{r\text{-}n} = F(P/F, r, n)$$
(3.24b)

The same comments under (1) apply for (2).

(3) If A is a series of discrete end-of-year payments,
$$F = A + Ae^r + Ae^{2r} \quad \dots + Ae^{(n-2)r} + Ae^{(n-1)r}$$
(a)

Multiply (1) by e^r:
$$Fe^r = Ae^r + Ae^{2r} + Ae^{3r} + \dots + Ae^{(n-1)r} + Ae^{nr}$$
(b)

Subtract (2) from (1):
$$F(1 - e^r) = A - Ae^{nr}$$

hence
$$F = A\left(\frac{e^{nr} - 1}{e^r - 1}\right) = A\overline{(\text{uscaf})}_{r\text{-}n} = A(F/A, r, n)$$
(3.24c)

If the effective interest i equals $e^r - 1$, then
$$F = A\left(\frac{e^{nr} - 1}{e^r - 1}\right) = A\left[\frac{(1 + i)^n - 1}{i}\right]$$

in which case the uniform-series compound-amount factors are the same for continuous and discrete interest if the payments are lump sum.

(4) The sinking-fund deposit factor is the reciprocal of the previous factor, and thus
$$A = F\left(\frac{e^r - 1}{e^{nr} - 1}\right) = F\overline{(\text{sfdf})}_{r\text{-}n} = F(A/F, r, n)$$
(3.24d)

and if the effective interest i is $e^r - 1$, then
$$A = F\left[\frac{e^r - 1}{e^{nr} - 1}\right] = F\left[\frac{i}{(1 + i)^n - 1}\right]$$

and the sinking-fund deposit factors are equal for discrete and continuous interest if the deposits are lump sum.

(5) To derive the capital recovering factor, we note from previous derivations that
$$A = F\left(\frac{e^r - 1}{e^{nr} - 1}\right) \quad \text{and} \quad F = P(e^{rn})$$

so that

$$A = P \left[\frac{e^{rn}(e^r - 1)}{e^{rn} - 1} \right] = P\overline{(\text{crf})}_{r-n} = P(A/P, r, n) \qquad (3.24e)$$

and, if the effective interest i is $e^r - 1$, then

$$A = P \left[\frac{e^{rn}(e^r - 1)}{e^{rn} - 1} \right] = P \left[\frac{i(1 + i)^n}{(1 + i)^n - 1} \right]$$

It follows that the capital recovery factors are equal for discrete and continuous interest if all the payments are lump sum.

(6) The uniform-series present-worth factor is the reciprocal of the previous factor, so that

$$P = A \left[\frac{e^{rn} - 1}{e^{rn}(e^r - 1)} \right] = A\overline{(\text{uspwf})}_{r-n} = A(P/A, r, n) \qquad (3.24f)$$

and, by the previous reasoning, the uniform-series present-worth factors are equal for discrete and continuous interest if the payments are lump sum.

In every case, therefore, we note that if the payments are lump sum and if the effective discrete interest equals the effective continuous interest, the interest factors for the discrete and the continuous systems will be equal. As a result, a set of discrete tables could be used to obtain the continuous interest factors for use with lump-sum payments. If one deals with *nominal* continuous interest, the corresponding effective interest rate may not be in any set of discrete interest tables. For example, given 20% nominal continuous interest, the corresponding effective interest of 22.14% is not in any set of discrete tables. In such a case, it may be easier to compute the factors directly with a handbook of exponential functions and a desk calculator than to interpolate from the discrete tables.

3.25 A VARIETY OF INTEREST TABLES

As the reader probably surmises, a variety of interest tables exists. In the first place, we have the conventional interest tables in which the periods and the payments are discrete, as illustrated in the first part of this chapter. A variation on this would be the so-called center-discounting system using the periods which begin and end at the midyear point instead of the year end.

As we have seen, many continuous interest tables are possible. First, we have those indexed by nominal interest and those indexed by effective interest. We have tables for lump-sum payments at continuous interest and tables for continuous payments at continuous interest. We have tables for continuous payments uniformly over 3 months, 6 months, and so on, over 5-year periods at continuous interest. We have continuous tables in which the periods begin and end at the midyear point instead of at the year end.

When the analyst encounters a new table, particularly a continuous interest table, he should take time to analyze it so that it will be used correctly. Considering the large variety of tables, we cannot always tell how to use a table from its title and description. Most continuous interest tables, for instance, do not say whether the interest rate is nominal or effective (in which case it is probably nominal but we cannot guess). The best advice we can give is to test a few of the factors by computing them from exponential tables.

3.26 THE CONVENTION USED IN THIS TEXT

With many possible conventions and interest tables available, it was decided that the most efficient method of presenting the subject and the least confusing to the student would be to use one convention and one interest concept throughout the book. We have, therefore, used the end-of-period convention for lump-sum payments at discrete interest. This is conventional interest and, together with lump-sum end-of-period payments, constitutes the standard practice in most engineering economy books today.

If efficiency in presenting this text required adoption of one method, it did not mean that the other methods were considered inferior. In fact, continuous interest formulas often simplify the solution of complex mathematical models, as will be noted in computing the cost of equity capital in Chapter 9. A point currently in favor of the discrete system is the general understanding that it enjoys among analysts. Other than this advantage, any of the systems could be used equally well. In that respect if an analyst prefers one of the continuous interest systems, he can solve any one of the examples in the text by merely substituting the values of the continuous interest factors for those of the discrete interest factors in the example. This is simple because both systems have the same factors, even if they are not numerically equal.

PROBLEMS

3.1 Give the following formulas in terms of the factors given in Section 3.10:
(a) For F if P is at the beginning of year 1 and F is at the beginning of year n. [*Ans.* $F = P(F/P, i, n - 1)$] (b) For F if P is at the end of year 1 and F is at the end of year n. (c) For F if P is at the end of year 1 and F is at the beginning of year n. (d) For P if P is at the end of year 1 and F is at the beginning of year n.

3.2 Give the following formulas in terms of the factors given in Section 3.10:
(a) For P if P is at the beginning of year 1 and A is at the beginning of each year. [*Ans.* $P = A(P/A, i, n - 1) + A$] (b) For P if P is at the end of year 1 and A is at the beginning of each year. (c) For P if P is at the end of year 1 and A is at the end of each year. (d) For F if F is at the end of year n and A is at the beginning of each year. (e) For A if P is at the beginning of year 1 and A is at the beginning of each year. (f) For A if F is at the end of year n and A is at the beginning of each year.

3.3 Prove that the following are identities:

(a) $\qquad\qquad (P/A, n) - (P/F, n) = (P/A, n-1)$

(b) $\qquad\qquad (A/P, n) - i = (A/F, n)$

(c) $\qquad\qquad (F/A, n) + (F/P, n) = (F/A, n + 1)$

3.4 Given only a table containing (F/P)'s and (P/F)'s derive all the other factors. You are allowed to add but not to divide or multiply; however, you may express a factor as a reciprocal quantity. Illustrate your answer from the 20% table.

3.5 If a sum of $1,000 is to be repaid in five equal year-end installments of $230.97, show how much of each installment is interest and how much is payment of principal. To make this easier, prepare a chart showing the following for the 5-year period: the year; the interest due at the year end; the total debt owed before payment of the installment; the debt owed after payment of the installment; the amount of principal in the installment.

3.6 (a) Given a table of only (F/A)'s show how to derive a table of (F/P)'s.
(b) Given a table of only (P/A)'s show how to derive a table of (P/F)'s.

3.7 Compute the effective annual interest of (a) 1% a month; (b) 2% a month; (c) 6% every 60 days.

3.8 Compute the interest on a loan of $6,000 for the following periods of time if the interest rate is (a) 6% simple interest, (b) 6% interest compounded monthly: 30 days; 60 days; 90 days. Assume 360 days in a year.

3.9 (a) Give the formula for the uniform annual equivalent of an increasing arithmetic series in which the annual gradient is G and the first term of the series, G, occurs at the end of year 1.
   (b) Give the formula for the lump-sum equivalent at time zero of an increasing arithmetic series in which the gradient is g and the first term of series, G, occurs at the end of year 2.
   (c) Give the formula for the uniform annual equivalent of an annual income I which decreases arithmetically by G dollars starting at the end of year 2.

3.10 Prove that the footnote for Eq. 3.21a is correct.

3.11 Derive the formula for the lump sum equivalent F at the end of year n if a sum of D dollars is deposited continuously over n years at interest r compounded continuously.

3.12 Compare the compound amount at the end of 10 years of $5,200 a year if the payments are (a) end-of-year; (b) weekly; (c) continuous. The effective interest per annum is 20%.

3.13 A sum of $10,000 is to be repaid uniformly over 10 years. The effective interest is 20% per annum. Compare the annual out-of-pocket payments if payments are (a) at the end of each year, (b) at the end of each week, (c) so frequent that they may be considered continuous.

3.14 (a) Give the formula for the lump-sum equivalent at time zero of $10,000,000 to construct a building if this cost was incurred uniformly and continuously during the year preceding its completion at time zero.

The effective interest is 20% per annum.

(b) Repeat this if the construction period of the $10,000,000 building was 3 years preceding time zero.

(c) Derive the formula for the lump-sum equivalent at time zero of a $100,000 reconstruction cost occurring uniformly and continuously during the tenth year of the life of the structure.

3.15 Compute the present worth at time zero of deposits of $1,000 a year for 10 years with nominal interest of 18.23% for (a) end-of-year deposits and continuous interest, (b) continuous-through-the-year deposits and continuous interest.

3.16 At 10% effective interest per annum, plot the curves of Dollars versus Years, from zero to 30 years for the following: (a) the compound amount of a deposit of $100 at time zero; (b) the annual cost of capital recovery of a $1,000 loan; (c) the compound amount of a deposit of $100 a year. All the payments are discrete.

4

Rate-of-Return Formulas Applied

4.1 RATE-OF-RETURN TABLES

Competence to use *all* the formulas developed in Chapter 3 will save a lot of time and effort. By these formulas we propose to avoid the labor of developing a formula for each situation or the labor of evaluating a proposal by having only one formula, such as the (P/F) factor, at our command instead of all eight basic formulas at least. We also propose to save labor by the use of tables for formula evaluation.

In the interest of speed and accuracy the following hints are offered.

1. Set up the entire equation first—*then* look up the values of all the factors at one time in the proper table.

2. When setting up the equation, realize that there are many equations that will give the same answer. Try to select the shortest and most direct formulation of the problem.

3. Use interpolation where it saves work; the results are usually accurate enough.

4.2 INTERPOLATION AND ERRORS

If we propose to save effort by interpolating, errors are introduced because the factors are not linear. How large or serious might these errors be?

EXAMPLE 4.2a Find $(A/P, .32, 15)$ if the tables give the factors only at 30% and 35%.

SOLUTION. By interpolation,

$$(A/P, .32, 15) = 0.305978 + 0.4(0.353926 - 0.305978) = 0.325157$$

The true value is 0.325051, so that the error is less than one-tenth of one per-cent. Although the approximation from interpolating is generally satisfactory, we should not disregard the possibilities of introducing large errors. One reason for accepting interpolation at all is the fact that predictions of costs and incomes are also approximations. But interpolation should be accompanied by good judgment relative to the extent of the error and its acceptability. The error will be greater for certain factors than others and will increase with the span of inter-polation as well as the values of i and n.

In the following example a large error in interpolating can be avoided as noted.

EXAMPLE 4.2b Find $(F/P, .15, 28)$ if the tables give values only at $n = 25$ and $n = 30$.

SOLUTION. By interpolation:

$$(F/P, .15, 28) = 32.919 + (0.6)(66.212 - 32.919) = 52.895$$

By a shortcut to an exact solution:

$$(F/P, .15, 28) = (1 + 0.15)^{28} = (1.15)^{25}(1.15)^3 = (32.919)(1.5209) = 50.066$$

The error due to interpolating is 5.7%.

4.3 SOLUTIONS FOR n

The following examples are intended to demonstrate the use of time scales, the formulation of the problem, and the use of the tables.

EXAMPLE 4.3a How long would it take for a sum to double itself if interest is 4% compounded quarterly?

SOLUTION.

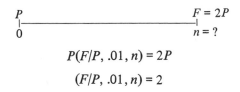

$$P(F/P, .01, n) = 2P$$

$$(F/P, .01, n) = 2$$

In the 1% table, this value of (F/P) occurs when n is approximately 70. There-fore, years $= 70/4 = 17^+$.

EXAMPLE 4.3b How many end-of-year payments of $500 must be made to repay a $5,000 debt if 6% interest is charged?

SOLUTION.

$$5,000(A/P, .06, n) = 500^1$$

$$(A/P, .06, n) = \frac{500}{5,000} = 0.1$$

In the 6% table, this value of (A/P) occurs when n is approximately 16.[2]

EXAMPLE 4.3c How many end-of-period sinking-fund deposits of $100 must be made to accumulate a sum of $1,000 if interest is 3%?

SOLUTION.

$$1,000(A/F, .03, n) = 100$$

$$(A/F, .03, n) = 0.1$$

In a 3% table, this value of (A/F) occurs when the number of periods, n, is approximately 9.

4.4 SOLUTIONS FOR *i*

EXAMPLE 4.4a At what rate of return will $1,000 double itself in 10 years?

SOLUTION.

$$P(F/P, i, 10) = 2P$$

$$(F/P, i, 10) = 2$$

For $n = 10$, this value falls between the (F/P)'s for 7% and 8% of 1.9672 and 2.1589, respectively; therefore,

$$i = 7 + (1)\left(\frac{2.0000 - 1.9672}{2.1589 - 1.9672}\right) = 7 + \frac{.0328}{.1917} = 7.2\%$$

EXAMPLE 4.4b At what interest will $1,000 be repaid by 10 equal end-of-year payments of $210?

---

[1] At first the student will probably write this as $P(A/P, i, n) = A$, but we expect that once he has learned to visualize the mathematical operations he will dispense with the letters entirely, a practice we will follow from here on.

[2] Hence, if there are 16 payments, the last will not be $500.

SOLUTION.

Investment ⌐―――――――― Annual Repayments ――――――――⌐

1,000	210	210	210		210	210
0	1	2	3	...	9	10

$$1{,}000(A/P, i, 10) = 210$$

$$(A/P, i, 10) = 0.21$$

When $n = 10$, this value of (A/P) falls between 15% and 20% interest.

$$i = 15 + \left(\frac{0.21000 - 0.19925}{0.23852 - 0.19925}\right)5 = 16.4\%$$

EXAMPLE 4.4c At what rate of return will $1,000 be 5 times as great in 5 years?

SOLUTION.

$$P(F/P, i, 5) = 5P$$

By logarithms,

$$(1 + i)^5 = 5$$

$$\log(1 + i) = (1/5)\log 5 = 0.13979$$

$$\text{antilog} = 1.3797$$

$$1 + i = 1.3797$$

$$i = 37.97\%$$

or, by interpolation between 35% and 40%,

$$i = 37.89\%$$

4.5 TIME VALUES OF SUMS AND SERIES

The time value of a sum or a series of sums of money is its value at compound interest at a specific date. The following are some examples.

EXAMPLE 4.5a What is the time value of $1,000 5 years hence if interest is 8%?

SOLUTION.

$P = 1{,}000$	$F = ?$
0	5

1.4693

$$F = 1{,}000(F/P, .08, 5) = \$1{,}469.30$$

At the same time, we can observe that the time value of $1,469 five years *earlier* is $1,000.

EXAMPLE 4.5b   A man and wife wish to save for the next 5 years to purchase a summer cottage which will cost $7,000. If interest is 4% compounded quarterly, how much must they deposit annually?

SOLUTION.

$$A = ? \qquad 7,000 = F$$

$$0 \qquad\qquad n = 20$$

$$0.04542$$
$$A = 7,000(A/F, .01, 20) = \$317.94$$

$$4.0604$$
The annual deposit $= 317.94(F/A, .01, 4) = \$1,290.84.$

EXAMPLE 4.5c   A 4% $1,000 bond matures on July 1, 1985, and interest payments are to be made twice annually. In the terms of the money market this means that the $1,000 principal is to be paid at the date of maturity and 2% interest on the principal is to be paid directly to the bondholder (redeeming his coupons) at the end of every 6 months.

How much is the bond worth on July 1, 1973, if the holder wants 6% return compounded semiannually?

SOLUTION.

$$\text{Payment} = \$20 \text{ per period} \qquad 1,000 = F$$

$$4 \quad 5 \quad 6 \quad 7 \quad 8 \quad 9 \quad 80 \quad 1 \quad 2 \quad 3 \quad 4 \quad 85$$

7/1/73

From July 1, 1973, to July 1, 1985, there will be 24 payments of $20 at the end of each period $\left(\dfrac{0.04}{2} \times 1,000\right)$. The time value P on July 1, 1973, of all the future payments will be

$$16.9355 \qquad\qquad 0.49193$$
$$P = 20(P/A, .03, 24) + 1,000(P/F, 24) = 338.71 + 491.93 = \$830.64$$

EXAMPLE 4.5d   A $10,000 mortgage is to be repaid uniformly over the next 15 years in end-of-year payments with interest at 5%. What are the annual payments?

SOLUTION.

$$P = 10,000 \qquad\qquad A = ? \qquad\qquad$$

$$0 \quad 1 \qquad\qquad\qquad\qquad 15$$

$$0.09634$$
$$A = 10,000(A/P, .05, 15) = \$963.40$$

4.6 TIME VALUES OF NONUNIFORM SERIES

In these problems the student will discover several ways of formulizing each problem, although all will give the same answer. As advised in Section 4.1, the student should seek the most direct solution to promote speed and accuracy. The following examples illustrate this.

EXAMPLE 4.6a   A man expects to receive an annual year-end bonus of $500 for the next five years and plans to invest it at 4% compounded quarterly. How much will he have at the end of 5 years?

SOLUTION.

```
0     500     500     500     500     500
├───────┼───────┼───────┼───────┼───────┤
0      4       8      12      16      20
```

Method 1

$$F = 500 \overset{0.24628}{(A/F, .01, 4)} \overset{22.019}{(F/A, 20)} = \$2,711.$$

Method 2

$$F = 500 \overset{0.25628}{(A/P, .01, 4)} \overset{17.258}{(F/A, 16)} + 500 = \$2,711.$$

Method 3

$$F = 500 \overset{1.1726}{(F/P, 16)} + 500 \overset{1.1268}{(F/P, 12)} + 500 \overset{1.0829}{(F/P, 8)} + 500 \overset{1.0406}{(F/P, 4)} + 500 = \$2,711$$

All the various methods will give the same answer, but one of them will be easier and faster.

EXAMPLE 4.6b   On January 1, 1975, a company leased a factory for the following 5 years by the payment of a lump sum. The lease provides that the company may extend the lease for another 5 years by the payment of $6,000 a year payable at the beginning of the year. On January 1, 1978, the company decides to employ some of its uninvested funds by immediately prepaying the rent on the last 5 years. If interest is 5%, what is a fair payment?

SOLUTION.

```
                              6,000 6,000 6,000 6,000 6,000    0
├──────┼─────┼─────┼─────┼─────┼─────┼─────┼─────┼─────┼─────┤
Jan. 1, 1975  '76   '77   '78   '79   '80   '81   '82   '83   '84   '85
```

The rent is paid through the end of 1979. On January 1, 1980, rent of $6,000 becomes due for the year 1980. Subsequent rental payments are shown on the time scale and will cover the rental of the premises through the end of 1984. It is now proposed to prepay these in one lump sum on January 1, 1978. This sum is

Method 1

$$P = 6,000 \overset{4.3295}{(P/A, .05, 5)} \overset{0.9524}{(P/F, 1)} = \$24,740$$

Method 2

$$P = 6,000 \overset{5.5256}{(F/A, .05, 5)} \overset{0.7462}{(P/F, 6)} = \$24,740$$

4.7 TIME VALUES OF ARITHMETIC SERIES

EXAMPLE 4.7   A machine costing $10,000 installed will require operating disbursements of $5,000 the first year. Disbursements are predicted to increase

$400 a year as the equipment ages. If interest is 10%, what is the total of all the costs at the end of 12 years of operation?

SOLUTION.

$$
\begin{array}{c}
\begin{array}{ccccccc}
 & & 400 & 800 & & 10(400) & 11(400) \\
 & & + & + & & + & + \\
10{,}000 & 5{,}000 & 5{,}000 & 5{,}000 & & 5{,}000 & 5{,}000 \\
\vdash & \!\!\!\!\!\!+ & \!\!\!\!\!\!+ & \!\!\!\!\!\!+ & \cdots & \!\!\!\!\!\!+ & \!\!\!\!\!\!+ \\
0 & 1 & 2 & 3 & & 11 & 12
\end{array}
\end{array}
$$

$$
\begin{array}{ccc}
3.1384 & & 4.3884 \quad 21.384
\end{array}
$$

$$F = 10{,}000(F/P, .10, 12) + [5{,}000 + 400(A/G, 12)](F/A, 12) = \$175{,}833.$$

4.8 COMPARING ALTERNATIVES

Until now we have attempted only to demonstrate the theory and techniques for computing the time value of given sums or series. Most of the problems in this text, however, will deal with the theory and techniques for comparing alternatives. These considerations are sufficiently complex to require a chapter or more of explanation, but the following simple examples anticipate this.

EXAMPLE 4.8a If interest is 8%, what must be the anticipated lowest repair bill 5 years from now to justify a present expenditure of $1,000 that will prevent the future repairs?

SOLUTION. There are two alternatives: to make the repair costing $1,000 now or to wait 5 years and make repairs increased by neglect.
The alternatives are

The time value of the first alternative at year 5 is $1,000(F/P, .08, 5) = \$1,469.30$. If the second alternative, the delayed repair, is expected to cost more than $1,469, it is more economical to make the repair now. This conclusion is also justified if the cost of the future repair is *equal* to $1,469, but this is subject to later proof.

EXAMPLE 4.8b How much can you justify spending now in order to save spending $1,000 at the end of each of the next 5 years if money is worth 8%.

SOLUTION.

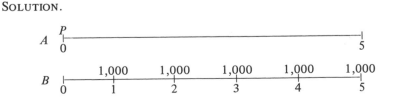

The statement of this example again implies the existence of alternatives: to spend $1,000 a year for 5 years or to spend P dollars now to produce the equivalent effect. The present time value of the second alternative is

$$P = 1,000 \overset{3.9927}{(P/A, .08, 5)} = \$3,992.71$$

It is not justifiable to spend more than $3,993 now, or, as we shall prove later, it is justifiable to spend *as much as* $3,993 now in order to avoid spending $1,000 a year for the next 5 years, if interest is 8%.

4.9 THE TEST OF INVESTMENTS

It is probably apparent that the examples in this chapter also illustrate investments. In Example 4.5a, computing the time value of $1,000 5 years hence at 8% interest is the same as computing the amount accumulated 5 years hence by investing $1,000 today at 8%.

In Example 4.8a, the question could just as well have been, "By investing $1,000 today, how much will you have in 5 years if interest is 8%?"

Although the following examples are expressed as investments, many other problems, which at first glance do not seem to be investments, are in fact investment situations.

EXAMPLE 4.9a What income must be received at the end of every year for 5 years to repay an investment of $1,000 if interest is 10%?

SOLUTION.

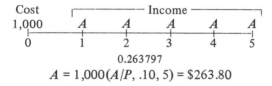

$$A = 1,000 \overset{0.263797}{(A/P, .10, 5)} = \$263.80$$

EXAMPLE 4.9b If an investment of $1,000 will bring an income of $350 a year for 5 years, what is the rate of return on the investment?

SOLUTION.

Cost | Income
1,000   350   350   350   350   350
0   1   2   3   4   5

Here again we observe both incomes and costs on the time scale. These can be labeled, as shown, or they can be identified with plus and minus signs.

The question is: If the time value of $1,000 expressed as a series is equal to $350, what must the interest be to achieve this?

$$1,000(A/P, i, 5) = 350$$

$$(A/P, i, 5) = 0.350$$

$$i = 22\%$$

EXAMPLE 4.9c How much can you afford to invest now in order to effect savings of $500 a year for 8 years if interest is 10%?

SOLUTION.

Cost				Savings				
P	500	500	500	500	500	500	500	500
0	1	2	3	4	5	6	71	8

The present time value of the saving must equal the investment P.

$$P = 500(P/A, .10, 8) = \$2{,}667.47$$

with 5.3349 above the factor.

The examples in this chapter are intended to create an awareness of the many different ways of expressing a problem and of the value of time scales in reducing words to a precise picture of the flow of cash, and to introduce the goals of comparing alternatives and evaluating investments.

4.10 LIMITING VALUES OF FORMULAS

A knowledge of the limits of the factors will prove helpful. If n is infinity,

$$(F/P, i, \infty) = (1 + i)^\infty = \infty \tag{4.10a}$$

$$(P/F, i, \infty) = \frac{1}{(1+i)^\infty} = 0 \tag{4.10b}$$

$$(F/A, i, \infty) = \frac{(1+i)^\infty - 1}{i} = \infty \tag{4.10c}$$

$$(A/F, i, \infty) = \frac{i}{(1+i)^\infty - 1} = 0 \tag{4.10d}$$

$$(A/P, i, \infty) = \frac{i(1+i)^\infty}{(1+i)^\infty - 1}$$

This is indeterminate, but it can be solved by noting that

$$(A/P, i, \infty) = (A/F, \infty) + i = 0 + i$$

whence

$$(A/P, i, \infty) = i \tag{4.10e}$$

$$(P/A, i, \infty) = \frac{1}{(A/P, i, \infty)} = \frac{1}{i} \tag{4.10f}$$

$$(A/G, i, \infty) = \frac{1}{i} \tag{4.10g}[1]$$

---

[1] See Problem 4.46 at the end of the chapter.

EXAMPLE 4.10a What is the perpetual annual income that will be provided by an endowment of $10,000 if the rate of return is 4%?

SOLUTION.

$$10{,}000 \qquad\qquad A = ?$$
$$\vdash\!\dashv$$
$$0 \qquad\qquad\qquad\qquad\qquad n = \infty$$

$$A = 10{,}000(A/P, .04, \infty) = 10{,}000i = \$400 \text{ a year forever.}$$

EXAMPLE 4.10b What is the required amount of an investment that will pay a perpetual annuity of $100 if the rate of return is 10%?

SOLUTION.

$$P = ? \qquad\qquad A = 100/\text{yr}$$
$$0 \qquad\qquad\qquad\qquad\qquad n = \infty$$

$$P = 100(P/A, .10, \infty) = (100)\left(\frac{1}{i}\right) = \frac{100}{0.10} = \$1{,}000$$

EXAMPLE 4.10c What is the amount of an endowment that will provide an annuity of $100 for the next 50 years if the rate of return is 10%?

SOLUTION.

$$P = ? \qquad\qquad A = 100/\text{yr}$$
$$0 \qquad\qquad\qquad\qquad\qquad 50$$
$$9.9148$$
$$P = 100(P/A, .10, 50) = \$991.48$$

But in Example 4.10b, $1,000 will provide an annuity of $100 forever; therefore $1,000 − 991.48 or only $8.52 will provide the annuity from 50 years to infinity. Examination of the tables confirms that the value for (P/A) and (A/P) for 50, 75, and 100 years are close to those for infinity. This would justify the use of capitalized costs, namely, finding the present worth to infinity, as a very close approximation for installations having long lives of 50 or more years.

Turning to the factor limits for $i = 0$, these are useful in rough-checking answers and also in the trial and error procedures, used in the rate-of-return analyses in Chapter 8.

These limits, the value of the factors when the time value of money is zero, can be written by inspection.

$$(F/P, 0, n) = 1 \qquad\qquad\qquad (4.10h)$$

$$(P/F, 0, n) = 1 \qquad\qquad\qquad (4.10i)$$

$$(F/A, 0, n) = n \qquad\qquad\qquad (4.10j)$$

$$(P/A, 0, n) = n \qquad\qquad\qquad (4.10k)$$

$$(A/F, 0, n) = \frac{1}{n} \tag{4.10l}$$

$$(A/P, 0, n) = \frac{1}{n} \tag{4.10m}$$

$$(A/G, 0, n) = \frac{n-1}{2} \tag{4.10n}$$

EXAMPLE 4.10d Uniform end-of-year payments over the next 10 years to recover \$1,000 if interest is 10% are computed to be $1,000(A/P, .10, 10) =$ \$162.75. Rough check this answer.

SOLUTION. With zero interest,

$$A = 1,000(A/P, 0, 10) = (1,000) \left(\frac{1}{10}\right) = \$100$$

If interest is greater than zero, A will be greater than \$100 a year, but, as visualized in Section 3.11, the uniform annual interest will not be 10% but roughly an average of 10% and zero. Taking 5% on \$1,000, or \$50 interest, gives a total of \$150, which is a reasonable check on \$162.75.

4.11 APPLICATIONS OF CONTINUOUS FORMULAS

The following example illustrates the use of the continuous formulas derived in Chapter 3.

EXAMPLE 4.11 Find the present worth (lump sum at time zero) of the payments on the following time scale. All the disbursements are assumed to flow uniformly through the year of occurrence. Each is located on the time scale during the year in which the disbursement has accumulated. The salvage value L, however, is a lump-sum end-of-year payment. The continuous interest is 20% (effective value).

SOLUTION. (Although we wrote r in the subscripts of the continuous formulas in Chapter 3, it is just as reasonable to write i, the effective interest. We suggest writing either r or i, depending on how your interest table is indexed.)

$\overline{100}$	$\overline{100}$	$\overline{100}$	$\overline{100}$	$\overline{100}$	$\overline{200}$	$\overline{200}$	$\overline{200}$	$\overline{200}$	$\overline{200}$	$L = 300$
0	1	2	3	4	5	6	7	8	9	10

$$P = \overline{100}(P/\overline{A}, .20, 5) + \overline{200}(P/\overline{A}, 5)(P/F, 5) - 300(P/F, 10)$$
$$= (100)(3.2806) + (200)(3.2806)(0.4019) - (300)(0.1615)$$
$$= \$543.29$$

Note that the (P/F)'s would be the same if taken from the discrete or continuous 20% tables.

4.12 CONTINUOUS FLOW AND INSTANT FLOW WITH CONTINUOUS INTEREST

The following example illustrates a situation in which we have continuous flow as well as instant flow of cash with continuous compounding. Formulas for the latter were derived and discussed in Section 3.23.

EXAMPLE 4.12   The completion of a project will take 4 years from the starting date. For a year after completion, expenses will be incurred for testing and adjusting the equipment. The payments are shown on the time scale; those in the top row, being instant, or lump-sum, payments, occur at the date shown, and those in the second row, being continuous-through-the-year payments, occur *during* the year in which they appear on the scale. The interest is continuous and its effective value is 20%. Find the value of the first cost P at time zero.

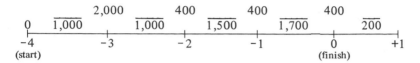

SOLUTION.

$$P = 2{,}000(F/P, .20, 3) + 400(F/A, 3) + \overline{1{,}000}(F/\overline{A}, 4) + \overline{500}(F/\overline{A}, 1)(F/P, 1)$$
$$+ \overline{700}(F/\overline{A}, 1) + \overline{200}(P/\overline{A}, 1)$$

$$= (2{,}000)(1.728) + (400)(3.640) + (1{,}000)(5.8885) + (500)(1.097)(1.2)$$
$$+ (700)(1.097) + (200)(0.91414)$$

$$= \$12{,}409$$

Note that in the first two terms of the equation the payments are instantaneous, so that the continuous interest factors would be the same as the discrete factors for 20% continuous interest. In the last four terms of the equation, the payments are continuous, and the formulas for them were derived and discussed in Section 3.21. We might point out that the sums $\overline{P} = \overline{500}, \overline{P} = \overline{700}$, and $\overline{F} = \overline{200}$ occur throughout the year and they are shown to occur on the time scale *during* a period inasmuch as they cannot be represented correctly on the time scale at any specific point in time. To treat them mathematically, they must be either compounded to the end of the year in which they occur or discounted to the beginning. For example, the $500 which flows uniformly through the period from -2 to -1 is $\overline{500}(F/\overline{A}, 1)$ at -1 in time.

PROBLEMS

4.1   Compute $(P/A, 135, 10)$ by interpolating between these tables: 30 & 40%, 25 & 45%, and 20 & 50%. Compute the Percentage Error compared to the exact factor. Plot this vs. the Interval of Interpolation. Is it linear?

4.2 If your school has a computer, program and run off interest tables (a) from zero to 6% in $\frac{1}{4}$ of 1% intervals; (b) from 1% to 50% in 1% intervals; (c) from 50% to 100% in 2% intervals; (d) to 150% in 5% intervals.

4.3 Compute $(P/F, 135.10)$ by interpolating between these tables: 30 & 40%, 25 & 45%, and 20 & 50%. Compute the Percentage Error compared to the exact factor. Plot this vs. the Interval of Interpolation.

4.4 Find how long it will take for $1,000 to double itself with the following interest rates: 3%, 4%, 6%, 10%, 20%, 30%, 50%.

4.5 Compute the years required for a deposit to equal twice, three times and so on up to 5 times its original value for interest rates of 4%, 10%, and 20% and plot the ratio F/P versus Years.

4.6 (a) How many payments of $120 must a purchaser make at the beginning of each month on an automobile costing $2,670 if the financing charge is 1% a month?

(b) How many deposits of $30 must an investor make at the end of every 3 months if he wants to accumulate $360 for a home appliance? The banks pays 4% compounded quarterly.

(c) An executive is planning a fund to finance his son's college education. He estimates he will need $10,000 at the end of 10 years from the present date, and over that period he can make a uniform deposit at the end of every 6 months. The fund into which he makes his payments earns 4% compounded quarterly. What should be the amount of each deposit?

(d) A company can lease a machine for $1,000 at the end of every month and become the owner at the end of the contract period. How many payments must be made if the lessor wants to receive the machine cost of $30,000 and 12% nominal interest?

4.7 If an investor wishes to double his $10,000 investment in 12 years, at what interest rate should he try to invest (assuming no appreciation or depreciation of the investment)?

4.8 A purchaser is required to pay $95 at the end of every month for 2 years for an automobile having a cash price of $1,700. What rate of return is the purchaser paying?

4.9 A lender expects to receive $100 at the end of every month for the next 20 months as repayment of a loan of $1,000. What interest rate is he charging?

4.10 An investor wants his estate to be worth $50,000 at the end of 8 years. He can acquire this by paying $5,000 a year at the end of every year through that date. At what rate of return must his deposits be invested?

4.11 If an investment of $1,000 is expected to become 10 times its present value in 10 years, what must be the rate of return on the investment?

4.12 What interest rate does the buyer pay if he purchases a $100 watch for $11 a month for the next 12 months, payments to be made at the first of each month starting on the day of purchase?

4.13 What is the time value of (a) $1,000 8 years hence if interest is 6%; (b) $1,000 8 years earlier if interest is 6%; (c) a present sum of $5,000 in 10 years if interest is 15%; (d) $8,000 paid 8 years from now if interest is

30%, compute the present time value; (e) deposits of $5,000 a year at the end of each year for the next 6 years if interest is 25%, compute the present time value; (f) a series of year-end payments of $1,000 for the next 10 years if interest is 15%, compute the time value at the end of 10 years; (g) a present sum of $10,000 if interest is 12%, compute the time value of this expressed as a future series of year-end payments for the next 8 years.

4.14 How much would one have to invest in an annuity policy paying 6% in order to receive $6,000 a year forever?

4.15 If an investor could buy a share of stock for $75 on the expectation of receiving $1.75 in dividends quarterly for an unlimited period (i.e., forever), what is the rate of return on his investment?

4.16 To earn 10% on an investment, how much should one pay for a property that will have a net income for an indefinitely long period of $11,500 at the end of every year?

4.17 Find the perpetual annual income to a college with an endowment of $17,000,000, if the investments earn $6\frac{1}{4}$%.

4.18 If a student proposes to save 10% of his salary over his professional carrer, estimated to be 40 years, how much will he have for "old age" if he invests it at 4% compounded annually? For simplicity, assume his salary starts at $5,000 and increases 50% every 10 years.

4.19 The student in Problem 4.18 proposes to save 10% of his salary over a 40-year earning period and invest it at 4% effective annual interest; how much will he accumulate at the end of this time assuming his starting salary is $5,000 and he receives a raise at the end of every year of $425?

4.20 A man, age 45, is incapable of working as a result of an injury. If ordinarily he would have had to retire in 20 years and his present salary is $12,000 a year, what lump-sum compensation to him would appear fair? What assumptions are inherent in your computation?

4.21 An investor needs money to organize a business. He proposes to sell 4% bonds redeemable in 10 years at $1,000. The interest payments will be made directly to the bondholders and will be made quarterly (each quarterly payment on this 4% bond will be $10). What must be the price if the purchasers want 6% return compounded quarterly?

4.22 A company is paying an investor $5,000 in royalties at the end of every year for the use of a patent which has 12 years to run. Assuming that the royalties will continue at this annual amount, what lump sum might the company offer the inventor if the company's minimum desirable rate of return is 15%? Is this price favorable to the company or to the inventor?

4.23 A man needs $30,000 immediately for the purchase of a house. He will be required to repay the loan in equal 6-month payments over the next 10 years at 6% interest compounded semiannually. What are the required payments?

4.24 A town must repay a $50,000, 5% bond issue in 20 years. Assume the 5% interest will be paid directly to the bondholders at the end of each year. However by law the town must establish a sinking fund to assure the repayment of the principal at the date of maturity. (a) What year-end annual deposit must be made into the sinking fund if it earns 4% compounded quarterly? (b) What is the town's total annual payment?

4.25   A company may pay for a $20,000 machine tool in 6 equal installments due at the end of every 6 months. The finance company to whom these payments will be made wants to earn 8% compounded quarterly. What will be the amounts of the payments?

4.26   A finance company is asked to make a loan of $2,800 for the purchase of an automobile. The company wants to earn 12% compounded monthly and recover its money in 24 equal end-of-month payments. How large are the payments?

4.27   How much must a father deposit every 3 months at 4% interest compounded quarterly to provide a lump sum of $10,000 at the end of 15 years for his child's college education? At the end of 10 years how much has he built up toward this goal? If at that time he inherits some money, how much could he deposit in a lump sum in lieu of continuing his quarterly payments?

4.28   Repairs to a factory roof can be made today for $3,000 or, if left to deteriorate, it will have to be replaced in 3 years for $5,000. The repaired roof will be as serviceable as a new roof and will last as long. If the company's minimum required rate of return is 35%, should the repairs be made?

4.29   A machine must be maintained and serviced at a cost of $300 at the end of its first year of operation, and this will increase by $30 a year over its entire 10-year life. If a redesign of the machine would completely eliminate these costs, how much could the company pay for this improvement if the company's minimum required rate of return is 25%?

4.30   A repair now will save future repairs. If present repairs will cost $5,000 and the time value of money is 20%, what would next year's repair bill have to be to justify repairing now? Take into account also that a failure to repair now will result in a cost of lost production of $400 by the end of the coming year.

4.31   What must be the prospective annual saving (use end-of-year convention) to justify spending $10,000 for a new machine if the machine is expected to perform for 8 years and if the company expects to receive a rate of return of 20% on any investments it approves?

4.32   If storm windows are expected to save $200 a year on a house's heating bill for the next 15 years, what could one afford to pay for them if he can get 6% on his money in other investments?

4.33   By spending $125 for a kitchen exhaust fan, an equipment vendor estimates that the home owner will need to paint his kitchen at the end of every 4 years instead of every 2. The cost of each painting is $30. Assume the life of the fan on this service is indefinitely long, what is the rate of return on the investment?

4.34   By spending $25,000 for a conveyor, a factory expects to save $6,000 a year for the next 7 years in the cost of handling material. If the conveyor will have zero value at that date, compute the company's rate of return on the investment in the conveyor.

4.35 What rate of return can be obtained by spending $10,000 now in order to save $2,000 a year (at the end of each year) for 10 years?

4.36 What rate of return will be earned by spending $5,000 now to save spending $8,000 5 years from now?

4.37 What is the single present value of six future year-end income payments of $700, a single income payment of $1,000 4 years from now, and an expense of $2,000 5 years from now if interest is 20%?

4.38 A company proposes to buy a machine for $6,000 that promises annual savings of $2,700 per year for the next 4 years. The maintenance expense for the 4 years is zero for the first year and increases by $200 each year. With interest at 10%, what is the present value of the project? Is the investment justified?

4.39 With interest at 20%, convert the following nonuniform series to a uniform annual series: a first cost of $10,000 with year-end operating costs of $2,000 for 5 years followed by operating costs of $3,000 a year for the next 5 years.

4.40 A machine can be rented for $3,000 a year on a 10-year lease. Payments are due at the end of the year. After 4 payments the owner is asked to name a lump sum he will accept in lieu of the remaining payments of rent. What should the figure be if the interest is 15%?

4.41 A tool can be purchased for a down payment of $4,000 and four payments of $2,000 to be made at the first of the following 4 years. When the second payment of $2,000 comes due, the company decides it might like to pay the remaining obligation in one lump sum. What amount would be acceptable to the company if its minimum acceptable rate of return is 20%?

4.42 With interest at 15%, convert the following nonuniform series into a uniform annual series: a sum of $20,000 occurs at the beginning of the first year; in the following 10 years, sums of $8,000 occur at the end of every year for the first 4 years and $10,000 at the end of every year for the last 6 years. Additional sums of $6,000 occur at the beginning of the third and sixth years of the 10-year period.

4.43 A company proposes to spend $20,000 for a new machine. What should the annual savings be over the next 10 years if the minimum acceptable rate of return is 20%? Make a rough check of your answer without the use of tables or factor formulas.

   If the year-end savings over this period are actually $4,000 a year, what is the rate of return on the investment? Make a rough check of this answer without the use of tables or formulas.

4.44 Rework the following problems if all of the *series payments* are continuous through the year instead of year end and if the interest is continuous instead of discrete. The interest rates in the given examples are the effective values. The *single payments* will continue to be lump sum at the dates given in the examples. Problems 4.10, 4.14, 4.16, 4.17, 4.22, 4.28, 4.30 through 4.40, 4.42.

4.45 Prove that the value of $A = G(A/G, i, n)$, if $i = 0$, is $(n - 1)/2$, as given in Eq. 4.10n.

4.46 Prove that the value of $A = G(A/G, i, n)$, if $n = \infty$, is $1/i$, as given in Eq. 4.10g.

5

Equivalence

5.1 EQUAL TIME VALUES

The factors developed in Chapter 3 enable us to compute the values at various points in time of a given sum or series.

Starting with a sum of $1,000 and a rate of 10%, the following time values can be computed using all of the factors.

(1)

$$\underset{0}{\overset{1,000}{\vdash\!\!\!-}{}}\underset{10}{\overset{F = ?}{\dashv}}$$

$1,000 today has a time value 10 years hence of $2,594:

$$\overset{2.594}{F = 1,000(F/P, .10, 10) = \$2,594}$$

(2)

$$\underset{0}{\overset{1,000}{\vdash\!\!\!-\!\!\!-\!\!\!-\!\!\!-\!\!\!-\!\!\!-\!\!\!-\!\!\!-\!\!\!-\!\!\!-\!\!\!-\!\!\!-\!\!\!-\!\!\!-\!\!\!-\!\!\!-\!\!\!-}{A = ?}}\underset{10}{\dashv}$$

Its time value expressed as a series over the next 10 years is $162.75 per year:

$$\overset{0.16275}{A = 1,000(A/P, .10, 10) = \$162.75}$$

(3)

$$\underset{0}{\overset{P = ?}{\vdash\!\!\!-}{}}\underset{10}{\overset{2,594}{\dashv}}$$

And the time value of a future sum of $2,594 occurring 10 years from now is $1,000 today:

$$\overset{0.3855}{P = 2,594(P/F, .10, 10) = \$1,000}$$

(4)

$$\underset{0}{\vdash\!\!\!-\!\!\!-\!\!\!-\!\!\!-\!\!\!-\!\!\!-\!\!\!-\!\!\!-\!\!\!-\!\!\!-\!\!\!-\!\!\!-\!\!\!-\!\!\!-\!\!\!-\!\!\!-\!\!\!-}{\overset{A = ?}{}}\underset{10}{\overset{2,594}{\dashv}}$$

68

And the time value of this future sum of $2,594 is $162.75 a year for the 10 years preceding it:

$$A = 2,594 \overset{0.06275}{(A/F, .10, 10)} = \$162.75$$

(5)

$$
\begin{array}{ll}
A = 162.75 & F = ? \\
\vdash\!\!\!-\!\!\!-\!\!\!-\!\!\!-\!\!\!-\!\!\!-\!\!\!-\!\!\!-\!\!\!-\!\!\!\dashv \\
0 & 10
\end{array}
$$

And the time value 10 years from now of a uniform series of $162.75 over the next 10 years is $2,594:

$$F = 162.75 \overset{15.937}{(F/A, .10, 10)} = \$2,594$$

(6)

$$
\begin{array}{ll}
P = ? \quad A = 162.75 & \\
\vdash\!\!\!-\!\!\!-\!\!\!-\!\!\!-\!\!\!-\!\!\!-\!\!\!-\!\!\!-\!\!\!-\!\!\!\dashv \\
0 & 10
\end{array}
$$

And the time value today of $162.75 a year for the next 10 years is $1,000:

$$P = 162.75 \overset{6.1446}{(P/A, .10, 10)} = \$1,000$$

These computations at 10% interest can be summarized as follows:

- $2,594 is the time value 10 years hence of $1,000 today.
- $1,000 is the present time value of $2,594 10 years from now.
- A series of $162.75 a year for the next 10 years is the time value of $1,000 today.
- $1,000 today is the time value of a series of $162.75 over the next 10 years.
- $2,594 is the time value 10 years hence of a series of $162.75 over the next 10 years.
- A series of $162.75 over the next 10 years is the time value of $2,594 10 years hence.

Therefore *each of these alternative sums or series is the time value of every other sum or series*, at 10%.

5.2 EQUIVALENCE DEFINED

The sums and series in the previous section are also "equivalent." Equivalence occurs whenever a sum or a series is the time value of another sum or a series. Therefore at 10% interest $2,594 10 years hence is the equivalent of $1,000 today. In fact each of the previous sums or series is the equivalent of every other sum or series.

It is important to observe that this does not mean, nor does it say, that these sums or the series are equal; they are not: only their time values are equal. For example, we have shown that the following sums or series are equivalent at 10% interest.

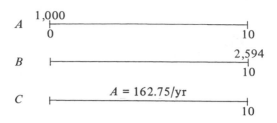

The sums are by no means equal; they are related only through their time values.

If the sums are not equal, (a) what is the reason for computing their equivalence and (b) what is the reality of equivalence? We will discuss these questions in the following sections.

5.3 EVALUATING ALTERNATIVES BY EQUIVALENCES

The equivalence concept is the basis for comparing alternative proposals for spending money. These proposals generally are described by a time series of costs which cannot be evaluated by mere inspection. By the use of equivalence it becomes possible to compare these alternatives, as examples will show.

EXAMPLE 5.3 Compare an alternative, A, costing \$10,000 and requiring cash outlays of \$5,000 a year for 10 years, with B, costing \$15,000 and requiring prospective cash outlays of \$4,000 a year for 10 years, if interest is 10%.

SOLUTION.

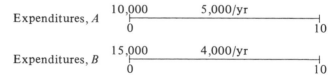

The equivalent of each alternative at time zero is

$$P_A = 10,000 + 5,000 \overset{6.1446}{(P/A, .10, 10)} = 10,000 + 30,723 = \$40,723$$

$$P_B = 15,000 + 4,000 \overset{6.1446}{(P/A, .10, 10)} = 15,000 + 24,578 = \$39,578$$

A decision to select Series A or B could not be made from a mere inspection of the time scales, but the decision can be made from their equivalents at the same point in time. The equivalent of B is lower than that of A, and since these are costs, not incomes, B should be selected.

Equivalence is therefore used as a yardstick for comparing alternatives. Just as a distance is converted into feet for purposes of evaluation, a time series is converted into an "equivalent." In the subject of valuation, equivalence serves a larger but similar purpose.

5.4 MEANING OF EQUAL EQUIVALENCE

Before we can make any choice between alternatives we must agree on a minimum required rate of return based on the assumptions, as in Section 2.9, that (a) we have funds, (b) the funds are limited relative to the opportunities, and (c) the funds must all be invested. To maximize the return on the investment, the limited supply must be invested only in the best investments, and this requires establishing a lower limit on the rates of return that we will approve. This limit becomes our minimum required rate of return. But note that thereafter, wherever we can invest at this minimum rate of return, we must do so because we chose it to be the cutoff between the investments we will take and those we will reject. It presumes that our capital has been budgeted to permit this. Therefore if we should reject opportunities promising the minimum required rate of return, the funds that this would free would be limited to opportunities below the minimum required. So it is understood that whenever the opportunity presents itself we must invest in every proposition down through the minimum required rate of return.

Suppose now that we had only three alternative propositions, as illustrated on the following time scales. Would we elect to spend $1,000 now as in A, $2,594$ 10 years from now as in B, or $162.75 a year for the next 10 years as in C? In this problem we will assume that by a capital budgeting viewpoint the minimum required rate of return has been established at 10%. The alternatives are

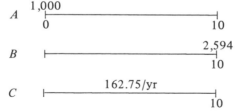

The equivalent of each alternative at time zero and 10% is

$$\text{For A,} \qquad\qquad\qquad\qquad\quad \$1,000$$
$$\text{For B,} \qquad\quad \overset{0.3855}{2,594\,(P/F,\,.10,\,10)} = \$1,000$$
$$\text{For C,} \qquad\quad \overset{6.1446}{162.75\,(P/A,\,.10,\,10)} = \$1,000$$

The equivalents of the three alternatives at a 10% minimum required rate of return are identical. Does this eliminate any basis of selection between them? It certainly seems to, but let us make a closer examination of the differences between the alternatives. The difference between A and B is that A requires an expenditure of $1,000 now whereas B requires an expenditure of $2,594 at the end of 10 years. Therefore, if we select A over B, we will spend $1,000 now and save spending $2,594 10 years from now, as illustrated on the following time scale.

Selecting A over B

	Cost		Savings
	1,000		2,594
	0		10

Selecting A over B is therefore the same as investing $1,000 to receive a return of $2,594 at the end of 10 years. The rate of return on this investment is

$$1,000\,(F/P, i, 10) = 2,594$$

$$(F/P, i, 10) = 2,594$$

whence

$$i = 10\%$$

This is the agreed-on 10% minimum required rate of return, so we are required to accept the investment.

Now compare alternatives B and C. Although their equivalents are equal and do not provide a clue to their differences, we note their costs are distributed at different points in time. This is the actual reality, and it alone would make them different even if their costs were for identical amounts. The time and money differences between B and C can be shown by subtracting their time scale as follows:

Selecting C over B

	Cost	Savings
	162.75/yr	2,594
	0	10

This is not a theoretical comparison; it is a statement of the real difference between the alternatives. Selecting C requires spending $162.75 a year but saves spending $2,594 at the end of the tenth year. This is the same as investing $162.75 a year to receive an income of $2,594 10 years from now.

The return on this investment is

$$162.75\,(F/A, i, 10) = 2,594$$

$$(F/A, i, 10) = 15.937$$

whence

$$i = 10\%$$

and, as it is the minimum required rate of return, we must approve investing in C.

The only remaining question is, should we select A over C?

Selecting A over C

	Cost	Savings	
	1,000	162.75/yr	
	0		10

Selecting A means we spend $1,000 now but we will save spending $162.75 a year for the next 10 years. This is a good investment, because the $1,000 will be recovered with 10% interest, the minimum required rate of return.

$$1,000(A/P, i, 10) = 162.75$$

$$(A/P, i, 10) = 0.16275$$

whence

$$i = 10\%$$

These examples demonstrate that where alternatives have equal equivalents, it does not mean that the alternatives themselves are equal. There is, in fact, a difference and a choice to be made between them. The difference between the alternatives arises because their costs occur at different points in time. The difference cannot be evaluated by inspection but only by computing whether the present expenditure will be recovered with a sufficiently attractive rate of return.

5.5 EFFECT OF CHANGING THE REQUIRED RATE OF RETURN

Let us consider the three alternatives again.

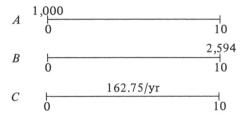

In the last section it was shown that at 10% interest each alternative is equivalent to a present sum of $1,000, and it was proved that, although the equivalents were equal, A would be selected if 10% were the minimum necessary rate of return.

At a different rate of return, however, (a) the equivalents will change and (b) the selection of alternatives may change. For example, the equivalent of each at 15% at time zero is

For A, $1,000

                         0.2472

For B, $2,594(P/F, .15, 10) = \$\ 641$

                         5.019

For C, $162.75(P/A, .15, 10) = \$\ 817$

Now the equivalents are all different, and if the minimum required rate of return is 15%, B will be selected, not A.

In this case B is selected because it has the lowest equivalent cost. It means that we will reject spending $1,000 today because $2,594 is not a large enough saving 10 years hence to recover the $1,000 with 15% interest (as seen in Section 5.4, it is only big enough to recover the $1,000 with 10% interest). Similarly, C is not selected because $2,594 is not a large enough saving at the end of 10 years to recover the series of annual investments of $162.75 with 15%

interest. Hence it is more economic to spend $2,594 at the end of 10 years and to save spending either $1,000 now or $162.75 every year.

Similar reasoning can be developed by comparing the alternatives at 5% interest; however, we have had sufficient opportunity to observe that (a) the equivalents exist only at the given rate of return and that (b) changing the rate of return can reverse the selection.

5.6 EQUIVALENCE VIS-À-VIS REALITY

We now realize that equivalence is only a kind of measure to permit the evaluation of alternative series of expenditures at some rate of return. The computation does not imply, however, that we will make an expenditure equal in amount of the equivalent. For example, if we have a series of year-end expenditures of $162.75 for 10 years, the equivalent at time zero at 10% interest is $1,000, but this does not mean that we will spend $1,000 today. Neither does it mean that we must invest $1,000 in order to have $162.75 a year. Equivalence is only a measure; it implies no procedure for purchasing, financing, investing, or reinvesting. In fact, as stated, the only reality is the actual time series.

5.7 EQUIVALENCE AND THE USAGE OF FUNDS

Although it seems to imply it, equivalence does not mean equal usage of funds. For example, if we compare alternatives A and B, the usage of funds is different, even though they are equivalent at 10%.

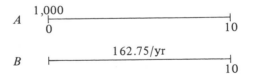

The person who receives $1,000 today will have a greater usage of funds than the person who receives $162.75 a year for 10 years. The same can be said of the usage given up by the persons who pay these sums. Therefore the person who exchanges the use of $1,000 today for the use of $162.75 next year and $162.75 each year thereafter can expect compensation for the usage he gives up. In this case his compensation is equal to 10% interest on the $1,000.

Equivalence does not imply equal usage, but it does imply that the unequal usage is compensated by the rate of return awarded to the person who parts with the usage of funds.

5.8 PRACTICAL EQUIVALENCE COMPARISONS

In most cases, the cost comparisons are between alternatives of different engineering efficiency, namely, one with a high first cost and low future disbursements compared to one with a low first cost and high future disbursements. These alternatives cannot be compared by mere inspection or even by addition and subtraction. The mere fact that the sums are distributed in time is sufficient to require equivalence measurements. The only exception occurs where the two alternatives have exactly the same time series, like this:

$$A \quad \overset{1,000 \qquad\qquad 100/\text{yr}}{\underset{0 \qquad\qquad\qquad\qquad\qquad\qquad 10}{\vdash\!\!\!\rule{5cm}{0.4pt}\!\!\!\dashv}}$$

$$B \quad \overset{1,000 \qquad\qquad 100/\text{yr}}{\underset{0 \qquad\qquad\qquad\qquad\qquad\qquad 10}{\vdash\!\!\!\rule{5cm}{0.4pt}\!\!\!\dashv}}$$

These are alike, with no numerical advantage of one over the other.

When we displace two sums in time like this, however,

$$\underset{0 \qquad\qquad\qquad\qquad\qquad\qquad 10}{\overset{0 \qquad\qquad\qquad\qquad\qquad\qquad 1,000}{\vdash\!\!\!\rule{6cm}{0.4pt}\!\!\!\dashv}}$$

$$\underset{0 \qquad\qquad\qquad\qquad\qquad\qquad 10}{\overset{1,000 \qquad\qquad\qquad\qquad\qquad\qquad 0}{\vdash\!\!\!\rule{6cm}{0.4pt}\!\!\!\dashv}}$$

their differences cannot be evaluated by inspection.

Equivalence comparisons are necessary and, in practice, conform to one of these generally accepted methods:

1. *Annual-Cost Method.* Each alternative is converted to an equivalent series of uniform end-of-year payments.

2. *Present-Worth and Capitalized-Cost Methods.* Each alternative is converted to an equivalent single sum located at time zero (or at a point regarded to be time zero).

3. *Rate-of-Return Method.* The rate of return is computed which will make the alternatives equivalent. This rate of return, therefore, is a direct evaluation of the alternatives.

These three practical methods of comparison are the subject of the next three chapters.

PROBLEMS

5.1 Refer to Table 3.11 in Chapter 3 and compute the lump sum equivalent at the end of year 5 of the following at 10% interest: (a) the 5-year series of interest (column 2) plus the 5-year series of capital recovery payments (column 6); (b) the $10,000 loan; (c) a $10,000 loan in which all the interest payments are equal and at the end of each year.

5.2 How many ways of repaying the $10,000 loan in Table 3.11 can you describe? Interest is 10%. Give numerical answers. Are these methods equivalent? What are the economical differences between them?

5.3 A company currently owes a bank $3,000 which it may repay at any one of the three following times: (a) $3,000 now, (b) $5,373 10 years from now, (c) $407.61 a year for 10 years.

Determine the company's best choice if its minimum required rate of return is (a) 10%; (b) 15%; (c) 8%.

5.4 A person may pay a bill for $1,000 now or pay $1,030 by waiting until the end of the year. His opportunities to invest are such that 6% is considered his minimum acceptable rate of return. Discuss the equivalents of the alternative choices in paying the bill.

5.5 A company can overhaul a machine now for $1,250 or wait until the end of the year; in the latter case $250 will be the cost by the year's end of idle labor caused by machine outages. Compare the equivalents of these alternatives if the company's minimum required rate of return is 20% and make a recommendation.

5.6 A company invests $2,000 in a piece of equipment that will save $800 per year in disbursements for materials. The economic life of the equipment is 6 years and the minimum required rate of return is 12%. How much of the yearly savings must be invested each year for 6 years at 12% to accumulate a sum equal to the amount that would be obtained if the $2,000 were invested at the minimum required rate of return?

5.7 A corporation can lease a new machine for $23,852 payable at the end of each year for 10 years or it can purchase the machine outright for $100,000. The economic life of the machine is 10 years and salvage is expected to be zero. If the minimum required rate of return is 20%, does it make any difference which alternative the corporation takes?

5.8 A company is considering two alternatives. Alternative A costs $6,000 and has an economic life of 8 years. Alternative B costs $4,000, has an annual operating expense that is $375 greater than A. It also has an economic life of 8 years. By an equivalence comparison, find the recommended alternative if the minimum required rate of return is (a) 20%; (b) 10%; (c) 5%.

5.9 Compare the usage of funds by the borrower under each of the plans of payment you suggested in Problem 5.2.

5.10 You can pay a debt of $1,000 now or you may put it off one year without penalty. In addition, a rich benefactor will give you $1,000 today or a year from now, the choice being yours. Using equivalence, what would you decide to do?

5.11 A man can buy a certain automobile at a reduction of $400; however, he estimates that this particular car will cost an extra of $100 a year for the next 4 years over a car for which he'd have to pay full price. By using equivalence, comment on his bargain. Assume the repairs are at the beginning of each year.

6

Annual-Cost and Annual-Worth Comparisons

6.1 ANNUAL-COST COMPUTATION

In the past, one of the most widely employed methods of evaluation has been based on the conversion of the cost of each alternative into an equivalent uniform series. This is well known as the Annual-Cost Method of Comparison.

Annual cost has been computed in practice by one of three methods which we will discuss:

1. Capital Recovery with a Rate-of-Return Method.
2. Sinking-Fund Method.
3. Straight-Line Depreciation plus Average-Interest Method.

The symbols[1] generally used are

P The investment in the equipment; the total first cost; the installed cost.
L The realizable value at the end of the economic life.[2]
n The economic life in years on the basis that the rate of return i in annual-cost problems is for a 1-year period.
I A series of equal end-of-year incomes.
D A series of equal end-of-year disbursements.
i The minimum required rate of return.
A The uniform end-of-period series equivalent to P or to P and L; the uniform annual equivalent investment cost.
AC The annual cost; the uniform end-of-period equivalent to all of the costs over the period n.[3]

---

[1] The symbols are for instant or lump-sum payments. The same symbols topped by a bar will represent continuous-flow payments as defined in Section 3.17.

[2] See Appendix re terms L and S.

[3] Whence $AC = f(A + D)$.

AW   The annual worth; the same as AC except that it is the equivalent of a stream of incomes or savings.[1]

6.2 REASONS FOR THE ANNUAL-COST COMPARISON

The annual-cost method is frequently used because people are more familiar with the concept of annual cost than with concepts of present worth (discounting), future worth (compounding), or perhaps even the concept of rate of return on the investment. Because understanding is a prerequisite to acceptance, we may often go far out of our way to compare alternatives in terms that are comprehensible to those whom we ask to adopt our conclusions.

In addition, the annual-cost method is easier to explain and justify than some of the newer and more complicated techniques, and it is reasonably easy to compute, especially compared to trial and error computations sometimes required in the rate-of-return method. As we shall see, the annual-cost equation is generally used in this text as the basis for setting up the other two methods of comparison, present worth and rate of return. Furthermore annual-cost comparisons may be used to complement present-worth or rate-of-return analyses if it seems advisable to present the conclusion from more than one viewpoint. In any event, true understanding of the subject is inconceivable without a knowledge of the principles of annual-cost comparisons.

6.3 MAKING AN ANNUAL-COST COMPARISON

The "annual cost" is merely the cost pattern of each alternative converted into an equivalent uniform series of annual costs at the minimum required rate of return i. The alternative with the lowest cost-series obviously is the more economic selection. This conversion is necessary because mere inspection will not show whether the alternative with the low first cost is better than the one with the low operating disbursements.[2]

The cost pattern will consist of the investment P, its salvage value L, and annual operating costs D. The equivalent uniform series of the *investment cost* is generally expressed by Eq. 6.3 derived as follows:

$$A = P(A/P, i, n) - L(A/F, i, n)$$

but

$$(A/F, i, n) = (A/P, i, n) - i$$

---

[1] Whence AW = f(I).

[2] We rarely encounter the machine with the low first cost and low operating cost. Conversely, the competitor with the high first cost and high operating cost will learn that he must lower one or the other or get out of business.

therefore,

$$A = (P - L)(A/P, i, n) + Li \qquad (6.3)$$

Equation 6.3 can be visualized to represent the recovery with interest of a portion of the capital, $P - L$, plus the interest on the remaining portion L. Recovery of the capital represented by L is not included in Eq. 6.3, because it is provided by the income from salvage.

EXAMPLE 6.3 Machine A costs $10,000, with $4,000 salvage value at the end of 6 years and annual operating disbursements of $5,000 a year for the first 3 years and $6,000 for the last 3 years. Machine B costs $8,000, with $3,000 salvage at the end of 6 years. Its operating disbursements are $5,500 a year for the first 3 years and $6,500 a year for the last 3 years. The increases in operating disbursements are the expected increases in maintenance and repair and the loss in efficiency with age. The minimum required rate of return is 15%.

SOLUTION.   The problem is presented on the time scales as follows:

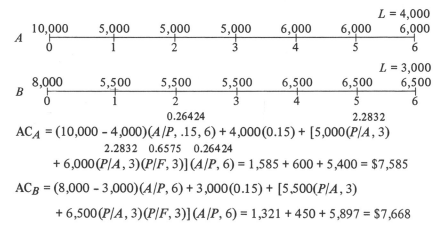

$$AC_A = (10{,}000 - 4{,}000)(A/P, .15, 6) + 4{,}000(0.15) + [5{,}000(P/A, 3)$$
$$+ 6{,}000(P/A, 3)(P/F, 3)](A/P, 6) = 1{,}585 + 600 + 5{,}400 = \$7{,}585$$

$$AC_B = (8{,}000 - 3{,}000)(A/P, 6) + 3{,}000(0.15) + [5{,}500(P/A, 3)$$
$$+ 6{,}500(P/A, 3)(P/F, 3)](A/P, 6) = 1{,}321 + 450 + 5{,}897 = \$7{,}668$$

6.4 SINKING-FUND CONCEPT

Analysis by the sinking-fund procedure is also known as "amortization with interest on first cost." The definition of amortize is to pay off or satisfy a debt by means of a sinking fund. A formula which combines (a) the annual cost of a sinking fund to repay the principal and (b) the annual cost of interest on the principal can be set up as follows:

From Eq. 6.3,
$$A = P(A/P, i, n) - L(A/F, i, n)$$

but
$$(A/P, i, n) = (A/F, i, n) + i$$

$$A = P(A/F, i, n) + Pi - L(A/F, i, n)$$

so
$$A = (P - L)(A/F, i, n) + Pi \qquad (6.4)$$

We observe that the first term is the annual cost of a sinking fund which will recover the capital, $P - L$ (since L is recovered from salvage), at the end of n years, and the second term, Pi, is the annual interest on the investment.

EXAMPLE 6.4 Equipment will cost $20,000 with salvage of $10,000 at the end of 10 years. The required rate of return is 10%. Compare the concept of annual investment cost by the capital-recovery method and the sinking-fund method.

SOLUTION. By Eq. 6.4,

$$A = (20,000 - 10,000)\overset{0.06275}{(A/F, .10, 10)} + (20,000)(0.10)$$

$$= \$2,628$$

or, by Eq. 6.3,

$$A = (20,000 - 10,000)\overset{0.16275}{(A/P, .10, 10)} + (10,000)(0.10)$$

$$= \$2,628$$

Obviously the annual cost by Eqs. 6.3 and 6.4 must be the same, since both were derived from the same equation; however, each formula presents a different concept of the factors comprising the cost of an investment. By Eq. 6.3 the borrower pays two sums: $1,628 a year to repay the entire debt with interest, except for salvage, and $1,000 to pay the annual interest on the amount which will be recovered by salvage. By Eq. 6.4 the borrower pays $628 into a sinking fund which will repay the debt without interest, and he also pays $2,000, the annual interest on the entire debt.

Either method is acceptable, so the objective is to adopt the concept which will be understood by those who must be convinced of the conclusion. "Understanding" must also extend to the fact that neither Eq. 6.3 nor Eq. 6.4 implies that the repayments will be made in that manner. These only provide a measure of each alternative. There is no requirement to set up a sinking fund or to make equal capital-recovery payments unless, of course, corresponding plans of repayment are actually intended. Section 6.5 illustrates such a situation.

6.5 PRACTICAL USE OF THE SINKING FUND

Because companies can earn higher rates of return by putting the money to work in their own businesses, they invest in machines, processes, and productive operations in their own companies rather than in sinking funds. Money acquired from a plowback of earnings or from the annual depreciation "reserves" will be reinvested in the business—not invested in sinking funds. As a general rule, therefore, sinking funds are not created out of earnings or depreciation.

The sinking-fund method has its practical application, however, where administrative policy or public law requires that an actual sinking fund be set up. Some public projects require that an actual sinking fund independent of all other revenues must be established to provide for the eventual replacement of the equipment and to assure that funds will not be diverted to other purposes. In these instances it is likely that the interest rate paid on the money in the sinking fund is not the same as that which must be paid on the first cost. This would occur, for example, if the investment represented by the first cost were obtained by a bond issue paying 6% and if the money in the sinking fund earned 3%.

EXAMPLE 6.5 Equipment cost for a public project is $10,000 with an expected life of 10 years. The minimum required rate of return is 7% based on the cost of borrowed money. The law requires that annual deposits be made into a sinking fund which will accumulate the $10,000 at the end of 10 years. Compute the annual investment cost if the sinking fund will earn 4% interest.

SOLUTION.

$$\overset{0.08329}{A = 10,000(A/F, .04, 10) + (10,000)(0.07)}$$

$$= 832.90 + 700 = \$1,532.90$$

6.6 STRAIGHT-LINE DEPRECIATION PLUS AVERAGE INTEREST

The method of straight-line depreciation plus average interest is an approximate method, unlike the two previous methods, because it adds and subtracts sums which do not occur at the same point in time.

The formulation assumes that the recovery of capital is on a straight-line basis, that is, an equal amount is recovered each year, as in Fig. 6.6. It will be noted that because the investment decreases each year by $(P - L)/n$, the annual interest charges are not equal, but since we want to compute *equal* annual costs we must use the average annual interest cost. This average is derived in the following manner:

Interest paid at the end of first year is $Li + (P - L) i$.

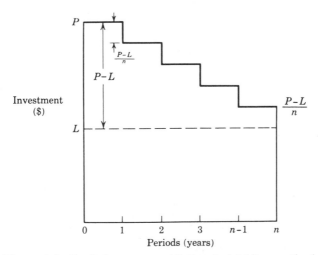

Figure 6.6   Capital recovery with the straight-line method

Interest paid at the end of last year is $Li + \dfrac{(P - L)}{n} i$.

The average of this equals $(P - L) \left(\dfrac{i}{2}\right) \left(\dfrac{n + 1}{n}\right) + Li$.

The annual cost is the annual depreciation plus this average interest:

$$\text{AC} = \frac{P - L}{n} + (P - L) \left(\frac{i}{2}\right)\left(\frac{n + 1}{n}\right) + Li \tag{6.6}$$

Examination of Eq. 6.6 reveals that the first term represents the recovery of capital, the middle term the interest on that part of the capital which depreciates (hence it must be an average), and the last term represents the interest on that part of the capital which does not depreciate, the salvage. It also serves to expose the fallacies of "shortcut" methods used in some engineering quarters, as noted in Section 6.8. Beyond the fact that it is a good tool to have in the bag, we will recommend against its use except for the purposes noted. One reason is that it is very inaccurate under the conditions described.

The method of straight-line depreciation plus average interest has been used by engineers and by financial executives probably because it is similar to the accounting concept of capital recovery, namely, straight-line depreciation. The method itself is not exact and, in fact, is very inaccurate in certain situations. Furthermore, it requires more work than the use of tables.

Among the few things to be said for this method is that it gives a quick approximation without a need for tables and can be quickly explained to those who have no understanding of the more precise methods. Although we recommend against its use, it has been employed and methods very similar to it have been proposed for use in industry.

As to the inaccuracies of this method, cost computed by it will be low. Table 6.6 indicates that the error will be considerable when the rate of return is high and the life period long. Errors of much greater magnitude than those in the table can result when comparisons are made between alternatives having unequal life periods.

Table 6.6 COMPARISON OF (crf)'s BY EXACT AND APPROXIMATE METHODS[a]

| Years, | 10% Interest | | | 15% Interest | | |
n	Exact	Approx.	Error (%)	Exact	Approx.	Error (%)
5	0.26380	0.26000	1.44	0.29832	0.29000	2.79
7	0.20541	0.20000	2.63	0.24036	0.22857	4.91
10	0.16275	0.15500	4.76	0.19925	0.18250	8.41
15	0.13147	0.12000	8.72	0.17102	0.14667	14.24
20	0.11746	0.10250	12.74	0.15976	0.12875	19.41

[a]The (crf) for the approximate method is computed from $\text{(crf)} = \dfrac{1}{n} + \left(\dfrac{i}{2}\right)\left(\dfrac{n + 1}{n}\right)$.

6.7 ONLY DIFFERENCES ARE RELEVANT

Since the sole purpose of an economic comparison is to select one alternative over another, we are not interested in the total cost of one or the total cost of the other but only whether one is greater or less than the other. In short, we are interested only in the difference between the two alternatives, namely, difference in annual costs, or difference in present worths or in the percentage earned on the difference (as we shall see later).

If, in the present case, we are only interested in the differences in annual costs between the alternatives, then obviously costs which do not contribute to this difference have no effect on the answer and may be omitted. This gives rise to the statement that *only the differences are relevant to the choice*.

EXAMPLE 6.7   Operation A has a first cost of $1,000 and the following estimated operating disbursements: fuel $500, maintenance $110, labor $700, insurance 1% of first cost, supervision $150, floor space $50. Operation B has a first cost of $800 and the following operating disbursements: fuel $680, maintenance $90, labor $700, insurance 1%, supervision $150, floor space $60. The life of each is expected to be 5 years with zero salvage. The minimum required rate of return is 8%.

SOLUTION.

$$A \quad \begin{array}{l} 1{,}000 \quad D = 500 + 110 + 700 + 0.01P + 150 + 50 \\ \vdash\!\!\!\!\!\!\!\!\!\!\rule{8cm}{0.4pt}\!\!\!\dashv \\ 0 \hspace{7.5cm} 5 \end{array}$$

$$B \quad \begin{array}{l} 800 \quad\; D = 680 + 90 + 700 + 0.01P + 150 + 60 \\ \vdash\!\!\!\!\!\!\!\!\!\!\rule{8cm}{0.4pt}\!\!\!\dashv \\ 0 \hspace{7.5cm} 5 \end{array}$$

	A	B
Investment Cost, $P(A/P, .08, 5)$ $	250	200
Labor	700	700
Fuel	500	680
Insurance, $0.01P$	10	8
Maintenance	110	90
Supervision	150	150
Floor Space	50	60
Annual Cost	$1,770	$1,888
Difference in favor of A	$ 118	

We would get the same advantage of $118 in favor of A if the costs of labor and supervision, which are alike for both alternatives, were omitted. Recognition of this fact has advantages. First, if we know that an item must be the same for both alternatives we can omit it and save the time and effort to compute it. In many cases the analyst knows that certain costs for each alternative will be the same without having to compute them. Second, by knowing that only the differences are relevant we can direct our efforts toward a more extensive search not only to find the differences but to make more accurate predictions of their cost patterns.

But now if we compile only *cost differences*, we must have it understood that the *annual cost* is not, or need not be, the *total cost*. This can be noted by adopting the term *comparative annual cost*.

6.8 MEANING OF AN ANNUAL-COST COMPARISON

An annual-cost comparison means something more than just concluding that machine *A* has a lower annual cost than *B* by so many dollars a year.

The first important interpretation of an annual-cost comparison is that the analysis concerns only the extra investment—nothing more or less—as illustrated in the following example.

EXAMPLE 6.8a Machine *A* costs $1,600 and is expected to have annual operating disbursements of $500 over its 5-year life. Machine *B* costs $1,200 with predicted annual operating disbursements of $650 for its 5-year life. Salvages are zero. The minimum required rate of return is 8%.

SOLUTION.   The time scales of the alternatives are

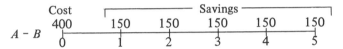

The difference between *A* and *B* is

The differences relevant to the choice between the two alternatives are (1) the extra investment in *A* and (2) the extra annual disbursements for *B*. If we make the extra investment in *A*, we save spending the extra disbursements in *B*. This is purely and simply an investment decision; the problem is to evaluate whether the savings are sufficient to recover the first cost with a minimum acceptable rate of return, in this case 8%. This is evaluated as follows:

$$0.25046$$
$$\text{Savings minus cost: } 150 - 400(A/P, .08, 5) = 150 - 100 = \$50/\text{yr}$$

We observe that this is the same as the difference in the annual costs of the alternatives:

$$0.25046$$
$$AC_B - AC_A = 1,200(A/P, .08, 5) + 650 - 1,600(A/P, 5) - 500 = \$50/\text{yr}$$

The only question resolved by an annual-cost comparison is whether to make the extra investment. This becomes apparent when we observe that we do not know any of the merits of *A*—we know only its demerits, its *costs*—nor do we know any of the merits of *B*; however, *between A and B* we know it is worthwhile to make the extra investment in *A* over *B*.

The conclusion in Example 6.8a may be expressed as follows: The extra investment in A is recovered with 8% interest plus a sum of $50 a year for 5 years.

EXAMPLE 6.8b Suppose the operating disbursements for B were $550 instead of $650 as they were in Example 6.8a:

SOLUTION.

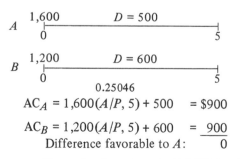

$$AC_A = 1,600(A/P, .08, 5) + 500 = \$900$$

$$AC_B = 1,200(A/P, 5) + 550 \qquad = \underline{850}$$
$$\text{Difference favorable to } B: \qquad \$ \ 50$$

Now the advantage is favorable to the lower cost machine: the one without the extra investment. Here the interpretation is: The extra investment of $400 fails to be recovered with 8% interest by $50 a year for 5 years.

Unfortunately we note that the differences are expressed in dollars and percent. This "apples-and-oranges" evaluation is the major disadvantage of the annual-cost method of comparison. The growing popularity of the rate-of-return method can be directly attributed to the fact that it expresses the comparison in one simple measure: percent.

Before finishing the interpretation of an annual-cost comparison let us look at this question: "What is the interpretation if the difference in the annual costs is zero?" The answer is illustrated in Example 6.8c.

EXAMPLE 6.8c Suppose the operating disbursements for B were $600 instead of $650 as they were in Example 6.8a:

SOLUTION.

A   1,600 $D = 500$
    0   5

B   1,200 $D = 600$
    0   5
       0.25046

$$AC_A = 1,600(A/P, 5) + 500 \qquad = \$900$$

$$AC_B = 1,200(A/P, 5) + 600 \qquad = \underline{900}$$
$$\text{Difference favorable to } A: \qquad 0$$

This situation means: The extra investment of $400 in A is recovered with *exactly* 8% interest. We must conclude that since 8% is the minimum required rate of return we will approve making the extra investment.

In summary we repeat that an annual-cost analysis deals solely with the advisability of making the extra investment. This should not discourage the reader, as it easily could, into believing that an analysis of only the extra investment is, therefore, only a partial treatment of the problem. It is actually a complete analysis because, for one thing, it achieves the sole objective of the analysis: to determine which of the two alternatives should be selected.

We must keep in mind that the analysis in Example 6.8a has (or should have) been preceded by an income-expansion analysis to decide the feasibility of the entire operation of which the present alternatives are only a part. For example, an earlier analysis of an income-expansion proposition should have decided that it was profitable to engage in an enterprise which incurred the proposed purchase of machine B, costing $1,200 (as well as other machines). The only question in Example 6.8a, therefore, is whether to invest another $400 in the function that machine B is intended to perform. If the extra investment is not justified, we shall, at least, purchase B (or keep B, as we shall see in Chapter 11 "Replacement Economy").

The process illustrated in Example 6.8a can be continued for other alternatives for comparison with machine A (since it won out over B in Example 6.8a) until the machine which can perform the function most economically is finally located.

6.9 CONCEPT OF ECONOMIC LIFE

In previous examples we were given the "life" of the equipment. Consideration of equipment life, or economic life, introduces a subject which is discussed at length in Chapter 10; however, some preliminary discussion perhaps will give the student enough understanding to satisfy his temporary requirements.

The economic life may be defined as the period of time that will elapse before the equipment—either present or proposed—is displaced from the intended service by more economic equipment. Or, restated, economic life is the period over which the equipment will continue to have the lowest annual cost compared to any contender for the service. It implies that the period will end with the appearance of equipment having lower annual cost.

The causes of replacement are, first, the deterioration of the equipment (this creates increasing costs relative to new equipment contending for the job) and, second, obsolescence of the equipment (this similarly causes higher annual costs relative to technologically improved equipments). These two causes, acting separately or together (according to various patterns), result in the gradual or in some cases the sudden decline of the equipment so that replacement is economically justified.

The concept of economic life is therefore inseparable from a consideration of replacement. Replacement or displacement is the result of a successful attempt by a superior equipment to terminate the service period of its predecessor.

6.10 COMPARISONS INVOLVING UNEQUAL LIVES

How do we compare alternatives that have different economic lives? What must we understand about the problem in order to make a logical comparison?

Let us first examine the problem.

EXAMPLE 6.10 Machine A costs $800 with an economic life of 5 years and operating disbursements of $600 a year. Machine B costs $1,500 with an economic life of 10 years and operating disbursements of $500 a year. Salvage values are considered to be negligible. The minimum required rate of return is 8%.

SOLUTION.

$$A \quad \overset{800}{\vdash} \qquad D = 600 \qquad \qquad \dashv \atop 0 \hspace{5.5cm} 5$$

$$B \quad \overset{1{,}500}{\vdash} \qquad\qquad D = 500 \qquad\qquad\qquad \dashv \atop 0 \hspace{7.5cm} 10$$

$$AC_A = 800 \overset{0.25046}{(A/P, .08, 5)} + 600 = 200 + 600 = \$800$$

$$AC_B = 1{,}500 \overset{0.14903}{(A/P, 10)} + 500 = 224 + 500 = \underline{724}$$
$$\phantom{AC_B = 1{,}500(A/P, 10) + 500 = 224 + 500 =}\ \ \$\ 76$$

The equivalent annual cost of A is $800 for 5 years, and B's is $724 for 10 years; if we disregard B's costs from years 6 through 10, the advantage of B is $76 a year for 5 years.

This situation is illustrated by substituting the uniform equivalent annual costs for the actual costs on the following time scales.

$$A \quad \overset{\;800\quad 800\quad 800\quad 800\quad 800}{\vdash\!\!\!\!+\!\!\!\!+\!\!\!\!+\!\!\!\!+\!\!\!\!+} \atop 0 \quad 1 \quad 2 \quad 3 \quad 4 \quad 5$$

$$B \quad \overset{724\ 724\ 724\ 724\ 724\ 724\ 724\ 724\ 724\ 724}{\vdash\!+\!+\!+\!+\!+\!+\!+\!+\!+\!+} \atop 0\ \ 1\ \ 2\ \ 3\ \ 4\ \ 5\ \ 6\ \ 7\ \ 8\ \ 9\ \ 10$$

By subtracting, the advantage of B over A is

$$\text{B over A} \quad \overset{\overbrace{\text{Savings}}\quad\overbrace{\text{Cost}}}{\overset{76\ \ 76\ \ 76\ \ 76\ \ 76\ \ 724\ \ 724\ \ 724\ \ 724\ \ 724}{\vdash\!+\!+\!+\!+\!+\!+\!+\!+\!+\!+}} \atop 0\ \ 1\ \ 2\ \ 3\ \ 4\ \ 5\ \ 6\ \ 7\ \ 8\ \ 9\ \ 10$$

In order to state that the advantage of B over A is $76 a year for 5 years, we must close our eyes to the costs of B after the fifth year. In one respect this procedure is not incorrect because, after all, the costs of B that occur after the fifth year belong to the comparisons that are to be made in that period. The question, it seems, is whether this comparison errs by disregarding all the possible events which might occur *on the time scale of A* after the fifth year. We will examine this question in detail in Section 6.13, but first let us look again at the philosophy which intentionally disregards all events after the fifth year. In the next section we will examine the study period which is based on this philosophy.

6.11 STUDY-PERIOD METHOD WHEN LIVES ARE DIFFERENT

The study-period method is a formalized name for essentially the same analysis we made in Example 6.10. In that example the study period would also disregard all the events or their effects in the period after year 5 if the selected study period were 5 years.

In the study-period approach, the mathematical model must be designed so that only those events and their costs are included which should be fairly charged to the period. In the case of A, if we select a 5-year study period, all its events occur within 5 years, so its annual cost is, as before,

$$\overset{0.25046}{AC_A = 800(A/P, .08, 5) + 600 = \$800}$$

In the case of B, the investment cost P, which pertains to the entire life period, must be prorated. The mechanism for distributing this over the 10-year life period and collecting the costs belonging to the 5-year study period can be observed from the following equation.

$$\overset{0.14903 \qquad 3.9927 \quad 0.25046}{AC_B = 1,500(A/P, .08, 10)(P/A, 3)(A/P, 5) + 500 = \$724}$$

We expect the same result as before, because Example 6.10 was based on the same philosophy: it, too, disregarded the entire stream of costs after year 5. The only basic difference between the procedure in Example 6.10 and the study-period approach is in the intentional selection of a study period. In this instance we purposely selected 5 years, the life period of A, but actually we could have selected any logical period. Of course if we select a period exceeding A's life, then we are faced anew with the responsibility of predicting the nature of the replacement for A.

6.12 IMPLICATION OF THE STUDY-PERIOD METHOD

The implication of the study-period method and of the conclusions in Example 6.10 are worth noting. We observed that both cases disregarded the stream of B's costs of $724 from year 6 through 10. Part of this stream represents the investment value in B, the value that expresses B's fitness to give service over the last 5 years. This investment value in B at year 5 may be computed as follows:

$$\overset{0.14903 \qquad 3.9927}{1,500(A/P, .08, 10)(P/A, 5) = \$893}$$

This is the theoretical salvage value L remaining in B at the end of year 5 (it also represents B's investment cost P at the beginning of year 6, the beginning of B's final 5 years of service).

Naturally this computed salvage value will give us the same annual cost as computed in Example 6.10 or in the study-period method:

$$\overset{0.25046}{AC_B = (1,500 - 893)(A/P, .08, 5) + (893)(0.08) + 500 = 152 + 72 + 500}$$

$$= \$724$$

It will also give the same cost stream as the one we disregarded over the last 5 years:

$$\overset{0.25046}{AC_B = 893(A/P, .08, 5) + 500 = 224 + 500 = \$724}$$

Mention of a salvage value suggests that to avoid any of the problems that arise with unequal lives we might have predicted the salvage value of B at the end of year 5. However, predicting a salvage value at year 5 and also predicting a 10-year economic life are not consistent: they are contradictory unless the predicted salvage value is $893 (if the minimum required rate of return is 8%). The computed annual cost is as low as $724 only because the economic life is 10 years. Computing the annual cost over a 5-year period based on the predicted salvage value at year 5 is expected to give a higher annual cost than that computed over the economic life period. From this we would also expect the salvage at year 5 always to be less than $893. If, however, it *is* greater than $893 we should use it, but in that case the economic life will not be 10 years. As we will see in Chapter 10, the lowest annual cost logically occurs over the period of the economic life, and if this occurs over a 5-year period, then the economic life is not 10 years. The question seems to be: Do you predict a 5-year or a 10-year economic life?

6.13 CONSIDERING FUTURE REPLACEMENTS

The question raised in Section 6.10 was whether we may disregard the events likely to appear on A's time scale after the first 5-year period. Are the possible replacements of A consequential in the selection between alternatives A and B? If they are, the study-period philosophy of disregarding the consequences after year 5 will have serious flaws.

The following example illustrates this situation.

EXAMPLE 6.13   The costs of machine A having a 5-year life and machine B having a 10-year life are reproduced from Example 6.10 on the following time scale. However, in this case, instead of disregarding the possible machines to follow A, the analyst foresees an improved machine which will become available in 5 years. This machine will also have a first cost of $800 with an estimated economic life of 5 years and zero salvage value but with annual operating disbursements of only $350.

The minimum required rate of return will be 8%, as before.

SOLUTION.

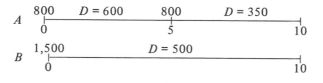

$$\overset{3.993}{} \qquad \overset{0.6806}{} \qquad \overset{3.993\quad 0.6806}{} \qquad \overset{0.1490}{}$$
$$AC_A = [800 + 600(P/A, .08, 5) + 800(P/F, 5) + 350(P/A, 5)(P/F, 5)](A/P, 10)$$

$$= [800 + 2{,}400 + 544 + 953](0.1490) = \$700$$
$$\phantom{= [800 + 2{,}400 + 544 + }0.1490$$
$$AC_B = 1{,}500(A/P, 10) + 500 \qquad\qquad = \underline{\ 724\ }$$
$$\text{The advantage of } A: \quad \$\ 24/\text{yr}$$

The advantage has now switched to A solely as a result of considering the replacement of A. In this case it has proved more economical to suffer the costs of operating the less economical machine A for 5 years in order to benefit from the improved machine that we expect to become available in 5 years.

6.14 COMPUTING MAXIMUM OR MINIMUM ADVANTAGES WHEN LIVES ARE DIFFERENT

Example 6.13 illustrated that the possible replacements for A, and for B, should be considered over a period that will terminate at a common date for both time scales. Beyond this point the same course of action will be equally available for A or B and therefore will be irrelevant to the choice. In Example 6.13 this occurred at the end of 10 years.

But now consider a very practical obstacle. We can reasonably predict the costs of machines A and B because they are machines of known designs, but we may not feel qualified to predict a machine that will appear in 5 years, as the analyst is presumed to have done in Example 6.13. What may we do in that case?

Of course we can use the study-period method and disregard all costs beyond the fifth year.

Another approach adopted by some analysts is to consider that A will be replaced with A, and B with B, until a period equal to the least common multiple of the lives is reached. This method is generally guilty of overstating the differences. For example, if the life of B happened to be 9 years and A is 5 years as given, the advantage claimed for B would be \$76 a year for 45 years, the least common multiple. Obviously the advantage of B has become a function of the least common multiple.

Another approach is based on the prediction, supported by historical fact, that machines of the future will be improvements on the most economical machines available today. As a *limit*, therefore, the future machines will be no less economical on the intended job than the most economical machine for the job today.

By assuming future replacements with the most economical machine available today we can at least compute the limit of the advantage or disadvantage of a choice of today's alternatives. This is illustrated in the following example.

EXAMPLE 6.14 Use the data in Example 6.10 except assume that all future replacements will be made with the most economical machine available today. The costs of machine A and B are reproduced from Example 6.10 on the time scales below:

SOLUTION.

The annual cost of machine A, computed in Example 6.10, was $800; that of B was $724. B is the more economical and by the given assumption will be the replacement machine in the future, as shown on the time scale.

Before stating a conclusion let us observe that an advantage of A, the machine with the shorter life, is the shorter commitment which attaches to it. By choosing A, management can take advantage of the improved machine that will likely be available in 5 years.

Therefore if B is the more economical (as in this case), then the quantitative *disadvantage* of selecting A (the machine that we would prefer in order to gain the short commitment) will be $76 a year for 5 years *or less*, depending on how superior the economy of the future machine may be.

On the other hand, if A, the short-lived machine, is more economical (let's say by $76 a year), then the quantitative *advantage* of selecting A will be *not less* than $76 a year for 10 years, depending on the extent of improvement in the new machine expected 5 years from now.

Research in this field has not developed to the point where we can make quantitative predictions of future improvements with any degree of confidence. The previous approach is only equal to saying that the improvements over the most economical machine today will be infinitesimal. With this assumption we may at least compute some limits to the advantage or disadvantage of selecting the machine with the shorter life.

In assuming that today's most economical machine and its cost pattern will be available in the future, we have disregarded the exceptional conditions where this may not be true. Such a condition may occur in certain instances of replacement analysis or in periods of increasing *real* costs.

6.15 THE ANNUAL COST OF A LIMITED SERVICE PERIOD

The previous sections of this chapter assumed that the need for the equipment was indefinitely long, which therefore resulted in a chain of continuing replacements of equipment into the indefinite future. When equipment lives were different we were obligated to predict or reasonably assume the nature and cost pattern of these replacements.

In some instances, however, we know the length of the required service and will use this for the period of comparison in preference to any other period. This is illustrated by the following example:

EXAMPLE 6.15 A construction job is expected to last 2 years. A belt conveyor costing $50,000 will have an operating cost of $20,000 and $25,000 salvage at the end of 2 years. Mobile equipment costing $30,000 could also be used having annual operating costs of $35,000 and $10,000 salvage at the end of 2 years. Either of these pieces of equipment would have economic lives on first line service longer than 2 years. The minimum required rate of return is 10%.

SOLUTION.

AC, conveyor:

$$\overset{0.57619}{(50,000 - 20,000)}(A/P, .10, 2) + (25,000)(0.10) + 20,000 = \$36,900$$

AC, mobile equipment:

$$(30,000 - 10,000)(A/P, .10, 2) + (10,000) (0.10) + 35,000 = \$47,520$$

6.16 COMBINED COST-REDUCTION AND INCOME-EXPANSION EXPENDITURES

In this chapter so far we have considered only cost-reduction expenditures. In each case the gross revenue was irrelevant because it was unchanged by the alternatives: it remained the same regardless of the choice. However, where the gross income is affected by the choice it must be included, as illustrated in the following example of a combined cost-reduction income-expansion expenditure.

EXAMPLE 6.16 Two processes are available for waterproofing cloth. One has a first cost of $35,000 with an annual operating cost of $12,000. The other costs $50,000 with an annual operating cost of $13,000. Purchasers will pay a total extra of $5,000 a year for the superior water-resisting qualities in the cloth produced by the second machine. The life of each is 12 years with zero salvage. The minimum required rate of return is 10%.

SOLUTION.

AC first process:

$$\overset{0.14676}{35,000(A/P, .10, 12)} + 12,000 = \$17,140$$

AC second process:

$$50,000(A/P, 12) + 13,000 - 5,000 = \$15,340$$

The increase in quality is sufficient to justify the extra investment.

6.17 LEVELS OF INVESTMENT BY ANNUAL-COST METHOD

In certain cases a number of alternatives may have to be (or should be) considered at one time to determine the most economic. The existence of these cases is not always apparent. For example, every time a machine is designed there are, theoretically at least, an infinite number of alternative designs starting with those having the lowest first cost and extending through those having the very highest operating efficiency. This is the case, for example, where successive increases in the first costs of a machine may result in increased automation and a reduction in operating labor costs. Specific examples occur in every field. In heat transmission we have the well-known illustration of progressively increasing the thickness of thermal insulation where each level of design more effectively reduces the heat loss; in fluid or gas transmission we note that progressively increasing the diameter of pipe reduces the pumping losses between terminals of the transmission line.

The objective in all of these problems is to find which of the various levels of investment is the most economic in a given situation.

EXAMPLE 6.17 The first cost of various thicknesses of insulation for a steam pipe are tabulated in column 2 of Table 6.17. The corresponding esti-

Table 6.17   LEVELS OF INVESTMENT IN INSULATION

(1) Thickness of insulation (in.)	(2) First cost	(3) Annual heat loss	(4) Annual cost of capital recovery	(5) Total annual cost
0	$ 0	$1,800	$ 0	$1,800
$\frac{3}{4}$	1,800	900	210	1,110
1	2,545	590	297	887
$1\frac{1}{2}$	3,340	450	390	840
$2\frac{1}{4}$	4,360	360	509	869
3	5,730	310	669	979
$3\frac{1}{2}$	7,280	285	851	1,136

mated annual costs of heat loss are given in column 3. It is estimated that the pipe will be required for 15 years. The minimum required rate of return is 8%.

SOLUTION.   The annual cost of each level of investment has been computed as follows:

$\frac{3}{4}$-inch $\underset{0}{\overset{1,800}{\vdash}} \qquad D = 900 \qquad \underset{15}{\overset{L = 0}{\dashv}}$

AC of $\frac{3}{4}$ -in. insulation: $1,800(A/P, .08, 15) + 900 = \$1,110$

On the basis of the lowest annual cost, $1\frac{1}{2}$-inch insulation will be selected.

Note that increasing the first costs, column 2, produces lower annual heat loss, column 3, but the *total* annual cost, column 5, declines only to a minimum and then rises. This is a mathematical illustration of the law of diminishing returns,[1] demonstrating that the cost of increased efficiency can no longer be recovered out of the savings. In this case the cost of insulating the pipe beyond $1\frac{1}{2}$ inches is not justified. These effects are illustrated in Fig. 6.17.

6.18 LEVELS OF INVESTMENT FROM STANDPOINT OF THE EXTRA INVESTMENT

Table 6.18, constructed from the data in Table 6.17, shows the economics of the extra investment in each added level of design. Table 6.18 shows that the extra investment of $795 for $1\frac{1}{2}$- over 1-inch insulation will save spending $140 annually for heat losses for the next 15 years. The annual capital recovery cost of this extra investment is $93, so that the net saving after recovery of capital with 8% interest is $47 a year. This is a worthwhile investment. We will note

---

[1] "A rate of yield that beyond a certain point fails to increase in proportion to additional investments of labor or capital." *Webster's New Collegiate Dictionary*.

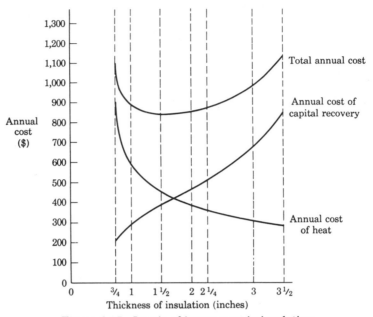

Figure 6.17   Levels of investment in insulation

that it does not pay to invest to the next level, because the extra investment of $1,020 fails to be recovered with 8% interest by $29.

Our conclusion will, of course, conform with the selection of $1\frac{1}{2}$-inch insulation in Section 6.17. However, Table 6.18 raises some further questions and conclusions. The first is this: If $\frac{3}{4}$-inch insulation gives the maximum *net* savings, $690, why is it not selected? In consideration of this question we should

Table 6.18 CONSIDERATION OF THE EXTRA INVESTMENT
IN EACH LEVEL OF INSULATION

(1) Thickness of insulation (in.)	(2) First cost	(3) Extra investment	(4) Capital recovery of extra investment	(5) Total annual heat loss	(6) Annual saving due to extra investment	(7) Net savings after recovery of extra investment
0	$ 0	$ 0	$ 0	$1,800	$ 0	$ 0
$\frac{3}{4}$	1,800	1,800	210	900	900	690
1	2,545	745	87	590	310	223
$1\frac{1}{2}$	3,340	795	93	450	140	47
$2\frac{1}{4}$	4,360	1,020	119	360	90	-29
3	5,730	1,370	160	310	50	-110
$3\frac{1}{2}$	7,280	1,550	182	285	25	-157

note that the net savings in column 7 are after the recovery of capital; in other words, the net savings comprise the return on the investment *over and above* the minimum required rate of return. In this connection we will remember that the investor has decided at some earlier date on a minimum required rate of return which would thereafter be sufficient to justify an investment. The net savings of $690 are therefore much more than he requires, and he will continue to increase the level of investment in that project as long as each level earns the minimum required return on the extra investment. In the given problem, therefore, he will certainly increase his level of investment through $1\frac{1}{2}$-inch insulation because it is recovered with 8% plus $47 a year.

Now for the second important observation. We observed in Section 6.8 that an extra investment would be satisfactory if it were recovered with exactly 8% and no more. This implies that somewhere between $1\frac{1}{2}$- and $2\frac{1}{4}$-inch insulation lies the most economical level of investment. This fact would be a very important guide to a designer in his search for the optimum design for his given set of conditions. For example, suppose he could design $1\frac{3}{4}$-inch insulation with a first cost of $3,845 and heat loss of $391. This represents an extra investment of

$$0.17683$$

$505 and a saving in heat of $59. Since $505(A/P, .08, 15) = 59, the *net* saving after recovery of capital will be found to be exactly zero, so that the extra investment is justified and the $1\frac{3}{4}$-inch insulation is the most economical—at an 8% rate of return.

Section 6.18 emphasizes the very important observation that each increment of extra investment and that each level of investment must stand the test of a satisfactory investment. Section 6.18 also illustrates the obligation to continue to invest in successive levels as long as each passes the test; failure to do so is failure to maximize profits.

6.19 THE CONFUSION BETWEEN FINANCING AND MAKING THE EXTRA INVESTMENT

Management sometimes rejects the purchase of new equipment with the remark that they "can't afford it." In most cases this is a mistake in reasoning based on an error in defining the problem. What they usually mean is that they "can't finance it;" nevertheless they are unaware of the fact that they have confused a problem in finance with one in engineering economy. If the truth were known it may be that although they cannot finance the purchase, neither can they afford *not* to make the purchase from the standpoint of its economy. If an economy study shows the extra investment is economical, then it is cheaper over the years to make that investment than not to make it. However, if inability to get funds or exceed a debt limit prevents making the extra investment, it should be understood that the barrier is a financial one, not an economic one.

PROBLEMS

6.1 A family plans to build a house for $20,000 including land. They estimate they will own it for 15 years, at which time they can sell for $20,000 as a result of the appreciation of the land. They estimate the following costs of annual operation: fuel $250; repairs $100; lawn maintenance and snow removal $40; insurance, $75; water $40; property tax 4% on the full value; and, at the end of every 3 years, painting and overhaul $300. They plan to finance this from bank deposits earning 4% compounded quarterly. Make an annual-cost computation.

6.2   Make an annual-cost computation of the following assets. As in the previous problem, these are to be total costs, not comparative costs. (a) a new automobile of a stated make; (b) a second-hand auto of a stated make and year; (c) a membership in a golf club having an initiation fee of $250; (d) a power-operated lawn mower (see a mail-order catalogue for data); (e) a business suit that you will wear 3 out of 5 days a week; (f) a summer camp; (g) a complete ski outfit.

6.3   An investment plan is expected to pay the following: $5,000 at the end of the first year, and subsequent annual income payments decreasing $200 each year. Compute the annual worth of this plan at a certain investor's minimum required rate of return of 5% if these incomes continue for 10 years.

6.4   A company can purchase a new special-purpose lathe for $7,000 installed. On the job intended for this machine the annual disbursement for all its operating costs, including labor, power, and maintenance, is $2,500. As an alternative, a new general-purpose lathe can be installed for $5,500 with operating disbursements of $3,000 a year. Both machines are expected to be operated on this service for 10 years, at which time their salvage values are expected to be $1,000 and $800, respectively. If the company's minimum required rate of return is 12%, which machine would you recommend based on an annual-cost analysis?

6.5   A sportsman plans to purchase an outboard cruiser for $2,500 and to keep it 5 years before replacing it. He believes he can sell it at that time for $800. His disbursements for gas, oil, maintenance and repair, storage, license, and landing privileges will be $700 the first year and will increase $50 a year thereafter. Find his equivalent annual cost of ownership if his minimum required rate of return in his venutres is 10%.

6.6   A company has received bids on a 2,000 kva (kilovolt-amperes) transformer from several manufacturers. One of these quotes $15,000 for a transformer having 98% efficiency at full load, 97% at three-quarter load, and 93% at half load. Another firm quotes $13,750 for a transformer having 96% efficiency at full load, 95% at three-quarter load, and 90% at half load. The company expects to keep the transformer on this service for 15 years, at which time salvage values are expected to be $300 and $275, respectively. Aside from these differences, the transformers are essentially equal.

Energy costs 2 cents per kilowatt-hour. The company's minimum required rate of return is 15%. Annual utilization of the transformer is expected to be 600 hours at full load, 1,800 hours at three-quarter load, and 600 hours at half load. Assume that the company's load is at unity power factor so that full load on the transformer is 2,000 kw. Make a recommendation from an annual-cost comparison.

6.7 A 36-inch pipeline can be installed for $98,000. Its operating costs including the cost of pumping as well as maintenance and repair, will be $22,000 a year. A 30-inch line can be installed for $73,000 but the operating cost will be $31,000. The line is expected to serve for 20 years with 10% salvage when replaced at that date. The company's minimum required rate of return is 20%. Compare the two by the annual-cost method.

6.8 A manufacturer is considering the purchase of a 500 hp diesel engine. Engine S costs $110,000 and has an efficiency of 0.41 pounds of fuel per brake horsepower-hour.   Engine I costs $125,000 and requires 0.38 pounds of fuel per brake horsepower-hour. It is believed that in all other respects the engines are alike. The engine will be on this service for 15 years and the estimated salvage at that date is expected to be $5,000 and $6,000, respectively. Fuel costs 3.5 cents a pound. The engine is to be used 8 hours a day, 250 days a year, for driving air compressors. Compare the two by the annual-cost method if the minimum required rate of return is 20%.

6.9 A railroad track runs down a street of a manufacturing complex and the freight cars frequently halt all movement on another company street which crosses it. The traffic holdup adds up to an hour a day and the total daily cost of idle labor caused by the delay is estimated to be $60. The factory works 250 days a year.

An underpass costing $65,000 will completely eliminate these delays. The useful life of the structure is predicted to be 15 years with no salvage of materials at that date. The cost of operating the underpass will be $2,000 a year for maintenance and for operating trucks on the grades in the tunnel under the tracks. The company's minimum required rate of return is 25%. Make an annual-cost analysis of whether to install the underpass.

6.10 A bulldozer costs $14,000 new and has a service life of 10 years. If its purchaser expects to use it only 2 years and then sell it for $9,000, what is his annual cost if the minimum required rate of return is 15%?

6.11 A city borrowed $500,000 on a bond issue which requires the city to pay it back in one lump sum at the end of 10 years. Annual interest on the loan is to be paid to the bondholders. The law requires the city to set up a sinking fund into which it must make annual deposits. The sinking fund is expected to earn 5%, and the interest on the loan is 6%. What is the total annual payment of the city?

6.12 A city is proposing to convert a slum area into a business and shopping center as part of its program of urban development. The bond issue will be $20,000,000 at a cost of 5% interest which must be paid annually. The bond matures in 20 years, and state law requires the city to make annual deposits into a sinking fund that will accumulate the amount of the issue in 20 years. The interest on the sinking fund is 4%. What is the city's total annual payment on this proposition?

6.13 Rework Problem 4.43 by using the method of straight-line depreciation plus average interest to find the annual cost. Compare it with the annual cost by the exact method.

6.14 A "standard" model of an automobile costs $2,000 and has an annual operating expense of $450. The auto will be replaced in 6 years when the salvage is expected to be $200. A "super" model can be purchased for $2,500 but will have a salvage of $700 when retired in 6 years. Its operating expenses are also $450 a year. The purchaser's other investment opportunities are 5%.

Compare the *total* annual costs of these models. Also compare their annual costs neglecting annual operating expenses. Discuss whether you consider the two comparisons give identical conclusions.

6.15 A manufacturer can purchase a second-hand machine tool for $4,000. He estimates the annual disbursements on the proposed operation will be $3,200, and when the equipment is replaced in 4 years it will have a salvage of $700. He can buy a new machine for $6,000 having operating disbursements of $2,600 a year. This machine will also be replaced in 4 years, when it will have a salvage of $900. Analyze the problem from the viewpoint of the extra investment.

6.16 The initial cost of an air compressor is $6,000. Operation and repair costs tend to increase year by year throughout its life as shown below:

Year	Operation and repair costs	Year	Operation and repair costs
1	$1,000	4	$1,400
2	1,100	5	1,600
3	1,200	6	2,200
		7	3,000

The salvage value is $3,600 after 1 year, and it decreases by $400 each year. With the required rate of return at 15%, determine the most economical year to replace the compressor.

6.17 A new automobile costs $3,380. At the end of each subsequent year its market value is expected to be $2,750, $2,200, $1,710, $1,290, $890, $575, $300, $200. The operating disbursements are expected to be $300 the first year. In subsequent years they are expected to be $305, $325, $370, $480, $605, $750, $925. The owner's investment opportunities will return 5% interest. Use an annual-cost analysis to determine the recommended economical life of the car.

6.18 Plan *A* requires an initial investment of $2,000 and has an economic life of 2 years. Plan *B* costs $4,500 and is expected to last 5 years. If the salvage value is zero in both cases and interest is 15%, which alternative is least expensive?

6.19 The purchasing agent of a large manufacturing concern is trying to decide whether to buy high carbon steel or carbide-tipped cutting tools for the metal shop's lathes. The carbide tools cost $2,000 and have an estimated life of 3 years. The steel tools cost $1,400 but only last 2 years. If the company's minimum required rate of return is 20%, which alternative is the best? Salvage values are zero.

6.20 Over what period do the advantages in Problems 6.18 and 6.19 exist? Explain your justification in comparing two alternatives over unequal periods of time. What assumptions did you make or must you make in your explanation? Prove your conclusions with a mathematical analysis.

6.21 As an alternative to buying the new car in Problem 6.17, a prospective buyer can purchase a second-hand car costing $1,290. Its selling price will decline in the following years as follows: $890, $571, $300, $200. The operating disbursements will be $570 in the first year of ownership and will increase in subsequent years to $620, $680, $750. Compare the alternatives by the annual-cost method if the buyer's opportunities for investment bring 5%. Over what periods do the advantages exist? Explain your answer as requested in Problem 6.20.

6.22 A manufacturer can purchase a new machine tool for $9,500 which will have operating disbursements on the intended service of $5,000 a year. These are expected to increase $200 a year as the tool ages. The expected life on the intended service will be 8 years with a salvage at that date of $3,300. As an alternative to this, a second-hand tool can be installed for $2,500. It will have a salvage at the end of one year of $2,250. Its next-year's operating disbursements will be $7,500 and they are expected to increase in future years by $325 or more. If the second-hand tool is more economic the management will approve it, even though it may have only a 1-year life. They also favor the shorter commitment as favorable to the early adoption of new technologies. If the manufacturer's minimum required rate of return is 25%, make a selection by the annual-cost method.

6.23 In the construction of a new office building, paint having a 5-year life can be used on exterior surfaces at a cost of $4,000. Less durable paint with a 3-year life can be obtained for $3,000. Renewals will cost the same. If the minimum required rate of return is 20%, which paint should be selected, based on an annual-cost analysis? Would your selection change if it is expected that the price of the less durable paint will drop to $2,000 in a year or at most 2 years, the cost of the more durable paint remaining the same?

6.24 A third-class railroad car costs $41,000 and has an annual operating cost of $13,000. A first-class railroad car costs $70,000 and costs $18,000 a year to operate. Both are expected to be obsolete in 5 years. Salvage value of the third-class car is $10,000; on the first-class car it is $15,000. The first-class car averages $15,000 more per year in revenue. If these can be used as alternatives on a given line, which should be selected if the minimum required rate of return for the railroad is 15%?

6.25 A manufacturing process can be designed for varying degrees of automation. The minimum required rate of return is 20% and economic life is 5 years. Salvage at that date is estimated to be zero. Which of the levels should be selected?

Level	First cost	Annual cost of labor	Annual cost of power	Annual cost of maintenance
1	$100,000	$70,000	$4,000	$1,000
2	175,000	55,000	5,000	1,500
3	300,000	35,000	6,500	2,200
4	500,000	20,000	8,000	3,000

6.26 Analyze Problem 6.25 from the standpoint of the extra investment.

6.27 Explain the meaning of the annual-cost comparison in Problem 6.4 if (a) the alternative selected by your analysis wins; (b) the two alternatives have equal annual cost; (c) the other alternative wins by $1,000 a year.

6.28 Repeat the previous explanation for Problem 6.7.

7

Present-Worth Analyses

7.1 PRESENT-WORTH COMPARISONS OF ALTERNATIVES

The present-worth method of comparison consists of reducing all the future differences between alternatives to a single equivalent present sum. This may also be made by computing the present worth of each alternative separately before subtracting their differences. The comparison may also be made by converting the annual cost difference as computed in Chapter 6 to a single present sum. In fact, in certain circumstances it is easier and quicker to make an annual-cost comparison first and then convert it to a present worth (see Section 7.9).

The fact that an annual-cost comparison can be converted to a present worth (and vice versa) is significant. It indicates that all the principles that applied to annual-cost comparisons can also be applied to present worth. Hence we can observe as before that (1) only the differences are relevant to the choice, (2) the present worth of each alternative is a *comparative* present worth, and (3) the present-worth comparison must be made over the same number of years for each alternative.

Some confusion can result from the fact that the term "present worth" is applied to costs as well as incomes. It is natural to think of "worth" as value or income instead of costs. We need only keep in mind that the present worth of a series of costs is a cost and the most economic alternative is the lower one, whereas the present worth of a series of incomes is an income and the most economic alternative is the higher one.

7.2 IMPORTANCE OF THE TIME PERIOD

The present worth of a series naturally depends on the number of terms in the series and therefore on the length of time over which the present worth is computed. The present worth of a $100 annual-cost advantage has one value over a 5-year period and another over a 10-year period. In a present-worth comparison we cannot escape a determination of the comparison period; we must establish it to get an answer and we must establish it correctly to get the right answer.

Over how long a period should the present-worth comparison be made? The answer, as stated earlier, is for as long a period as the cost differences between alternatives are expected to exist. This means that the entire consequences of the choice between the alternatives should be included and the computation should cover the entire period of time during which these differences will exist. Sections 7.5 and 7.6 are concerned with illustrating this problem.

7.3 EQUAL ECONOMIC LIVES

If the alternatives have equal lives, the present-worth comparison is made for this common period of time. This is proper because any action taken at the conclusion of this period is irrelevant inasmuch as it will be the same for both alternatives.

EXAMPLE 7.3   Two operations are expected to have economic lives of 4 years. The first will cost $1,000 installed and is expected to have annual operating costs of $800 and a salvage value of $100. The second costs $800 with annual operating costs of $900 and zero salvage. The minimum required rate of return is 8%.

SOLUTION.

$$A \quad \begin{array}{ccc} 1{,}000 & D = 800/\text{yr} & L = 100 \\ \vdash & & \dashv \\ 0 & & 4 \end{array}$$

$$B \quad \begin{array}{ccc} 800 & D = 900/\text{yr} & L = 0 \\ \vdash & & \dashv \\ 0 & & 4 \end{array}$$

$$\overset{0.7350}{} \qquad \overset{3.312}{}$$
$$\text{PW}_A = 1{,}000 - 100(P/F, .08, 4) + 800(P/A, 4) = \$3{,}576$$
$$\overset{3.312}{}$$
$$\text{PW}_B = 800 + 900(P/A, 4) \qquad\qquad\qquad = \$3{,}780$$
$$\text{Advantage of } A: \quad \$3{,}780 - \$3{,}576 \qquad = \$\ \ 204$$

All decisions made after 4 years are irrelevant to the choice, so the entire difference between these alternatives is represented by a present sum of $204.

7.4 MEANING OF A PRESENT-WORTH COMPARISON

In the previous section Operation A had a present-worth advantage of $204. What does this mean?

The meaning of a present-worth comparison is best approached by extending the interpretation of an annual-cost comparison given in Section 6.10. We noted there that, if the difference in the annual cost between the alternatives is zero, the extra investment is exactly recovered with the required rate of return. The interpretation is the same where the difference in the present worths of the alternatives is zero. We also noted that, if the asset with the extra investment has the lower annual cost, the extra investment is recovered with the required rate of return *plus* the difference in the annual costs over a certain period of years. If we interpret the present worth of this difference, we conclude that the extra investment is recovered with the required rate of return plus a present sum of money. Illustrating these points from Example 7.3, the difference in the time scales is as follows:

Cost	Savings	Income
200	100/yr	100

0   3.312   0.7350   4

$$PW = 100(P/A, .08, 4) + (P/F, 4) - 200 = \$204, \text{ advantage of } A$$

The $200 cost is seen to be recovered out of future savings discounted at 8% plus a present sum of $204, or, more precisely, the extra investment will be recovered over a 4-year period with 8% plus a present sum of $204.

Now if the present worth of the difference is zero, we note from the above illustration that the future savings discounted at 8% would exactly equal the extra investment. This is another way of saying that the extra investment will be recovered over 4 years with exactly 8%.

For the case where the alternative with the higher investment also has the higher present worth, the interpretation is that the extra investment fails to be recovered with 8% interest by the amount of the present-worth difference.

7.5 STUDY-PERIOD METHOD OF ANALYSIS WHEN LIVES ARE UNEQUAL

In Chapter 6 we examined techniques for analysis when the economic lives of the alternatives are not equal. We observed two basic philosophies for handling this problem:

1. Disregard the future events and their consequences beyond the life of the shorter-lived machine or beyond some study period.

2. Predict the future events, i.e., the replacements for the present machines, in order to make a prediction over equal periods for both alternatives.

Before examining these in the light of the present-worth technique, we should restate the general observation that *the alternatives must be compared over equal periods of time*. This truth seems obvious, because to compare a long period of service (and its long stream of costs) with a short period of service (and its short stream of costs) is an unfair comparison.

EXAMPLE 7.5 An old machine costing $8,000 is expected to have a life of 3 years with zero salvage value and operating disbursements of $16,000 a year.

A new machine will cost $40,000 and have an 8-year economic life with zero salvage and operating costs of $11,000 a year.

If the minimum required rate of return is 10%, make an analysis based on the philosophy of a study period.

SOLUTION.

$$A \quad \begin{array}{c} 8,000 \quad D = 16,000 \\ \vdash\!\dashv \\ 0 \qquad\qquad\qquad 3 \end{array}$$

$$B \quad \begin{array}{c} 40,000 \qquad\qquad\qquad\quad D = 11,000 \\ \vdash\!\dashv \\ 0 \qquad\qquad\qquad\qquad\qquad\qquad\qquad\quad 8 \end{array}$$

For academic reasons let us first observe the result of an annual-cost analysis.

$$\begin{array}{c} 0.40211 \\ AC_A = 8,000(A/P, .10, 3) + 16,000 = \$19,217 \end{array}$$

$$\begin{array}{c} 0.18744 \\ AC_B = 40,000(A/P, .10, 8) + 11,000 = \underline{\ 18,498} \end{array}$$

Advantage of B: $\qquad\qquad\qquad$ $ \ 719/\text{yr}$

By the annual-cost method we would disregard the stream of B's costs of $18,498 from years 4 through 8. Therefore the period of comparison would be limited to 3 years and the advantage of B would be specified as $719 a year for 3 years.

By the present-worth method we will also disregard events after 3 years but we will treat differences as lump sums instead of series. For example, if we selected a 3-year study period:

$$\begin{array}{c} 2.487 \\ PW_A = 8,000 + 16,000(P/A, .10, 3) \qquad = \$47,792 \end{array}$$

$$\begin{array}{c} 0.18744 \qquad\qquad 2.487 \\ PW_B = [40,000(A/P, 8) + 11,000](P/A, 3) \quad = \ \underline{\ 46,004} \end{array}$$

Advantage of B: $\qquad\qquad\qquad$ $ \ 1,788$

The PW_B is the cost of B disregarding those effects occurring after year 3.

And the advantage of $1,788 is also the present worth of the 3-year annual-cost advantage, that is: $719(P/A, .10, 3) = \$1,788$.

7.6 COMPARISONS INVOLVING PREDICTIONS OF FUTURE MACHINES

As pointed out in Chapter 6, the preferred approach where lives are not equal is to predict the nature of events to follow: the kind of machines to become available in the future. One of the goals of administrators is to make short commitments so they will always be in position to adopt the most economic alternatives when they become available. The penalty for overlooking this opportunity was made apparent in Example 6.13.

Research has not progressed to the point where we readily accept predicted cost patterns of future machines,[1] so we usually shy from making these predictions. We can, nevertheless, by the method described in Section 6.14, predict the limits pertaining to the improved machine of the future.

---

[1] George Terborgh has proposed several patterns; see *Dynamic Equipment Policy* (New York: McGraw-Hill, 1949).

EXAMPLE 7.6   Solve Example 7.5 from the viewpoint that, historically, future machines will be no less economical than the most economic machine today. By assuming replacements with the most economic machine available for the job today, we set a lower limit on the economic advantage of future replacements.

(a) Using this pattern for future replacements, determine the advantage or disadvantage of installing A, the machine with the shorter life.

(b) If the decision can be reversed by the appearance of improved machines in the future, how much would the improvement have to be?

SOLUTION.   In Example 7.5 we noted that B, with an annual cost of $18,498, was the more economic machine on this job and we conclude that, as a limit, future machines will be no less economical.   On the time scale this will be as follows:

A 8,000 $D = 16,000$ 40,000   ········· $D = 11,000$ ·········   40,000   ········· ∞
0   ·····   3   ·····   11

B 40,000   ········· $D = 11,000$ ·········   40,000 $D = 11,000$ ········· ∞
0   ·····   8

$$\text{PW}_A = 8{,}000 + 16{,}000 \overset{2.48685}{(P/A, .10, 3)}$$
$$+ [40{,}000 \overset{0.18744}{(A/P, 8)} + 11{,}000] \overset{10.0}{(P/A, \infty)} \overset{0.7413}{(P/F, 3)} = \$186{,}764$$
$$\text{PW}_B = [40{,}000 \overset{0.18744}{(A/P, 8)} + 11{,}000] \overset{10.0}{(P/A, \infty)} \qquad = \underline{\;184{,}976\;}$$

Advantage of B: $\$\quad 1{,}788$

This, of course, gives the same numerical answer as a 3-year study period but in this case we can say that the quantitative disadvantage of selecting A, the machine with the shorter life, will not be greater than $1,788.   If future machines are no better than the best machine today, then it will be $1,788.   How much less it might be depends on how much improved the future machines might be. If they are vastly improved, the disadvantage of A can be considerably less than $1,788 up to the point that alternative A becomes the most economic choice. In fact, this conclusion can become the basis of a break-even analysis.   In the break-even model, the present worth of the advantage of the improved machines of the future over today's most economic machine must exceed $1,788.   (Note: the PW is at time zero and the future machines are replacements on the time scale.)   Inspection of a pattern that would give this sum should enable the analyst to decide whether he can reasonably expect the particular degree of improvement.

Another method of comparison, also mentioned in Chapter 6, uses the period of the least common multiple.   In the given example this is 24 years, and the present worth of the advantage of B is greatly inflated solely because the LCM happened to be 24 instead of 3 years.

7.7 COMPARISONS OVER SPECIFIED SERVICE PERIOD

Where equipment is to be used on a job of known duration, the present-worth comparison is, of course, made over that period.   This is a situation likely to occur in contract work such as construction jobs or perhaps defense contracts, and the period is generally short enough to be within the normal economic life of the same equipment employed on similar functions where the service requirements are longer.

EXAMPLE 7.7   On a construction job expected to last 2 years, a conveyor costing $10,000 with annual operating disbursements of $7,000 is proposed as one alternative for hauling material. The analyst estimates the salvage value at the end of two years will be $4,000. As an alternative, the contractor is able to subcontract the entire hauling job at $1,500 a month. Make a present-worth comparison if the minimum required rate of return is 8%.

SOLUTION.

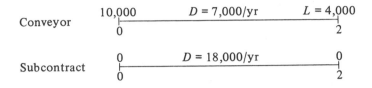

Conveyor:
$$PW = 10,000 + 7,000\overset{1.783}{(P/A, .08, 2)} - 4,000\overset{0.8573}{(P/F, 2)} = \$19,052$$

Subcontract:
$$PW = 12(1,500)\overset{1.783}{(P/A, 2)} = \$32,094$$

The advantage lies with purchasing the conveyor.

7.8 CAPITALIZED-COST COMPARISONS

A capitalized-cost comparison is a present-worth comparison for a period assumed to be infinite.

Capitalized-cost analyses are especially suited to situations where economic lives are indefinitely long in the eyes of the analyst. In the early days of railroad construction and expansion, capitalized-cost analyses predominated because roadbeds, tracks, and bridges were considered to have the mathematical equivalent of perpetual lives.[1]   Aqueducts, tunnels, canals, dams, and perhaps some highways are in the same category. A typical analysis of this type is illustrated in the following example:

EXAMPLE 7.8   A dam costing $100,000 to construct will cost $15,000 a year to operate and maintain. Another design costing $150,000 to build will cost $10,000 a year to operate and maintain. Both installations are felt to be permanent. The minimum required rate of return is 5%.

---

[1] A. M. Wellington, *The Economic Theory of Railway Location* (New York: Wiley, 1887).

SOLUTION.

First design $\begin{array}{c} 100,000 \\ \vdash \\ 0 \end{array}$ $\begin{array}{c} D = 15,000 \\ \\ \end{array}$ $n = \infty$

Second design $\begin{array}{c} 150,000 \\ \vdash \\ 0 \end{array}$ $\begin{array}{c} D = 10,000 \\ \\ \end{array}$ $n = \infty$

Capitalized cost of first design:

$$100,000 + 15,000 \overset{20.0}{(P/A, .05, \infty)} = \$400,000$$

Capitalized cost of second design:

$$150,000 + 10,000 \overset{20.0}{(P/A, \infty)} = \$350,000$$

This shows an advantage of $50,000 in favor of the second design.

7.9 CAPITALIZED-COST COMPARISON IF BOTH LIVES ARE NOT INFINITE

Sometimes the alternatives have vastly different lives, particularly if economic lives are established by the physical duration of the equipment.

EXAMPLE 7.9 A city is investigating alternative designs for an aqueduct, and their considerations reduce to a rock tunnel and a pipeline. A rock tunnel of indefinitely long life will cost $100,000 and $4,000 to operate. A wooden pipeline having a 20-year life will cost only $35,000 and have an operating expense of $5,500. Interest is 5%.

SOLUTION.

Tunnel $\begin{array}{c} 100,000 \\ \vdash \end{array}$ $\begin{array}{c} D = 4,000 \\ \end{array}$ ∞

Pipe $\begin{array}{c} 35,000 \\ \vdash \end{array}$ $\begin{array}{c} D = 5,500 \\ \end{array}$ 20

Annual cost of rock tunnel:

$$(100,000)(0.05) + 4,000 = \$9,000/\text{yr to infinity}$$

Annual cost of wooden pipeline:

$$35,000 \overset{0.08024}{(A/P\ .05, 20)} + 5,500 = \$8,308/\text{yr for 20 years}$$

Some conclusion must be reached regarding the procedure after the expiration of the first wooden line. Since it is the more economical, one assumption is that it will be duplicated, so the advantage of installing a pipeline over a rock tunnel will extend to infinity, and the present worth is

Capitalized cost·

$$(9,000 - 8,308) \overset{20.0}{(P/A, \infty)} = \$13,840$$

This analysis presumes that future installations of the pipeline are not expected to cost more or less; otherwise, these outlooks become relevant to the choice.

Another approach in this case would be to evaluate the advantage of deferring the extra investment, that is, the advantage, if any, of installing the rock tunnel now versus deferring the *consideration* to install it.

Rock tunnel:

$$100{,}000 \qquad 4{,}000/yr$$

$$0 \qquad\qquad\qquad\qquad\qquad\qquad\qquad\qquad\qquad \infty$$

Fabricated tunnel:

$$35{,}000 \qquad\quad 5{,}500/yr \qquad\quad 100{,}000 \qquad\quad 4{,}000/yr$$

$$0 \qquad\qquad\qquad\qquad\qquad\qquad 20 \qquad\qquad\qquad\qquad\qquad \infty$$

Advantage of deferment:
$$\overset{12.462}{(9{,}000 - 8{,}308)(P/A, .05, 20)} = \$8{,}624$$

To the quantitative advantage of $8,624 must be added the irreducible advantage of installing the short-lived asset now and thereby gaining a greater opportunity to install the best design that will become available in 20 years. On the basis that future designs are always better, not worse, than present designs, this is always an advantage.

7.10 UNIQUE VALUE OF PRESENT-WORTH COMPARISONS

The present-worth method of analysis demonstrates the advantages or disadvantages of a choice in ways which are not possible with annual-cost comparisons. These possibilities arise from the fact that the differences in alternatives can be expressed as single sums instead of series of sums.

A good example is found in demonstrating to the price-conscious buyer the difference between the price and the total cost of buying the equipment. In the first chapter we observed that a decision to purchase is a commitment to pay for all the operating expenses during its service; therefore, comparing the price and the total commitment expressed as a single sum demonstrates the relative importance (or unimportance) of first cost to total cost. The following example illustrates this.

EXAMPLE 7.10a   The management of a company believes that $30,000 is too much to pay for mechanizing a process. A competing supplier has offered to mechanize it for $24,000. The first method requires annual operating disbursements of $19,500 and the second $22,000. Economic life is predicted to be 10 years and the cost of capital is 10%. Make an analysis to show the relative insignificance of first cost.

SOLUTION.

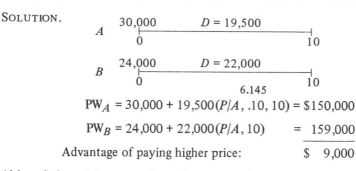

$$PW_A = 30{,}000 + 19{,}500(P/A, .10, 10) = \$150{,}000$$

$$PW_B = 24{,}000 + 22{,}000(P/A, 10) \quad = \ 159{,}000$$

Advantage of paying higher price: $ 9,000

Although bargaining over the selling price will remain a game between buyer and seller, a present-worth analysis illustrates the relative unimportance of price compared to total cost and the error of judging on price alone. In this example, the price of the cheaper equipment is actually more than $9,000 high instead of $6,000 low. If it were priced at $15,000, the higher-priced machine should still be purchased if the minimum required rate of return is 10%.

The following example carries this to an interesting extreme by using a present-worth analysis to show that the buyer couldn't accept the equipment as a gift.

EXAMPLE 7.10b A machine costs $20,000 with a 10-year life and an annual operating cost of $10,000. An alternate machine undersells it by 15% and has an annual operating cost of $13,000. Its economic life is the same. The minimum required rate of return is 8%.

SOLUTION.

$$\begin{array}{l} A \quad \begin{array}{l} 20{,}000 \qquad\qquad D = 10{,}000 \\ \underset{0}{\vdash}\rule{12em}{0.4pt}\underset{10}{\dashv} \end{array} \\[1em] B \quad \begin{array}{l} 17{,}000 \qquad\qquad D = 13{,}000 \\ \underset{0}{\vdash}\rule{12em}{0.4pt}\underset{10}{\dashv} \end{array} \end{array}$$

$$\overset{6.710}{PW_A} = 20{,}000 + 10{,}000(P/A, .08, 10) = \$ \ 87{,}100$$

$$\overset{6.710}{PW_B} = 17{,}000 + 13{,}000(P/A, .08, 10) = \ 104{,}200$$

PW of the advantage of A: $ 17,100

Based on price alone, machine A might be viewed as over-priced compared to its competitor's. Actually it would be more accurate to say that machine B couldn't be accepted as a gift (unless accompanied by a bonus of more than $100).

We can see, therefore, that present worth provides the technique for computing the value of equipment, processes, real estate, stocks, bonds. It can be employed to advantage in sales, purchasing, pricing, rate-making, and even judicial decisions. In fact, in some of these fields it is indispensable if the problem concerns property valuation. Valuation, a specialized field in itself, is introduced in Section 7.19.

7.11 DEFERRED INVESTMENTS

In problems involving growth and planned expansion it is often more economic to install a full-size plant in advance of the need for it than to defer the addition until the required date. Some of the economic factors which make it advantageous to install full-size plants in advance of their needs are prospective increases in real costs, possible dislocation of business when the addition is tied in, and the important economic observation that a large installation costs less per unit of capacity than two small-size installations.   On the other hand, a number of economic factors work against installing all future requirements before they are needed, so the answer, as usual, is to make an economy analysis.

EXAMPLE 7.11   A plant to provide the company's present needs can be constructed for $120,000 with annual operating disbursements of $30,000. It is predicted that at the end of 10 years the production requirements could be doubled, which will necessitate the addition of an extension costing $120,000. A plant to provide the entire eventual capacity can be constructed for $200,000, and its operating disbursements will be $32,000 when operating on half capacity (for the first 10 years) and $58,000 on full capacity. The plants are predicted to have indeterminately long life. The required rate of return is 8%.

SOLUTION.

Deferred expansion:

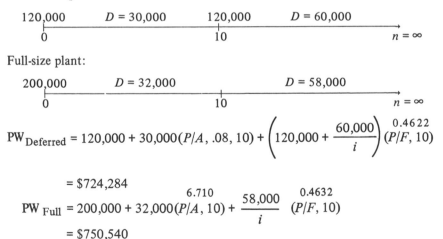

$$PW_{Deferred} = 120,000 + 30,000(P/A, .08, 10) + \left(120,000 + \frac{\overset{0.4622}{60,000}}{i}\right)(P/F, 10)$$

$$= \$724,284$$

$$PW_{Full} = 200,000 + 32,000\overset{6.710}{(P/A, 10)} + \frac{58,000}{i}\overset{0.4632}{(P/F, 10)}$$

$$= \$750,540$$

The analysis indicates the advantage of deferring the investment in a full-size plant until it is needed 10 years from now by proving that the extra investment today of $80,000 fails to be recovered with 8% by $26,256.

Example 7.11 also illustrates some of the economic factors that prevail in a deferred investment situation. We have seen that the half-size plant costs more than half the first cost of the full-size plant. This is generally the result of fixed costs or overhead, which are inelastic with changes in size, as well as the extra work necessary to coordinate and join the two halves. Another element is observed by the fact that the operating disbursements at equal outputs are not the same for each alternative. This expresses the fact that (a) the operating efficiency of large equipment may be greater than the efficiency of a small unit at all loads and (b) equipment running at half capacity will likely have poor efficiency. This explains why the small plant has low disbursements during the first 10 years but two half-size units have higher disbursements in subsequent years.

7.12 USE OF A STUDY PERIOD IN DEFERRED INVESTMENTS

The study period, introduced in Chapter 6, is a useful technique in deferred investment problems, as illustrated in the following example.

EXAMPLE 7.12   Equipment to provide waste disposal for a factory for the next 10 years can be installed for $30,000 with annual operating expenses of $5,000. In 10 years this capacity must be doubled by the installation of identical equipment. Alternatively, equipment to provide the full anticipated capacity can be installed now for $50,000 with annual operating disbursements of $6,000 for the first 10 years and $9,500 thereafter. Each piece of equipment is estimated to have a 20-year economic life from its date of installation. The minimum required rate of return is 10%.

SOLUTION.

Deferred plan:

```
 30,000    5,000/yr   30,000     10,000/yr
 ├─────────────────────┼────────────────────────┼────────────────────────┤
 0                     10                        20                       30
```

Full plan:

```
 50,000    6,000/yr              9,500/yr
 ├─────────────────────┼────────────────────────┼────────────────────────┤
 0                     10                        20                       30
```

By adopting a 20-year study period, we need not predict the equipment to be installed at the end of 20 years except to predict that the deferred equipment installed in the tenth year will continue to serve the business during the last 10 years of its economic life. As a result, only the first 10 years of the investment cost of the deferred equipment is prorated to the study period.

$$\mathrm{PW}_{Deferred} = 30{,}000 + 5{,}000\overset{6.145}{(P/A, .10, 10)} + 10{,}000\overset{6.145}{(P/A, 10)}\overset{0.3855}{(P/F, 10)}$$

$$+ 30{,}000\overset{0.11746}{(A/P, 20)}\overset{6.145}{(P/A, 10)}\overset{0.3855}{(P/F, 10)} = \$\ 92{,}762$$

$$\mathrm{PW}_{Full} = 50{,}000 + 6{,}000\overset{6.145}{(P/A, .10, 10)} + 9{,}500\overset{6.145}{(P/A, 10)}\overset{0.3855}{(P/F, 10)}$$

$$= \underline{109{,}375}$$

Advantage of deferment: $ 16,613

7.13 LEVELS OF INVESTMENT

In the previous chapter we noted that theoretically a host of alternatives exists in every economic situation, even though some may not yet be on the market or perhaps not even conceived. This will not prevent the designer from suggesting a series of alternative designs and arranging these alternatives in a series of present worths, observing the trend that points to the most economic.

This is not to imply that such an analysis is only theoretical. Many practical problems cover a host of design alternatives which have not yet been tried. A typical illustration is determining the economic height of a proposed office building. In problems of this kind, a practical approach is to analyze all the prospective alternatives together, rather than two at a time.

Example 7.13   Rework Example 6.17, which was analyzed by the annual-cost method, from the standpoint of a present-worth analysis. The data given in Example 6.17 is reproduced in the first three columns of Table 7.13.

Table 7.13   PRESENT-WORTH ANALYSIS OF THE LEVELS OF INVESTMENT IN INSULATION

Thickness of insulation (in.)	First cost	Cost of annual heat loss	Present worth of all costs; 15-year life—8%
0	$ 0	$1,800	$15,401
$\frac{3}{4}$	1,800	900	9,503
1	2,545	590	7,595
$1\frac{1}{2}$	3,340	450	7,192
$2\frac{1}{4}$	4,360	360	7,441
3	5,730	310	8,383
$3\frac{1}{2}$	7,280	285	9,719

SOLUTION.   The present worth of each level is computed as follows:

$$\overset{8.559}{\text{PW of } \tfrac{3}{4} \text{ in.}} = 1,800 + 900(P/A, .08, 15) = \$9,503$$

as arrayed in the fourth column. Selection of the lowest present worth shows that $1\frac{1}{2}$-inch insulation is the most economic installation, but actually the most economic alternative is not on the list, as illustrated in the next section.

7.14 SIGNIFICANCE OF THE EXTRA INVESTMENT

Let us reexamine Example 7.13 from the viewpoint of the extra investment.

EXAMPLE 7.14   The data from Example 7.13 is rearranged in Table 7.14a, which shows the extra investment in column 3 and the saving in heat loss in column 5.

Table 7.14a ANALYSIS OF THE EXTRA INVESTMENT IN INSULATION

(1) *Thickness of insulation (in.)*	(2) *First cost*	(3) *Extra investment*	(4) *Annual heat loss*	(5) *Annual savings in heat*	(6) *Present-worth advantage of making the extra investment*
0	$ 0	$ 0	$1,800	$ 0	$ 0
$\frac{3}{4}$	1,800	1,800	900	900	5,898
1	2,545	745	590	310	1,908
$1\frac{1}{2}$	3,340	795	450	140	403
$2\frac{1}{4}$	4,360	1,020	360	90	-249
3	5,730	1,370	310	50	-942
$3\frac{1}{4}$	7,280	1,550	285	25	-1,336

SOLUTION. The present-worth analysis of the extra investment in 1-inch over $\frac{3}{4}$-inch insulation is

$$\overset{8.559}{310(P/A, .08, 15)} - 745 = \$1,908$$

This is the advantage of making the investment because the savings exceed the cost.

As observed in column 6, $1\frac{1}{2}$-inch insulation is the most economic because the extra expenditure of $1,020 to install $2\frac{1}{4}$-inch insulation fails to be recovered with 8% return by $249. The test of economy is to show that the extra investment is recovered with the minimum required rate of return. The first three levels of investment exceed this minimum (by $5,898, $1,908, and $403, respectively); however, we note in column 6 that, mathematically at least, there is an alternative between $1\frac{1}{2}$-inch and $2\frac{1}{4}$-inch that should just meet our minimum economic requirements. This situation would be satisfied if the following alternative of $1\frac{3}{4}$-inch insulation could be designed.

In this case $1\frac{3}{4}$-inch insulation would be selected as the alternative that conforms to the goal of maximizing profits with limited funds and limited opportunities.

Table 7.14b MAXIMIZATION OF THE INVESTMENT IN EQUIPMENT DESIGN

Thickness of insulation (in.)	*First cost*	*Extra investment*	*Annual heat loss*	*Annual savings in heat*	*Present-worth advantage of making the extra investment*
$1\frac{1}{2}$	$3,340	$795	$450	$140	$403
$1\frac{3}{4}$	3,845	505	391	59	0
$2\frac{1}{4}$	4,360	515	360	31	-249

7.15 INCOME-EXPANSION EXPENDITURES

Having considered only cost-reduction expenditures, let us look at situations where gross income, expanded or contracted by the choice of alternatives, becomes relevant to the choice. Examples would include plant-expansion projects or propositions that affect the unit selling price or the quantity of units sold.

EXAMPLE 7.15   A company is contemplating creating a new division that will cost $400,000. The gross income from sales will be $250,000 a year and the operating disbursements for all activities relative to the division will be $150,000 a year, except that the cost of replacing machines and equipment will amount to another $20,000 a year. To provide working capital an additional sum of $50,000 will be required. The management contemplates that the divisional activity can be counted on for 20 years before developments in this field may make it obsolete. Salvage at that date for the plant and equipment (some of which will be reasonably new as a result of replacement policies) is expected to be $100,000. The minimum required rate of return on the enterprise is 20%.

SOLUTION.

$$I = 250,000/\text{yr}$$

450,000 $D = 170,000/\text{yr}$ $L = 150,000$

0 ———————————————— 20

The complete salvage will include the $50,000 working capital. The present worth of the income will be computed as follows:

4.8696   0.02608
$$PW = 80,000(P/A, .20, 20) + 150,000(P/F, 20) - 450,000 = -\$56,520$$

The proposal is not recommended as the investment is not recovered with the required rate of return.

7.16 LEVELS OF INCOME-EXPANSION INVESTMENTS

Let us examine alternative designs in which each design represents a higher level of investment, as shown in the following example:

EXAMPLE 7.16   Successive levels of investment, A through E, which can be

Table 7.16   LEVELS OF INVESTMENT IN AN INCOME-EXPANSION PROPOSAL

(1) Size	(2) Investment	(3) Annual gross income	(4) Annual disbursements	(5) Present worth of the operation
A	$1,000	$ 800	$ 500	$ 843
B	1,500	1,150	650	1,572
C	2,300	1,475	825	1,694
D	3,300	1,800	1,025	1,462
E	4,500	2,135	1,250	938

made in a small business are given in Table 7.16. The required rate of return is 10% and the economic life is 10 years.

SOLUTION. The present worth of each level of investment is computed as follows:

$$\overset{6.1446}{\text{PW of } A = (800 - 500)(P/A, .10, 10) - 1,000 = \$843}$$

Investment level C with the highest present worth will be selected. In the next section, examination of this from the standpoint of the extra investment will help to develop a deeper understanding of this conclusion.

7.17 INCOME-EXPANSION EXPENDITURES FROM STANDPOINT OF THE EXTRA INVESTMENT

Using the data in Example 7.17, let us now examine the problem from the standpoint of the extra investment.

EXAMPLE 7.17 The data is presented in Table 7.17.

Table 7.17 ANALYSIS OF THE EXTRA INVESTMENT IN AN INCOME-EXPANSION PROPOSITION

(1)	(2)	(3)	(4)	(5)	(6)
		Extra	*Income less*	*Extra income less extra*	*Present worth of the*
Size	*Investment*	*investment*	*disbursements*	*disbursements*	*operation*
A	$1,000	$1,000	$300	$300	$843
B	1,500	500	500	200	729
C	2,300	800	650	150	122
D	3,300	1,000	775	125	-232
E	4,500	1,200	885	110	-524

SOLUTION. Analysis of the extra investment in each level over the previous level proceeds as follows:

$$\overset{6.1446}{\text{PW of Level } C = 150(P/A, .10, 10) - 800 = \$122}$$

As in Example 7.16, this method selects investment level C, but it also proves that the extra investment in D over C of $1,000 fails to be recovered with 10% return by $240. This example shows that in income-expansion propositions, it is correct to select the alternative with the highest present worth as we did in Example 7.16.

7.18 MUTUALLY EXCLUSIVE PROPOSALS

Cost-reduction alternatives are mutually exclusive;[1] we select one or the other of the alternatives, but not both, because only one of these can be used. While this is obviously the case for cost-reduction alternatives, it is not always true for multiple income-expansion alternatives. In Example 7.15 the proposal was to invest $450,000 in a new division of the company. Obviously this is mutually exclusive with investing the money elsewhere in the company. But suppose another proposal had been made to invest a large sum of money in a new division located in another part of the country. If there are two separate divisions in which the company can invest simultaneously, both will be selected if each meets the test of recovery of capital with the minimum required rate of return. But if only one can be selected, if they are mutually exclusive, then only the better one will be selected, even though both meet the test of recovery of capital with the minimum required rate of return. The latter situation is illustrated in the following example.

EXAMPLE 7.18 Proposal A requires an investment of $250,000, which will bring an annual income of $100,000 from annual disbursements of $40,000. The life of the project is expected to be 20 years with $75,000 salvage at that date. Proposal B requires $175,000 investment with annual income of $90,000 and disbursements of $50,000. At the end of 20 years its salvage will be $60,000. The proposals are mutually exclusive although the company may turn down both if neither is acceptable.

The minimum required rate of return is 20%.

SOLUTION.

$$
\begin{array}{llll}
 & I = 100,000 & \\
\quad 250,000 & D = 40,000 & L = 75,000 \\
A \quad \vdash\!\!&\!\!\rule{4cm}{0.4pt}\!\!&\!\!\vdash \\
\quad\quad 0 & & 20
\end{array}
$$

$$
\begin{array}{llll}
 & I = 90,000 & \\
\quad 175,000 & D = 50,000 & L = 60,000 \\
B \quad \vdash\!\!&\!\!\rule{4cm}{0.4pt}\!\!&\!\!\vdash \\
\quad\quad 0 & & 20
\end{array}
$$

$$
\overset{}{PW_A} = (100,000 - 40,000)\overset{4.8696}{(P/A, .20, 20)} + 75,000\overset{0.02608}{(P/F, 20)} - 250,000
$$

$$
= \$44,132
$$

$$
PW_B = (90,000 - 50,000)\overset{4.8696}{(P/A, .20, 20)} + 60,000\overset{0.02608}{(P/F, 20)} - 175,000
$$

$$
= \$21,349
$$

[1] These are not to be confused with instances where expenditures are mutually independent; for example, proposals to reduce the operating cost of a machine tool by adding devices for the automatic feeding of stock, automatic ejection of the piece, automatic feeding of the tool, and so on. These are not alternatives to each other: each can be done without excluding the other; one or all or none can be installed, depending on the test of profitability. Each, however, is only mutually exclusive with making no installation or mutually exclusive with another method of feeding stock.

Both of these proposals, by themselves, are satisfactory inasmuch as they recover the investment with more than the required 20% return, but since they are mutually exclusive only the better one should be selected. This is Proposal A, with the highest present worth. The test is simple but the reasoning is deceptive. The conclusion to select A over B is based on the fact that the extra investment in A's level of investment is justified along the lines of reasoning developed in Section 7.17.

We should also note that both of these income-expansion proposals would be rejected if neither met the test.

7.19 VALUATION

Valuation has been defined "as the art of estimating the fair monetary measure of the desirability of ownership of specific properties for specific purposes."[1]

Valuation encompasses an area too large to be covered in its entirety in a text on engineering economy. Its wide scope of applications is suggested by the following items.

Valuation for property taxes
Condemnation of property for public use
Public utility rate cases
Valuation of land
Valuation of good will
Valuation of patents and trade secrets
Valuation of stocks and bonds
Valuation of an enterprise
Valuation of mines, timberlands, oil properties

As implied in the definition, the fair market value is the cornerstone of valuation. In many instances no market has been established and the incomes not only lie entirely in the future but must be predicted. The basis of valuation in the absence of a known existing fair market value is the present worth of all future incomes minus future expenses computed at a fair rate of return. The following examples will illustrate some aspects of valuation.

EXAMPLE 7.19a A 20-year, 4%, $1,000 bond pays interest coupons semiannually. The first payment is due 6 months hence. What will be the value or price of the bond to yield 6% compounded semiannually?

SOLUTION.

$$
\begin{array}{lll}
& & \text{Income} \\
P = ? & I = 20/\text{period} & 1,000 \\
\vdash\!\!\!-\!\!\!-\!\!\!-\!\!\!-\!\!\!-\!\!\!-\!\!\!-\!\!\!-\!\!\!-\!\!\!-\!\!\!-\!\!\!-\!\!\!-\!\!\!-\!\!\!-\!\!\!\dashv \\
0 & & 40
\end{array}
$$

[1] Anson, Marston, et. al., *Engineering Valuation and Depreciation*, 2nd ed. (Ames: Iowa State University Press, 1964).

The 4% bond pays 2% interest every 6-month period. The value to yield 6% compounded semiannually is the present worth of the stream of 40 end-of-period payments at 3% per period.

$$\text{Value} = 20\,\overset{23.115}{(P/A, .03, 40)} + 1{,}000\,\overset{0.30656}{(P/F, 40)} = \$768.86$$

This would be a fair market price if the purchaser's minimum required rate of return is 6% compounded semiannually.

EXAMPLE 7.19b How much should a company pay for a second-hand machine, based on the value to the company, if the machine is to perform the following job on a contract that will last 3 years? The machine can be obtained for $5,000; delivery and installation will cost another $500. The machine cost $25,000 when new 10 years ago. A new machine can be obtained for $20,000 installed and will cost $8,000 a year to operate compared to $12,000 for the used machine. Three years from now the new machine will have a salvage of $15,000, whereas it is expected that the second-hand machine can still be sold for $5,000. The company's minimum required rate of return is 15%.

SOLUTION.

$$
\begin{array}{lll}
\text{Used} & \begin{array}{ccc} P = ? & D = 12{,}000/\text{yr} & L = 5{,}000 \\ \vdash\!\!\!-\!\!\!-\!\!\!-\!\!\!-\!\!\!-\!\!\!-\!\!\!-\!\!\!-\!\!\!-\!\!\!\dashv \\ 0 & & 3 \end{array}
\end{array}
$$

$$
\begin{array}{lll}
\text{New} & \begin{array}{ccc} 20{,}000 & D = 8{,}000/\text{yr} & L = 15{,}000 \\ \vdash\!\!\!-\!\!\!-\!\!\!-\!\!\!-\!\!\!-\!\!\!-\!\!\!-\!\!\!-\!\!\!-\!\!\!\dashv \\ 0 & & 3 \end{array}
\end{array}
$$

$$(20{,}000 - P) = 4{,}000\,\overset{2.283}{(P/A, .15, 3)} + 10{,}000\,\overset{0.6575}{(P/F, 3)}$$

whence

$$P = \$4{,}293$$

At the price of $4,293 or less for the used machine, it is economical to make the extra investment. The proposed price of $5,000 is therefore too high.

PROBLEMS

7.1 A motorcar company is considering two propositions for the design of a new production line. The first is as automated as present technology permits and costs $1,500,000. The second, less automated but inherently more flexible, will cost $900,000 but will have annual labor costs $310,000 higher than the other proposal. Changes in car models will necessitate redesign of the production lines every 2 years; the cost of reconstruction will be $300,000 for the fully automated line and $100,000 for the other. The economic lives will be 8 years with $100,000 salvage values for both lines. Compare the propositions by the present-worth method if the minimum required rate of return is 20%. Explain the meaning of your answer.

7.2 Using the present-worth method, what is the cost commitment of a forming tool priced at $9,500 if the installation cost is $500, operating disbursements for labor and power are $6,800 a year, property taxes are 4%

of first cost, and inspection, maintenance, and repair are expected to be $300 the first year, increasing by $100 a year thereafter? The economic life is predicted to be 11 years with $1,250 salvage at that date. The company's minimum required rate of return is 25%.

7.3   A retired executive is contemplating the purchase of a new car for $3,890 with the idea of keeping it for 10 years. Salvage at that date, he expects, will be $200. His annual cost of gas, oil, maintenance, insurance, license, and storage space will be $800. He estimates that repairs will be insignificant for the first 3 years, $40 at the end of the fourth year, and thereafter they will increase 20% each year over the previous year. What is his contemplated cost commitment if he can obtain 6% on his investments?

7.4   A prospective builder can insulate his house against excessive heat loss during the winter months for $975. His furnace will cost $2,100 and the annual fuel bill is expected to be $550. Alternatively, he can procure thicker and better quality insulation for $1,360. This expenditure will reduce his annual heating bill to $350 and will also enable him to use a smaller heating plant costing $1,900 installed. He plans to keep the premises for 15 years, at which time he expects that the house, excluding the land, will sell for 50% of its first cost. Annual property taxes are 5% of first cost. If he can get 6% on his investments, make a present-worth analysis to determine which proposition to install. Explain the meaning of your answer.

7.5   In the previous problem explain your answers under the following situations. (a) The alternative wins based on the given data in Problem 7.4. (b) The other alternative wins by a $200 lower present worth. (c) The alternatives have equal present worths.

7.6   Various types of roofing material are available to a prospective builder in a community in the northern United States. He can install a very durable material having an estimated life of 20 years for $2,000. After 10 years repairs are expected which are estimated to be $200. Alternatively, he can install a less durable material, expected to last 10 years, for $1,500. He estimates repairs costing $150 will be necessary after 5 years. Make a present-worth comparison if the owner can get investment opportunities at 7%. Explain the meaning of your answer.

7.7   Rework Problem 7.6 if all future replacements will cost an added $250 to remove the old roofing material prior to installing a new roof. Will this alter your analysis and your conclusions?

7.8   An airline is considering replacement of an airliner which is estimated to have an economic life of 3 years, an investment value P today of $280,000, and annual operating disbursements of $750,000. The proposed machine, a jet liner costing $1,700,000, is expected to have a 10-year economic life with zero salvage value. The annual operating disbursements are $300,000. The minimum required rate of return is 25%. (a) Compare the alternatives by the present-worth method using a 3-year study period. (b) A company analyst claims that the study-period method is incorrect. He maintains that the predicted salvage value at the end of 3 years should be used in the computation. If this is $250,000 for the new liner and zero for the old, what action would he recommend? (c) Which method do you think is correct and why?

7.9 In a certain northern community, deterioration of an automobile from road salt used in the winter months may require early replacement of body parts if not the whole car. Alternative methods of handling this situation from the standpoint of a certain owner are as follows:

(a) Use "standard" body undercoating at a first cost of $30. As this is not entirely effective, deterioration necessitates replacement of the car after 6 years of operation. The estimated salvage is $350.

(b) Use a special coating and body materials costing $350 which will protect the car through a 10-year life, at which time the salvage of the car is $150. After the sixth year, however, the other parts of the car will require extra maintenance estimated at $150 a year (begins end of year 7).

(c) Use "standard" body undercoating, as in (a) and then rebuild the body for $400 at the end of year 6. Salvage of the car at the end of 10 years will be $175. The added annual maintenance for other repairs will be the same as in the second method.

The original cost of the car is $3,500. If the buyer can invest at 7% in other opportunities, what course of action do you recommend?

7.10 A company is considering new versus used machinery to perform intermittent jobs in a fabricating department. The comparative data in the tabulation shows that the used machine is expected to have a shorter life. The company's minimum required rate of return is 30%.

	Used	New
First cost, installed	$3,000	$6,000
Estimated life	6 years	9 years
Estimated salvage value	$ 500	$1,500
Annual disbursements	$2,000	$1,000

Use the present-worth method of comparison, employing various approaches to the problem of analysis where lives are different: study period, replacement with the machine having the extra investment, and least common multiple. Discuss the meaning of each and compare the conclusions.

7.11 Two sources of minerals are available to a company, either of which can supply its future needs. Deposit *A* is sufficient to last 10 years and will have a land value (salvage) at that date of $15,000. The purchase price is $120,000 and the annual cost to extract the deposits and operate the mine is $20,000. Deposit *B* will last 20 years, at which time the land value will be zero because the restoration cost will equal the sale price. The cost of mining and operating will be $10,000. The first cost of Deposit *B* is $180,000. If the minimum required rate of return is 15%, compare the two by the present-worth method. You may presume that similar deposits will be available elsewhere in the future.

7.12 Two designs are suitable for housing track and field events. Design *N* costs $800,000 with annual upkeep costs, including maintenance, repair, heat, and janitor service, of $25,000 a year. Its life is expected to be permanent. Design *T* costs $450,000 with annual upkeep costs for the previous items of $35,000 a year; however, with this design repairs costing $15,000 will be required every 5 years, and the life will be 25 years with a probable salvage at that date of $50,000. The minimum required rate of return is

10%. In your present-worth analysis compare the capitalized-cost method with the study-period method.

7.13 Two designs of store fronts are proposed for a department store on a famous street in New York. Design G costs $25,000, will be replaced every 2 years, and has a salvage of $8,000. Maintenance will cost $3,000 a year. Design O costs $50,000 and will last 6 years with $10,000 salvage. Maintenance will cost $4,000 a year. The minimum required rate of return is 17%. Using the present-worth method, which design is recommended—assuming both are equal from a marketing viewpoint?

7.14 Two designs of vehicular tunnels are proposed to eliminate highways that presently go around a cliff on the outskirts of an expanding city. The first design will cost $300,000 to build. It is estimated that reconstruction costing $100,000 will be required every 30 years. Its annual operating expenditures will be $25,000 for the first 15 years and $40,000 a year thereafter. The alternative design requires an initial investment of $550,000 followed by reconstruction costs of $50,000 every 30 years. Its annual operating expenditures will be only $15,000. Both installations are considered permanent. If the minimum required rate of return is estimated to be 15%, which design, using the capitalized-cost method of analysis, should be selected?

7.15 A grocery chain, prior to installing markets in communities throughout the state, is examining alternative designs prior to adopting one as standard. One of these, called the Parthenon design, is expected to be less likely to go out of style; in fact, it is expected to be more durable from the standpoint of deterioration as well as obsolescence. This design costs $75,000 and will have a 35-year life with $7,500 salvage and annual upkeep costs for repairs of $2,500. The other, known as the Pendulum design, costs $50,000 and has an estimated 20-year life with $5,000 salvage value. Its annual repair cost will be $4,000. If the minimum required rate of return is 20%, compare the alternatives by their present worths. Handle the differences in lives by investigating all the approaches—such as study period, capitalized cost, least common multiple, and replacement with the most economic.

7.16 A young couple have two plans to provide future housing needs. The first is to construct a single-level house costing $15,000, which they predict will be adequate for their needs for the next 5 years. At that time, they would meet their needs for more space by adding to the house a wing costing $10,000. The alternative plan is to construct a house now which will be adequate for all their future needs. Such a house, they estimate, will cost $20,000. In any event they plan to move into a smaller house in 30 years, and they estimate that the salvage of both houses would be equal at that date. If they can invest at returns of 10%, which house, using the present-worth method, is their best buy?

7.17 A town has plans for installing a water tower and pumping system. The first plan, costing $350,000, will take care of the town's needs for the next 10 years and will have annual pumping costs of $26,000. At the end of 10 years the town plans to install an additional tower and pumps, identical to the first, to provide the needed extra capacity. This addition will cost

$350,000 and the total pumping costs will become $52,000. The towers will be considered permanent but every 20 years from the date of installation some equipment costing $125,000 will have to be replaced.

The alternative proposal is to install a large tank and pumping equipment now and operate at half capacity for the next 10 years. This installation costs $500,000. The annual pumping costs will be $28,000 now and $50,000 later. The tank will be considered permanent but 20 years from the date of installation some equipment costing $200,000 will have to be replaced.

If the minimum required rate of return is 15%, which plan should be recommended? Use the present-worth method of analysis.

7.18 Automatic switching equipment in a toll center can be installed to provide the needs of the area for the next 8 years. It will cost $240,000 and have a 15-year life with zero salvage value. Operating costs, including maintenance, repair, and taxes, will be $65,000. At the end of 8 years, the system will have to be enlarged at a cost of $220,000. The additional equipment will have a 15-year life from that date with zero salvage value. The added operating costs will be only $45,000.

The alternative to this is to install a system that will take care of all the load for the next 15 years. This can be done for $390,000 with operating costs over the next 8 years of $75,000 and of $110,000 after that date. Its salvage at the end of 15 years will be zero.

The minimum required rate of return is 10%. Which plan is favored, using a present-worth analysis?

7.19 A state turnpike can be built for $12,000,000 which will serve the traffic needs for the next 10 years, at the end of which it must be enlarged at an additional cost of $12,000,000. Maintenance of the highway during the first 10 years will be $40,000 a year.

Alternatively, the right-of-way needed for future expansion can be acquired now and graded at the same time the present turnpike is constructed. The total cost will be $16,000,000. The maintenance cost of the highway and the added right-of-way will be $58,000 a year for the first 10 years. During that period there will also be a loss of revenue from the taxable property reclaimed by the state in providing the right of way. This amounts to $80,000 a year. After 10 years the highway can be enlarged with less dislocation of the existing roadbed so that the cost of enlargement will be only $5,000,000. Maintenance after that date will be the same as for the other design.

It is predicted that the life of the highway will be 25 years from the present date as a result of obsolescence. Salvage will be $3,000,000 in either case. If the minimum required rate of return is 6%, which plan is recommended? Use a present-worth analysis.

7.20 A sports arena is planned in a growing metropolis. The administrative offices and entrance halls to the arena face on a street that is expected to show great commercial progress. Two plans are offered for the construction of this part of the arena. Plan I is to construct a three-story building with provision for adding 12 stories at a future date. The cost of this initial building, designed to take the future loads, will be $3,100,000. In

10 years the stories can be added at a cost of $11,200,000. The life of the entire structure, including the arena, is expected to be 35 years with zero salvage.

Plan II is to construct for $1,110,000 a three-story building which will be demolished in 10 years and replaced by a 15-story structure at a cost of $15,300,000.

The maintenance of Plan I will be $40,000 and of Plan II, $35,000 for the first 10 years. After that they will be alike. The property taxes will be 4% of the first costs of the structure. The minimum required rate of return will be 20%. Make your recommendation based on a present-worth analysis.

7.21   A car owner who operates his car commercially is contemplating certain equipment changes on his automobile to correct its high gasoline consumption. He currently is getting 11.4 miles per gallon under the test conditions. He drives an average of 30,000 miles a year and gasoline costs 32.6 cents per gallon. He estimates that the improvements will serve for 3 years, at which time he plans to sell the car. However, they are not expected to increase the sale price at that time.

Item	Cost of improvement	Expected improved mileage (mpg)
C	$ 120	1.3
F	400	2.6
E	225	1.0
D	660	1.8
B	300	2.0
A	180	3.1
Total of A to F	$1,885	11.8

The equipment changes are independent; that is, any one can be installed alone or in addition to any other. For example, all can be installed, in which case the gas mileage will become 11.8 + 11.4 = 23.2 mpg.

Which items of improvement should be made if the owner's minimum required rate of return is 15%? Use present-worth analysis. Explain your answer from the viewpoint of the "extra investment."

7.22   In the previous problem, suppose the equipment improvements were not independent because they had to be installed in a certain order. For example, if the order is ABCDEF, then A must be installed first, B cannot be installed unless A has been, and so on. What equipment should be installed if the order is (a) ABCDEF; (b) BCADEF; (c) CABDEF; (d) DABCEF. Explain your answer from the viewpoint of the extra investment.

7.23   Four alternative heights have been proposed for an office building in a small western city:

Number of Stories	2	3	4	5
Building first cost	$200,000	$250,000	$310,000	$385,000
Annual operating cost	15,000	25,000	30,000	42,000
Annual income	40,000	60,000	90,000	106,000

The economic life of the building is predicted to be 40 years, at which time it will be demolished at zero salvage. The above costs are for the building only; the cost of the land is $30,000 in each case and is predicted to be the same at the end of the life period. Taxes and insurance are included in the listed operating costs. The minimum required rate of return is 15%. Which should be built, if any? Explain your answer from the standpoint of the extra investment.

7.24 The Acme Cab Company has been experimenting with various grades of automobiles as taxis; they find that a higher priced car attracts more customers, is less expensive to maintain, and has less time out for repairs. The question is whether these justify the higher first cost.

Car	Price of car	Salvage value	Annual repair expense	Annual income
A	$2,000	$ 800	$630	$ 8,000
B	2,600	1,000	550	8,300
C	3,100	1,200	540	9,000
D	4,200	1,350	460	10,100
E	6,000	2,000	300	11,000

The expected economic life of the cars is 3 years. The minimum required rate of return is 10%. Explain your answer from the standpoint of the extra investment.

7.25 In Problem 7.24, an officer of the firm maintains that "the best buy is the $2,600 car; the worst buy is the $6,000 car, which is $2,000 overpriced." From the data in Problem 7.24, what should the prices of these two cars be for them to just qualify (i.e., within one dollar) as the best buy?

7.26 Based on the data in Problem 6.19, what price could the purchasing agent afford to pay for the carbide-tipped tools?

7.27 In Problem 6.8, the manufacturer of Engine I is asked to cut his price $15,000 in order to equal the price of Engine S offered by a competitor. Based on the data given in that problem, show whether this price reduction is equitable or what it should be to give a fair price in the given situation.

After some additional bargaining, the manufacturer of Engine I decides to offer a price for his engine which would make it impossible for the customer to accept Engine S as a gift unless accompanied by a bonus. What price would satisfy this situation?

7.28 Which of the following problems in Chapter 7 are mutually exclusive: 20, 21, 22, 23? Explain why.

7.29 If you conclude that the alternatives in Problem 7.23 are mutually exclusive, restate the problem so the alternative heights of buildings become mutually independent. If they are mutually independent alternatives, what investment decision would you make? Explain your answer in terms of the extra investment.

7.30 A $1,000 bond matures in 20 years and pays 4% interest. The interest is payable at the end of every 6 months. What is the price of the bond to yield 6% compounded semiannually?

7.31 A 6%, $1,000 bond pays interest at the end of every 6 months. The bond matures in 12 years. What is the price of the bond to yield 8% compounded quarterly?

7.32 A promissory note has 10 annual payments of $425 remaining, each one at the end of the year. What should the market price of the note be to yield the investor 8% interest compounded quarterly?

7.33 The annual dividends of Company *A* and Company *B* are $6.40, and these are expected to continue at this amount indefinitely. A shareholder who buys stock with the expectation of permanent ownership will buy *A*'s stock if it yields 8% and *B*'s only it it yields 12%. What price is he willing to pay for each? What logical reason would he have for paying more for one company's stock if both promise to pay the same dividends?

7.34 A patent for a control attachment to a machine tool has 12 years to run and the inventor by contract with one of the licensee's under the patent is to receive $25 for each attachment sold. Predictions place next year's sales at 1,000 units with an increase of 100 units every year thereafter. The inventor needs money to develop and promote a new product and suggests that he receive a lump sum payment for his future stream of income. What is a fair price if he can get 6% compounded semiannually on his investments?

7.35 The contract of a manager of a baseball team has 3 years to run and calls for an annual salary of $40,000. The owners of the team want to hire a new manager. They believe the man they want will take the job under a 3-year contract at $46,000 a year. They estimate that the new manager will increase annual attendance by a minimum of 30,000 people or at most by 200,000 people. The club receives $2.00 net after all expenses on the average from each admission. The owner's minimum required rate of return is 12%. Without losing money, what amount could they reasonably offer the present manager to buy up his contract? How much might the manager reasonably want?

8

Rate-of-Return Comparisons

8.1 ANALYSIS OF INCOME-EXPANSION INVESTMENTS BY RATE-OF-RETURN METHOD

The theory of the rate-of-return method of analysis is based on the observation that the gross income in any enterprise is used for just two purposes: to repay all costs and to pay a rate of return. This observation is the basis for the mathematical conclusion that *the rate of return is the interest which makes the costs equivalent to the income.*

The mathematical model simply equates costs to income; but the solution of the model, unfortunately, in most cases requires a trial-and-error solution. On the bright side, however, much of the labor can be reduced by planned procedures in conducting the trials.

The general model of equivalence will be:

$$(P - L)(A/P, i, n) + Li + D = I \tag{18.1}$$

where I is the uniform annual gross income and i is the interest rate, the unknown factor in the equation.

8.2 GENERAL SOLUTION IN INCOME-EXPANSION EXPENDITURES

The solution of the general equation for an income-expansion problem contains i to some power of n in two or more terms and is best handled by trial and error, simplified by a planned procedure such as the one illustrated in the following example.

EXAMPLE 8.2 An income-producing property which can be purchased for $30,000 has an annual gross income of $5,000 and an annual operating cost of $2,000. It is estimated that the resale price will be $15,000 in 10 years.

SOLUTION.

$$I = 5,000/\text{yr}$$

30,000 $D = 2,000/\text{yr}$ $L = 15,000$

0   10

$$(P - L)(A/P, i, n) + Li + D = I$$

$$(30,000 - 15,000)(A/P, i, 10) + 15,000i + 2,000 = 5,000$$

First Trial, $i = 0\%$

Selecting zero in the first trial shows whether the income is actually sufficient to recover the costs. From this trial we can also approximate the magnitude of the rate of return. The symbol, $\triangleq$, employed to mean "set equal to" acknowledges that AC $\triangleq$ AW may subsequently prove to be an inequality in the given trial.

AC $\triangleq$ AW

0.10

$$15,000(A/P, 0, 10) + (15,000)(0) + 2,000 \triangleq 5,000$$

$$3,500 \triangleq 5,000$$

$$0 \triangleq 1,500$$

Therefore, at 0%,

AC $<$ AW by $1,500

Interpretation of this result shows that the investment is recovered with zero rate of return plus $1,500 a year, or an *approximate* rate of return after recovery of capital of

$$i \cong \left(\frac{1,500}{30,000}\right)(100\%) \cong 5\%$$

As we will show in Section 8.2.1, the true rate of return will be higher than the approximate rate of return—probably between 5% and 7%. So try 6%.

Second Trial, $i = 6\%$

$$15,000(A/P, .06, 10) + (15,000)(0.06) + 2,000 \triangleq 5,000$$

$$4,938 \triangleq 5,000$$

$$0 \triangleq 62$$

Therefore, at 6%,

AC $<$ AW by $62

Hence the true rate of return is still higher, so try 7%.

Third Trial, i = 7%

$$15,000 \underset{0.14238}{(A/P, .07, 10)} + (15,000)(0.07) + 2,000 \overset{\wedge}{=} 5,000$$

$$5,186 \overset{\wedge}{=} 5,000$$

$$186 \overset{\wedge}{=} 0$$

Therefore, at 7%,

$$AC > AW \text{ by } \$186$$

This shows that at 7% interest the costs exceed incomes, or, explicitly, the investment fails to be recovered with 7% return by $186 a year.

Since the return on the investment is $186 short of 7% and $62 greater than 6%, we can interpolate:

$$i = 6\% + \left(\frac{62}{62 + 186}\right)(1\%) = 6.25\%$$

Therefore, the rate of return on the $30,000 investment after recovery of capital is 6.25%.

The steps in a planned trial-and-error procedure are as follows:

1. Equate annual costs to annual incomes.
2. Make first trial assuming $i = 0$. Use this and the direction finder in the next section to predict i for the next trial.
3. By successive trials, straddle the true rate of return and interpolate.

A guide that may be helpful between trials is illustrated as follows:
With data from the second trial in Example 8.2, the approximate rate of return after the second trials is

$$i \cong 6\% + \left(\frac{62}{30,000}\right)(100\%) \cong 6.21\%$$

The true rate of return will be slightly higher than that indicated by the direction finder. It appears that a trial of 7% would give a straddle (as it did).

By using the planned procedure, three or at the most four trials should be sufficient.

8.2.1 A DIRECTION FINDER

In Example 8.2, which appeared as follows,

$$I = 5,000/\text{yr}$$

30,000	$D = 2,000/\text{yr}$	$L = 15,000$
0		10

we computed that the approximate $i = 5\%$ (obtained from the first trial, $i = 0$) and the true $i = 6.25\%$.

From this example we can make these observations:

1. The income is early in the life of the project (or, roughly, $P > L$).
2. The true i > approximate i.

These observations are but illustrations of a more general conclusion that we can make:

If income is early, true i > approximate i (and vice versa). This can be roughly reduced to

$$\text{If } P > L, \text{ true } i > \text{ approximate } i.$$

This conclusion can be tested by taking some limiting cases. For example:
(a) If the income were distributed so $L = 0$, i.e., $P > L$,

$$I = 6,500/\text{yr}$$
$$30,000 \qquad\qquad D = 2,000/\text{yr} \qquad\qquad\qquad L = 0$$
$$0 \qquad\qquad\qquad\qquad\qquad\qquad\qquad\qquad\qquad 10$$

then a test shows that the approximate $i = 5\%$ but the true $i = 8.1\%$.
(b) If the income were distributed so that $L = P$,

$$I = 3,500/\text{yr}$$
$$30,000 \qquad\qquad D = 2,000/\text{yr} \qquad\qquad L = 30,000$$
$$0 \qquad\qquad\qquad\qquad\qquad\qquad\qquad\qquad\qquad 10$$

Analysis shows that the approximate $i = 5\%$ and the true $i = 5\%$, also.
(c) If the income were distributed so that $P < L$.

$$30,000 \qquad\qquad\qquad I\text{-}D = 0 \qquad\qquad L = 45,000$$
$$0 \qquad\qquad\qquad\qquad\qquad\qquad\qquad\qquad\qquad 10$$

Analysis shows that the approximate $i = 5\%$ but the true $i = 4.1\%$.

These examples also demonstrate that the first trial, $i = 0$, in a trial-and-error procedure is mathematically equivalent to a situation in which $P = L$ (and the incomes are uniform); therefore we must gauge our actual incomes and disbursements relative to that kind of a situation in order to detect the location of the true rate of return.

8.3 NONUNIFORM INCOME

If incomes and disbursements are not uniformly distributed, the models will have many "unknown" terms, but the number of trials should be no greater than in the previous example.

EXAMPLE 8.3 An income-producing property can be purchased for speculation for $20,000 and sold in 5 years for a predicted $30,000. The expected income after costs at the end of each of the next 5 years is $1,000.

SOLUTION.

20,000 $I = 1,000/\text{yr}$ $L = 30,000$
┠──┨
0   5

Annual costs = Annual worth of income

$$20,000(A/P, i, 5) = [1,000(P/A, i, 5) + 30,000(P/F, i, 5)](A/P, i, 5)$$

First Trial, $i = 0\%$

$$(20,000)\left(\frac{1}{5}\right) \triangleq [(1,000)(5) + (30,000)(1)]\left(\frac{1}{5}\right)$$

$$4,000 \triangleq 7,000$$

$$0 \triangleq 3,000$$

whence

$$i = \frac{3,000}{20,000} = 15\%$$

Since $P < L$, the true rate of return will be less than 15%, so in the next trial use 13%. The results of the subsequent trials are as follows:

Second Trial, $i = 13\%$
AC > AW by $57

Third Trial, $i = 12\%$
AC < AW by $174

By interpolating,

$$i = 12 + \frac{174}{174 + 57} = 12.8\%$$

8.4 DIRECT METHODS OF SOLUTION

Trial-and-error procedures are required except in a few instances. Direct solutions are possible if $L = P$ or $L = 0$ and incomes and disbursements are uniformly distributed, or at any other time if the equation contains only one unknown factor. Nevertheless we find trial and error used in problems capable of direct solution. This is likely to occur if the analyst has command of only one interest factor. In many discounted cash-flow sheets only the single-payment compound-amount factor is used and therefore trial and error is required in every solution.

The analyst will be rewarded by commanding all the factors not only to make direct solutions but to simplify the more complex mathematical models.

8.5 LEVELS OF INCOME-EXPANSION INVESTMENTS

Various levels of income-expansion expenditures were tested by the present-worth method in Example 7.16. We now propose to compare these by the rate-of-return method in the following example.

EXAMPLE 8.5 The alternative levels of investment, A through E, proposed in Example 7.16 are reproduced in Table 8.5a. The minimum required rate of return is 10% and the economic life is estimated to be 10 years. Using the rate-of-return method of analysis, which level should be selected?

SOLUTION. First determine the rate of return on the *total* investment in each level:

Size A: $1,000(A/P, i, 10) + 500 = 800$

   $(A/P) = 0.300$, whence $i = 27.3\%$

Size B: $1,500(A/P, i, 10) + 650 = 1,150$

   $(A/P) = 0.333$, whence $i = 31.1\%$

Size C: $2,300(A/P, i, 10) + 825 = 1,475$

   $(A/P) = 0.283$, whence $i = 25.3\%$

Size D: $3,300(A/P, i, 10) + 1,025 = 1,800$

   $(A/P) = 0.235$, whence $i = 19.6\%$

Size E: $4,500(A/P, i, 10) + 1,250 = 2,135$

   $(A/P) = 0.1967$, whence $i = 14.7\%$

Next, determine the rate of return on the *extra* investment:

Size A over none = same as computed above $i = 27.3\%$

Size B over A: $500(A/P, i, 10) + 150 = 350$

   $(A/P) = 0.4$, whence $i = 38.5\%$

Table 8.5a PROPOSED LEVELS OF INVESTMENT

Size	Investment, P	Annual operating disbursements, D	Annual gross income, I
A	$1,000	$ 500	$ 800
B	1,500	650	1,150
C	2,300	825	1,475
D	3,300	1,025	1,800
E	4,500	1,250	2,135

Size C over B: $800(A/P, i, n) + 175 = 325$

$$(A/P) = 0.1875, \text{ whence } i = 13.4\%$$

Size D over C: $1{,}000(A/P, i, n) + 200 = 325$

$$(A/P) = 0.125, \text{ whence } i = 4.3\%$$

Size E over D: $1{,}200(A/P, i, n) + 225 = 335$

$$(A/P) = 0.0917, \text{ whence } i = 0$$

Table 8.5b shows that the maximum level of investment should be C if the minimum required rate of return is 10%. The extra \$1,000 investment in D over

Table 8.5b RATE-OF-RETURN ANALYSIS OF PROPOSED
LEVELS OF INVESTMENT

Size	Investment, P	Annual operating disbursement, D	Annual gross income, I	Rate of return on extra investment (%)	Rate of return on total investment (%)
A	$1,000	$ 500	$ 800	27.3	27.3
B	1,500	650	1,150	38.5	31.1
C	2,300	825	1,475	13.4	25.3
D	3,300	1,025	1,800	4.3	19.6
E	4,500	1,250	2,135	0	14.7

C brings a return of only 4.3%. Similarly, the extra investment of E over D does not meet the minimum required rate of return. Therefore, levels D and E must be rejected in spite of the fact that the *total* investment at level D has 19.6% rate of return and level E has 14.7% rate of return.

We must remember that these levels are mutually exclusive: if one level is selected, no other can be. And in mutually exclusive comparisons the test is whether the *extra* investment satisfies the minimum required rate of return. This observation was not so obvious in present-worth comparisons, where we simply selected the level of income expansion with the highest present worth, but the reader will recall that we proved that this was implicit in the present-worth test.

Sometimes a situation is found where a level of investment which fails to meet the required rate of return is followed by a level of investment which does meet the required rate. In this case it is possible that both levels *combined* may meet the requirement and thereby qualify for acceptance.

8.6 COST-REDUCTION INVESTMENTS

It has been noted that although the gross income is not altered by the choice, the net income after disbursements will be increased by the installation of cost-reduction expenditures. Consider an operation having a first cost of $10,000 with an annual operating cost of $5,000 and a second operation having a first cost of $7,000 with an annual operating cost of $6,000, both having 5-year lives and zero salvage. Installing the first operation will save spending $1,000 a year in the next 5 years thereby increasing the annual net income $1,000 during this period but the investment cost responsible for this increase is $10,000 − $7,000 = $3,000. On one hand there are investment costs and on the other incomes from these investments; consequently the rate of return in cost-reduction problems can be determined in the same manner as in income-expansion problems: equate annual cost to annual income (i.e., savings) and solve for the interest rate that makes them equal. Therefore:

$$(10,000 - 7,000)(A/P, i, 5) = 6,000 - 5,000$$

$$3,000(A/P, i, 5) = 1,000$$

$$(A/P, i, 5) = 0.333$$

whence

$$i = 19.9\%$$

Therefore, 19.9%, the rate of return which makes the cost equivalent to the income, is the rate of return on the investment.

8.7 ANNUAL COSTS ARE EQUIVALENT AT TRUE RATE OF RETURN

In Section 8.6 the annual costs were equated to annual incomes as follows:

$$(10,000 - 7,000)(A/P, i, 5) = 6,000 - 5,000$$

Algebraically transposing terms, we get

$$10,000(A/P, i, 5) + 5,000 = 7,000(A/P, i, 5) + 6,000$$

This equation shows that the rate of return, i, *also makes the annual costs equivalent.* This observation is very practical because in certain problems it is much simpler to equate the annual costs of the two alternatives than to equate the extra investment to the annual net savings. This is particularly true in problems having unequal economic lives or in problems having both positive and negative net savings.

8.8 ANALYSIS OF THE EXTRA INVESTMENT

If we set costs equal to incomes as they were in Section 8.6,

$$(10,000 - 7,000)(A/P, i, 5) = 6,000 - 5,000$$

we note that the left-hand member is the $3,000 extra investment in the more expensive alternative. This illustrates again what has been said in a number of places, that the entire analysis is only a test of whether to make the extra investment.   This is but another way of saying that the analysis only provides us with a means of selecting one of two alternatives.

The rate of return computed in the analysis is the rate of return on the extra investment and not the rate of return on the total investment.   The analyst cannot compute the latter without knowing the total income resulting from the total investment, and in cost-reduction expenditures the total income is not only irrelevant to the choice but is actually unknown.

Perhaps a better proof of this point is this: If the analysis shows that the alternative with the lower first cost is the more economic, what is the rate of return on it?   In a cost-reduction expenditure one hasn't the slightest idea!

8.9 GENERAL SOLUTION IN COST-REDUCTION INVESTMENTS

The planned procedure outlined in Section 8.2 for income-expansion investments serves equally well for cost-reduction investments.   The following example illustrates this.

EXAMPLE 8.9   An operation costing $1,000 has an annual operating cost of $850 with an economic life of 5 years.   A second operation costing $1,500 has an annual operating cost of $800 with an economic life of 8 years.   The minimum required rate of return is 8%.

SOLUTION.

Equate annual costs as observed in Section 8.7.

$$1,000(A/P, i, 5) + 850 = 1,500(A/P, i, 8) + 800$$

First Trial, i = 0%

$$(1,000)\left(\frac{1}{5}\right) + 850 \triangleq (1,500)\left(\frac{1}{8}\right) + 800$$

$$1,050 \triangleq 988$$

Therefore, at $i = 0$,

$$AC_A > AC_B \text{ by } \$62$$

This shows that the operation involving the extra investment has the lower annual cost at zero rate or return, which is to say there is an annual advantage of $62 if the extra investment is made at zero rate of return.   This advantage may be expressed as an approximate rate of return on the *extra investment* of $500.

$i = 62/500 \cong 12.4\%$, but $P > L$; therefore, true $i >$ approximate i, so use a higher return in the next trial.

$$\textit{Second Trial, } i = 15\%$$

$$\overset{0.29832}{1,000(A/P, .15, 5)} + 850 \overset{\triangle}{=} \overset{0.22285}{1,500(A/P, .15, 8)} + 800$$

$$1,148 \overset{\triangle}{=} 1,134$$

Therefore, at 15%,

$$AC_A > AC_B \text{ by } \$14$$

Again the annual cost of the operation involving the extra investment is lower, and this advantage of $14 may be expressed as a rate of return over and above the assumed rate of return of 15%. Therefore,

$i = 15 + 14/500 = 15 + 2.8 \cong 17.8\%$. The true i will be higher but perhaps not higher than 20%.

$$\textit{Third Trial, } i = 20\%$$

$$\overset{0.33438}{1,000(A/P, .20, 5)} + 850 \overset{\triangle}{=} \overset{0.26061}{1,500(A/P, .20, 8)} + 800$$

$$1,184 \overset{\triangle}{=} 1,191$$

Therefore, at 20%,

$$AC_A < AC_B \text{ by } \$7$$

Now the annual cost of the operation having the extra investment is higher, indicating that the true i is less than 20%.

Interpolating between 15 and 20%:

$$i = 15\% + \left(\frac{14}{14 + 7}\right)(5\%) = 18.3\%$$

The rate of return on the extra investment of $500 is 18.3%, and since a minimum required rate of return is only 8%, an investment in the $1,500 operation is justified.

8.10 ASSUMPTIONS PERTINENT TO THE RATE-OF-RETURN ANALYSIS

In Chapters 6 and 7, if the economic lives were different, we used a study-period approach or considered likely patterns for the chain of replacements. We also included like-for-like replacements to the least common multiple of years, or replacement with the most economic machine available today.

Although we made no assumptions in solving Example 8.9, what, if any, assumptions are inherent in the solution or implicit in the mathematics?

By making some tests we can show this: it is immaterial which of the above approaches are used because they all give the same rate of return. This can be quickly demonstrated by an example.

EXAMPLE 8.10 Show that a study-period approach over the life of machine A gives the same answer as in Example 8.9.

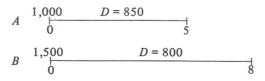

SOLUTION. In Example 8.9, i was found to be 18.3%. Using this rate of return in present-worth analysis of a study period, we get

$$PW_A = 1,000 + 850\overset{3.1063}{(P/A, .183, 5)} = 1,000 + 2,640 = \$3,640$$

$$PW_B = 1,500\overset{0.24754}{(A/P, .183, 8)}\overset{3.1063}{(P/A, 5)} + 800\overset{3.1063}{(P/A, 5)} = 1,153$$
$$+ 2,485 = \$3,638$$

At 18.3%, therefore, the present worths are equal (or would be equal except for the error of interpolation), showing that the study-period approach and the method in Example 8.9 give the same quantitative results.

By another test we can show that replacement with the most economical machine available today will also give the same quantitative results. No doubt this has already been obvious to the reader without demonstration.

The conclusion, however, is that although the numerical results are the same, the assumptions and predictions which support them are different and of some significance. The reader is referred to Chapters 6 and 7 for further discussions.

8.11 LEVELS OF COST-REDUCTION INVESTMENTS

EXAMPLE 8.11a As in the two previous chapters, we will analyze the levels of investment in insulating a steam pipe if the minimum required rate of return is 8% and the life is 15 years. The data are reproduced in Table 8.11a.

Table 8.11a ANALYSIS OF LEVELS OF INVESTMENT BY THE RATE-OF-RETURN METHOD

Thickness of insulation (in.)	First cost	Extra investment	Annual heat loss	Annual savings in heat loss	Rate of return on extra investment (%)
0	$ 0	$ 0	$1,800	$ 0	0
$\frac{3}{4}$	1,800	1,800	900	900	50
1	2,545	745	590	310	41.3
$1\frac{1}{2}$	3,340	795	450	140	15.6
$2\frac{1}{4}$	4,360	1,020	360	90	3.7
3	5,730	1,370	310	50	0
$3\frac{1}{2}$	7,280	1,550	285	25	0

SOLUTION. The rate of return on the extra investment in each level is analyzed as follows:

$$\text{For } \tfrac{3}{4}\text{-inch insulation over no insulation:}$$

$$1,800(A/P, i, 15) + 900 = 1,800$$

$$(A/P, i, 15) = 0.5, \text{ whence } i = 50\%$$

The results are tabulated in the last column of Table 8.11a.

Each successive level through the third is justified because each meets the minimum required rate of 8%, but beyond this no level passes the test.

Table 8.11b ANALYSIS OF A BREAK IN THE ACCEPTABLE LEVELS OF INVESTMENT

Thickness of insulation (in.)	First cost	Extra investment	Annual heat loss	Annual savings in heat loss	Rate of return on extra investment (%)
0	$ 0	$ 0	$1,800	$ 0	0
$\frac{3}{4}$	1,800	1,800	900	900	50
1	2,545	745	825*	75*	5.7*
$1\frac{1}{2}$	3,340	795	450	375*	47 *
$2\frac{1}{4}$	4,360	1,020	360	90	3.7
3	5,730	1,370	310	50	0
$3\frac{1}{2}$	7,280	1,550	285	25	0

EXAMPLE 8.11b Now let us make one change in the data in the previous example: revise the heat loss at 1-inch insulation from $590 a year to $825. The new savings with heat loss and the new rate of return on the extra investment are shown in Table 8.11b, marked with asterisks for your inspection.

SOLUTION. Here we see that 1-inch insulation with a return of only 5.7% would be rejected but that $1\frac{1}{2}$-inch insulation with a return of 47% would be accepted. Naturally, the $1\frac{1}{2}$-inch level cannot be installed unless it is preceded by the 1-inch increment; therefore, the test is to combine the levels and analyze them as a single increment, namely, $1\frac{1}{2}$-inch over $\frac{3}{4}$-inch, as follows:

$$3,340(A/P, i, 15) + 450 = 1,800(A/P, i, 15) + 900$$

$$(A/P, i, 15) = 0.292$$

whence

$$i \cong 29\%$$

The installation through a level of $1\frac{1}{2}$-inch insulation is justified. This points up a practical problem which may occur whenever methods of design, construction, or procedure must be changed before further increases in size are possible.

For example, in office building design, the need to expand service facilities at certain heights, including elevator space and size of halls and stairways, may make the next few floors uneconomical without the addition of subsequent levels. The analyst must look beyond the level where this break occurs to determine if the combined levels pass the test of economy.

8.12 IMPORTANCE OF RATE-OF-RETURN METHOD OF COMPARISON

Three basic methods have been presented for the analysis of equipment investment problems. These methods are equivalent but the methods of communication are quite different as noted in the following example.

EXAMPLE 8.12 A machine costing $8,500 will have annual operating disbursements of $4,500. An alternative process will cost $7,000 with operating disbursements of $4,800 a year. Both will have 10-year economic lives and the minimum required rate of return is 10%. Compare these by all three methods.

SOLUTION.

A. 8,500 ——— 4,500/yr ——— 0 — 10

B. 7,000 ——— 4,800/yr ——— 0 — 10

$$AC_A = 8{,}500(A/P, .10, 10) + 4{,}500 = \$5{,}883 \quad [0.16275]$$

$$AC_B = 7{,}000(A/P, .10, 10) + 4{,}800 = \underline{5{,}939} \quad [0.16275]$$

Annual-cost advantage of A: $\$\quad 56$

Present-worth advantage of A: $56 \cdot {}_{.10\text{-}10}\text{uspwf}^{6.1446} = \$344$
Rate of return on the extra investment in A:

$$1{,}500(A/P, i, 10) = 300$$

$$(A/P, i, 10) = 0.2$$

whence

$$i = 15.1\%$$

Each of these suggests equivalent conclusions but may convey different meanings unless one correctly interprets the story each conveys. A familiarity with the accounting viewpoint of cost may make it difficult for the uninitiated to realize that a $56 annual cost advantage for A is the advantage after the recovery of capital with 10% return, or that A will still be recommended if the annual cost advantage is zero. It is this "apples and oranges" evaluation that makes annual-cost comparisons difficult for the untrained person to understand. The same is true of present-worth comparisons.

For this reason a rate-of-return analysis has merit. It is a straightforward communication of the advantages of making the extra investment. Even if one does understand the meaning of an annual-cost analysis, it is still difficult to visualize what "a $56 advantage after recovery of capital with 10% return" equals in terms of a rate of return on the extra investment.

Yet all of these methods seem to have their place. At a certain level or in a certain location in an organization annual cost may have more practical meaning, even if it is not thoroughly understood. Foremen, supervisors, and workers are perhaps better schooled by experience to deal with costs than rates of return. On the other hand, purchasing organizations might compute present-worth valuations of equipment to determine the price that should be paid. But top management invariably prefers rate-of-return analyses to determine the projects to which the firm's limited funds should be appropriated. (This problem of laddering projects is covered in Chapter 9.)

There may be good reason, therefore, to analyze a problem by all three methods and in addition to include a break-even analysis as a test of the "factor of safety." (This technique is covered in Chapter 16.)

8.13 ACCOUNTING VERSUS ENGINEERING ECONOMY VIEWPOINTS ON RATE OF RETURN

If the accountant and the economy analyst do not see eye to eye it is not because of errors in the techniques of their respective profession, but a respective misunderstanding of what each is doing. However, a mutual understanding should be developed, because the economist must work with the accountant or his books of accounts to get data for predicting future projects or auditing past projects; and top financial executives with accounting training must often approve or reject, with good reasons and good conscience, the demands for capital expenditures.

The accountant can easily disagree with the rate-of-return method of analysis because the formulas charge interest rate i to the cost of each alternative, whereas the accountant never charges a cost of interest unless it is a disbursement. Obviously, each is talking of different things. The economist, working entirely in the future, adds "i" not as interest but as the "profit" that must be earned in the future to insure the continuance of the business. (At that, this is a complex "profit" involving income tax and the "cost of capital" considerations which we have not yet studied in detail.) The accountant, on the other hand, is examining the past and does not add this profit rate i to his books because the net result of his efforts is to *find* this figure which represents the net profit from past operations. The economist is allowing for this "interest" so that the accountant may subsequently find it—as profit.

Another area of misunderstanding may be the difference in life periods used by the accountant and the economist in computing the firm's profit. This and other differences will be discussed when each becomes pertinent to the topics in subsequent chapters.

8.14 REJECTION OF THE EXTRA INVESTMENT

Suppose two alternatives will have the following expenditures:

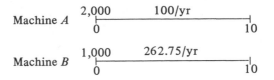

The problem of selecting A over C will be expressed on the time scale as follows:

```
                     Cost              Savings
Selection of        1,000              162.75
 A over C             0                                              10
```

The mathematical test of this investment is

$$1,000(A/P, i, 10) = 162.75$$

$$(A/P) = 0.16275$$

whence

$$i = 10\%$$

We could therefore conclude that if the minimum required rate of return is 10% or less we should select A over C, because we will recover the investment of $1,000 in A with the 10% minimum required rate of return.

However, if the minimum required rate of return is greater than 10% if it is 11% or higher—we will select C over A. This selection would appear on the time scale as follows:

```
                    Savings              Cost
Selection of        1,000             162.75/yr
 C over A             0                                              10
```

By selecting C over A, we make an immediate saving of $1,000 followed by an obligation to spend $162.75 a year for the next 10 years. The saving of $1,000 is therefore money available for investment elsewhere in the company[1] since we have rejected the alternative of investing it in A.

For example, the investment of the $1,000 savings elsewhere in the firm at 11% or more will provide an income at least equal to

$$\overset{0.1698}{1,000(A/P, .11, 10)} = \$169.80$$

This investment, the result of selecting alternative C, will earn $169.80 a year, more than enough to cover C's annual disbursements of $162.75.

---

[1] Consistent with the concept of the time value of money, all funds are presumed to be at work in projects demanding these funds. Where funds may be held idle as reserves of working capital, a cost of "interest" may be acknowledged.

On the other hand, we note that by the concept of selection of a minimum required rate of return we shall select A and reject C if that rate is exactly 10%. In that case selecting C would mean rejecting an opportunity to invest $1,000 in machine A at 10% in favor of investing it elsewhere in the company at 10%. In budgeting capital we adopted the concept of minimum required rate of return at which we would invest whenever and wherever we found the opportunity. Therefore we should select A. Furthermore, it is ridiculous to reject an opportunity to invest in A at a 10% rate of return in order to accept another opportunity to invest at 10%.

8.15 ANALYSIS IF SAVINGS PRECEDE COSTS

Up to this point our test of the extra investment has been whether to invest money *now* in order to receive future savings. Let us observe that by "acceptance" the investment cost precedes the savings but by "rejection" of the extra investment the savings precede the costs.

Since we frequently enough reject the extra investment and since the savings precede the costs whenever we reject the extra investment, the thought of an analysis in which savings precede costs should not be too disturbing. Furthermore, we find some examples which are framed in that manner.

EXAMPLE 8.15 Maintenance of a machine to keep it in permanent working order is $225 a year indefinitely. However, by cutting the annual maintenance to only $100, a replacement costing $1,000 will be required at the end of every 10 years. To put it more directly, we can save $125 annually in maintenance and spend $1,000 at the end of 10 years to replace instead of maintain equipment. The minimum required rate of return is 10%.

SOLUTION.

$$
\begin{array}{ccc}
\text{Savings} & & \text{Cost} \\
125/\text{yr} & & 1,000 \\
\hline
0 & & 10
\end{array}
$$

With the reduced maintenance plan represented on the above time scale, the savings of $125 a year will be invested elsewhere in the firm. (Incidentally, the reduced maintenance plan will be selected at any minimum required rate-of-return, because even if it is zero the savings will more than recover the cost of $1,000.)

While this may look like a special problem, it is not, as the following time scales illustrate:

Full maintenance, plan A

$$
\begin{array}{cc}
& 225/\text{yr} \\
\hline
0 & 10
\end{array}
$$

Reduced maintenance, plan B

```
                    100/yr                    1,000
       ├─────────────────────────────────────┤
       0                                      10
```

Selection of A over B

```
                            Cost            Savings
                           125/yr            1,000
       ├─────────────────────────────────────┤
       0                                      10
```

The costs now precede incomes, and the question, as in all such cases, is whether or not to make the extra investment. To be sure, the extra investment is now a series of costs instead of a lump sum at time zero, but that does not alter the problem or the test of the extra investment. In this case we will reject the extra investment in A because the savings do not recover the investment.

8.16 INCOME-EXPANSION PROJECTS IN WHICH THE SAVINGS PRECEDE COSTS

The discussion in the two previous sections applies equally to income-expansion projects.

To begin with, in most income-expansion propositions the cost precedes the income as follows:

EXAMPLE 8.16a An income-expansion proposal is shown by the following time scale:

```
            Cost         Income
           1,000         200/yr
           ├──────────────────────────────────┤
           0                                   10
```

SOLUTION.

$$1,000\,(A/P, i, 10) = 200$$

$$(A/P, i, 10) = 0.2$$

whence

$$i = 15\%$$

Here, if the minimum required rate of return is 15% or less, the investment will be approved. This is illustrated in Fig. 8.16a.

In the following example, however, the income precedes the cost. This situation might occur in a lease of an income-producing property in which the contract requires the tenant, in some way, to restore the property at the end of the lease to a condition as good as it was when new. The income I is the net income after operating disbursements, including the annual rent required by the lease. This situation is illustrated in the following example.

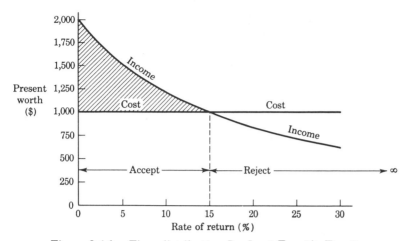

Figure 8.16a   Time distribution $P - I$ and $\Sigma_{i=0}\, I > \Sigma_{i=0}\, P$

EXAMPLE 8.16b The predicted net income and the capital expenditure from the standpoint of the lessee are given on the following time scale.

$$I = 470/\text{yr} \qquad \qquad \text{Cost} \atop 10{,}000$$

0   10

SOLUTION.

$$470 = 10{,}000(A/F, i, 10)$$

$$(A/F, i, 10) = 0.0470$$

whence

$$i = 16\%$$

Under the lease, \$470 a year for 10 years will become available for investment.   The money will be invested elsewhere in the busines, and if the projects in which it is invested return 16% or more, the \$10,000 will be re-

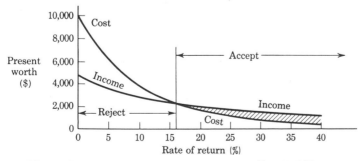

Figure 8.16b   Time distribution $I - P$ and $\Sigma_{i=0}\, I < \Sigma_{i=0}\, P$

covered at year 10 with a 16% return or more. Therefore if the firm's minimum required rate of return is 16% or more, the lease is justified. This is illustrated in Fig. 8.16b.

In the graphs of the two previous examples, we accept the propositions in the areas where the present worth of the income exceeds the present worth of the cost. The shaded area graphically represents that situation. Note that this area is to the left of the break-even point in Example 8.16a, and to the right of the break-even point in Example 8.16b.

EXAMPLE 8.16c In this example the net income after disbursements is $150 a year and a capital expenditure of $1,000 must be made at the end of the 10th year, as shown on the following time scale.

$$I = 150/\text{yr} \qquad \begin{array}{c} \text{Cost} \\ 1,000 \end{array}$$

$$0 \qquad\qquad\qquad 10$$

SOLUTION.

$$150(F/A, i, 10) = 1,000$$

whence

$$i = 0$$

In this case, even if i is zero the invested income will accumulate the cost; therefore the proposition will be accepted for any minimum required rate of return, as shown in Fig. 8.16c.

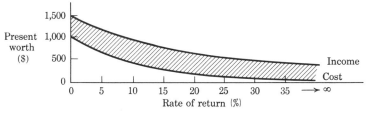

Figure 8.16c   Time distribution $I - P$ and $\Sigma_{i=0} I > \Sigma_{i=0} P$

8.17 INCOME-EXPANSION PROJECTS WITH DUAL RATES OF RETURN

In the two preceding examples, 8.16b and 8.16c, the required capital expenditure occurred at the very end of the income-expansion proposition. Now suppose the required expenditure occurred before the end of the lease.

EXAMPLE 8.17a Assume the contract required the lessee of the factory to replace the electrical distribution system, which was in a state of decline, during the tenancy, as illustrated in the following time scale.

SOLUTION.

Cost
16,000
↓

$I = 1,000/\text{yr for 15 yrs}$

0 1 2 3 4 5 6 7 8 9   14 15

AW savings = AC costs

$$1,000 = 16,000(P/F, i, 8)(A/P, i, 15)$$

Try $i = 9\%$.

$$1,000 \triangleq (16,000)(0.50187)(0.124059)$$

$$1,000 \triangleq 996$$

income > cost by $4 per year

Try $i = 8\%$.

$$1,000 \triangleq (16,000)(0.54027)(0.11683)$$

$$1,000 \triangleq 1,010$$

income < cost by $10 per year

Therefore,

$$i = 8\% + \frac{10}{14} = 8.7\%$$

If the minimum required rate of return is 8.7% or greater, the investment
will be accepted. Figure 8.17 demonstrates that, for any minimum required
rate of return less than 8.7%, the present worth of the costs exceeds the incomes

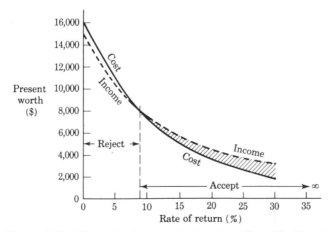

Figure 8.17   Time distribution $I - P - I$ and $\Sigma_{i=0} P > \Sigma_{i=0} I$

and the project will be rejected; but at any minimum required rate of return higher than 8.7%, incomes exceed the costs and the investment will be accepted.   Figure 8.17 also suggests why, in the trial-and-error process, the second trial should have been at 8% instead of 10%. This is observed from the fact that, to the left of the break even point (which represents the true rate of return), the present worth of costs exceeds income, but incomes exceed costs to the right of it. Obviously, 9% was to the right of the break-even point and therefore the next trial should be 8%.

In the example the income during the first 8 years will be invested elsehwere in the firm at the minimum required rate of return or greater. For the purpose of illustration we will assume that this income is invested at the company's minimum required rate of return of 15%. Then if we allow for the compound amount accumulated by these annual investments over the period of 8 years, the equivalent *net* expenditure required at the end of 8 years will be only

$$\overset{13.727}{P = 16,000 - 1,000(F/A, .15, 8) = \$2,273}$$

The earnings on this investment from the seven subsequent years of income will be

$$2,273\,(A/P, i, 7) = 1,000$$

$$(A/P, i, 7) = 0.44$$

whence

$$i \cong 40\%$$

This has shown that if the first 8 years' incomes are invested at the minimum required rate of return, the earnings on the "net investment" in the eighth year will be 40%, which, being greater than the minimum required rate of return, is acceptable.

If the income during the first 8 years had been invested at a higher rate of return or if the minimum required rate of return had been higher, the rate of return on the "net investment" would also be higher. For example, if the first 8 years' savings were invested at 17% instead of 15%, the "net investment" in the eighth year would be less and consequently the return on it from the ensuing 7 years of income would be even greater than 40% (it would be 80%). This merely substantiates the statement that the project is acceptable if the minimum required rate of return is 9% or greater.

In examples like the previous one, where the outlay of capital occurs neither at the beginning nor at the end of the investment period, it is sometimes possible to get a multiple solution for the true rate of return, as illustrated in the following example.

EXAMPLE 8.17b The incomes and disbursements for a lease contract are shown on the following time scale. The incomes are the net profit after payment of rent and other operating disbursements. The capital outlay in the fourth year is for the major overhaul of the power plant, which by the contract of lease must be performed at the expense of the tenant.

SOLUTION.

Cost
10,000
↓ $I = 1,000/\text{yr}$ for 20 years

0   1   2   3   4   5   6   7   8   20

$$AC = AW$$

$$10,000(P/F, i, 4)(A/P, i, 20) \triangleq 1,000$$

Try $i = 20\%$.

$$(10,000)(0.48225)(0.20536) \triangleq 1,000$$

$$990 \triangleq 1,000 \text{ (income exceeds cost)}$$

$$0 \triangleq 10$$

Try $i = 25\%$.

$$(10,000)(0.4096)(0.2529) \triangleq 1,000$$

$$1,036 \triangleq 1,000 \text{ (cost exceeds income)}$$

$$36 \triangleq 0$$

Therefore,

$$i = 20 + \left(\frac{10}{46}\right)(5) = 21\%$$

However, by a method discussed later we can reasonably predict that this project will have two rates of return. Let us test for the second root as follows:

Try $i = 50\%$.

$$10,000(P/F, i, 4)(A/P, i, 20) \triangleq 1,000$$

$$988 \triangleq 1,000 \text{ (income exceeds cost)}$$

$$0 \triangleq 12$$

Notice that at 25%, which was above the true rate of return, cost exceeded income. Therefore, if income exceeds cost at 50%, there must be a crossover at some interest rate below it. This indicates the existence of another root between 50% and 21%.

Try $i = 45\%$.

$$(10,000)(0.2262)(0.45027) \triangleq 1,000$$

$$1,019 \triangleq 1,000 \text{ (cost exceeds income)}$$

$$19 \triangleq 0$$

whence

$$i = 45 + \left(\frac{19}{31}\right)(5) = 48\%$$

Here is a project in which the true rate of return is 21% *and* 48%. How can this be? The answer is offered in the next section.

8.18 EXPLANATION OF DUAL RATES OF RETURN

The present worths of the income and the capital cost for the previous example are plotted in Fig. 8.18. The graph shows that, below 21% interest, income exceeds cost; also above 48% interest, income exceeds cost; and between these rates, cost exceeds income. It seems logical to conclude, therefore, that if the minimum required rate of return is 21% or less, or 48% or more, we should accept the project, but if it is between these rates we should reject it. The following computation will support this.

In this illustration, let us suppose that the minimum required rate of return is 15%. If the first 4 years' income is invested at the minimum, the "net investment" in year 4 will be

$$P = 10,000 - 1,000 \overset{4.993}{(F/A, .15, 4)} = \$5,007$$

and rate of return on it will be

$$5,007(A/P, i, 16) = 1,000$$

whence

$$i = 19\%$$

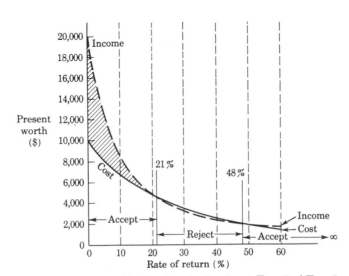

Figure 8.18   Time distribution $I - P - I$ and $\Sigma_{i=0} P < \Sigma_{i=0} I$

and the proposition is acceptable. But if the minimum required rate of return is 30%:

$$P = 10,000 - 1,000 \overset{6.187}{(F/A, .30, 4)} = \$3,813$$

$$3,813 (A/P, i, 16) = 1,000$$

whence

$$i = 25.5\%$$

and the proposition is unacceptable. Or if the minimum required rate of return is 60%:

$$P = 10,000 - 1,000 \overset{9.256}{(F/A, .60, 4)} = \$744$$

$$744 (A/P, i, 16) = 1,000$$

whence

$$i = 134\%$$

and the proposition is acceptable.

Table 8.18 shows the results of these computations for various minimum required rates of return. If the minimum required rate of return (first column) is 21% or less, the project is acceptable because the "net" investment in year 4 is recovered with a rate of return (second column) equal to or greater than the minimum required; for example, if the minimum required is 12%,

Table 8.18 SUMMARY OF THE TEST FOR DUAL RATES OF RETURN

If the first 4 years' savings are invested at (%)	Rate of return earned on the "net" investment in year 4 is (%)
0	15
2	15.5
5	16
10	17.3
12	18
18	20
20	20.5
21	21
25	22.3
30	25.5
40	34.2
48	48
54	69
60	134

the rate of return on the net investment is 18%. Similarly, we observe that if the minimum required is 48% or more, the return on the net investment will be equal to or greater than the minimum; for example, if the minimum required is 54%, the return on the net investment is 69%.

However, if the minimum required is 30%—or any percentage from 22 to 47—the return on the net investment is less than the required so that the investment is not approved.

Furthermore, if the minimum required rate of return is 21% or less and the first 4 years' income is invested elsewhere at a rate *higher* than the minimum required, the earnings on the "net" investment will always be higher than the minimum required. For example, if the minimum required is 18% and the income is invested at 30%, the rate of return will be 25.5%. Since this is higher than the minimum required, the lease is acceptable.

8.19 PREDICTING EXISTENCE OF TWO OR MORE RATES OF RETURN

When do dual rates of return occur? Since they do occur, we should have some way of predicting them in advance. The following guidelines suggest the possible existence of dual rates of return. Dual rates may exist just outside the boundary of the guideline or fail to occur just within it.

(a) The time distribution of I, annual income, and P, the investment cost, is

$$
\begin{array}{ccccccccc}
 & I & I & I & & P & & I & I & I \\
\end{array}
$$
$$
\underset{0}{\vdash}\!\!+\!\!+\!\!+ \cdots + \cdots +\!\!+\!\!+\underset{n}{\dashv}
$$

that is, any time sequence I-P-I, and if $P < \Sigma_{i=0} I$,

(b) or if the time distribution of I and P is

$$
\begin{array}{cccccc}
P & & I & I & I & P \\
\end{array}
$$
$$
\underset{0}{\vdash}\!\!- \cdots +\!\!+\!\!+ \cdots \dashv \underset{n}{}
$$

that is, any time sequence P-I-P, and if $\Sigma_{i=0} P > \Sigma_{i=0} I$.

Where two rates (or more) are possible, the above examples suggest guidelines for their prediction. Thus if the distribution is I-P-I-P-I, the four "reversals" suggest a possibility of four rates of return if $\Sigma_{i=0} P < \Sigma_{i=0} I$.

Example 8.17b, which had two rates of return, illustrates guideline (a) above, because the time distribution is I-P-I and $P < \Sigma_{i=0} I$. However, Example 8.17a, which did not satisfy the guide, had only one rate of return. The two examples are summed up as follows:

$$
\begin{array}{c}
\text{Cost} \\
16{,}000 \\
\downarrow \quad\quad I = 1{,}000/\text{yr}
\end{array}
$$

Example 8.17a $P > \Sigma_{i=0} I$ $\quad \underset{0}{\vdash}\!\!\rule{2cm}{0.4pt}\!\!\underset{8}{+}\!\!\rule{2cm}{0.4pt}\!\!\underset{15}{\dashv}$

And Fig. 8.17 (p. 144) demonstrates that only one rate of return exists.

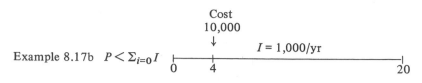

Example 8.17b $P < \Sigma_{i=0} I$

And Fig. 8.18 (p. 147) verifies the existence of two rates of return.

8.20 ARGUMENTS REGARDING THE RATE-OF-RETURN AND OTHER METHODS

Unless the reader encounters these arguments he may not feel concerned with them at this time, since he has already observed that the annual-cost, present-worth, and rate-of-return methods all give the same conclusions. However, enjoyment of this subject comes from thoroughly understanding what you are doing, so it is more than a matter of deferring understanding until the moment one's reasoning is questioned by the person whose acceptance you need—a moment when it may be too late. We hope, too, that this discussion will emphasize that an analyst should never "go by the numbers" without thoroughly understanding their meaning.

One question to resolve is whether the validity of the rate-of-return method depends on reinvestment of the funds at the computed return. The computed rate of return is merely a measure to permit comparisons, not to dictate realities. Similarly the net present worth or net present value (NPV) is only a comparative measure of value which does not dictate depositing the computed sum in order to meet future obligations. Note that measuring a vehicle's rate of speed between two cities doesn't require traveling exactly at that rate at every instant throughout the trip in order to equal the measured rate.

Another point to note is that the discovery of two or more rates of return does not imply that the rate-of-return method is giving the wrong answers. In fact the method would be wrong if it didn't reveal two rates when they exist. As we noted they will also be revealed by present-worth techniques, too, if the computation covers a complete spectrum of interest rates. Naturally the *standard* present-worth evaluation doesn't encounter two rates since it is computed at a single interest rate.

We should, of course, recognize that while the annual-cost, present-worth, and rate-of-return methods are in total agreement, they express their conclusions differently and each may even perform a unique function not attained by another method. For example, net-present-worth or net-present-value method as noted is unique in providing for property valuation. It also may enhance graphic illustrations as noted in Figure 8.18. Considering the uniqueness of the rate-of-return method, we should recognize that it actually computes more than required for a mere selection between two alternatives; it places each investment in a position for laddering in a capital budgeting situation—something not directly achieved by the present-worth method. While this can be an advantage of great significance, the same point of view makes the rate-of-return method more acceptable and more easily understood by business managers.

The rate-of-return method is efficient in selecting mutually exclusive income-expansion investments, but the method may be a source of difficulty for some analysts. Unfortunately the difficulty seems to stem from a misunderstanding of the basic principles of the entire subject: every *comparison*, annual cost, present worth, or rate of return, tests only the recovery of the *extra* investment with an acceptable return on it. At the risk of some repetition let us examine the following situation.

EXAMPLE 8.20a The following income-expansion opportunities are mutually exclusive. If the minimum required rate of return is 15% which should be selected?

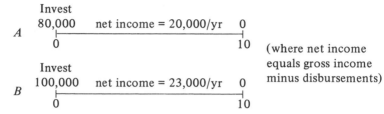

SOLUTION: By the present-worth method

$$PW_A = 20,000 \overset{5.0188}{(P/A, .15, 10)} - 80,000 = \$20,376$$

$$PW_B = 23,000 \overset{5.0188}{(P/A, .15, 10)} - 100,000 = \$15,432$$

Advantage of B over A = (minus) \$4,944
(The extra investment of \$20,000 in B fails to be recovered with 15% by a present sum of \$4,944.)

By the rate-of-return method:

Advantage of B over A = $20,000(A/P, i, 10) = 3,000$ whence $i = 8.1\%$

so B should be rejected.

Advantage of A alone = $80,000(A/P, i, 10) = 20,000$ whence $i = 21.4\%$

so A should be accepted.

An error in understanding will result if one computes the rate of return on B's investment and concludes that since it is 18.9% and higher than the minimum required rate, it should be adopted. Adopting numerical evaluations without understanding them would result in investing an extra of \$20,000 in B to receive a drop in the rate of return from 21.4% to 18.9%. Logically this can result only if the \$20,000 is earning something less than 21.4%—perhaps considerably less. In the given example it is only 8.1%—not enough to justify investing \$20,000. We understand, too, that the conclusion would be different if the alternatives were mutually independent investments.

It has been suggested that the rate-of-return method fails to alert the investor to his future commitments and obligations. None of these methods do since they are not designed for that purpose. (For example, a net present worth of zero signals an acceptable commitment.) The best display of comparative obligations, as we have noted throughout the text beginning with Chapter 1, is a time scale of each alternative.

Infinite rates of return do not signal a failure of the rate-of-return method. In fact, a manager essentially hits the jackpot in investment economics when he discovers, for example, that an inspection process costing $50,000 a year can be eliminated without any disadvantage. Since the cost of eliminating it may be little more than organizational and procedural changes, the yield or the net present worth will be exceptionally great (infinite returns are difficult to conceive as some first cost actually exists).

Akin to this there is a unique and quite rare situation in which the investment *is* zero but *no* rate of return can be calculated—although the situation can be explained by the rate-of-return method and easier in all respects by the PW method.

EXAMPLE 8.20b Given the following case, should the opportunity be accepted if the minimum required return is 15%?

SOLUTION: If the company invests the $1,000 income at its minimum required rate of return whatever that may be, zero or above, it will in all cases have a net surplus after paying the $800 cost. Thus the rate-of-return explanation is: no matter what the chosen rate of return we always have a net surplus at the end of year 1. (A mathematical analysis will show that a yield cannot be computed.) The present-worth method gives a direct answer for any specific minimum acceptable rate of return. Furthermore, a plot of present-worth valuations for all interest rates, zero to infinity, will reveal that the curve of incomes always exceeds and never intersects the curve of costs.

Should this situation occur the analyst will be forewarned by using the rate-of-return method by the pattern of income preceding costs and

$$\sum_{i=0} I > \sum_{i=0} P$$

Our summary of the discussion is that we use all three methods with equal enthusiasm and suggest that with an ability to use all methods the analyst has the great advantage of selecting any one that may best serve the needs of each situation.

8.21 USING CALCULATORS OR COMPUTERS

The mathematical sentences by which problems are expressed in this text can be put into a computer exactly as written. Inputting these statements, com-

```
? COMMENT: SOLVE EXAMPLE 8.20a
? SOL I: 20000*CRF(I,10)-3000
THE SOLUTION IS 8.14417
? SOL I:80000*CRF(I,10)-20000
THE SOLUTION IS 21.4065
? SOL I: 100000*CRF(I,10)-23000
THE SOLUTION IS 18.9411
? LET A=20000 #LET I=15 #LET N=10 #LET B=80000
? EVA A*USPWF(I,N)-B
 20375.4
? LET A=23000 #LET B=100000
? EVA
 15431.7
? LET A=3000 # LET B=20000
? EVA
- 4943.69
? COMMENT: SOLVE EXAMPLE 8.20b
? LIMITS
ENTER LEFT ENDPOINT, RIGHT ENDPOINT, # OF INTERNALS,
# OF SOLUTIONS
? 10,50,5,2
? SOL I: 1000*SPPWF(I,4)*CRF(I,20)-1000
2 SOLUTIONS FOUND:
    20.8355
    48.1343
? STOP
```

Figure 8.21   Illustration of computer solutions

pared to inserting the problem piecemeal, saves time and effort, and the computer itself provides significant additional savings since it computes each factor without the use of tables and automatically iterates for an unknown rate of return.

The input/output reproduced here (Figure 8.21) illustrates computer usage at Dartmouth College. The program, written in BASIC, is linked to a time-sharing arrangement and is used at Dartmouth and other colleges and businesses. At a convenient terminal the user may call the library program **ECON** and type in commands or input data (**boldface** in the figure, to distinguish the input from the computer's responses).

The following capabilities of **ECON** are illustrated. The user can:

1. Solve for i (**SOL I**).
2. Evaluate the annual cost or present worth (**EVA**).
3. Eliminate the need to retype the mathematical sentence for each computation by using "**LET**" statements. We illustrate the process in Figure 8.21 by computing the present worths in Example 8.20a. In the same manner we need not have retyped the sentences in computing i.

4. Solve for multiple rates of return. Here the analyst must type "**LIMITS**" if he suspects more than one rate, and he must suggest the number.

PROBLEMS

8.1 A granite company estimates it can increase sales if it had the capacity to cut more stone. A new cutter costs $30,000 installed at the quarry. The increased capacity can be sold for $22,000, but the increased annual cost of operation, including labor, power, maintenance and repair, taxes and insurance, raw materials, transportation, and the added cost of sales and administration will be $17,500. The life of the operation is expected to be 12 years with $4,000 salvage at that date. What is the rate of return on the investment?

8.2 A realty corporation plans to invest $70,000 in a building containing stores and offices. The annual income from rentals is estimated to be a minimum of $34,000. The annual expenses for taxes, insurance, maintenance and repair, heat, light, and all the building services are expected not to exceed $29,900. The company estimates that neighborhood property values will reach a maximum in 10 years, at which time they can sell the property for $100,000. Assuming uniform annual income and expenses, compute the expected minimum rate of return on the investment in the property.

8.3 An investor purchased 100 shares of stock in the Ajax Mutual Fund for $2,000. He received no dividends the first year, $1.75 a share dividends at the end of each year for the next 4 years, and $2.50 a share at the end of each of the 5 following years. After holding the stock for 10 years, he sold it for $5,500. What was the true rate of return on his investment?

8.4 A professional pilot is planning to go into business for himself. Based on his survey of the market, he predicts that if he buys a $22,000 plane he can earn an annual gross income of $28,300 with expenses of $11,200 for taxes, insurance, maintenance and repair, fuel, and hangar and airport charges. He also plans to allow himself a salary of $12,000 a year. He expects an 8-year life of the plane with 10% salvage value. If the income and expense are assumed to be uniform over this period, what is the prospective rate of return on his investment in the business, i.e., the $22,000 in the plane?

8.5 Solve Problem 7.23 by the rate-of-return method.

8.6 Solve Problem 7.24 by the rate-of-return method.

8.7 A small business, identified by the prospective buyer as Project *A*, can be purchased for $65,000, which will give annual receipts for the next 20 years of $33,190 with annual disbursements of $25,550. Alternatively, a similar enterprise, Project *B*, can be purchased for $80,000, which will give annual receipts for the next 20 years of $35,990 with annual disbursements of $23,210. The salvage values at the end of 20 years are assumed to be zero. The purchaser intends to buy only one of these businesses. If his minimum required rate of return is 10%, which business should he purchase? Explain why.

8.8 A small business, identified as Project *C*, can be purchased for $60,000, which will give annual receipts for the next 25 years of $29,400 with annual disbursements of $20,110. Alternatively, a similar business, Project *D*, can be purchased for $75,000, which will give annual receipts for the next 25 years of $34,750 with annual disbursements of $26,180. The salvage values at the end of 25 years are assumed to be zero. The purchaser intends to acquire only one of these businesses. If his minimum required rate of return is 10%, which business should he purchase? Explain why.

8.9 A small business, identified as Project *E*, can be purchased for $70,000, which will give annual receipts for the next 20 years of $36,332 with annual disbursements of $28,110. Alternatively, a similar business, Project *F*, can be purchased for $85,000, which will give annual receipts for the next 20 years of $40,984 with annual disbursements of $31,000. The salvage values at the end of 20 years are assumed to be zero. The purchaser intends to acquire only one of these businesses. If his minimum required rate of return is 10%, which business should he purchase? Explain why.

8.10 A 4%, $1,000 bond which matures in 20 years is for sale for $793. Interest is payable semiannually beginning 6 months from now. What is the nominal interest rate that a purchaser will receive?

8.11 A $4\frac{1}{2}$%, $1,000 bond which matures in 15 years can be purchased for $802. Interest is payable quarterly beginning 3 months from today. What is the nominal interest rate that a purchaser will receive?

8.12 A promissory note calls for 20 payments of $750 to be made semiannually beginning 6 months from today. The note can be purchased for $11,000. What is the nominal rate of return on the investment?

8.13 A promissory note calls for 24 monthly payments of $60 beginning one month from today. The note is for sale for $1,200. What are the nominal and the effective annual interest rates?

8.14 A bank offers an automobile loan at the following terms: "On a $2,000 loan financed for 30 months, the total monthly payment is $77.50." Assuming all payments are end-of-month, find the nominal and effective interest rates paid by the borrower.

8.15 A machine tool can be purchased for cash as follows:

Basic machine	$12,700.00
Coolant pump	295.00
Bar-feed attachment	435.00
Tooling	2,508.75
Total	$15,938.75

The same machine can be obtained on a lease plan at $331.07 per month rental with the first 5 months' rental payable in advance. This amounts to a $1,655.35 down payment. The rental charges are due on the first of each month. If the lease is continued for 5 years, the lessee becomes the owner of the machine. The salvage of the machine at the end of 5 years is expected to be $6,000. What rate of return is the purchaser paying?

8.16 The subscription rates in the United States and Canada for a news magazine are 1 year, $7.50; 2 years, $12.00; 3 years, $16.00; 5 years, $22.00. Compute the rate of return on the investment for purchasers of 2-year, 3-year, and 5-year subscriptions.

8.17 A speculator can buy land for $20,000 which he estimates will increase 50% in value at the end of 5 years. He will derive no income from the property but he must pay taxes and liability insurance on it amounting to $800 a year, payable at year end. On selling the land 5 years hence, he must pay a sales commission of 6% and furnish a title guaranty costing $75. What rate of return can the speculator expect on his investment?

8.18 A subscription to a local newspaper is $2 a month or $20 a year, all payable in advance. What is the rate of return on the investment in a year's subscription?

8.19 Two pumps are being considered for use over the next 15 years. The Delta pump has a first cost of $1,500 and an annual cost of $1,700 for the electrical energy it uses. The Alpha pump costs $1,200, but, being less efficient, its pumping costs are $65 a year more. Salvage values are zero. Compare the alternatives by the rate-of-return method. What is the rate of return on the Delta pump? On the Alpha pump? Explain your answers. In addition, prove that the rate of return is the interest which makes the annual costs equal.

8.20 The Specific Electric Company sells two motors in the 100-hp range. Model A-38 costs $2,400 and has a full load efficiency of 91%. Model A-40 costs $2,000 and has a full load efficiency of 89.5%. Nutronics Corporation has an operation that requires one 100-hp motor to operate at full load for 1,800 hours a year. Energy costs 2 cents a kilowatt-hour. (0.746 KW = 1 hp, and kilowatt-hours equals the number of kilowatts input times the number of hours of operation.) These motors are expected to serve 12 years and have 25% salvage value. If they are equal mechanically in all respects except efficiency, what selection should be made based on a rate-of-return analysis?

8.21 A company is planning to purchase 10 compressed-air-operated screwdrivers costing $109.50 each. The increased production caused by the 10 tools is expected to show a total annual savings of $2,190. The anticipated economic life is 8 years with zero salvage at that time. What is the rate of return on the investment? Give the meaning of your answer.

8.22 Solve Problem 7.4 by the rate-of-return method.

8.23 Solve Problem 6.8 by the rate-of-return method.

8.24 A manufacturing plant owns a floor-cleaning machine which has a current investment value P estimated to be $3,500. The machine uses the full time of one operator and $2,000 worth of cleaning materials a year. The salesman that sold this machine is offering an improved model costing $4,500. The machine uses the same labor but requires only $1,700 worth of cleaning substances a year. The remaining economic life of the old machine is estimated to be 4 years and that of the new one, 7 years. Both will have zero salvage. Compare the alternatives by the rate-of-return method. Explain the meaning of your answer.

8.25 What assumptions are mathematically inherent in the solution of the previous problem? Which assumption would you prefer? Does it make any difference which assumption you made?

8.26 Solve Problem 6.19 by the rate-of-return method. Explain the meaning of your answer.

8.27 Solve Problem 7.1 by the rate-of-return method. Explain the meaning of your answer.

8.28 Solve Problem 7.22 by the rate-of-return method.

8.29 An automobile company is planning to install inspection procedures to reduce the high cost of repairs arising out of their new-car guarantees. Alternative plans have been worked out as shown. The equipment consists of mechanized test stands to be installed at various points in the production line. The annual cost of labor to operate the inspection equipment increases with the degree of inspection; however, even the increased inspection will not entirely eliminate the need for repairs under the guarantee. The economic life is 10 years with zero salvage.

The company's minimum required rate of return is 25%. How much money should be invested based on a rate-of-return analysis?

Plan	Equipment	Annual cost of labor	Cost of repair under car guarantee
	—	—	$1,585,000
A	$1,400,000	$40,000	680,000
B	1,700,000	50,000	610,000
C	1,800,000	60,000	300,000
D	2,000,000	70,000	230,000
E	2,600,000	80,000	180,000
F	3,000,000	85,000	165,000

8.30 Solve Problem 6.22 by the rate-of-return method.

8.31 Solve Problem 7.23 by the rate-of-return method.

8.32 Solve Problem 6.7 by the rate-of-return method.

8.33 Assuming that the rate of return which you computed in Problem 8.19 is less than the company's minimum required rate of return, draw a time scale of the cash flow that will result from rejecting the extra investment.

8.34 A company is organized to sell trading stamps to stores and to redeem them from the customers of these stores for merchandise. The company sells the stores a book of 1,200 stamps for $3.50. The company's cost of these stamps, including administrative, clerical and other overhead costs, but not including the cost of the merchandise, is $1.00. The company plans to exchange merchandise retailing for $31.00 for 10 books. It is estimated that the average customer will take 1 year to collect 10 books. The company purchases all articles at 40% off of the list (retail) price. If the company's minimum required rate of return is 10%, what percentage is the company making on each item of merchandise it exchanges for 10 books?

8.35 A company plans to avoid spending $10,000 for a new machine. Instead, it will spend $3,000 a year for the manual labor the machine would have eliminated. If purchased, the machine would have performed this job for 8 years and it would have had no salvage value. The $10,000 saved by not buying the machine will be invested in bonds paying 4% interest. Assume the company's minimum required rate of return should be (a) 15%; (b) 40%. What is the gain or loss to the company in each situation?

8.36 Impellers on pumps handling very corrosive liquids in a chemical plant can be made to last indefinitely by a monthly cleaning which will cost $3,000 a year. The alternative is to replace the impellers at the end of every 3 years at a cost of $10,000. What procedure is recommended if the minimum required rate of return is (a) 5%; (b) 20%? Draw the time scales of the cash flow in (a) and (b).

8.37 A shipping line can lease tankers and, after paying the rent and the operating disbursements, have a net profit on its business of freighting oil of $40,000 a year. In addition to the rent, the lessee must pay for the overhaul and repair of equipment. It is predicted that the vessel and its power plant will have to be overhauled at the end of the fourth year at a cost of $400,000. The net profit of $40,000 does not include any allowance for this expense of overhauling the equipment. Should the shipping firm engage in the lease if it is to run for 12 years?

8.38 Mr. A can purchase a tract of land from Mr. B for $145,000 and can sell part of it at once for $100,000. Mr. A therefore wants to acquire title (ownership) at once but he is unable to produce the cash to make the purchase. However, Mr. B agrees to an immediate sale, allowing Mr. A to defer actual payment for 1 year, at which time he will pay $145,000 plus interest. Mr. A also expects he can sell the remaining parcels of land for $440,000 at the end of 15 years. Neglecting taxes, should Mr. A proceed with the transaction?

8.39 Mr. X can lease forest land for 20 years. The rental is negligible, but the cost for reforestation and road construction required by his contract will be considerable in certain years. If he leases he can take out trees at once (time zero) worth $100,000. One year later his cost will be $150,000 for reforestation and construction of roads required for fire control. At the end of 14 years from that time he can cut trees from another section of the land worth $440,000. At this point the lease has 5 years to run. Under the contract he must complete certain road construction and reforestation prior to the end of the lease. These will cost $440,000 but may be put off until the end of the contract—the end of the twentieth year. Although Mr. X is spending more money than he receives, it will be noted that his income precedes his disbursements. Would this make it advisable for Mr. X to lease? Thoroughly explain your answer.

8.40 If Mr. X wishes to take a 100-year lease instead of 20 as in Problem 8.39, his estate will receive income of $60,000 at the end of the hundredth year. The costs and incomes for the earlier years will be the same as in the previous problem. Regardless of Mr. X's decision in Problem 8.39, what should he do now for the benefit of his heirs. Explain your answer.

9

The Cost of Capital

9.1 SOURCES OF CAPITAL

A company's supply of capital may come from several sources and each source may have a different cost.[1] To estimate the total cost of capital the company must determine its sources of supply and compute the cost of each. For simplicity, we presently assume that the cost of each source is independent of the cost of the other sources. Limited space prevents discussion of the effects of one class of capital on the cost of another as the proportions of the capital mix are extended. The questions of establishing the best mix and therefore the questions of the intereffect of the costs of the classes of capital in the mix are truly important in the subject of finance, but must be held to be beyond the scope of this text.

There are three basic sources: debt capital, plowback capital, and new equity capital.

1. *Debt Capital* This is capital obtained by long-term borrowing, such as by bonds and mortgages.

2. *Plowback Capital* This is capital obtained largely by retaining earnings instead of paying them in dividends; it includes funds earmarked for retention in the business as a result of depreciation accounting, funds from the sale of assets, and funds from excess working capital. This source is commonly referred to as plowback capital, equity capital, or even retained earnings (as this is the largest component of this source). In general, plowback capital is the greatest source of funds for internal investment. Very often it is the only source.

3. *New Equity Capital* This is capital obtained by the sale of additional shares of stock.

---

[1] This is the generally accepted view, but an interesting counteropinion appears in Franco Modigliani and Merton H. Miller, "The Cost of Capital, Corporation Finance, and the Theory of Investment," *American Economic Review*, vol 48, no. 3 (June 1958), pp. 261–297.

9.2 COST OF DEBT CAPITAL

Capital borrowed by the company for investment is generally contracted on a long-term basis. Such debt is known as funded debt, fixed liability, or long-term debt. It may be secured by mortgages or bonds having long maturity dates.

Industry is well aware of the hazards of borrowing. These stem from the unfailing legal obligation to pay both interest and principal when due and from the contract, under which, upon nonpayment, the creditors could take over the business. These fears cause most companies to set themselves a debt limit and to to tap this source of capital only lightly in spite of its apparent cheapness. The lender prices it cheaply because he takes little risk of not being paid, and the company finds it economical because, unlike earnings, the interest on the debt is tax free.

The contract between the company and the lender will specify certain costs and dates of interest payments but the estimate of the true cost of debt capital should include every conceivable cost, such as a reduction in asking price to assure the sale of the bond issue, commission to the agents, and expenses of administering and handling the issue.

In the following example the cost of debt capital is computed without consideration of the effects of the capital mix on the cost of capital—as stated, this is a matter reserved for a text on finance.

EXAMPLE 9.2   A 6% $100 bond series is offered to the public for $94 to assure its sale by a broker, who, after his commission, turns over $92 to the firm. If the interest is paid annually and date of maturity is 10 years, what is the cost of capital to the company?

$$P = 92 \qquad\qquad\qquad I = 6/\text{yr} \qquad\qquad\qquad L = 100$$

$$0 \qquad\qquad\qquad\qquad\qquad\qquad\qquad\qquad\qquad 10$$

SOLUTION:

$$92 = 6(P/A, i, 10) + 100(P/F, i, 10)$$

Try 7%.

$$0 \triangleq 0.98$$

Try 8%.

$$5.42 \triangleq 0$$

whence

$$i = 7 + \left(\frac{98}{640}\right)(1) = 7.15\%$$

The cost of debt capital for this company is therefore 7.15%, not 6.0%.

The price paid by the public ($94 in the preceding example) will be lower in proportion to the public's evaluation of the company and the risk involved. This increases the cost of capital to poorly managed companies, and we can observe that a good business gets a low rate and a poor business gets a high rate on its cost of capital. It follows, too, that if both classes of companies can get all the capital they need, the good business with its lower cost of capital can invest in opportunities down to a lower minimum required rate of return and, by indulging in more economies, can improve its position over a poor business.

9.3 COST OF EQUITY OR PLOWBACK CAPITAL

The corporation must satisfy the shareholders' expectations of profits. New shareholders purchase stock expecting to receive a return on their investment, the purchase price. Similarly, having purchased the stock, they continue to own it based on the expectation of receiving a return on their investment in the stock, that is, on the price they could receive for it if they sold it. Consequently, the prospective shareholders and existing shareholders can be viewed alike in that both expect a future stream of income as a return on their investment represented by the present market value of the stock. The market price specifies the amount of money each foregoes—one in buying the stock and the other in keeping the stock in order to receive a future stream of income (neglecting the difference introduced by transfer costs). In short, therefore, the corporation is expected to pay its shareholders the rate of return which they expect on their investment in the stock. The corporation's internal investment program in methods and equipment should therefore promise earnings from which the shareholders' expectations can be satisfied.

In view of the fact that payment to shareholders for the use of equity capital is not a contractual obligation, the term "cost of capital" has caused some misunderstanding.[1] However, no management can disregard the obligation without fear of being replaced by a more responsible management.

9.4 WHAT DOES THE SHAREHOLDER EXPECT TO RECEIVE?

The shareholder expects to receive a rate of return on his investment in the stock. The rate of return on his ownership will be the rate which makes the dividend series equivalent to the current price of the stock.

The shareholder as owner of the business is presumed here to be interested in a permanent association with the business. We are assuming for the purpose of our analysis that he does not contemplate a future selling date or a speculative selling price, and for that reason the shareholder's expectations will be expressed as a stream of dividends, indefinitely long.

Let us try to conceive a logical pattern for this future stream of dividends. First, we note that all the earnings or yield Y on each share of stock is not paid out to the shareholder. Only a part is paid as dividends D, and the remainder or retained earnings is plowed back into the firm. Retained earnings, per se, are of

[1]Professor John A. Griswold, of the Amos Tuck School, Dartmouth College, for this reason has suggested the term "capital-use rate."

no value to the shareholder, since he never gets them, but we must include in our prediction all dividend increases caused by earnings on the retained earnings. The following section develops such a pattern of dividends.

9.5 COMPUTING COST OF CAPITAL RETAINED IN BUSINESS[1]

Suppose P_0 is the market price of a share of stock at time zero and D_t is the dividend per share paid in any year t.

We will designate k as the interest rate which makes this stream of future dividends equivalent to the market price of the stock. This, we have noted, is the company's obligation to the shareholder; it is the rate of return which the company must count on paying to the shareholder.

Then

$$P_0 = D_0 + D_1(P/F, k, 1) + D_2(P/F, k, 2) + D_3(P/F, k, 3) + \cdots \infty$$

or

$$P_0 = \sum_{t=0}^{t=\infty} D_t \cdot (1 + k)^{-t} \tag{9.5a}$$

But the dividend stream is a consequence of the flow of earnings, and earnings on earnings, which can be developed as follows:

Y_0 is the earnings per share at time zero after corporate income tax.

b is the fraction of earnings retained in the company, not paid out in dividends. This ratio of retained earnings to earnings is assumed to be constant for the convenience of our solution. Disregarding the business fluctuations that cause unusual troughs or peaks in earnings, this assumption of a constant b is reasonable. We are not predicting that it is permanent, but we are not setting up a basis for predicting its change nor for predicting the variation of P_0 with a prospective change in b.

bY_0 therefore is the retained earnings per share at time zero.

B_0 is the book value per share at time zero.

r is the rate of return on the book value of the common stock. Its ratio is assumed to be constant from the standpoint of our solution. We assume it reflects the ratio of earnings on book value in a typical year and disregards business fluctuations or the effects of the long pull. As with b, we are not predicting a permanent value for r in spite of the assumption that it is constant in the formula.

$$r = \frac{Y_0}{B_0} = \text{constant}$$

At time zero, the retained earnings, bY_0, will be added to the book value of the capital stock. It will also be put to work in the company and during the

---

[1] This solution is based on Myron J. Gordon and Eli Shapiro, "Capital Equipment Analysis: The Required Rate of Profit," *Management Science*, vol. 3, no. 1 (October 1956).

ensuing year show the average rate of earnings on the book value. At the end of year 1 the earnings on the previous year's earnings will be $r(bY_0)$. Therefore the earnings at year 1, Y_1, will be greater than Y_0, the earnings the year before, as follows:

$$Y_1 = Y_0 + rbY_0 \tag{9.5b}$$

and, similarly,

$$Y_2 = Y_1 + rbY_1$$

Substitute Eq. 9.5b, which simplifies to

$$Y_2 = (Y_0)(1 + rb)^2$$

or, in any year,

$$Y_t = (Y_0)(1 + rb)^t \tag{9.5c}$$

Now the dividend D_0 at time zero is the earnings minus the retained earnings:

$$D_0 = Y_0 - bY_0 = (Y_0)(1 - b)$$

similarly,

$$D_t = (Y_t)(1 - b)$$

Therefore, multiplying both sides of Eq. 9.5c by $(1 - b)$:

$$D_t = (D_0)(1 + rb)^t$$

Substituting in Eq. 9.5a,

$$P_0 = \sum_{t=0}^{t=\infty} (D_0)(1 + rb)^t (1 + k)^{-1} \tag{9.5d}$$

So that we may integrate, convert Eq. 9.5d from discrete to continuous functions, noting that

$$(1 + rb)^t = e^{rbt}$$

and

$$(1 + k)^{-t} = e^{-kt}$$

So

$$P_0 = D_0 \int_0^\infty e^{rbt} e^{-kt} \, dt \tag{9.5e}$$

$$P_0 = D_0 \int_0^\infty e^{-t(k-rb)} \, dt$$

$$P_0 = -D_0 \left[\frac{e^{-t(k-rb)}}{k - rb} \right]_0^\infty$$

$$P_0 = \frac{D_0}{k - rb}$$

$$k = \frac{D_0}{P_0} + rb \qquad \text{(Eq. 9.5)}$$

Equation 9.5 is the rate of return on the purchase price of the common stock in the market. It is the shareholders' expectations of profit. This statement applies not only to those who will buy the stock at the existing figures but also to those who continue their ownership when they might have sold the stock (disregarding the differences produced by transfer fees). This is also sometimes called the market rate of profit.

As Gordon and Shapiro have pointed out, if management's objective is "the maximization of the value of the stockholder's equity"[1] then it has been shown by several authorities that this will occur when the market rate of profit is established as the marginal rate of return required in investments—namely, the minimum required rate of return. We take the liberty of calling this the cost of equity capital. This applies to retained capital as well as new equity.

EXAMPLE 9.5 The present after tax earnings are $3.40 a share for stock selling at $36.00. The current dividends are $1.67. The ratio of retained earnings to earnings is expected to remain constant in the future. The present book value of the stock is $19.50 a share and it is expected that the percentage earnings on the book value will be held constant by management action. What is the firm's cost of capital?

SOLUTION. Use the method derived in Eq. 9.5.
$D_0 = 1.67$ and $P_0 = 36.00$.

r = ratio of earnings to book value

$$= \frac{Y_0}{B_0} = \frac{3.40}{19.50} = 0.1744$$

b = ratio of retained earnings to earnings

$$= \frac{Y_0 - D_0}{Y_0} = \frac{3.40 - 1.67}{3.40} = 0.51$$

$$k = \frac{D_0}{P_0} + rb = \frac{1.67}{36.00} + (0.1744)(0.51) = 0.0464 + 0.0889 = 13.5\%$$

The reader will note that the expected rate of return k is the current dividend rate plus the growth rate. Therefore k is greater than the dividend-price ratio,

[1]Gordon and Shapiro, p. 103.

D_0/P_0. Obviously, k is not the capitalization rate of a fixed dividend, D_0, but of all future dividends after allowing for the continuous increase in dividends resulting from the annual profit made on the plowback of earnings.

This formula is one of the most logical attempts to quantify the rate of return expected by shareholders in a company. Other work has been done; the earnings-price ratio approach is presented in Section 9.7, and other methods are expected as research continues on this subject.

We do not pretend that the formula does more than give an estimate of the cost of capital. However, for economy analyses in many companies, the cost of capital does not need to be quantified with great accuracy. This is especially true whenever the demand exceeds the supply of capital, because in that case a cutoff rate will be used which exceeds the cost of capital, as we will see in Section 9.11.

Before leaving this topic we should recognize that if the stock of a company is not traded, market prices and dividends are not available for use in the formula. This is typical of privately held companies as well as many small firms and partnerships. One approach to this problem is to compute the cost of capital of a firm (whose stock is being traded) which might be viewed as similar in the eyes of the public—a company of similar risk and similar management ability to earn profits. Another approach is to observe that the cost of capital is established by the opportunity cost of the owners—whether the firm is owned by one or by many persons. This is discussed more fully in Section 9.16.

9.6 EFFECT OF RETAINED EARNINGS ON BOOK VALUE

We observed that as a result of the earnings made by the retained earnings, the earnings in any year t were expected to be

$$Y_t = (Y_0)(1 + rb)^t \tag{9.5c}$$

and, since

$$Y_t = rB_t$$

we can write

$$B_t = (B_0)(1 + rb)^t$$

and

$$D_t = (D_0)(1 + rb)^t$$

These values are illustrated in Table 9.6, in which $r = 0.1744$, $b = 0.51$, $Y_0 = \$3.40$, and $B_0 = \$19.50$.

Although the retained earnings belong to the shareholder, he can receive value only from the payments that are made to him, namely, the dividends. The shareholder can therefore benefit only by the increase in dividends resulting from the profitable reinvestment of the retained earnings.

Table 9.6 THE RESULT OF RETAINING EARNINGS IN THE CORPORATION

Time	Earnings, Y	Dividends, D	Book value, B	Retained earnings, bY
0	$3.40	$1.67	$19.50	$1.73
1	3.70	1.81	21.23	1.89
2	4.03	1.97	23.11	2.06
3	4.39	2.15	25.17	2.24
4	4.78	2.34	27.41	2.44
5	5.21	2.55	29.85	2.66

Nevertheless, we should inquire whether retained earnings, as accretion to book value, can be regarded as valuable from that viewpoint alone. Reasoning will indicate that purchasers of shares in successful companies do not purchase stock for its book value. For example, in the present company, where the book value of a share is $19.50, no one would pay anything for the stock, not even $19.50, if there were no prospects whatsoever of future dividends. Where there is no promise of dividends, the stock is worthless in spite of a high book value, except in the eyes of those who might purchase an unsuccesful company based upon their expectation of profits by liquidating the firm's assets. (Certainly liquidation of the firm's assets might prove profitable to anyone who is making a business of trading in assets, or it might prove profitable to someone who deals in reorganizing unsuccessful companies.)

Before we leave this discussion, it should be noted that the retention of earnings as liquid asset reserves to smooth out dividend performance over the peaks and valleys of business activity is outside the bounds of this problem, because we have assumed that r, the rate of return on book value, is constant year in and year out.

Table 9.6 is intended solely to enable the reader to visualize the structure of Eq. 9.5. Table 9.6 therefore is not an attempt to predict the future but a statement that if the future consists of this stream of values—and this includes the assumptions that r and b will be constant—the value of k will follow from Eq. 9.5.

9.7 EARNINGS-PRICE RATIO

As stated in Section 9.5, there are and will continue to be other methods suggested for quantifying the cost of capital. A method which has found considerable acceptance is the Earnings-Price Ratio,[1] which is computed as follows:

P = selling price of a share of common stock, based on reasonable recent averages—say the last 12 months.[2] ($34.50)

[1] Recommended by the Finance Management Committee of the Controller's Institute in "Cost of Capital," *The Controller*, May 1956, p. 207.

[2] The report explains at length that these averages must not represent "an especially good year or an outstandingly bad one" and suggests averaging over the past 3 to 5 years or taking into account prospective future earnings.

Y = average annual earnings with adjustment for prospective future earnings. ($\$4.06$)

k' = cost of capital computed by the Earnings-Price Ratio method.

If $P = Y_{k'-\infty}$ uspwf, then

$$k' = \frac{Y}{P} \qquad (9.7)$$

It will be observed that the cost of capital by this method is the earnings-price ratio, and it is the result of capitalizing the earnings. With the given data, the cost of capital by the earnings-price ratio is

$$k' = \frac{4.06}{34.50} = 11.8\%$$

9.8 COMPARISON OF METHODS FOR COMPUTING COST OF CAPITAL

Based upon the reasoning in Section 9.6, the earnings-price ratio should not give correct results, because it counts as benefits to the shareholder those retained earnings which he never gets. By coincidence, however, the two methods give somewhat similar results. This can be demonstrated as follows:

We know that

$$Y = D + bY$$

Substituting this in Eq. 9.7,

$$k' = \frac{D}{P} + \frac{bY}{P} \qquad (9.8a)$$

then, from Eq. 9.5,

$$k = \frac{D_0}{P_0} + rb$$

where

$$r = \frac{Y_0}{B_0}$$

so

$$k = \frac{D_0}{P_0} + \frac{bY_0}{B_0} \qquad (9.8b)$$

Equations 9.8a and 9.8b demonstrate the basis of difference between the two methods for estimating the market rate of profit. The essential difference is that the Gordon-Shapiro method uses the book value in the denominator of the second term, whereas the earnings-price method uses the market value. If the market value of the stock happened to equal its book value (and if the analyst predicted the same dividends and earnings for use in each formula), k and k', will be equal. In the same circumstances, if $P > B_0$, then $k > k'$; or if $P < B_0$ then $k < k'$. We note, therefore, that k and k' can be at wide variance—or in close agreement.

The student interest in a critical discussion of the two methods would do well to study the Gordon-Shapiro paper. One reason for not continuing the discussion here is that the minimum required rate of return is often something other than the cost of equity capital. This is illustrated in Sections 9.11 through 9.13.

9.9 COST OF NEW EQUITY CAPITAL

As with debt capital, the cost of new equity capital must include all costs such as broker's commission, handling charges, and the cost of underpricing to increase the demand for the issue.

As expected, Eq. 9.5 is applicable whether the capital is new equity or plowed-back equity. However, P_0, the current market value for new equity, would be reduced by the costs noted in the previous paragraph.

EXAMPLE 9.9   Compute the cost of new equity capital[1] proposed for an expansion program if the current earnings are $3.40 a share of common stock, dividends are regularly 49% of earnings, the consistent rate of earnings on book value is 17.44%, and the current market price is $36 a share. In the proposed issue, P_0, after underpricing, broker's fees, and handling, will be $29.

SOLUTION.   By Eq. 9.5,

$$k = \frac{D_0}{P_0} + rb = \frac{0.49(3.40)}{29} + (0.1744)(0.51) = 14.6\%$$

9.10 DEPRECIATION AND CASH FLOW

From a profit-and-loss statement for the past year we could show the following summary of earnings. In it we have assumed that the depreciation for the year has been set at $100,000 by the accounting procedures.

Income from sales		$2,000,000
Cost of labor, material, manufacturing supplies	$900,000	
Depreciation	100,000	
Cost of manufacturing		1,000,000
		$1,000,000
Less cost of administration, sales, taxes,		
supplies, etc.		650,000
Net earnings		$ 350,000
Dividends declared	$150,000	
Retained earnings	200,000	

---

[1] These illustrations disregard the effect of the shareholder's income tax. A discussion of this can be found in Franco Modigliani and Merton H. Miller, "The Cost of Capital, Corporation Financing, and the Theory of Investment," *American Economic Review*, vol. 48, no. 3, (June 1958), pp. 294–296.

As a result of the year's operations, the supply of capital in the business has been increased by $300,000.

The $100,000 charged for depreciation remains as capital in the business because it has not been paid out to anyone—neither to the owners nor to outside vendors, as would be the case for materials, labor, and supplies. It is one of the elements of plowback capital along with retained earnings.[1] In fact, the term "cash flow" is applied to this flowback of profit plus depreciation from a given project.

9.11 CAPITAL BUDGETING

The budgeting of capital is a very important and very necessary process; two of the outstanding reasons are (1) the company's demands for capital generally exceed the supply of capital, and (2) the prospective returns on these demands cover a wide range relative to the cost of capital. In these instances it is not only important that none of the limited capital should be appropriated to aggressive demands at rates of return less than the cost of capital but it is important that the limited funds should be given only to the very best investments.

Without capital budgeting as a management device, substantial losses can occur. The appropriation of money to projects based on demand alone invariably means satisfying loss ventures or poor ventures at the expense of the best ventures. Capital budgeting, therefore, necessitates an organized procedure for generating alternatives, evaluating each alternative, listing or laddering all the alternatives in the order of their merits, determining the sources of capital and their costs, and appropriating the supply to the best of the demands. This process, capital budgeting, is essential, because money cannot be properly appropriated unless the demands have been studied and evaluated.

Capital budgeting is possible only through the participation and cooperation of all the members of the firm for the improvement of every production unit, department, and division of the company. The creative demands of each of these units should then be laddered together so that they compete for the firm's limited supply of money.

The budgeting itself, therefore, implies the separate existence of management machinery that will make budgeting not only possible but practical.

The demands schedule is constructed from the budgetary requests made by departments and divisions of the business for the investment funds they will require for the coming period for each project, together with the merit of each, usually in the form of the expected rate of return. These requests would be laddered as shown in Table 9.11. For simplicity we have not listed any demands for strategic investments which cannot be quantified. Budgeting for irreducible investments is discussed separately in a later section. For simplicity we are also assuming that irreducible considerations are not deemed to be governing factors in any of the laddered projects.

---

[1]Clearly there must be a sufficient flow from operations for depreciation to remain as capital in the business.

Table 9.11 LADDERING THE DEMANDS

Laddered increments of demand		Cumulative amounts (total demand)
Amount	Rate of return (%)	
$100,000	70 and up	$ 100,000
150,000	60–69	250,000
200,000	50–59	450,000
175,000	45–49	625,000
200,000	40–44	825,000
220,000	35–39	1,045,000
310,000	30–34	1,355,000
280,000	25–29	1,635,000
275,000	20–24	1,910,000
300,000	15–19	2,210,000
340,000	10–14	2,550,000
400,000	5–9	2,950,000
450,000	0–4	3,400,000

If all the projects listed in the demands schedule, Table 9.11, are satisfied, the total requirement for capital is $3,400,000. But now suppose the total supply of capital for the period is expected to be plowback amounting to $1,500,000 at a cost of 15%, this sum must be appropriated to only the most profitable demands. Examination of Table 9.11 indicates that this supply will satisfy all projects down through those promising between 25% and 29% or, let us say, precisely 27%. At this point the supply intersects the demand schedule. This establishes the *minimum required rate of return* at 27% because satisfying a project at any lower rate of return results in insufficient money to invest in some project promising 27% or more.

In this context we can see how the obvious term, *cutoff rate*, has also been applied to the minimum required rate of return.

Figure 9.11 shows the cumulative demand, except that for simplicity a smooth curve has been constructed through the steps of the increments of demand. This figure illustrates the earlier comment that the demands for capital may exceed management's ability to provide the supply. In the given example, approximately $700,000 of good investments promising returns between 15% and 27% will be rejected because of the company's inability to finance them. The greater the spread between the cutoff rate and the cost of capital, the greater the pressure on management to increase the supply by employing outside funds. Under these circumstances, we observe that whenever the supply does not satisfy the demand, the cost of capital remains as a floor under the cutoff rate.

Actually, the problem is not one of just increasing the supply, but of planning over an extended period so that a supply can be provided to meet the demands for all projects promising rates of return down through the cost of capital. This is discussed in the following section.

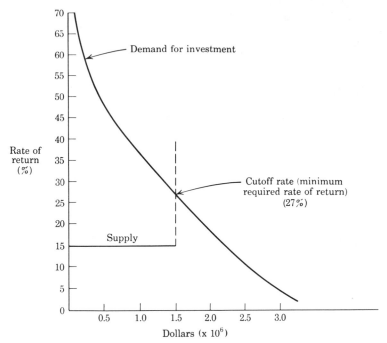

Figure 9.11   The cutoff rate with insufficient supply of capital

9.12 PERIOD PLANNING

Capital budgeting is a multiperiod problem. The annual budget cannot be set up in complete independence of future needs and future supplies. The prospective improvements of a company take the form of 5-year and 10-year plans and the annual budget in any year is but the integration of these needs—long and short—into a one-year step. This planning for the capital equipment requirements of the company must also be matched by a long-term planning of the supply of funds to meet these needs.

In this situation the long-term plans must consider the effect on the cost of capital of extending the amounts of debt, plowback, and new equity in the capital mix with the aim of providing an adequate supply at an optimal mix.

The aim of successful planning of demand and supply is to avoid rejecting good opportunities for lack of funds. With successful planning, Fig. 9.11 might be redrawn as shown in Fig. 9.12. The supply of $1,500,000 has now been increased from various sources to about $2,000,000 and the cost has increased as the supply has been expanded. The intersection of demand and supply at 18% gives a cutoff rate at the cost of capital.

As a result of long-term planning, the cutoff rate is regarded as a multiperiod value rather than one that disregards the needs of future years.

When necessary, the cutoff rate will be adjusted in any year, but with the

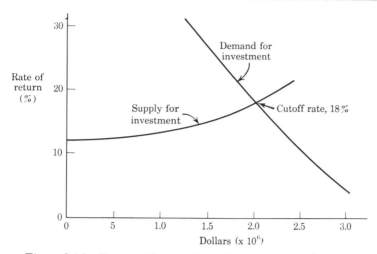

Figure 9.12   The cutoff rate with sufficient supply of capital

long-term pull in mind and if funds cannot be provided in sufficient amount, the situation will fall between Figs. 9.11 and 9.12. As noted, the plowback cannot be varied greatly, and the amount of debt capital invested in the business cannot be increased in total disregard of the amount of equity funds invested, as we will indicate in Section 9.18.

If perchance the supply is consistently more than adequate for the demands, a rather quick observation is to return the excess funds to the shareholders on the basis that they can invest them more profitably than the business. However, a firm in the enviable position of having enough funds should plan a program to educate its management to find ways to invest them internally for the betterment of the company.

In the long pull, where the plans for financing are aimed at the best possible mix, the cost of the mix will be regarded as somewhere between the cost of the highest cost component, equity, and the lowest cost component, debt capital, as would be approximated by a weighted average. Discussion of this, we feel, belongs, with the discussions of optimal mix, in a separate text on finance.

9.13 VARIATIONS IN CUTOFF RATE

The cutoff rate, determined by the intersection of the supply and demand curves, can therefore be expected to vary as a result of factors that bring about changes in supply or demand.

The supply of money for economy investments will decrease in bad times. With a shrinkage of earnings, less money is available for plowback after payment of dividends and after supplying the requirements of a possibly depleted working capital. Not only does the supply shrink, but management may withhold it from equipment investment to create reserves against the storms that may be ahead during the recession.

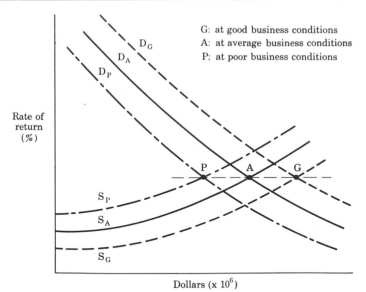

Figure 9.13   Variations in the cutoff rate

The demand for capital should vary primarily with the ability of the firm's personnel to create improved methods in which capital can be profitably invested. However, investment opportunities do tend to shrink during poor times unless management plans for the long instead of the short run. During poor times, when operating disbursements are low because of low machine utilization, the savings that justify investments are low and discourage investing unless the long-run figures are introduced.

In Fig. 9.13, point A, the intersection of the demand D_A and supply S_A establishes the cutoff rate during a period of average business conditions. When business improves, the opportunities for investment increase and the demand D_G is greater. At this time, also, more funds are available from each source at about the same percentage cost. When business is good, more plowback will be available from greater profits and more debt capital can be introduced. The supply loosens, as illustrated by curve S_G, and the cutoff point now occurs at G. Conversely, in poor business periods the demand lowers and the supply tightens, producing a cutoff at P. In spite of changing conditions, the cutoff rate tends to be stable, because we note in Fig. 9.13 that the cutoff rates corresponding to P, A, and G are essentially the same in spite of the changes in supply and demand.

9.14 ROLE OF THE EXTRA INVESTMENT

In the laddering process we noted that each demand for investment is listed with its prospective rate of return. In cost-reduction investments only the rate of return on the *extra* investments is known; therefore the ladder presumably contains only the extra investment for cost-reduction projects (but contains the total investment in income-expansion projects). This would seem to suggest at first glance that insufficient capital would be allotted for the purchase of cost-reduction equipment.

A brief explanation is sufficient to indicate the answer. Take as an example a case where cost-reduction means replacing an existing machine with a modern new machine. If the total cost including all installation parts of the new machine is $10,000, and if the *net realizable value* of the old machine (which we will show in Chapter 11 is its investment *P*) is $4,000, then the extra investment is $6,000 and is all that we need provide in the budget, because the old machine will be liquidated for its $4,000 net realizable value. Suppose, on the other hand, that the old machine is retained in the business. This should occur only if that machine wins a position in a degraded post against a more obsolete machine. For the sake of simplicity, if this machine presently has zero salvage value, then the $4,000 extra investment in that project can appear on the capital budget.[1] Therefore, by budgeting for only the extra investment, sufficient money ($10,000 in the given example) will be allotted for total acquisition of the cost-reduction property.

9.15 RATIONING FOR STRATEGIC INVESTMENTS

Some investments are sufficiently irreducible so that they cannot be quantitatively evaluated as investments and aligned in the demand schedule according to expected earnings. In spite of this they may be necessary investments in the judgment of management. An example would be an investment in an employees' clubhouse which management feels it must provide to match competition in the labor market. Another example would be investing money in a new line of goods necessary to maintain the firm's leadership but where the calculable returns are insignificant.

"Strategic investments," as they are usually called, are necessary investments in which a low or negligible rate of return is overwhelmed by irreducible advantages.

In spite of this method of approval, every effort should be made to qunatify all facts and to call fewer and fewer spending decisions irreducible. Too often one takes for granted that problems cannot be quantified when some study will reveal how they can be. But even when problems are positively irreducible they should be *viewed* as investments and the benefits at least visualized in order to appreciate their value.

Management may follow a system for allotting funds to irreducible investments. One method is to annually apportion a certain percentage of the total supply solely for use in strategic projects. Another method is to consider the needs of each year as they arise without establishing prior budgetary restrictions.

---

[1] That is, in theory; in practice the approaches can vary widely.

9.16 OPPORTUNITY COST OF CAPITAL

We sometimes hear that the cost of capital is established by the firm's opportunity cost, so we ask, how does this concept relate to the ideas expressed in thic chapter?

Opportunities available to management for the use of the firm's funds in lieu of internal investments are to invest in government bonds or the securities of other firms.

Certainly funds should not be approved for internal investment at lower rates of return than they would bring if invested externally. Theoretically, external opportunities can be viewed as establishing a floor under internal investments, but actually the external investment of funds is rarely a practical course of action, because industry invariably has unlimited opportunities for internal investments at returns considerably in excess of those obtainable on the outside. In fact, if the best opportunities exist outside the firm, there is no excuse for further investments in the firm or, in short, for continuing the business.

Management's other external opportunity is to return the money to the shareholders and creditors. It seems apparent that if money cannot be invested at a return equal to that expected by the shareholders or that required by the lenders of debt capital it should be refunded to them. We have already seen that management will hurt its own position by retaining money which it cannot invest to meet those expectations. It would seem to be clear that the firm's opportunity cost is established by the opportunity cost of the investors in the firm. When they invest in the firm by the purchase of stock, or by keeping their stock ownership, or by lending money to the firm, they reject opportunities to invest that money at like risk elsewhere. Their opportunities, their expecta- in turn become the firm's opportunity cost.

9.17 COST OF CAPITAL AND EARNINGS ON NET WORTH

Sometimes we hear that money should not be invested at a rate of return less than the return that has been earned on net worth. This means, in other words, that the cost of capital should not be less than the earnings on net worth. Let us examine this viewpoint mathematically.

To simplify the problem, let us assume that the entire source of capital is to be obtained by a new issue of stock. Present stock ownership consists of 1,000 shares. Suppose the annual earnings are $15,000, neglecting income tax (to simplify the problem). This is $15 a share. If the new stock is predicted to sell at $150 a share, then the cost of capital using the earnings-price ratio, Eq. 9.7, is 15/150, or 10%. If management proposes to sell 200 shares to bring in a needed $30,000, this $30,000 invested in new equipment at the minimum required rate of return of 10% will bring in a new income of $3,000.

Under the foregoing conditions the question is, "Will this sum invested at 10% reduce the present earnings of $15 a share being received by the present shareholders?" The answer appears in Table 9.17.

Table 9.17   ILLUSTRATION IF THE MINIMUM REQUIRED RATE
OF RETURN IS LESS THAN THE RETURN ON NET WORTH

	Present	*Proposed*
Total shares of stock	1,000	1,200
Added profit	$ 0	$ 3,000
Total profit	15,000	18,000
Income per share	15	15

Obtaining new equity capital at a cost that is lower than the rate of return on net worth and investing this at prospective rates of return that are lower than the return on net worth does not, in spite of appearances, lose money for the present owners.

The reader will recognize that this is not only a restatement of the irrelevance of book value in establishing the cost of capital but of the conclusions reached in Section 9.5 on the cost of capital. A failure to realize this and to maintain the investments are not justified at less than the earnings-on-net-worth ratio leads to a grave fallacy in reasoning. If this were true, the better companies with a high return on their net worth could justify only investments promising a high rate of return while weak companies with low returns on net worth could justify almost every economy that comes along, down through very low rates of return. In this way, the poor companies would get better and and the better companies would get poorer. Actually, the reverse is true; the better companies have the competitive advantage, because at their lower cost of capital they can justify the greater number of economic investments.

9.18 LIMITS ON FINANCING AND INVESTING

As long as investments can be made at a rate of return exceeding the cost of capital, there is an incentive to make them. A broad objective, therefore, is to saturate all investment opportunities down through the cost of capital. On the other hand, management is reluctant to engage in financing when it creates heavy debt, and management is cautious of building up high fixed assets with their resultant high fixed costs. The result, therefore, is management's limitation on the acquisition of equipment.

Management has never agreed on any precise limits for debts, fixed assets, and other balance-sheet elements, but nevertheless at some point management will draw the line on increasing these elements. Although analysts will avoid naming specific limits, we note that most seem willing to be guided by the balance-sheet and profit-and-loss ratios published for the industry to which they belong. The median and upper and lower quartile ratios of many balance-sheet, profit-and-loss relationships are available through various publications.[1]

[1] For example, Dun and Bradstreet periodically publishes "14 Important Ratios in 72 Lines of Business," which gives median and upper and lower quartiles.

A bold attempt to clarify these undefined limits has been the aim of Roy A. Foulke,[1] vice president of Dun and Bradstreet. Foulke also publishes median and quartile ratios by industries, but in addition he defines certain ratios in his "maxims," as he calls them, which we will quote here. Our purpose in doing so is to suggest to the economy analyst that a resistance will be raised by the financial management to the thought that all good investment opportunities should be saturated or that, in the absence of funds, the organization should borrow the money needed to make the investment.

Foulke's maxim for the relationship between current liabilities and tangible net worth reads as follows (p. 229):

"Experience in the analysis of many thousands of balance sheets in all lines of business activity in good times and in poor has indicated that when a commercial or industrial concern has a tangible net worth between $50,000 and $250,000, its operation should be carefully analyzed if the current liabilities exceed two-thirds the tangible net worth; if the tangible net worth is greater than $250,000, its affairs should be studied closely if the liabilities exceed three-quarters of the tangible net worth."

As to the relation between total liabilities and tangible net worth, Foulke offers this maxim (p. 253):

". . . it is obvious that a ratio of total liabilities to tangible net worth in excess of 100.0 percent is unusual. Rarely, if ever, should total liabilities of a commercial or industrial concern exceed the tangible net worth, as in such cases creditors have more at stake in a business enterprise than the stockholders or the owners."

In connection with the ratio of funded debt to net working capital, Foulke's maxim suggests (p. 275):

"The examination of thousands of balance sheets in all lines of industrial and commercial activity has led to the conclusion that rarely, if ever, should the aggregate of funded liabilities exceed the net working capital."

And in relation to the amount of fixed assets, Foulke's maxim reads (p. 297):

"When a business enterprise has a tangible net worth between $50,000 and $250,000, experience has shown that its condition should be carefully analyzed if the depreciated book value of its fixed assets is more than two-thirds of its tangible net worth. When the tangible net worth exceeds $250,000 the affairs of the concern should be followed closely if the depreciated book value of its fixed assets totals more than three-quarters of its tangible net worth."

While these thoughts suggest that resistance to heavy accumulation of assets or heavy spending can be expected, most companies have not reached levels where such resistance should begin. On the contrary, therefore, most companies suffer from a failure to make the investments that without jeopardizing the safe financial position of the company could be made in economical equipment.

[1] Roy A. Foulke, *Practical Financial Statement Analysis*, 6th ed. (New York: McGraw-Hill, 1968).

Again we must point out that Foulke's contributions toward the overall picture cannot substitute for a detailed study of debt-equity proportions provided by a course in finance.

PROBLEMS

9.1 What is the cost of debt capital to a company that borrows $450,000 by issuing 6% bonds? The plan is to sell 5,000 bonds which will be redeemed at the end of 20 years for $100 each. Four percent interest will be paid; interest coupons worth 2% of the face value of the bond can be redeemed by the holder at the end of every 6 months. The cost of administering these interest payments is estimated to be 25 cents per bond every 6 months. It is predicted in the initial offering that the company will receive $90 net per bond after allowances for underpricing and broker's fees. Compute the nominal and the effective interest rates.

9.2 Rework Problem 9.1 under each of the following revised conditions: (a) the bond must be redeemed in 10 years instead of 20; (b) the company receives only $80 instead of $90 net from the sale of the bond. Assume a 20-year life as before, but now 5,625 bonds must be sold to produce the required $450,000. In (a) and (b) all other costs and incomes will be the same as in Problem 9.1.

9.3 What is the cost of debt capital to a company which has the following $100,000 mortgage on its property? The debt must be repaid in equal installments of $5,000 at the end of every 3 months for 5 years together with quarterly interest payments at the rate of 6% per annum on the balance. For example, the interest will be: $1,500 at the end of the first quarter, $95,000(0.015) = $1,425$ at the end of the second quarter, $90,000(0.015) = $1,350$ at the end of the third quarter, and so on.

9.4 The book value of a share of common stock of a large manufacturing company is $98.40. The stock is currently paying annual dividends of $2.55 out of earnings of $4.64 a year. Based on a widely accepted stock guide, the above dividend yield would establish a fair current price, excluding fluctuations, of $52.10. Compute the firm's cost of equity capital using the Gordon-Shapiro method.

9.5 A corporation has 216,232 outstanding shares of common stock. The money paid in by share owners on the purchase of common stock plus the retained earnings in the business brings the total book value to $7,092,115. The current earnings per share of common stock are $3.50 and the dividend is $2.30. The current market price of the stock disregarding fluctuations is estimated to be $48. Compute the firm's cost of equity capital using the Gordon-Shapiro method.

9.6 A corporation has 88,861 outstanding shares of common stock. The share owner's equity consisting of the amount paid to the firm for common stock plus the earnings reinvested in the company amounts to $1,513,421. The current earnings are $2.77 per share and the dividends are $2.00. The current market price is estimated to be $65.75. What is the firm's cost of equity capital using the Gordon-Shapiro method?

9.7 For the data in Problem 9.6, prepare a table showing the prospective future annual earnings, dividends, and book values of a share of common stock in order to illustrate the mathematical model of the Gordon-Shapiro formula.

9.8 In Problems 9.4 through 9.6 compare your computed cost of capital with the rate of return on the book value of the common stock. Why not use the rate of return on the book value as the cost of capital? Explain how these rates can be different.

9.9 Compute the cost of capital for three different corporations of your own choice. Get your own data from the companies' financial statements and from stock guides giving market quotations.

9.10 (a) Use the data in Problems 9.4 through 9.6 to compute the earnings-price ratio. Compare these with the cost of capital, computed by the Gordon-Shapiro formula. (b) Repeat part (a) except assume that the earnings are as follows: Problem 9.4, $4.90; Problem 9.5, $4.03; Problem 9.6, $2.95. Also assume the dividends are $2.70, $2.65, and $2.13, respectively. The other data will be the same. (c) Use the data in Problems 9.4 through 9.6 except assume the *retained* earnings are: (1) 100% of the total earnings, (2) 50% of the earnings, (3) zero. Compute and compare the cost of capital by the Gordon-Shapiro formula and the earnings-price ratio.

9.11 Create a fictitious profit and loss statement and use it to demonstrate that the "cash flow," namely, the internal supply of capital, equals the retained profits plus the depreciation.

9.12 A company has grouped all the demands from its plants for the coming year according to the prospective rates of return on the investments; for example, plants A,B,C, and D can invest a total of $320,000 at prospective rates of return from 50.0% to 54.9%. The complete demand schedule for all plants prepared by the corporate planning department is as follows:

Demand	Estimated rate of return (%)
$ 200,000	65 or more
220,000	60–65
260,000	55–60
320,000	50–55
400,000	45–50
500,000	40–45
620,000	35–40
760,000	30–35
920,000	25–30
1,110,000	20–25
1,300,000	15–20
1,550,000	10–15
1,790,000	5–10

The supply which the corporation can make available for the coming year is $5,000,000 at a cost of 12%. What minimum required rate of

return should be established with regard to next year's budget? What
suggestions can you make in regard to future budgets?

9.13 Prepare a laddered budget for a company that has the following proposals
for capital equipment for the coming year:

In Department A, a new planer costing $25,000 after installation is
expected to replace an existing planer. The savings indicate a 50% rate
of return. The old planer with a net realizable value of $10,000 will be
used to replace a still older machine which can be sold to a dealer for
$2,500. If displaced, no economic use can be found for the old machine.
The rate of return on this replacement is expected to be 25%.

In Department B, a conveyorized spray-booth costing $15,500 will re-
place individual paint stations. The expected rate of return is 30%. The
existing stations will be sold as junk for $1,500.

In Department C, an existing boring machine will be replaced by a new
one costing $30,000. The expected rate of return is 40%. The existing
machine which has a net realizable value of $6,000 will then represent
excess equipment but it is proposed that this excess capacity be employed
to attract additional contract work at a rate of return of 15%.

In Department D, a standby machine will be purchased second-hand
for $500 to replace an ancient machine which can be sold for $100. The
expected rate of return is 20%.

The company's cost of capital is 10% and it appears that a maximum
supply of $70,000 will be available.

9.14 A stock having a market value of $100 has just paid a $5.00 dividend.
What should be the dividend position of the shareholders *next* year if
(a) this dividend is 100% of the earnings; (b) this dividend is 50% of the
earnings per share and the retained earnings are invested in the company
at a rate of return not less than the current earnings-price ratio?

9.15 The following is a typical balance sheet of a certain manufacturing
company. In this company the opportunities for internal investment are
very great, but the supply of capital provided entirely by plowback funds
is grossly inadequate. As a result of capital shortage many excellent
opportunities will be rejected unless new funds are sought. The management rejects the idea of diluting ownership through an issue of new
equity and therefore proposes creating a large funded debt. The opportunities are presumed to be so great that any amount can be profitably
invested.

The present balance sheet is as follows:

Balance Sheet on December 31

Current assets	$500,000	Current liabilities	$225,000
		Funded debt	25,000
Fixed assets	250,000	Net worth	500,000
	$750,000		$750,000

If the amount of the loan will be set only by the limiting ratios suggested by R. A. Foulke, how much should be borrowed? Assume that
the entire amount of the loan will be used for fixed assets and that the

balances of the current assets, current liabilities, and net worth will not be altered as a result of acquiring the debt.

Discuss the dangers of oversimplification occurring from the use of the above rule of thumb. What are all the considerations that should limit the size of the proposed loan or the amount of investment in capital equipment?

9.16 Review the balance sheets of three corporations and decide how much their internal investments in capital equipment may be increased by the use of funded debt according to the limit inferred by R. A. Foulke. Discuss all the considerations that should be the basis of this decision.

10

Economic Life

10.1 EFFECT OF CHOOSING WRONG LIFE PERIOD

The life period must not be established by an arbitrary decree of management. This occurs when management selects a fixed payout period for all equipment as a substitute for a free and independent prediction of economic life by persons familiar with the equipment being analyzed. Selecting the wrong life period can be serious: it can reverse the conclusion and pick the wrong piece of equipment, as illustrated in the following example.

EXAMPLE 10.1a A manual operation costs $7,000 a year for labor. The hand tools used in the operation have negligible value. The job can be performed by a machine costing $10,000 with annual operating costs for labor. power, and maintenance of $4,000. Although a correct prediction would place the economic life at 10 years, the analyst must conform to a management decree of a 3-year recovery period for all equipment. Salvage is presumed to be zero. The minimum required rate of return is 10%. What is the loss to the company if the economic life is actually 10 years?

SOLUTION.

Machine
$$\overset{10{,}000}{\underset{0}{\vdash}} \quad \overset{D = 4{,}000}{\underset{10}{\quad\quad}}$$

Manual
$$\overset{D = 7{,}000}{\underset{0}{\vdash} \quad \underset{10}{\quad}}$$

10-year economic life:

$$
\begin{array}{ll}
& \quad\quad\quad\quad\quad 0.1628 \\
\text{AC machine:} & 10{,}000(A/P, .10, 10) + 4{,}000 = \$5{,}628 \\
\text{AC manual:} & \quad\quad\quad\quad\quad\quad\quad\quad\quad\quad = \underline{\ \ 7{,}000} \\
\text{Annual advantage of machine} & \quad\quad\quad\quad\quad\quad\quad = \$1{,}372
\end{array}
$$

Three-year economic life:

AC machine: $10,000(A/P, .10, 3) + 4,000 = \$8.021$

(note above: 0.4021 over the $(A/P, .10, 3)$ term)

AC manual: $= \underline{\ 7,000}$

Annual advantage of manual method $= \$1,021$

By using the incorrect 3-year life, the manual operation will be retained and the company will reject savings of $3,000 a year which they can purchase for $10,000. This loss of income will last until the manual operation is actually displaced, that is, until a machine appears which can be proved in over a 3-year capital recovery period. It is very unlikely that such a machine will appear within the next 10 years if it is logical to predict a 10-year life for today's machine. If we assume, then, that the replacement of the manual method will be deferred for 10 years, then how much has the company lost by erroneously rejecting this investment?

If the investment recovered only the 10% minimum required rate of return, the company has lost the interest on $10,000 after recovery of capital. For example, $10,000 invested today at 10% interest for 10 years would accumulate to $25,940, an enrichment of $15,940. However, in the given case we can invest $10,000 and receive, not 10% a year, but $3,000 a year. What we will have at the end of 10 years depends upon the interest rate at which we can reinvest the $3,000.[1] We can reinvest it at least at the minimum required rate of return, 10% in the present example, and we will have $3,000 (F/A, .10, 10) = \$47,811$, (note above the $(F/A, .10, 10)$ term: 15.937) an enrichment of $37,811 from the initial $10,000 investment. Using a different approach in the given case, we can observe that the company has rejected an opportunity equivalent to investing $10,000 at 27%, i.e., $(A/P, i, 10) = 0.3$, whence $i = 27\%$.

The *net* loss depends on the investment we make in lieu of this one. The rejection of this investment, and the similar rejection of good investments, reduces our stock of opportunities. Instead of saturating all our opportunities down through the cost of capital, we will have artificially erased some. This may well result in an insufficiency of opportunities or, if it does not, it may result in an investment in some of the less profitable ones.

Of course we can err on the other side, too, by adopting life periods that are too long. This error is not likely to arise from management decree, but it can very well occur if the analyst arbitrarily adopts accounting lives or ownership lives extending beyond the term of the economic life.

EXAMPLE 10.1b   A manual operation costs $2,400 a year. A machine which can be purchased for $10,000 has annual operating disbursements of $1,000. The analyst, unfamiliar with the concept of economic life, adopts the 20-year accounting life and 10% salvage. The economic life, if he had understood the nature of it, is 6 years with $4,500 salvage at that date. The minimum required

---

[1] The $3,000 savings is the cash flow—the supply available for investment.

rate of return is 10%. What is the loss to the company if the economic life of the machine is 6 years, not 20?

SOLUTION.

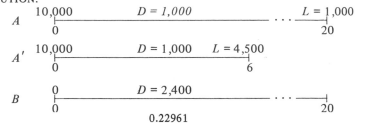

$$\text{AC of } A': \overset{0.22961}{(10,000 - 4,500)(A/P, .10, 6)} + (4,500)(0.10) + 1,000 = \$2,713$$

$$\text{AC of } A: \overset{0.11746}{(10,000 - 1,000)(A/P, .10, 20)} + (1,000)(0.10) + 1,000 = \$2,157$$

$$\text{AC of } B: \hspace{8cm} = \$2,400$$

Computed on the 6-year life, the machine is rejected; on a 20-year life, acceptance of the machine based on using the wrong life results in a loss to the company which can be expressed as in the last example. The investment of \$10,000 at the minimum required rate of return will accumulate to $\overset{1.772}{10,000(F/P, .10, 6)} = \$17,720$, but investment in this machine accumulates only to $\overset{7.716}{14,000(F/A, .10, 6)} + 4,500 = \$15,300$; or the investment in the machine recovers the \$10,000 with 6.1% rate of return instead of the minimum required rate of 10%.

Our object in this chapter, therefore, is to promote better prediction of the life of equipment. As an aid to this, we suggest creating basic classifications of equipments according to the factors that influence their life periods. The following five classifications have been suggested solely to assist the analyst in his predictions of economic life.

1. One-horse shay
2. Military aircraft
3. Like-for-like
4. Deterioration and obsolescence
5. Military aircraft with deterioration gradient

10.2 ONE-HORSE SHAY TYPE

The "wonderful one-hoss shay" conceived by Oliver Wendell Holmes is a reasonably accurate prototype of certain pieces of equipment. A careful examination of this class of equipment indicates that its life period is not the result of obsolescence or of reparable deterioration. Neither of these factors should figure in the determination of the economic life period of one-horse shay equipment.

Deterioration, of course, causes the demise of the equipment, but it is latent until the physical collapse of the equipment. This deterioration is not accompanied by any cost effects although we would expect to allow for the cost of normal maintenance and repair.

We can readily identify certain pieces of equipment which behave like the one-horse shay, such as electric light bulbs, fluorescent tubes, many cutting tools, and wooden telephone poles. We observe that the life of this class of equipment is purely and simply its physical life. In each case, however, we must be doubly assured that maintenance and repair will not contribute to the subsequent extension of the predicted life, although certain items of maintenance such as, for example, cleaning bulbs, uniform sharpening of tools, and routine painting, may well exist.

The life of this class of equipment can be determined with considerable accuracy by scientific observation of the mortality of identical equipment under identical conditions. This prediction, therefore, assumes the availability of statistical records.

Obsolescence must not be ruled out without careful consideration. In the modern world, obsolescence will lurk in the future of all one-horse shay types as a far more likely cause of retirement than physical destruction. The appearance of the automobile would more likely end the life of the shay long before it disintegrated. Electric bulbs can be terminated by fluorescent lighting. Cutting tools become obsolete by the endless appearance of new cutting methods or even by foundry methods that eliminate machining. Telephone transmission poles can be displaced by underground cables or microwave relaying. Only when these factors do not exist can the equipment be said to be the one-horse shay type.

For equipment to qualify as the one-horse shay type, maintenance and repair costs must not become relevant factors in determining the life period. If maintenance and repair increase with age, replacement may be dictated not by physical life but by mounting costs compared to a new asset. And as stated earlier, if maintenance and repair costs do exist they must have no effect on *prolonging* the life, either.

10.3 MILITARY AIRCRAFT TYPE

Military aircraft provide a model of the economic life of certain pieces of individual equipment. The life period of military aircraft, in wartime or peace, is established by sudden obsolescence. The event is produced by the sudden appearance of a superior model, possibly of enemy origin—in warfare, that makes all existing models obsolete and uneconomical for the intended purposes. We must observe that deterioration is not a factor, because the equipment may be as efficient or reliable the day it is displaced as the day it was placed in service.

This type of equipment meets its end as suddenly and, perchance, with as little warning as the one-horse shay type.[1] The event that conveys the death

---

[1]We do not wish to be misunderstood—the military aircraft is not shot down but merely displaced, intact even with all its polish and paint. If shot down, this is the end of its physical life—a one-horse shay situation.

blow does not appear gradually but all at once. The impending event therefore is not preceded by annual obsolescence (if it is, the life pattern falls into another classification, as we shall see). Just as the one-horse shay type encounters sudden and complete deterioration, the military aircraft type meets with sudden and complete obsolescence.

Many pieces of industrial equipment fall into this category. Wherever research and invention are stimulated, a new process or machine can appear almost overnight to replace equipment that in all respects can be termed brand new. New chemical processes, new metal working processes and machines, new textile materials can cause this sudden obsolescence.

Estimating economic life often relies on the past as a possible indication of the future. Past experience may provide some indication of how long it may be expected before the enemy will counter an advantage or how long before research and invention will again materially improve a certain process or machine. People close to these processes and with a knowledge of the forces at work to improve them should be called on to provide such forecasts.

The military aircraft type generally exists where this stimulation to make improvements is very strong, as in warfare or heavy competition. It is a prevalent type, and the insidious threat of a new and superseding invention being somewhere around the corner must be considered for all prospective equipment. Reasonably careful investigation should reveal whether this is likely.

10.4 LIKE-FOR-LIKE TYPE

Some pieces of equipment do not become obsolete during their life period but deterioration causes the annual costs of maintenance and repair to mount until the equipment must be replaced. Because obsolescence is essentially zero, replacement is made with like equipment. Equipment in this class can be designated as like-for-like.

Economic life for this class can be computed if past maintenance and repair records have been maintained and if they can be interpreted for use with the proposed equipment. A few companies have recorded this data and more companies can be expected to do so as research into operations continues.

The following example illustrates the computation of the economic life period of a piece of equipment from its prospective maintenance costs.

EXAMPLE 10.4 A proposed machine has a first cost of $1,000. Its operating disbursements, as predicted below, are rising as a result of increased maintenance and repair as well as lowered operating efficiency.

First year	$112
Second year	163
Third year	315
Fourth year	377
Fifth year	440
Sixth year	904

To simplify the illustration, salvage is presumed to be zero at the end of each life period. The minimum required rate of return is 10%. With no obsolescence and a like-for-like replacement, compute the economic life for the proposed machine.

SOLUTION.

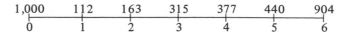

We compute the uniform annual costs for various life periods in a search for the period which gives the minimum annual cost. This period is the economic life because (a) rising costs signal the time for replacement with more economic equipment and (b) this replacement will not be made prior to reaching the period of least cost.

The computations are illustrated for a 3-year life period as follows:

$$AC_3 = 1{,}000 \overset{0.4021}{(A/P, .10, 3)} + [112 \overset{0.9091}{(P/F, 1)} + 163 \overset{0.8265}{(P/F, 2)} + 315 \overset{0.7513}{(P/F, 3)}] \overset{0.4021}{(A/P, 3)}$$
$$= \$592$$

The results are summarized in Table 10.4 and Fig. 10.4.

Because the uniform annual investment costs decrease with longer life and uniform annual operating disbursements increase as the equipment deteriorates with time, we can expect a minimum total cost at some life period. In Example 10.4 this occurs at a 5-year life.

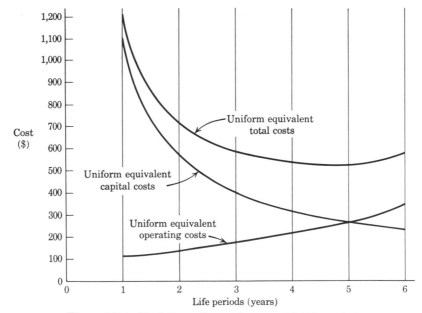

Figure 10.4   Variation of annual costs with life periods

Table 10.4 LIKE-FOR-LIKE REPLACEMENT: VARIATION OF UNIFORM
ANNUAL COSTS WITH LIFE PERIODS

Life (yr)	Capital recovery	Uniform equivalent operating disbursements	Total cost
0	$1,000	$ 0	$ ∞
1	1,100	112	1,212
2	576	136	712
3	402	190	592
4	315	231	546
5	264	265	529
6	230	348	578

10.5 PREDICTING A PATTERN OF DETERIORATION

It is more than likely that we do not have past statistics on which to base predictions of the rising disbursements and therefore we cannot make a precise mathematical analysis as in Example 10.4. In the absence of these statistics we may resort to reasonable approximations. One method is to assume a mathematical pattern. For example, we might believe that disbursements will increase by a constant sum each year, an increasing arithmetic series as in the following example.

EXAMPLE 10.5 A proposed machine has a first cost of $1,000. Next year's operating disbursements are expected to be $112. Operating disbursements will rise every year as a result of deterioration, and in the best judgment of the people concerned with the piece of equipment this rise is predicted to be $75 a year. The minimum required rate of return is 10%.

Table 10.5 ANNUAL DETERIORATION BY A GRADIENT

Life period (yr)	Uniform annual costs		
	Investment cost	Operating disbursement	Total AC
1	$1,100	$112	$1,212
2	576	148	724
3	402	182	584
4	315	216	531
5	264	248	512
6	230	279	509
7	205	309	514
8	187	337	524
9	174	365	539
10	163	392	555

SOLUTION. The stream of disbursements will be

$$
\begin{array}{ccccccc}
 & G & 2G & 3G & & (n-2)G & (n-1)G \\
1,000 & 112 & 112 & 112 & 112 \ \cdots & 112 & 112 \\
\hline
0 & 1 & 2 & 3 & 4 & n-1 & n
\end{array}
$$

In this case $G = 75$, and we may compute the annual cost by Eq. 3.16b. For example, at a 10-year life,
$$
AC_{10} = 1,000\underset{0.16275}{(A/P, .10, 10)} + 112 + 75\underset{3.73}{(A/G, 10)} = \$555.
$$

These costs are listed in Table 10.5. The low point establishes 6 years as the most economic life period. (Section 10.12 discusses a quick method for locating the economic life.)

10.6 PREDICTING A DETERIORATION GRADIENT

In the absence of detailed yearly records, in Section 10.5 we predicted a gradient increase in operating disbursements of $75 a year. Certainly this prediction, guided by the judgment of persons familiar with the equipment, would be based on past records as far as they were available.

An interesting guide to the prediction of a deterioration gradient can be observed from the following illustration of an old piece of equipment which has presently reached its fourth year of life.

$$
\begin{array}{cccccc}
\text{Present} & 0 & 112 & 163 & 315 & 377 & 440 \\
\hline
\text{machine} & 4 & 3 & 2 & 1 & 0 &
\end{array}
$$

The predicted operating disbursement for the forthcoming year is $440, whereas the predicted operating disbursement for a proposed new machine, otherwise duplicating the present machine, is $112. Inasmuch as the new machine and the old machine when new cost $112 to operate the first year, there is no obsolescence, and the difference between next year's disbursements of $440 for the present machine and $112 for a similar new machine will be solely the accumulation of deterioration over a 4-year period (not 5 years, because the cost of deterioration does not occur until the second year). With no information other than the age of the machine and a prediction of next year's operating costs, we can observe that the total deterioration was $328 over four years—or an arithmetic gradient of $82 if we assume an arithmetic pattern of deterioration. If our considered judgment predicts a future gradient of $75, we can proceed with the solution as in Example 10.5.

This approach indicates the deterioration which a machine has accumulated over its life to date, providing that none of the superiority of the proposed machine is the result of obsolescence. Of course, this gives us no basis for predicting the *pattern* of accumulation; for that we require additional evidence. The question is, can we predict a reasonable pattern? Of one thing we seem certain, however: the costs of deterioration will rise. In many cases, too, we can anticipate unusual costs in certain years for overhaul or major repair.

In the complete absence of data, that is, in most cases, the analyst tries to predict the economic life itself instead of the gradient or the pattern of deterioration. The reason is that he feels more competent to predict the life period than the rise in disbursements. In most cases, therefore, the analyst disregards the increase in costs in computing the uniform annual cost. This, of course, will result in a lower cost than the true cost and will improperly favor the installation of the equipment computed in this manner.

We will see later that it is not necessary to disregard completely the effects of rising costs during the lifetime of the equipment.

10.7 FACTORS DETERMINING DETERIORATION

Deterioration may be defined as the lowering of the engineering efficiency of equipment compared to that existing when the equipment was new.

Disbursements will increase from the following aspects of deterioration:

1. Increased fuel and power caused by lower machine efficiency.
2. Increased maintenance and repair due to failure of parts.
3. Increased labor idle-time due to increased frequency of breakdowns.
4. Increased spoilage and increased labor and material wastage due to unreliability.
5. Increased labor due to reduced speed and lower productivity.
6. Increased inspection costs due to loss of reliability.
7. Loss of revenue from returned sales or higher sales expense if product is inferior.
8. Increased overhead due to unreliable equipment.

10.8 FACTORS DETERMINING OBSOLESCENCE

Obsolescence may be defined as the lowering of the engineering efficiency of equipment when new, compared to the best engineering efficiency currently available. The machine's obsolescence is established by comparing its operating cost when new with the operating cost of the latest model. We should observe that this is a prediction of technological inferiority, not deterioration, and therefore as we would expect, the comparison is between *new* machines. Deterioration, we note, has no part in the accumulated inferiority caused by obsolescence.

Obsolescence of a machine results in costs relative to the best machine available each year. The following items illustrate some cost differences resulting from technological inferiority in design.

1. Higher fuel and power consumption because of lower design efficiency.
2. Lower productivity because of lower productive speeds.
3. Higher maintenance and repair due to inferior design planning.

4. More breakdowns from design weaknesses.
5. Less reliability because of poorer design calculations.
6. Greater spoilage from less accurate design.
7. More labor and supervision because design is not as highly automated.
8. More floor space from less compact design.

Obsolescence is not entirely a one-way street; for example, a more automatic design may greatly reduce labor, supervision, spoilage, and floor space, but may increase fuel, power, inspection, maintenance, and repair. The combined effect of the technological improvement, however, is to reduce the total operating disbursements.

10.9 DETERIORATION AND OBSOLESCENCE TYPE

The economic life of many pieces of equipment is fashioned by the combined forces of deterioration and obsolescence; eventually this accumulation of inferiority will signal that replacement by improved equipment is an economic necessity.

A machine tool is a typical example of this type of equipment; the factors of deterioration and obsolescence listed in the two previous sections are obviously present.   As a result of progressive deterioration and obsolescence a year will be reached in the life of the machine tool when the improved machine of the moment will have sufficient economic advantage to displace the installed machine.

In this class of equipment, the operating disbursements rise with age as a result of deterioration, but in addition to this the equipment becomes more obsolete by the steady emergence of improved machines.   Such equipment experiences progressive deterioration and obsolescence. In predicting the date of displacement the analyst therefore tries to be guided by his opinion of the rate at which technological improvements are being brought forth in new equipment and by his opinion of the rise in operating costs as a result of deterioration.

In spite of the fact that this sounds like an impossible prediction, analysts generally feel that they have a reasonable opinion of the economic life period and are not stopped by the prospect of having to predict it.

10.10 OBSOLESCENCE AND DETERIORATION AS AN ANNUAL COST

In Sections 10.4 and 10.5 we computed the annual cost including the rising disbursements resulting from deterioration.   However, to include obsolescence in the cost equation is entirely another matter and one of some complexity. Obsolescence as a cost depends on the existence of unequal life periods and therefore arises almost exclusively in a "replacement" situation. Consequently, this is somewhat less than a general case but we present it now as it does contribute to a better understanding of economic life.

It is probably apparent that if the two alternatives which we are comparing have the same economic life the cost of obsolescence is irrelevant. We will see from a comparison of time scales that obsolescence becomes relevant only under a deferred investment situation.

A way of dealing with this class of equipment is through the prediction of a deterioration and obsolescence pattern which will account for annual increases in deterioration and obsolescence. In the following illustration, the pattern is assumed to be an increasing arithmetic series like the one in Section 10.5.

EXAMPLE 10.10 A proposed machine costs P dollars (we propose to use a symbol for first cost for the time being) and its operating disbursement for the coming year is $5,000. The annual cost of operating is presumed to rise $20 every year as a result of deterioration. Let us also presume that new machines are brought out annually which have operating disbursements $30 less than the machine the year before and that these new machines also deteriorate by a gradient of $20 a year. Assume that all new machines have the same first cost P and that all salvage values are zero whenever the machine will be retired. Let us also assume (until we can prove that it should be something else) that the economic life of all new machines is 4 years. The cost pattern for the proposed machine and its successors will therefore be

```
                    P                          P
                    +                          +
           20   40   60            20   40   60
  P        +    +    +             +    +    +
    5,000 5,000 5,000 5,000 4,880 4,880 4,880 4,880 4,760
   +----+----+----+----+----+----+----+----+----  ... ----> ∞
   0    1    2    3    4    5    6    7    8    9
```

Inasmuch as a new machine appears annually with operating disbursements $30 lower than the one the year before, the machine installed 4 years hence will be $4 \times 30 = 120$ better than the proposed machines, as noted on the time scale. This shows the effect of obsolescence relative to the operating disbursements of successive machines; but note that obsolescence does not yet show up on the cost of the proposed machine. Its gradient is solely the result of deterioration.

Obsolescence only appears as a comparative cost, and so we must compare the above time scale with an alternative. Let us assume that the alternative to the proposed machine is a manual process having a labor cost of $9,000 a year with zero first cost. The minimum required rate of return is 10%. Now let's ask this question: "Should we install the proposed machine now or defer it one year?"

SOLUTION. The two alternatives can now be shown on the time scales:

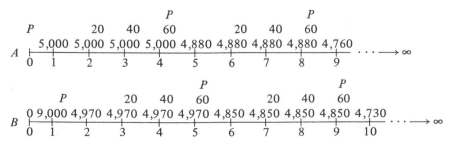

Note that the advantage of deferring the machine operation one year is to get a technologically improved machine, namely, next year's machine, which is $30 better than the present machine when it was new. This advantage lasts for 3 years, at which time the proposed machine will be replaced with the best machine then available; but, the year after, the advantage reverts to the deferred investment plan for another 3 years. This is shown by subtracting the two time scales (except for the first year's operating disbursements):

$$
\begin{array}{c}
\quad P \;\; -P \qquad\qquad P \quad -P \qquad\qquad P \quad -P \\
\quad\;\; 50 \;\; 50 \;\; 50 \;\; -150 \;\; 50 \;\; 50 \;\; 50 \;\; -150 \;\; 50 \\
A - B \;\; \vdash\!\!-\!\!+\!\!-\!\!+\!\!-\!\!+\!\!-\!\!+\!\!-\!\!+\!\!-\!\!+\!\!-\!\!+\!\!-\!\!+\!\!-\!\!+\!\!-\!\cdots\longrightarrow \infty \\
\quad\;\; 0 \;\;\; 1 \;\;\; 2 \;\;\; 3 \;\;\; 4 \;\;\; 5 \;\;\; 6 \;\;\; 7 \;\;\; 8 \;\;\; 9 \;\;\; 10
\end{array}
$$

This can be rewritten:

$$
\begin{array}{c}
\qquad\qquad\qquad\qquad P \quad -P \qquad\qquad\qquad P \quad -P \\
\qquad\qquad\qquad\qquad\quad\; -200 \qquad\qquad\qquad -200 \\
\quad P \;\; -P \\
\quad\;\; 50 \;\; 50 \;\; 50 \quad 50 \quad 50 \;\; 50 \;\; 50 \quad 50 \quad 50 \\
A - B \;\; \vdash\!\!-\!\!+\!\!-\!\!+\!\!-\!\!+\!\!-\!\!+\!\!-\!\!+\!\!-\!\!+\!\!-\!\!+\!\!-\!\!+\!\!-\!\!+\!\!-\!\cdots\longrightarrow \infty \\
\quad\;\; 0 \;\;\; 1 \;\;\; 2 \;\;\; 3 \;\;\; 4 \;\;\; 5 \;\;\; 6 \;\;\; 7 \;\;\; 8 \;\;\; 9 \;\;\; 10
\end{array}
$$

If we exclude the $4,000 savings at the end of year 1, the present worth of the foregoing stream is the cost of today's machine plus the disadvantage of installing it now instead of deferring the installation to get at the better machine. Let us compute this present worth at Point 1 in time so that we may compare it directly with the $4,000 savings which also occurs at that time. The present worth at year 1, excluding the $4,000 savings, is

PW of $A - B$ at year 1:

$$
PW_1 = P(1 + i) - P + [P(1 + i) - P]\left[\frac{A/F,\, i,\, 4}{i}\right] + \frac{50}{i} - \frac{200}{i} \; (A/P, 4)
$$

$$
= P[i + (A/F, 4)] + \frac{50}{i} - \frac{200}{i} \; (A/P, 4)
$$

$$
= P(A/P,\, i,\, 4) + \frac{50}{i} - \frac{200}{i} \; (A/F, 4) \tag{10.10a}
$$

In the above equation, $50 is the gradient resulting from deterioration of $20 a year plus obsolescence of $30 a year, which we may call the deterioration and obsolescence gradient.

We also discover that the $200 in this equation equals nG, where n is 4, the economic life we selected, and G is $50, the deterioration and obsolescence gradient.

We also note that the first term in Eq. 10.10a is the investment cost of the proposed machine, that the second term is the cost of infinity of installing now instead of deferring the installation one year, and that the third term is the saving in the year following each replacement of the proposed machine.

Rewriting Eq. 10.10a in general terms,

$$\text{PW of } A - B \text{ at year 1: } P(A/P, i, n) + \frac{G}{i} - \frac{nG}{i} (A/F, n) \qquad (10.10b)[1]$$

Equation 10.10a is now in its general form for any value of economic life n. In other words, had we selected any economic life n instead of 4 years, we would have derived Eq. 10.10b.

The next step is to recognize that Eq. 10.10b, as a mathematical expression, must have a minimum for some value of n. If the first cost P of the machine had been \$1,000, the present worth at year 1 will be

$$\text{PW}_1 = 1,000(A/P, .10, n) + \frac{50}{0.10} - \frac{n50}{0.10} (A/F, n)$$

which by successive trials n (not shown here) gives a minimum at 7 years.

The PW of $A - B$ does not include the first year's operating disbursements, which we purposely omitted to simplify the explanation. The time scale values that were omitted were

so the complete PW of $A - B$ at year 1 is

$$\text{PW}_1 = 1,000 \overset{0.2054}{(A/P, .10, 7)} + \frac{50}{0.10} - \left(\frac{7 \times 50}{0.10}\right) \overset{0.1054}{(A/F, 7)} + 5,000 - 9,000$$

$$= -\$3,664$$

This is the advantage of A (because negative values represent incomes), and it means that the extra investment in A is recovered with 10% interest plus \$3,664 at the end of 1 year.

Observe that 7 is the life period that gives the lowest comparative cost, and this is the economic life of the proposed machine, not 4 years.

We may observe, too, that when we considered a 1-year deferment, the concept of a deterioration and obsolescence gradient arose. However, if the deferment period equals the economic-life period of the proposed equipment, the only gradient is the \$20 deterioration gradient, that is, no obsolescence gradient appears.

Although the problem is illustrated by the consideration of only a 1-year

---

[1] The student should note the PW_1 is the difference of A and B—the same result as computing the present worths of A and B separately and subtracting. The comparative cost is the same either way, although the former method works with the combined gradient, \$50, and the latter uses two, \$20 and \$30. Both methods give the same minimum for various values of n.

deferment, the same type of analysis can be applied to a longer deferment. Several problems are presented in the homework section to cover these situations. However, a 1-year deferment is usually the most applicable situation.

In view of the fact that B has only a 1-year life, we may find more reason to express the 1-year advantage of $3,664 computed in Example 10.10 as the conclusion reached by an annual-cost instead of a present-worth evaluation. In general we find it easier to do so. The next section is aimed at developing an approach from the standpoint of *comparative annual costs* which is simple to understand and to compute.

10.11 A COMPARATIVE-COST MODEL FOR THE DETERIORATION AND OBSOLESCENCE TYPE

The differences, $A - B$, between the alternatives in the problem presented in Section 10.10 are summarized on the time scale as follows:

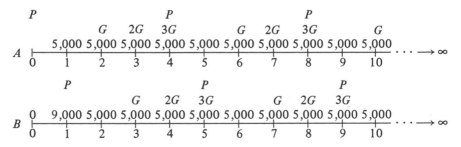

The term G is the deterioration and obsolescence gradient; n is the economic life which, to simplify the illustration, is shown on the time scale as 4 years; P is the first cost of the proposed machine and its successors as well as the deferred machine and its successors; and minus $4,000 is the next year's advantage of today's machine over the manual process.

We can see that an equivalent difference would result if alternatives A and B had been represented on time scales as follows:

We must remember that the above representations are only *comparative* costs, not the true annual costs, but in comparison they give the same differences and the same conclusions as if we had used the true costs.

Realize that the comparative cost of the proposed machine differs from the actual cost disbursement in several respects. In the first place, the actual cost disbursements do not include obsolescence. (The actual disbursements, illustrated in the first time scale in Section 10.10, consists only of disbursements for deterioration.) Secondly, all future machines have lower operating dis-

bursements as a result of technological improvements, whereas the comparative cost shows all future machines to be alike. Why, then, use this model
of comparative cost? Because, for one thing, it permits us to better visualize
the effect of a deterioration and obsolescence gradient, and secondly—and
most important of all--the mathematical comparison is made much easier
as follows:

$$AC_A = P(A/P, n) + 5,000 + G(A/G, n) \tag{10.11}$$

$$AC_B = 9,000$$

As shown on the time scale, after one year the uniform equivalent annual
costs of the alternatives will be the same. The equivalent annual cost difference
therefore exists only at year 1 and thus, using the data in Example 10.10, equals

$$AC_A = 1,000 \overset{0.2054}{(A/P, .10, 7)} + 5,000 + 50 \overset{2.62}{(A/G, 7)} = \$5,336$$
$$AC_B \qquad\qquad\qquad\qquad\qquad\qquad\qquad\qquad = \underline{\quad 9,000}$$
$$\text{Advantage of } A \text{ at end of year 1} \qquad\qquad = \$3,664$$

We note that this is the entire difference arrived at more laboriously in
Section 10.10.

We should note, in passing, that had there been no gradient, the comparison,
based on the assumption of a 1-year deferment of the extra investment and
a 7-year economic life, would be

$$AC_A = 1,000 \overset{0.2054}{(A/P, .10, 7)} + 5,000 = \$5,205$$
$$AC_B = \text{for a 1 year life} \qquad\qquad = \underline{\quad 9,000}$$
$$\text{Advantage of } A \text{ at end of year 1} \quad = \$3,795$$

Now the advantage of installing the machine is $3,795, whereas the correct
advantage after allowing for the effects of deterioration and obsolescence was
$3,664—a difference of $131. The advantage of $3,795 is also only a 1-year
advantage—occurring at the end of the next year.

10.12 DIFFERENTIATING THE ANNUAL-COST MODEL

Before passing from this model (Eq. 10.11) we should note that the economic
life is the year at which the low point of the cost curve occurs. Therefore by
differentiating Eq. 10.11 with respect to n, equating to zero, and simplifying,
the economic life n can be determined:

$$n \cong \frac{Pi}{G} + \frac{1}{i} - \frac{(P/F, n)}{i} \tag{10.12a}$$

Assuming we have predicted G, we can solve for n by trial and error. This requires but little effort if we observe that n must be less than the first two terms on the right-hand side of the equation. Obviously, this is much easier than constructing Table 10.5.

Interestingly enough, the same result as in Eq. 10.12 can be obtained from a different concept. This concept derives from the MAPI[1] technique explained in Chapter 17. The MAPI method formulates the fact that the equipment will be replaced when the next year's cost will exceed the uniform equivalent annual cost of the prospective replacement. Thus, if we stand at point "n" in time, next year's cost will be $D + nG$, assuming for simplicity that the salvage values at this age of the equipment will be zero. The comparative uniform annual cost of the replacement will be

$$P(A/P, n) + D + \frac{G}{i} - \frac{nG}{i} (A/F, n)$$

Although the next year's cost, $D + nG$, will be greater than this, the two costs approach each other as a limit at which point we may write

$$P(A/P, n) + D + \frac{G}{i} - \frac{nG}{i} (A/F, n) = D + nG \qquad (10.12b)$$

By solving for n we get

$$n \cong \left[\frac{P}{G} (A/P, n) + \frac{1}{i} \right] \div \left[1 + \frac{(A/F, n)}{i} \right]$$

which will simplify into Eq. 10.12a

Inasmuch as our purpose in this chapter is to discuss economic life, we reserve discussion which might lead into the MAPI method for Chapter 17.

We should point out before leaving the topic that if the analyst chooses to predict the life n, namely, to predict the year at which the low point on the annual cost curve will occur, he can solve for the gradient that produces that curve. Now with values for n and G, and for a given i, he can compute the comparative uniform equivalent annual cost. This is a basis for development of the MAPI formula.

10.13 ESTIMATING A DETERIORATION AND OBSOLESCENCE GRADIENT

Outside of the MAPI method, gradients have not found much application in industry; yet as we can see in Section 10.6 their prediction seems reasonable. However, there is no doubt that much more research is needed in this area of the subject.

As we have observed, the alternative to predicting a gradient is to assume it is zero. This lowers the uniform annual cost and favors the installation of

[1]George Terborgh, *Business Equipment Policy* (Washington, D.C.: Machinery and Allied Products Institute, 1958).

the new equipment, whereas predicting a gradient for new equipment favors the retention of the existing equipment. We shall observe more about this in the subsequent chapter on replacement analysis.

The following example serves to suggest one approach to the prediction of a gradient.

EXAMPLE 10.13 A machine purchased 10 years ago will require operating disbursements during the coming year of $7,320. If sold at once it would bring a net price of $1,000, and if sold next year, $800. A new machine to perform the same function will cost $10,000 and its first year's operating disbursements will be $4,000. Its salvage at any time is assumed (for simplicity) to be 20% of the first cost. The only question we propose to ask at this time is, "Should the present machine be kept for 1 more year?" (Note this is equivalent to saying, should we install the new machine now or defer the installation for one year?) The minimum required rate of return is 10% and the investment value P of the present machine is zero.

SOLUTION. Before we solve this example let us reproduce the first time scale in Section 10.10.

```
P                           P
           20    40    60        20    40
       5,000 5,000 5,000 5,000 4,880 4,880 4,880
   ├─────┼─────┼─────┼─────┼─────┼─────┼─────     · · · ───→ ∞
   0     1     2     3     4     5     6     7
```

In that problem the gradient was $50, consisting of $20 for deterioration and $30 for obsolescence. Now if we had been standing in time at year 4, the old machine, if continued for another year, would cost $5,000 + 80 = $5,080, and the new machine would cost $4,880 for the coming year. Therefore, in 5 years of life the old machine will have accumulated $200 inferiority. If we assume this occurred by an arithmetic series, then, because the inferiority in any year of life is the gradient times the age of the equipment minus one, we can write

$$(t - 1)G = 200$$

where $t = 5$ years, so that

$$G = \$50$$

Since we need to know only the next year's disbursements for both machines to establish the inferiority of the old machine relative to the newest machine currently available, we can estimate a gradient in Example 10.13. The inferiority is $7,320 - 4,000 = $3,320, which will be accumulated over 11 years, so from $(t - 1)G = \$3,320$, G is $332 a year based on the assumption of an arithmetic series.

This, of course, is the gradient of the old machine and, subject to the considerations expressed in Section 10.6, must be projected into the future. Will technology improve at a different rate or by a different pattern in the future?

Will deterioration in the future be the same as in the past? In the present example let us assume the analyst feels that history will repeat itself and he predicts an arithmetic gradient of $332.

The comparative annual cost for the new machine computed by Eq. 10.11 is

$$AC = (P - L)(A/P, .10, n) + Li + G(A/G, n) + D$$

$$= (10,000 - 2,000)(A/P, .10, n) + 2,000i + 332(A/G, n) + 4,000$$

The annual cost is computed for various lives (the shortcut suggested by Eq. 10.12a indicates that the economic life occurs at about 8 years), and the results are given in Table 10.13 and Fig. 10.13. As noted in the table, the

Table 10.13 UNIFORM ANNUAL COSTS WITH A DETERIORATION AND OBSOLESCENCE GRADIENT

Life period n (yr)	Capital recovery	First year's disbursement, D	Deterioration and obsolescence, G(A/G, i, n)	Total uniform equivalent cost
5	$2,310	$4,000	$ 600	$6,910
6	2,035	4,000	740	6,775
7	1,845	4,000	870	6,715
8	1,700	4,000	1,000	6,700
9	1,590	4,000	1,120	6,710
10	1,500	4,000	1,240	6,740

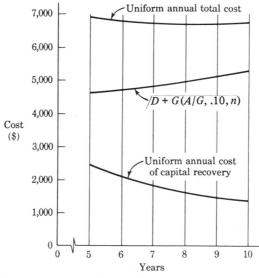

Figure 10.13   Annual cost with deterioration and obsolescence gradient

minimum point in the annual-cost equation occurs at year 8. This is the economic life of the equipment for the simple reason that it is cheaper to keep it 8 years than for 7 or 9 or any other number of years.

The annual cost of the present machine is

$$AC = (10,000 - 8,000)(A/P, .10, 1) + (800)(0.10) + 7,320 = \$7,620$$

Now let us compare the uniform equivalent cost of the proposed machine with the plan to defer installation one year:

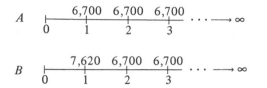

The difference of $920 at year 1 favors the installation of a new machine A, now.

10.14 MILITARY AIRCRAFT TYPE WITH DETERIORATION GRADIENT

We have examined at one extreme the military aircraft type in which a sudden stroke of obsolescence ends the life of equipment almost overnight and, at the other, the like-for-like type in which deterioration whittles away at the life of the equipment until the accumulated deterioration makes replacement economically essential.

Conceivably, we can have a combination of these types: equipment which deteriorates annually, by some gradient perhaps, but, before these effects accumulate sufficiently to terminate its life, it succumbs to the sudden appearance of a greatly improved machine. This certainly is a deterioration and obsolescence type, but unlike the type in the last three sections the obsolescence is not annual but at much longer periods.

This requires the prediction of the appearance of the superseding machine, as in the military aircraft situation, and the prediction of the pattern of rising costs with age, as in the like-for-like type.

EXAMPLE 10.14 A proposed machine which will cost $2,000 is expected to last 8 years before displacement by the appearance of a superior machine. The salvage at that date is predicted to be $350. The annual operating disbursements will be $500 and an arithmetic gradient of $50 is predicted for deterioration. At present the company is employing a manual process with disbursements of $800 a year. If not displaced by the proposed machine, the manual process will have nothing to challenge it for the next 8 years when the next machine is predicted. The minimum required rate of return is 10%.

SOLUTION.

$$L = 350$$

$$AC_A = (2,000 - 350)(A/P, .10, 8) + 350(0.10) + 50(A/G, .10, 8)$$

$$+ 500 = \$994$$

$$AC_B \qquad\qquad\qquad\qquad\qquad = \$800$$

Advantage of *B:* $194

A test of various lives shows that the optimum life for deterioration alone would have been 10 or 11 years except for the predicted appearance of the superior machine at year 8.

This method has the advantage of permitting the analyst to predict the life of the equipment which will be terminated by sudden obsolescence and yet allow for predictions of rising costs. The method envisages another equipment classification resulting from combined obsolescence and deterioration.

10.15 FUNCTIONAL DEGRADATION

At this point we are going to take an academic look at a machine over its entire useful life from the day it is installed until it is retired. During this period machines are, in many cases, functionally downgraded from prime service and so on, over a succession of degraded positions ending with eventual liquidation. Every utility company can illustrate the historical degradation of a generator from operation on base load through several stages of peak load service, to its final use on standby duty. Metalworking companies can illustrate the degradation of a machine tool from main line production, through secondary and then occasional service, until it winds up as a standby. In these cases we note that the new equipment performs on prime service until another machine is purchased to replace it. In turn, an economic contest for second place will occur in which it will displace the equipment in that post. As a rule, equipment displaced from prime service seldom fails to win a post on degraded service because history shows that, for most machines, the period of ownership or useful life is in excess of the prime service life.

As a general rule, too, when equipment is degraded its utilization is less. If utilization did not diminish, or if it increased, the post would be filled by modern prime-service equipment. As a rule, therefore, equipment gives less service over the course of downgrading, and as a rule the operating disbursements decrease with lessened utilization. In other words, the pattern is "declining costs with declining service."

For the case we are discussing, the useful life will be a series of economic lives each representing functional degradation and each having a lower cost plateau. It is also more than likely that the costs over the period of each job assignment will rise with age.

At the beginning of each service period the net realizable value of the equipment is the investment tied up in it if we continue the use of the equipment. This is also the salvage value of the equipment when displaced from higher service. These values are not theoretical computations of worth to the owner but are predictions of actual values in the open market at the time. If a market value is low compared to the service obtained by the user, the equipment can show a high rate of return, and vice versa. This, of course, is the essence of all analyses: the comparison of the extra investment with the savings it causes.

The problems of prediction probably are insurmountable when we attempt prediction of services beyond the prime service. When forecasting the costs on prime service we know all the guiding forces: we know the intended service, we can describe each alternative, and we can visualize the required utilization to perform the job. But on subsequent services, can we even begin to predict what the services will be, or describe the alternatives, or estimate the degree of utilization, or establish the net realizable values of the alternatives, or even guess the length of each service?

We will temporarily cast aside these insurmountable difficulties for some academic crystal gazing and we will presuppose that one could forsee the entire life of the equipment. The easiest way to present this panorama on time scales, where identification of future contenders is unknown, is to show the predicted *difference* between the proposed equipment and the machines it displaces as in the following example.

EXAMPLE 10.15 The extra investment to install the most modern equipment is $10,000 and the annual savings will be $3,000 for an estimated 6-year economic life. At the end of this period, the equipment will be displaced but will win a post on second-line service. Its extra investment over the equipment which had been performing that second-line function is $3,000 and its saving, $1,500. At the end of 6 years, it will be displaced but will win a post in third-line duty. Its extra investment over the third-line equipment used to that date is $1,000 and the saving is $750. At the end of 18 years the machine is retired with no salvage value. Compare returns from this equipment on each of its services.

SOLUTION.

(P)		(P)		(P)		
10,000	$I = 3,000$	3,000	$I = 1,500$	1,000	$I = 750$	
0		6		12		18

Compute the rate of return on prime service:

$$(10,000 - 3,000)(A/P, 6) + 3,000i = 3,000$$

Try $i = 20\%$.

$$\text{Cost} < \text{Income by } \$295/\text{yr}$$

Try $i = 25\%$.

$$\text{Cost} > \text{Income by } \$122/\text{yr}$$

$$i = 20 + \left(\frac{295}{417}\right)(5) = 23.5\%$$

Compute the rate of return on the first degraded service:

$$(3,000 - 1,000)(A/P, 6) + 1,000i = 1,500$$

Try $i = 40\%$.

$$\text{Cost} < \text{Income by } \$177/\text{yr}$$

Try $i = 50\%$.

$$\text{Cost} > \text{Income by } \$96/\text{yr}$$

$$i = 40 + \left(\frac{177}{273}\right)(10) = 46.5\%$$

Compute the rate of return on the second degraded service:

$$1,000(A/P, 6) = 750$$

$$(A/P, 6) = 0.750$$

$$i = 75\%$$

The rates of return for the three services are 23.5%, 46.5%, and 75%, respectively. The example illustrates, as we would expect, that the rate of return on each service is different and that it can be higher on degraded service even though the utilization is less.

The lifetime rate of return, namely, computing the rate of return on the initial extra investment from the lifetime savings, as we might expect, will show a return higher than 23.5% but lower than 75%. But we are not required for any reason to compute the lifetime return; it is not necessary to combine into one answer all the economic contests the equipment will win on each service. It is not necessary to fight these contests in advance; these can be analyzed and decided on the threshold of employing the equipment for degraded service. We need only to decide the contest for the prime service now.[1]

[1]We should mention that MAPI has suggested that, by using their predicted cost pattern (called Variant B) over the useful life of the machine, the annual cost can be computed over the useful life regardless of functional degradation. The discussion of Variant B is given in Terborgh, *Business Investment Policy*.

Even if our crystal gazing made it possible to predict these degraded functions, to compute the composite rate of return would be the equivalent of weighting the return on a particular service by the returns (whether plus or minus) on subsequent services. Obviously, we should not purchase uneconomical equipment for prime service on the basis of its value on degraded service.[1]

10.16 1-YEAR LIFE

In previous sections we have considered a one-year deferment of the extra investment. This is equivalent to using a 1-year life for one of the alternatives. Now we ask ourself, "Might there be an advantage to using a 1-year life for both alternatives?"

Using a 1-year life reduces predictions to almost a certainty—if we may call predictions of costs and salvage values 1 year away reasonably certain. It eliminates predictions of the economic life period as well as the salvage value in the dark uncertain future.

On the other hand, the use of a 1-year life introduces inaccuracies of its own which, unless it is used with great understanding, rule it out as a method of analysis for new equipment. Conversely, the use of a 1-year analysis for old or used equipment is often correct.

If we examine the equation of annual cost computed over the economic life of a new piece of equipment we make these observations:

1. It must be a minimum over the economic life period compared to any other period.
2. The uniform annual investment cost decreases as the investment is spread over a longer period.
3. The annual operating disbursements are constant for some classes of equipment or increase over the life period with other classes. They do not decrease.

If we are analyzing a used piece of equipment whose investment cost, because of its age, is insignificant, we can see from the above that the next year of operation will give the lowest cost. Even if the present purchase price of the old equipment is not zero, it is bound to be much lower than a new piece of equipment, and if at the same time its operating disbursements are greatly increasing—more than the small investment costs are decreasing—a 1-year life will again give the minimum annual-cost point.

The reverse is true of new equipment. In the first few years of life the investment cost is dropping and the operating cost is increasing only slightly or not at all, depending on the class of equipment, so the annual cost over a 1-year life will be higher than over a longer life period. To use a 1-year period of analysis

---

[1] It would be equally wrong to assume that the savings on the prime service extend over the center service life of the equipment. This would give an inflated rate of return (about 30% instead of 23.5% in the present case).

for the new equipment would therefore be inaccurate and it would tend to prevent the installation of new equipment.

In fact, sometimes the first or the first few years' costs are exceptionally high as a result of testing and adjustment, the inefficient use of the equipment during the learning period, extra spoilage of material, and so on. Furthermore, the first few years' utilization may be below the anticipated capacity (i.e., will all the expected work be assigned to the new machine?). These costs will even further prevent the installation of new equipment using a 1-year analysis compared to analysis over the full economic life period.

The following example is given to illustrate a 1-year analysis period.

EXAMPLE 10.16 A new machine costing $10,000 is predicted to have a salvage value of $9,095 at the end of next year and to have a 20-year *useful* life with 15% salvage when it is retired at that date. It is also believed reasonable to assume that salvage values will decrease by a constant percentage. The first year's operating disbursements will be $6,000 and a deterioration gradient of $135 is predicted. Like-for-like replacement is anticipated.

A used machine can be acquired for $1,000. Operating disbursements for the coming year are predicted to be $8,000 and thereafter to increase $175 a year. Salvage value for next year is expected to be $930, for the year after that $870, and the following year $810. The minimum required rate of return is 10%. Compare the conclusion suggested by an analysis over the economic life with that over a 1-year life.

SOLUTION. The objective is to compare the annual cost of the new machine for a 1-year life with the minimum annual cost corresponding to the economic life period.

It was assumed that the salvage values for future years decline by a constant percentage over 20 years, at the end of which time the final salvage is 15%. If salvage values decline by a constant percentage, the ratio of the salvage value in adjacent years will be constant. If x is the constant salvage ratio and s is the ratio of salvage at year n to the first cost, then $x^n = s$, so $x = (0.15)^{0.05} = 0.9095$. In the given problem, annual salvage values computed from this ratio are listed in Table 10.16a. (Note that the analyst's prediction of a first-year's salvage of $9,095 purposely corresponds—for the simplicity of our example—with that computed by the salvage ratio.) This table shows that the annual cost over a 1-year life, $7,905, is higher than the annual cost over the 5-year economic life, $7,862. We can also see that if the equipment had been the military aircraft type with no gradient and if the economic life had been predicted to be 7 years, the annual cost, $1,511 + 6,000 = $7,511, would also be lower than the annual cost over the 1-year period.

Now let us consider the old machine. We see in Table 10.16b that the old equipment has its minimum annual cost in the first year, and a 1-year analysis happens to be correct because the economic life as 1 year—a situation likely to be true of old equipment but very unlikely for new.

An important observation should be made: even with a 1-year analysis

Table 10.16a NEW MACHINE: UNIFORM ANNUAL COSTS FOR VARIOUS LIFE
PERIODS

Year	Salvage	Capital recovery	First year's disbursement	G(A/G, i, n)	Total AC
1	$9,095	$1,905	$6,000	$ 0	$7,905
2	8,272	1,824	6,000	64	7,888
3	7,523	1,748	6,000	126	7,874
4	6,842	1,680	6,000	186	7,866
5	6,223	1,618	6,000	244	7,862
6	5,660	1,562	6,000	300	7,862
7	5,148	1,511	6,000	354	7,865
8	4,682	1,464	6,000	406	7,870
9	4,258	1,422	6,000	455	7,877
10	3,873	1,383	6,000	503	7,886

Table 10.16b OLD MACHINE: UNIFORM ANNUAL COSTS FOR VARIOUS LIFE
PERIODS

Year	Salvage	Capital recovery	First year's disbursement	G(A/G, i, n)	Total AC
1	$930	$170	$8,000	$ 0	$8,170
2	870	162	8,000	83	8,245
3	810	157	8,000	164	8,321

the new machine would win, and if it wins with a 1-year analysis there is no
point in trying a longer life because the annual cost will be lower! We find
that many pieces of equipment that have been proved in by elaborate analysis
over the predicted economic life period would also have won on a 1-year
analysis.   Nevertheless we are not advocating elimination of the complete
study over the economic life. To do so would suggest action without an attempt
to foresee as much of the future as possible.

10.17 DEFINITIONS OF ECONOMIC LIFE

Here we should be able to propose some definitions of economic life which
will be more meaningful as a result of previous discussions and illustrations. In
doing this we are not attempting to coin one definition that will suit all circumstances for, as we observed, economic life depends on more than one factor.
We believe, therefore, that economic life is best defined by considering all of
the following definitions.

Economic life is the period over which the given equipment has its lowest
uniform equivalent annual cost.

Economic life is the period that will be terminated when a new piece of
equipment has a uniform annual cost lower than the cost of keeping the equipment one or more years longer.

Economic life is the period that will elapse before the proposed equipment will be displaced by another as the result of a future economy analysis.

Economic life is the period spent on the *intended* service prior to degradation to a new service (or liquidation).

The economic life is the period during which the equipment will perform on the service or function for which it is being proposed. Along the same line is the statement, which should not be used out of context for obvious reasons, that economic life is the period for which we can predict the annual operating disbursements. This statement presumes that we can predict disbursements only for the intended service but not for subsequent degraded services because the analyst does not even know what they might be.

From the illustrations in this chapter we observe that each degradation of a piece of equipment terminates its economic life period. Like the proverbial cat, each piece of equipment may have a number of successive economic lives. The one-horse shay class of equipment is clearly an exception, but it is generally true of the other classes of equipment. The military aircraft type, for example, may pass from primary equipment on the major front, to major equipment on a secondary front, to training equipment for new pilots, to standby aircraft held for a big offensive. The termination of economic life, therefore, signals replacement but not necessarily disposal of the equipment.

The succession of economic lives which many pieces of equipment experience may be under one ownership or under several. If under one ownership we see that the ownership life, or useful life, of the equipment exceeds the economic life. If the equipment is disposed of, it may go on to additional economic lives under a new owner. We have noted trolley cars serving in distant places of the world long after their economic displacement on mainline and suburban service in New York City.

10.18 KINDS OF LIVES

A piece of equipment can have several kinds of lives, and a brief observation of them might promote a better understanding of economic life. For example:

1. *Economic life:* The period defined in the previous section.

2. *Ownership life:* The period until the equipment is sold or otherwise disposed of.

3. *Useful life:* The period over which the equipment will produce useful service. Practically speaking, it should therefore be the ownership life, although technically it may be argued that there can be a difference. It is usually *intended* to mean the life until disposal, the ownership life.

4. *Accounting life:* The period selected by the accountant over which the equipment will be depreciated in the books of the company. The accountant uses a period equal to the useful life, although when permitted by tax rules he may accomplish a fast writeoff of the equipment. (In general, however,

the accountant will explain a "fast writeoff" on the basis of a predicted short, useful life.)

5. *Physical life:* Usually longer than any of the lives previously stated. One piece of equipment may have several owners, several useful lives, but it may be physically sound even after it can find no useful service to perform.

6. *Primary service life:* The first economic life period of a piece of equipment.

7. *Service life:* This usually means the useful life described earlier.

10.19 HEEDING ALL FACTORS IN ECONOMIC LIFE

Predicting the life period cannot be based on a formula, so it is hoped that the previous classifications of equipment will sharpen predictions rather than lull the analyst into a false sense of security. For example, the fact that telephone poles are typical of the one-horse shay class does not preclude the possibility of an early decision to replace them with underground cables.

Similarly, like-for-like equipment can be displaced by sudden obsolescence prior to the optimum life established by its deterioration gradient. A reciprocating-engine aircraft in a given commercial service can be displaced, before the date necessitated by its increased operating costs, when new turbo-prop or jet-engine aircraft become available.

Another illustration occurs in the situation where the engineers predict an economic life of 8 years, based on military aircraft considerations, but top management, based on special knowledge, predicts that the company will not be producing the particular product made by this machinery for more than 5 years. In this case the obsolescence period of the product is shorter than the obsolescence period of the machine.

PROBLEMS

10.1 Machine *A* costs $10,000 with operating disbursements of $4,950 a year for 8 years with $2,500 salvage at that time. Machine *B* costs $8,000 with operating disbursements of $5,500 a year with $2,000 salvage at the end of 8 years. The minimum required rate of return is 15%. (a) By the annual-cost method of analysis, which machine should be selected? (b) If management decrees the adoption of 4-year economic lives with zero salvage for all equipment, which machine must be selected? Describe the loss to the company, if any. (c) Suppose the economic life of the machine selected in part (a) does turn out to be 4 years, what will be the loss to the company, if any?

10.2 Suppose a company can save $4,000 a year by replacing a manual process with a machine costing $12,000, but rejects this opportunity. Describe the resulting loss in money if the economic life of the machine is 10 years with $3,000 salvage and if the minimum required rate of return is 15%. On the other hand, describe the loss, if any, if the company approves the installation and the economic life proves to be 4 years.

10.3 The class of economic life depends on circumstances, not on the equipment itself. Show how circumstances can place each given item into any one of several different classes: a suit of clothes, a radio set, an automobile, a summer cottage, a pneumatic hand tool, an automatic machine tool, a chemical processing plant.

10.4   A machine costs $11,000 and will have operating disbursements in the first year of $5,000. As a result of deterioration, these disbursements are expected to increase arithmetically by $400 a year. The salvage value is expected to be $1,000 whenever the equipment is retired. The minimum required rate of return is 15%. Assuming like-for-like replacement, compute the economic life of the machine. Plot the following uniform equivalent annual costs versus years: investment cost, operating disbursements, and total cost. Also, plot the actual yearly operating disbursements.

10.5   A machine costing $20,000 is expected to have operating disbursements of $8,000 the first year, but these are expected to increase 5% each year over the year before for the life of the machine. Its net realizable value will decline 15% a year, making the first year's salvage value $17,000, the second year's $14,450, and so on. The minimum required rate of return is 20%. Assuming like-for-like replacement, determine the economic life and the annual cost for that period.

10.6   Rework Problem 10.4 if it is believed that the given machine will be superseded as a result of a military aircraft replacement situation at the end of 6 years. Also in this case state what the maximum annual cost and the maximum economic life can be.

10.7   An 8-year-old machine is expected to have operating disbursements for the coming year of $7,600. Its present value is $2,000, and this is expected to be constant for the remaining life of the machine. A new machine, otherwise identical, costs $20,000 and will have operating disbursements on the same job of $4,400. Its salvage is expected to be $2,000 whenever it is retired. If it is assumed that the operating disbursements increase by an arithmetic gradient similar to the pattern established by the old machine, what is the economic life and the annual cost of each machine for that life? The minimum required rate of return is 15%.

10.8   A new machine costs $8,000 and its anticipated operating disbursements for the coming year are $5,000, but they are expected to increase $100 a year due to deterioration. Improved machines are predicted to appear every year that will do the same job for $150 less than its predecessor of the year before. The salvage value of new machines will be zero whenever they are retired. The minimum required rate of return is 20%.

An existing machine has an investment value of $2,000 which will decrease to $1,500 at the end of the coming year. Its operating disbursements for this year will be $7,500. Derive a comparative annual-cost equation similar to Eq. 10.11 in the text. Should the existing machine be kept for one more year? Compute the economic life and the comparative annual costs of the machines.

10.9   Rework Problem 10.8 deciding whether the existing machine should be kept for 2 more years. Its operating disbursement at the end of the second year will be $7,700 and its salvage value at that time will be

$1,200. Derive a comparative annual-cost equation similar to Eq. 10.11 in the text. Also determine the economic life and the comparative annual costs of the machines.

10.10 Rework Problem 10.8 deciding whether the existing machine should be kept for 3 more years. Its operating disbursement for each of these years will be $7,500, $7,700, and $7,900, respectively. Its salvage value at the end of that time will be $1,050. Derive a comparative annual-cost equation similar to Eq. 10.11 in the text. Determine the economic life and the comparative annual costs of the machines.

10.11 Rework Problem 10.8 deciding whether the existing machine should be kept for the next 4 years. Its operating disbursements for each of these years will be $7,500, $7,700, $7,900, and $8,100, respectively. Its salvage value at the end of that time will be $900. Determine the economic life and the comparative costs of the proposed machines.

10.12 Compare your solutions for Problems 10.8 through 10.11 (or for the ones that you were assigned) with the answers that you would get had there been no deterioration and obsolescence gradients.

10.13 Differentiate the annual-cost model as suggested in Section 10.12 to verify Eq. 10.12a.

10.14 Prove that Eq. 10.12b equals Eq. 10.12a.

10.15 A machine costs $15,000 with a next-year operating disbursement of $4,000, a 10-year economic life, and zero salvage at that time. Its life on this service will be terminated by deterioration and obsolescence. The gradient is assumed to increase arithmetically. The minimum required rate of return is 15%. (a) Compute its comparative annual cost for use in a 1-year deferment test. (b) Draw a time scale showing the cost of each year's operation. (c) Using the gradient computed in part (a) compare the uniform total annual cost of operating 9 years, 10 years, 11 years, and of operating 1 year from the tenth to the eleventh. Assume the salvage is zero in each case.

10.16 Rework part (a) of Problem 10.15 if the salvage at the end of the 10-year economic life is $1,600 instead of zero. In that case the salvage at the end of the eleventh year will be $1,300.

10.17 Derive Eq. 10.12a if the salvage of the proposed machine, instead of being zero, is 20% of the machine's first cost, regardless of when the machine is retired.

10.18 Take the uniform equivalent annual costs listed in the last column of Table 10.13 and compare each with the annual costs of 1 more year of operation. For example, compare $6,910, the uniform equivalent annual cost for 5 years of operation, with the cost of operating the machine for only year 6. Proceed in the same way for all the others. In computing the cost of this single year of operation, assume that the investment value P at the beginning of the year is 20% of the original cost and that it will not decrease with one year of operation (this is consistent with the statement of Example 10.13). Interpret the results of your comparisons.

10.19 A tool with fully programmed electronic control of its operations costs $45,000, installed. Annual operating disbursements are expected to be

$16,000 for the first year and to increase $1,000 a year as a result of repairs and down time. The management believes that at the end of 6 years an improved machine will appear on the market which will make replacement economically feasible. Salvage at that date is expected to be 50%. The present tool can be salvaged for $15,000 (i.e., its present investment value) and if kept for another year the salvage value will decline to $12,000. Its operating disbursements for that year are expected to be $25,000. The minimum required rate of return is 20%. Should the proposed machine be acquired?

10.20   Suppose the analyst predicts an economic life of 6 years as in Problem 10.19 but he expects that this will be the result of combined annual obsolescence and deterioration in the form of an arithmetic gradient. Assume that the salvage value will be 50% of the first cost whenever the machine is disposed of. Compute the annual cost. All other data will be the same as in Problem 10.19.

10.21   What is the composite or lifetime rate of return over the 18 years of useful life in Example 10.15 in the text? Should you use this in deciding whether to purchase the equipment at time zero?

10.22   In a business with which you are familiar, name some equipments that (a) are subject to discrete functional degradation; (b) are subject to continuous degradation; (c) can be classified as "like-for-like;" (d) can be classified as military aircraft type; (e) can be classified as the one-horse shay type.

11

Replacement Economy

11.1 THE MEANING OF REPLACEMENT

T he term *replacement* is so broad that almost the entire subject of engineering economy comes under it. The term is used with the widest implications. For example, replacement does not mean that equipment will be duplicated at the end of its life; it does not imply like-for-like substitution. No resemblance between the present incumbent and its replacement is necessary. Replacement in this sense occurs even if a manual process is superseded by a machine or if a group of machines is superseded by one large machine.

A broader understanding results if we observe that replacement is synonymous with displacement. Replacement then means that the present incumbent process will be displaced by a more economic one. From this standpoint we can replace a financial policy, an entire business operation, a factory, a manufacturing process, a machine, or a manual operation with a better one.

In considering replacement, we must observe that a proposal to do something, such as a proposal to manufacture a product, can replace an existing policy of not manufacturing it. In every situation there may be many alternatives, but one of these always is the alternative of doing nothing, of maintaining the status quo. The question of replacing a policy of doing nothing with a positive policy underlies every comparison. Even a comparison of two new machines, although not a replacement problem itself, only exists because of a prior decision to replace the status quo with an income-expansion proposition requiring one of these new machines. Therefore every problem in equipment investment is also a replacement problem or at the very least, part of a larger replacement situation.

The principles of engineering economy that we have studied apply to all replacement problems, but some new principles will be examined at this time which are best understood in the light of specific replacement situations.

11.2 DEGRADATION VERSUS DISPOSAL

What happens to equipment that is displaced as the result of an economy analysis?

One might assume that replacement means the end of the life of that equipment with the company, namely, that it means retirement and disposal of the equipment. It is more likely that, on replacement, equipment will be retained for service on a degraded job somewhere within the company. In this manner, a machine can be replaced a number of times, each in a different service, before its final retirement.

As an example, a turbogenerator installed in a power plant will probably be degraded a number of times before its final disposal. Initially, while its efficiency is the highest of the installed machines, it will be on primary service supplying the base load. After some obsolescence and deterioration it will be replaced by a more efficient machine and degraded to secondary service with respect to the best units. Eventually it will be replaced in this service and degraded to peak load service for operation only a few hours a day. From this service it might be degraded to serve only as a standby in emergencies. When displaced from this it is then ready for retirement.

Each of these degradations represents an economic life period in a different service. However, the equipment should gain entry to each new service only as the result of an economy study. When displaced from one service it can become the proposed machine in a degraded service, and if it wins in an economy study it will, only then, displace the present machine in that service. In its contest for a degraded post it should compete not only with the present incumbent but with any new or second-hand equipment that may seem to be reasonable contenders for the post.

Displaced equipment is neither automatically retired nor automatically assured a position in a degraded service. Even for standby service the equipment should earn the privilege based on an economy comparison. Unless equipment can hold its own in an economy test, it should be removed from the company assets on the balance sheet.

11.3 DEPRECIATION

Depreciation has many definitions. In the *value* sense it refers to the loss caused by deterioration and obsolescence. Depreciation in the *accounting* sense refers to writing off unamortized cost over the useful life of the equipment. The first cost of equipment is treated in accounting very much like a prepaid expense: it is set up as an asset, and each year, over the assumed life of the equipment until its disposal, some proportion of this unamortized cost is charged to expense.

The life period over which the accountant depreciates an asset is not the economic life defined in Chapter 10. The accountant estimates depreciation over the entire life of the equipment until its disposal, which, as we noted in

Section 11.2, may cover several degraded services. The accountant's life period for assets may therefore be much longer than the economist's prediction of the prime service life.

For the computation of income taxes, the accountant is required by Internal Revenue Service rules to depreciate the asset over its useful life. Consequently we would expect useful life, tax life, and accounting life to be identical, but economic life to be less than accounting life in the case of assets that will be retained for useful service but degraded as superior assets appear.

The Treasury Department publishes guidelines of useful lives for different classes of equipment, as mentioned in Chapter 15, and the accountant will ordinarily stay within the ranges allowed by the guidelines unless he is in a reasonable position to prove that the useful life he wishes to adopt in a given situation is something else. Obviously, too, having computed the income tax payments correctly, the accountant may then adopt a different accounting life, perhaps longer or shorter than the tax life, in computing after-tax profits in his report to the shareholders. While this may introduce still another depreciation period, and the maintenance of two sets of books, business reasons may justify them. The fundamental objective in accounting depreciation is the proper absorption of capital wastage (depreciation) at the correct rate over the correct period of time.

As stated, the accountant prorates the cost of the asset (less any predicted salvage value on disposal) against each year's earnings, and his mathematical model of distribution defines the effect of depreciation on each year's profits. Furthermore, charging too little depreciation expense represents overstatement of earnings and payment of false profits by neglecting some of the costs of capital wastage; conversely, charging too much depreciation in a given year causes the declared earnings to be too low. The accountant is concerned with the amount of depreciation in a given year and to this end employs formulas which affect the pattern of the distribution of the cost of the asset and the amount of depreciation in each of the various years of the asset's useful life. The following is a list of some of the formulas in use.

1. Straight line: gives uniform depreciation.
2. Sum-of-the-years digits: gives rapid depreciation in early years.
3. Double-rate declining balance: gives rapid depreciation in early years.
4. Sinking fund: gives rapid depreciation in late years.

The mathematical formulas for the important methods of depreciation appear in Chapter 15, where they are used in the computation of corporate income tax and where, in fact, depreciation must be discussed in more detail. In the present chapter we are only concerned with the topic in relation to the discussion of book value and its relevance to economy comparisons.

Before discussing book value, let us note that the economy analyst doesn't use the accountant's formulas, because it is not his role to apportion the savings to capital recovery in any year (except as it may affect income taxes) as long as the capital is recovered by the end of the economic life period.

11.4 BOOK VALUE

Book value is the unamortized cost of the asset which still appears on the accounting books of the business. It is a sum which is solely the result of past depreciation procedures and past decisions. For example, the useful-life period and the annual depreciation charged in past years both result from past predictions which seemed appropriate to the accountant at the time.

If the accountant had selected straight-line depreciation, the present book value would be as follows:

$$\text{Book value} = P - t\left(\frac{P - L}{n}\right)$$

where

$$\frac{P - L}{n} = \text{annual depreciation}$$

t = number of years that the equipment has been depreciated to date

In establishing t, we should note that many companies charge one-half year's depreciation in the year that the equipment is purchased in recognition of the fact that these acquisitions occur at random throughout the year. Where this is done, the same charge is made in the year the equipment is retired.

We should note that book value is not market value, not the liquidated value of the asset. If depreciation could be predicted perfectly, book and market value would be identical, but this coincidence can be expected only as a matter of chance. Book value is strictly an accounting fiction.

Nevertheless, the existence of an unamortized cost on the books will raise the following questions which must be answered.

1. How does book value enter into an economy analysis—if at all?
2. In a replacement analysis, what investment value, P, should be used for the present equipment?
3. If book value is not used, how does the discrepancy between book value and market value affect the conclusion?

We will attempt to answer these questions in the next few pages.

11.5 INVESTMENT VALUE OF EXISTING EQUIPMENT

The investment cost P is always the installed cost of the equipment. But then what is the investment cost P of a machine presently operating on the intended service?

The *installed cost* of a machine that is *already installed* on a given service is

(a) its "as-is" price; (b) the net income that will be tied up in the equipment by electing to keep instead of sell it; (c) the net salvage value, the value that will be rejected if we retain the unit in its present service; (d) the money that we could have on hand, but will forego by keeping the unit on its present service; (e) the so-called *net realizable value*, NRV, of the unit. All of these give the installed cost of a unit already installed, its investment value P. These concepts are illustrated in the following example.

EXAMPLE 11.5a In Fig. 11.5, what is the investment cost P of the machine presently installed in Department A in an economic study of its replacement?

SOLUTION. In the given figure, $1,500 can be realized for the equipment f.o.b. cars. But to realize this we must dismount it ($75), box it ($100), and move it to the cars ($25). These costs are necessary to the sale; hence the net proceeds from the sale are $1,500 – 200 = $1,300. This is the NRV.

Note that $1,300 is also the *installed cost*, because it is the investment value of the machine in place ready to run on the intended service. It is also the NRV, because it is the as-is price of the unit. A dealer should give $1,300 for it as is, because if it is worth $1,500 f.o.b. cars, he has to spend $200 to convert it from "as-is installed" to "f.o.b. cars," assuming that his costs are the same as ours.

In the case of a unit *already installed* on the intended service, the *installed cost* is therefore the NRV.

However, the investment cost or installed cost of a unit not yet installed has nothing to do with its NRV. The installed cost of a new unit is its purchase price plus all the costs incident to buying it, installing it, and making it fully ready to operate on the intended service. For example, if we can purchase a new unit, either brand new or second-hand, for $1,500 f.o.b. cars with freight allowed to our railroad siding, and if the costs of installation are

Unboxing:	$ 10
Moving from cars to site:	25
Mounting and connecting up the unit:	125

then the installed cost of the purchased unit = $1,500 + 160 = $1,660.

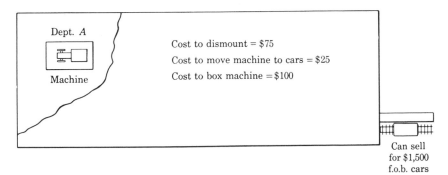

Figure 11.5 Considering the investment in an existing machine

Incidentally, this supports the logical conclusion that it is more expensive to purchase than to retain ownership of an identical unit even if it is possible to buy the unit at the same price as we could sell it for in the market place.

A more difficult problem than determining the investment cost of a purchased unit or of a unit already installed is to determine the installed cost at a new location of a machine already owned but installed elsewhere in the company.

EXAMPLE 11.5b   Take the case of the above machine now installed in Department *A* which has an NRV or investment cost of $1,300 as computed above. Suppose it is displaced in Department *A* and we propose to test it for a position in Department *B* if the cost of moving it to Department *B* is $25 and the cost of mounting and connecting it up is $125. Now what is its investment value?

SOLUTION.   The point to remember is that the NRV of $1,300 is the installed cost in Department *A*, so to the other costs we must add the $75 cost of dismounting it from its location in *A*. Now the installed cost in *B* will be

$$\$1,300 + 75 + 25 + 125 = \$1,525$$

Note that the installed cost of this unit is not its NRV, although it is an element in the computation.

After the machine is installed in Department *B*, however, its installed cost, for any test of whether it should stay in Department *B*, is its NRV. For example, if the selling price of the machine is $1,500 f.o.b. cars on our siding, then the NRV is $1,500 minus the cost of making it f.o.b. cars—namely, minus $75 for dismantling, $25 for moving, $100 for boxing—a net of $1,300. Now if we proposed to test whether to *keep* this machine on the intended service after we installed it, the correct investment value or installed cost becomes $1,300. (This assumes that the cost of dismounting, disconnecting, moving, and boxing totals $200, the same as before.) But the installed cost for the same machine, on the basis that we propose to dismount it from its foundations in Department *A* and install it in Department *B*, is $1,525. The instant it is installed, however, its NRV in defending its right to stay there is $1,300.

Realize that the investment cost of a machine once installed has to be less; if it is more, then it would be economical to take the machine out immediately and replace it with a like machine and the machine on the outside would continuously win the battle for replacement. However, using the correct reasoning we discover that once a machine is installed it is immediately harder to replace it.

11.6   THE IRRELEVANCE OF BOOK VALUE

The reader will note that in establishing the investment value of installed equipment or relocated equipment—equipment that we already own—the book value was immaterial, in no way did it enter the computation. In view of the fact that book value is employed by some analysts in establishing the investment value and strong arguments are advanced for its use, let us examine the reasons why it should not be used.

One reason for the irrelevance of book value in an economy study is that only future differences between alternatives are relevant to the choice. Book value results from a past decision and the commitment to write it off in the future will exist regardless of any future equipment selection. The commitment to write off the book value may be termed a sunk cost. This term arises from the fact that money spent in the past or committed as a result of past decisions, like water over the dam, cannot be altered by future decisions. Sunk costs, therefore, are irrelevant to the choice. The following example illustrates this:

EXAMPLE 11.6a An asset was purchased 5 years ago for $1,000 and has a present net realizable value of $600. It has been depreciated over a 20-year useful life by the straight-line method with zero salvage expected at that date. Management is now considering replacement of the asset by a new machine. Show how the book value of the present asset is irrelevant to the decision of whether to keep it or replace it.

SOLUTION. As the result of a past decision 5 years ago, management decided to write off the asset over a 20-year life, apportioning the expense equally in each year. Solely as a result of these two past decisions, the book value today happens to be

$$1,000 - 5\left(\frac{1,000}{20}\right) = \$750$$

Therefore, $250 of the asset has been charged as expense and $750 must still be written off. Now let us note that if the equipment is retained in its present job it must be written off, if it is displaced it must be written off, if it is retired it must be written off. Regardless of any alternatives involving this equipment, we cannot alter the fact that $750 must still be charged as expense in the future. It is a sunk cost and irrelevant. The net realizable value of $600, however, is relevant because it is the investment cost which will be incurred only if the unit is continued in its present job.

EXAMPLE 11.6b In the previous example, management insists that book value must be included in the computations. If it must be included, show how it can be. The investment cost of the proposed machine is $2,000.

SOLUTION. If book value is omitted, the comparison is between the following alternatives:

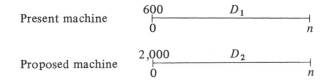

and the question is whether to make the extra investment of $1,400 out of the savings caused by the proposed machine.

If the book value is included, we must continue to write it off regardless of which alternative we select. Consequently, if we must include the book value of $750 we must add it as a cost to *both* sides:

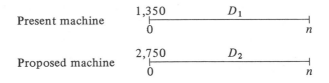

Present machine

Proposed machine

The extra investment is still $1,400 and we will arrive at exactly the same answer. Unnecessary as this example may be to the initiated, the method can save a lot of explaining to anyone who asserts that the $750, being a future expense (and it is), must be included in the analysis. Unfortunately, one method in use was to add the "loss on disposal" (the excess of the book value over the net realizable value of the present asset) to the investment cost of the proposed equipment. The failure again was to observe that, if this expense is included at all, it must be added to all alternatives, not just to the proposed equipment.

Another erroneous practice, where book value may be higher than net realizable value, is to use the book value of the present equipment instead of its net realizable value. Surely this is the place to point out that the investment cost of retaining equipment should not be greater for the owner of the equipment than for its prospective purchaser. This was also inferred in Section 11.5.

Actually, it is not correct to say that book value is entirely irrelevant to the choice because, as we shall see in Chapter 15, the annual disbursement for income tax is computed from book value, not net realizable value, and therefore, in that respect, it is a relevant factor.

11.7 LOSS ON DISPOSAL OF EQUIPMENT

Regardless of the statements in the previous section, management may debate the alleged irrelevance of book value if it is to be written off all at once instead of over an extended period of time. The former can occur if equipment is retired and liquidated, because it is general accounting practice to write off the loss on disposal immediately. Therefore, if equipment is *retired* as a result of replacement and if book value is *higher* than the net realized on the sale, a loss in excess of usual depreciation will occur in that year. This reduces that year's earnings, and any reduction in earnings does not make management happy.[1]

It is, of course, understandable that management is fundamentally opposed to a reduction in profit in the year they approve a replacement (or in any other

---

[1] Accounting practice permits charging a material loss on disposal directly to earned surplus without reducing current earnings. This recognizes the inadequacy of past depreciation and the inappropriateness of charging the current year with the entire loss. The procedure adjusts the earned surplus account to the balance it would have had if the correct depreciation had been recorded in the past.

year), but it is false economy to keep uneconomical equipment merely to avoid acknowledging a sunk cost.

Another reason why management might oppose replacement is that a loss on disposal suggests a prior error in management judgment. It appears to give evidence that management has previously authorized a purchase which has proved unwise, whereas this might be only a failure to predict the rate at which the equipment should have been depreciated. However, it is better that management admit an error, regardless of its origin, than permit it to be the cause of the serious error of not approving economic replacement.

It might be mentioned here that the income tax effects, as we will see in Chapter 15, favor a sudden or immediate write-off instead of one distributed over a future period.

Although much discussion is given to the problem of loss on disposal, we should note that disposal seldom occurs as a result of replacement. In most cases the equipment is not retired but is retained for use on a degraded service. In that event, the accountant merely continues to write off this equipment as before, regardless of its present realizable value. The problem is not very serious because (a) until equipment nears its predicted useful life the odds are against its retirement and (b) then, when it is eventually retired at the end of a long, useful life, discrepancies between its fully amortized book value and its realizable value will be small or, for that matter, may be gains. The blow is also softened by the tax savings from a loss on disposal.

11.8 INCLUSION OF ALL RELEVANT COSTS AND REVENUES

While creating an awareness to irrelevant costs, it is also appropriate to point out that special care should be given to including all the relevant costs. A helpful procedure is to prepare a check list for the type of equipment being considered. Examples of items that might be considered for a check list are:

Labor for operating, handling, setting up, putting away
Inspection
Fuel and energy
Supervision and indirect cost *differences*
Scrap or waste
Labor, material, and indirect costs lost in spoilage
Property tax on first cost or valuation
Insurance
Uninsured cost of risks
Maintenance (Materials, labor, overhead)
Periodic overhaul, repairs, or other capital expenditures

In setting up cost equations. the analyst must identify all the differences inherent in the alternatives, then precisely define them and finally quantify them in dollars.

A good example occurs in establishing the differences in overhead cost between alternative projects. By his familiarity with the present and proposed methods, the analyst can sense whether the latter is likely to result in changes in any of the overhead items. For example, might the supervision in the proposed automatic process be less than the present normal process? The detection of differences will stimulate research for the actual cost differences. Seldom are costs available to point out where differences do exist, so the analyst must be imaginative in predicting where differences will exist and then locate the costs to prove or disprove the point. The difficulty is increased because either one or both of the alternatives is not now on the intended service and cost records do not exist.

As we shall see, there are some helpful guides in establishing certain comparative cost differences such as floor space or inherent productive capacity; however, one of the first differences is examined in the next section; a possible difference in economic life.

11.9 SELECTING ECONOMIC LIFE OF PRESENT EQUIPMENT

In many replacement problems the present equipment can be expected to have a shorter economic life than the proposed equipment. In some cases we are moved to make a replacement test based on the belief that the present equipment is perhaps at or near the end of its life.

For equipment conforming to like-for-like or deterioration-and-obsolescence types it is not unusual to test the present equipment for one more year of life. We will note that with increasing deterioration if the net realizable value P is zero, the annual cost for any period in excess of one year will be greater than next year's. In fact, even if the investment cost is not zero, the deterioration could be increasing so rapidly relative to the low investment cost of old equipment that the lowest annual cost still occurs for a one-year life.

A very helpful observation in testing the present equipment is this: if the present equipment wins, based on a one-year economic life, consideration of a longer period is unnecessary. On the other hand if it loses with a one-year life, the new must decide whether a longer life will result in a lower uniform equivalent annual cost.

The previous observation is true, in fact, for all equipment, present or proposed, but because the first year's annual cost of new equipment is usually much higher than the annual cost over the economic life period, a one-year life is seldom employed in testing new equipment.

If capital expenditures for major overhaul and repair are required at this time, the most likely economic life of the equipment is longer than one year. The life may then extend until another major overhaul is required, depending, of course, on the class of equipment. For example, if it is the like-for-like type, the life will extend until the rising expense predicts replacement.

Fundamentally, the economic life of the present equipment is based on the same considerations given in Chapter 10. The classifications of equipment will also apply here, modified by the fact that the present equipment may be at or near the end of its economic life.

First, let us note that while the life of the present equipment may approximate one year, the economic life of the *proposed* equipment is expected to be much longer, and therefore its equivalent annual investment cost will be lower than for a one-year life. This statement must take into account the usual early decline in salvage values.

11.10 MILITARY AIRCRAFT TYPE

The following example illustrates a replacement situation in which both alternatives are viewed by the analyst to be in the military aircraft class of equipment.

EXAMPLE 11.10   The equipment now on the job was installed five years ago at a cost of $8,000. Its present net realizable value is $1,500. If the machine is continued on this service for another year, its operating cost is predicted to be $10,650 and its salvage value will drop $500.

A new machine has just appeared costing $10,000, installed and ready to run, and its operating cost is expected to be only $8,000. Maintenance and repair is a uniform routine expense included in the stated operating costs. No special or increased costs for maintenance are anticipated for either machine. The new machine will likely exist on this service until an improved model appears. The field is technologically stimulated and it is expected that such a machine might appear in 5 years. Salvage at that date is likely to be $2,000. If the present machine is kept 5 years, its salvage is expected to be $400 at that date. The minimum required rate of return is 10%.

SOLUTION.

$$D = 10,650$$

Present machine $NRV = 1,500$ $L = 1,000$

0   1

New Machine   10,000 $D = 8,000$ $L = 2,000$

0   5

The proposed machine would appear to have an economic life of 5 years.

The present machine will either be replaced by the model that has just appeared or it will last until a better one appears, that is, in 5 years, when the next model is expected.

With constant operating disbursements and salvage values decreasing by a smaller differential each year, the present machine will have its lowest annual cost over a 5-year life. Of course, the present machine may be tested over a 1-year life, but if it loses, the analyst must test it over a 5-year period, as illustrated in the two solutions that follow.

Proposed machine:

$$\overset{0.2738}{AC = (10{,}000 - 2{,}000)(A/P, .10, 5) + (2{,}000)(0.10) + 8{,}000 = \$10{,}310}$$

Present machine (first solution):

1-year AC:

$$\overset{1.10}{(1{,}500 - 1{,}000)(A/P, 1) + (1{,}000)(0.10) + 10{,}650 = \$11{,}300}$$

Since the machine has failed on a 1-year test, the analyst must make another over a 5-year period. The only advantage of the 1-year test is that if the present machine wins, the analyst will have avoided the difficulties of making long-term projections of its costs.

Present Machine (second solution):

5-year AC:

$$\overset{0.2638}{(1{,}500 - 400)(A/P, 5) + (400)(0.10) + 10{,}650 = \$10{,}980}$$

In this case the present machine loses on both tests.

11.11 ONE-HORSE SHAY TYPE

The following example is intended to illustrate a replacement situation in which both alternatives are classified by the analyst as the one-horse shay type. Replacement of one-horse shay equipment is not signalled by an economy test but by the failure of the equipment itself; for example, we replace an electric light bulb because it has burned out. Therefore, replacement analyses can apply only to special situations such as group replacement of equipment prior to the expiration of individual items (in order to save installation costs), treatment of equipment prior to its expiration to extend its life, replacement of that portion of the equipment that has failed in service, and so on. The latter is illustrated in the following example.

EXAMPLE 11.11 A wooden telephone pole is 11 years old and inspection reveals that decay at the base demands its prompt removal. Inspection also shows that by placing a new butt in the ground to which the upper will be strapped, the life can be prolonged another 5 years. The net realizable value of the present pole if sold to a dealer is $2. The cost of a butt is $10 installed and its salvage value at any time is zero.

A new pole can be installed for a total cost of $28. Mortality tables predict an average life of 12 years in this geographic locality. Salvage value of an old pole is $2.

The minimum required rate of return is 10%.

SOLUTION.

Butted pole

$$
\begin{array}{lll}
10 + 2 & & L = 2 \\
\vdash\!\!-\!\!-\!\!-\!\!-\!\!-\!\!-\!\!-\!\!-\!\!-\!\!-\!\!-\!\!-\!\!-\!\!-\!\!-\!\!-\!\!-\!\!\dashv \\
0 & & 5
\end{array}
$$

Proposed pole

$$\underset{0}{\overset{28}{\vdash}} \quad \rule{0pt}{0pt} \overset{L\,=\,2}{\underset{12}{\dashv}}$$

0.14676

New pole, AC = $(28 - 2)(A/P, .10, 12) + 2(0.10) = \$4.02$

0.2638

Butted pole, AC = $(12 - 2)(A/P, .10, 5) + 2(0.10) = \$2.84$

11.12 LIKE-FOR-LIKE TYPE

Replacement of like-for-like equipment is brought about by the increasing costs of maintenance and repair, as illustrated in the following example.

EXAMPLE 11.12 A truck being considered for replacement is 4 years old. Its net realizable value of $1,400 is expected to drop to $1,100 if the truck is used another year. The operating cost for the coming year is expected to be $4,100.
A new truck of equal capacity will cost $4,500. Operating costs predicted from past records include maintenance, repair, fuel, tires, tax, hiring other carriers when equipment fails, and so on. The following predictions were made of market values of trucks of various ages as follows:

Year	Operating costs	Year-end value
1	$3,000	$3,300
2	3,200	2,500
3	3,500	2,000
4	3,900	1,600
5	4,400	1,300

The minimum required rate of return is 10%. Based on the predicted costs, what is the economic life of the equipment?

SOLUTION. The annual cost of the present truck will be lowest for the coming year because rising operating costs more than offset decreases in capital costs.

Present truck, AC:

1.10

$$(1,400 - 1,100)(A/P, 1) + (1,100)(0.10) + 4,100 = \$4,540$$

The minimum annual cost of the proposed truck can be located by computing the costs over successive life periods. The results of the computation are as follows:

Economic life, years	Uniform equivalent annual cost
1	$4,650
2	4,500
3	4,420
4	4,430
5	4,510

This demonstrates that if an asset *wins* based on assuming that its life is one year, testing it over a longer life period is not necessary. However, if an asset *loses*, it must be tested over a longer life period if that will give a lower annual cost.

11.13 DETERIORATION AND OBSOLESCENCE TYPE WITH ESTIMATED GRADIENT

In Chapter 10 we considered a class of equipment in which it was predicted that deterioration and obsolescence were increasing uniformly by some fixed annual pattern. The following example illustrates a replacement situation for this class of equipment.

EXAMPLE 11.13 The present machine is 10 years old and its operating disbursements for the coming year are expected to be $20,000. Its net realizable value is $1,500, which is not expected to go lower whenever the equipment is retired. The proposed machine can be purchased for $19,000 and will cost $1,000 to install. Salvage value is predicted to be 15% at the conclusion of the economic life, whenever that may be. Operating disbursements for the coming year are computed at $18,000. The minimum required rate of return is 10%. Which machine should be selected?

SOLUTION:

Proposed machine
$$\overset{\displaystyle \underset{0}{20{,}000}}{\vert} \quad D = 18{,}000 + (t-1)G \quad \ldots \quad \overset{\displaystyle \underset{n}{L = 3{,}000}}{\vert}$$

Present machine
$$\begin{array}{cc} & D = 20{,}000 \\ \underset{0}{1{,}500} & \underset{1}{L = 1{,}500} \\ \vert & \vert \end{array}$$

The old machine will cost $2000 more to operate than the new machine in the coming year. This is the inferiority accumulated by the old machine over an 11-year period. Accepting the basic assumption of uniform accumulation of obsolescence and deterioration and adopting the arithmetic gradient explained in Section 10.11, we can compute a gradient for the old machine:

$$(n-1)G = 2{,}000$$

where

$$n = 11$$

whence

$$G = 200$$

But how will the prospective accumulation of inferiority of the new machine, both as to amount and distribution, relate to this past experience? The answer is not easy; this is certainly an area where more research and study are needed to support predictions of this type. For the present problem, however, the analyst must predict a gradient in which he has some confidence. Let us assume in this case that he believes that future technological growth will parallel the past and that the gradient of the proposed machine will be the same as the old, $200.

To make an annual cost comparison we must now find the minimum annual cost resulting from this gradient. The comparative uniform annual cost is given by Eq. 10.11.

$$AC = (P - L)(A/P, i, n) + Li + D + G(A/G, n) \qquad (10.11)$$

and from Eq. 10.12a the minimum will occur when

$$n \cong \frac{(P - L)i}{G} + \frac{1}{i} - \frac{(P/F, n)}{i} \qquad (10.12a)$$

$$n = \frac{[20,000 - (0.15)(20,000)](0.10)}{200} + 10 - 10(P/F, n)$$

$$n = 18.5 - 10(P/F, n)$$

By trial and error in this equation, the life is between 16 and 17 years. By using 17 years in Eq. 10.11, the *comparative* cost of the proposed machine, the deferred machine, and all future machines is

$$AC = (20,000 - 3,000)(A/P, .10, 17) + (3,000)(0.10) + 18,000 \overset{0.12466}{\underset{5.8071}{}}$$
$$+ 200(A/G, 17) = \$21,581$$

The annual cost of the present machine will be the lowest in the coming year because its investment value P can never be any lower, and its operating cost in future years will be higher as the process of deterioration continues. Therefore a 1-year life gives the lowest annual cost and establishes the economic life of the present machine.

$$AC = (1,500)(0.10) + 20,000 = \$20,150$$

The present machine has the lower annual cost; therefore installation of the proposed machine should be deferred for 1 year, and when that date arrives an analysis may indicate continued deferment.

Before passing from this example we should note that the uniform annual cost curve of the proposed machine is very flat and that a variation in life by a few years, one way or another, will change the annual cost very little. It is interesting to note also that disregarding the gradient entirely and predicting a life of 20 years or less the proposed machine, even without the cost of obsolescence or deterioration, would not win. Some analysts do just that and, if the proposed machine loses, they proceed no further, on the basis that the gradient only makes the cost of the machine higher.

11.14 COMBINED MILITARY AIRCRAFT AND GRADIENT TYPE

It is conceivable that a piece of equipment might experience the annually increasing costs of deterioration, as in the like-for-like class, although sudden obsolescence might be the actual cause for replacement, as in the military aircraft type. The mathematical model would show an annual gradient for deterioration alone, whereas obsolescence would be expressed in longer discrete intervals, i.e., occurring at the end of each life period.

EXAMPLE 11.14 An engine is 5 years old and its operating disbursements, including fuel, maintenance, and annual overhaul and repair for the coming year, are expected to be $8,650. From past records it is estimated that this is $1,500 greater than the operating cost when this engine was new, and it is also estimated that the annual disbursements have been increasing arithmetically and will continue at the same rate in the future. Its present net realizable value is $10,000.

An improved engine has just been marketed which will cost $22,000 and have operating disbursements for the first year of $5,000. Because of improved design and materials, the added operating disbursements resulting from deterioration are expected to be two-thirds those experienced by the present engine.

It is estimated that another improved engine will appear in 5 years which will make this engine obsolete. The salvage of the proposed engine at that date is expected to be $6,250, and that of the present engine, $2,500.

The minimum required rate of return is 15%.

SOLUTION. The deterioration gradient of the present engine is $(n - 1)G = 1,500$ where $n = 6$, the age at the end of next year, from which G equals $300.

$$\text{Present} \quad \begin{array}{ccc} 10,000 & D = 8,650 + (t - 1)(300) & L = 2,500 \\ \mid & & \mid \\ 0 & & 5 \end{array}$$

$$\text{Proposed} \quad \begin{array}{ccc} 22,000 & D = 5,000 + (t - 1)(200) & L = 6,250 \\ \mid & & \mid \\ 0 & & 5 \end{array}$$

Present engine, AC:

$$\overset{0.29832}{} \qquad\qquad\qquad\qquad\qquad\qquad \overset{1.72}{}$$
$$(10,000 - 2,500)(A/P, .15, 5) + (2,500)(0.15) + 8,650 + 300(A/G, 5) = \$11,778$$

Proposed engine, AC:

$$\qquad\qquad\quad \overset{0.2983}{} \qquad\qquad\qquad\qquad\qquad \overset{1.72}{}$$
$$(22,000 - 6,250)(A/P, 5) + (6,250)(0.15) + 5,000 + 200(A/G, 5) = \$10,980$$

The advantage of the proposed engine is $798 a year. Except for the predicted appearance of the improved machine, the lives of either machine could be longer than 5 years, if deterioration were the only replacement factor.

On the other hand, without considering deterioration, the advantage of the new engine would have been only $626 instead of $798. Obviously, it is more conservative to include the rising costs of deterioration if they can be predicted.

11.15 WHICH METHOD OF ANALYSIS?

We remind the reader that we are still laying a groundwork of theory. The process of learning new principles is often made easier for the student by the use of simple, direct illustrations which will not detract from the principle on display. For that reason we have in most examples employed annual-cost illustrations in preference to the more complex rate-of-return solutions or even to present-worth solutions.

We are not permanently deferring a discussion of the techniques of analysis that might be preferred in practice: annual cost, present worth, rate of return, or variations of these methods. Such a discussion will be the main objective of Chapter 17, and we will find at that time that an understanding of these techniques will require a good understanding of basic theory.

The student will recall that setting up the uniform annual-cost equation is usually the first step in the rate-of-return method as presented in this text. Any extra training in setting up annual-cost equations in this and other chapters will not be wasted.

11.16 REPLACEMENT DUE TO INADEQUATE CAPACITY

So far we have discussed the selection of economic life of the present equipment in a replacement situation, with illustrations for various classes of equipment. Let us continue now with another problem found in replacement situations: inadequate capacity of the present equipment. This situation may occur because of inadequate capacity alone or because of inefficiency as well as inadequacy.

A principle, true in every economy analysis of mutually exclusive alternatives, is that the comparison must be made over equal outputs. Each alternative must be *producing equal quantities*. Of course the *inputs* will be different, because each project has a different engineering efficiency. However, the input dollars must never reflect differences in output; input dollars must purchase equal units of output.

In the case where the production capacity of the present equipment is too small, a comparison with a larger unit can be made only by supplementing the present equipment with a new unit of sufficient size to make up the required output. This is shown in the following example.

EXAMPLE 11.16a A 3-year-old screw machine is too small for future production needs. In the past year the company had to subcontract half of the total production requirements. A new machine otherwise duplicating the present machine can be purchased and installed for $6,000. The net realizable value of the present tool is $4,000. Both tools are expected to have economic lives of 6 years from this date. At the conclusion of this period the salvage value of the new machine is expected to be $900 and that of the old machine $800. The operating disbursements of each machine running at full capacity are $4,000.

A single machine can be obtained to do the job, in fact it will deliver 125% of the combined output of the two smaller machines. Its installed cost is $11,000 with a salvage value of $1,650 at the end of its predicted 6-year economic life. Its annual operating disbursements are $7,500 when it is producing at its rated capacity and $6,000 when equaling the total output of the two smaller machines. The minimum required rate of return is 10%.

SOLUTION:

Added unit

$$
\begin{array}{lcc}
6{,}000 & D = 4{,}000 & L = 900 \\
\vdash & & \dashv \\
0 & & 6
\end{array}
$$

Present unit

$$
\begin{array}{lcc}
4{,}000 & D = 4{,}000 & L = 800 \\
\vdash & & \dashv \\
0 & & 6
\end{array}
$$

Large unit

$$
\begin{array}{lcc}
11{,}000 & D = (0.8)\,7{,}500 & L = 1{,}650 \\
\vdash & & \dashv \\
0 & & 6
\end{array}
$$

If operating disbursements for each alternative do not purchase identical production outputs, one of the alternatives will be unjustly burdened with costs not charged to the other. The first alternative, one large machine, is therefore computed at an output equaling the combined output of the two small machines as follows:

$$
\overset{0.22961}{AC_1 = (11{,}000 - 1{,}650)(A/P, .10, 6) + (1{,}650)(0.10) + 6{,}000 = \$8{,}312}
$$

The second alternative represents the combined output of the two small machines.

$$
\overset{0.22961}{AC_2 = (4{,}000 - 800)(A/P, 6)} + 800(0.10) + \overset{0.22961}{(6{,}000 - 900)(A/P, 6)}
$$

$$
+ (900)(0.10) + 2(4{,}000) = \$10{,}076
$$

The advantage, therefore, lies with the single large machine.

In replacement problems, the present equipment may have a shorter life than the new equipment, a situation which usually opens the door to a number of alternative possibilities when the present equipment also has inadequate capacity, as we shall see in the following example.

EXAMPLE 11.16b   An existing 5-year-old furnace will supply only half of the predicted heat-treating requirements. Its present net realizable value is $800 and operating disbursements are $3,000. Its expected economic life is 5 years with zero salvage.

A modern furnace of the same capacity costs $3,200 with operating costs of $2,500. A large furnace equalling the total capacity of the two small furnaces costs $6,000 with operating costs of $4,500 a year. The economic life of either of the new units is expected to be 10 years with zero salvage at that date (to avoid complicating our illustration).

The minimum required rate of return is 10%.

SOLUTION: We conceive the following alternative plans to be possible.

1. Replace the present furnace and install a new full-size furnace.
2. Supplement the present furnace with a new half-size furnace and make all future replacements with the new half-size furnace.
3. Supplement the present furnace with a new half-size furnace and replace *both* in 5 years.

Of course, other alternatives are possible, such as supplementing the present furnace with another used furnace, but the above three alternatives will serve to illustrate the problem as follows:

Plan 1
Full-size unit

6,000 $D = 4,500$ $L = 0$
0   10

Plan 2
Old Unit

3,200
800 $D = 3,000$ | $D = 2,500$ $L = 0$
0   5   15

plus
New half-size unit

3,200 $D = 2,500$ $L = 0$
0   10

Plan 3
Old unit

800 $D = 3,000$ $L = 0$
0

plus

New half-size unit

$P = 6,000$ $D = 4,500$ $L = 0$
3,200 $D = 2,500$ L = 800   15
0   5

To compare these three plans we will adopt a 10-year study period.

$$\text{PW}_1 = 6{,}000 + 4{,}500 \overset{6.1446}{(P/A, .10, 10)} = \$33{,}651$$

$$\text{PW}_2 = 800 + 3{,}000 \overset{3.791}{(P/A, 5)} + [3{,}200 \overset{0.16275}{(A/P, 10)} + 2{,}500]\overset{3.791}{(P/A, 5)}\overset{0.6209}{(P/F, 5)} + 3{,}200$$

$$+ 2{,}500 \overset{6.1446}{(P/A, 10)} = \$37{,}845$$

In the third plan we predict the disposal value of the new half-size furnace to be $800 (based on the fact that the net realizable value of today's 5-year-old machine is $800).

$$\text{PW}_3 = 800 + 3{,}200 + [(6{,}000 - 800)\overset{0.16275}{(A/P, 10)} + 4{,}500]\overset{3.791}{(P/A, 5)}\overset{0.6209}{(P/F, 5)}$$

$$+ (3{,}000 + 2{,}500)\overset{3.701}{(P/A, 5)} = \$37{,}435$$

The comparison shows the extra investment in Plan 1 is recovered with 10% plus $3,784 relative to the second-place plan, Plan 3, of deferring the installation of the larger unit for 5 years by a temporary installation of a half-size unit.

11.17 TREATMENT OF INHERENT EXTRA CAPACITY

We have seen that if comparisons are not made on equal outputs one alternative will be unfairly charged with extra operating costs arising solely out of its extra productive capacity. If anything, inherent extra capacity, which will be available when and if needed, is more likely to be an asset than a disadvantage. Let us see how it might be treated.

Any excess capacity beyond the required output on the proposed job is an irreducible factor with values over and above the quantitative evaluation. At first glance, excess capacity beyond the *required* capacity is pointless. On the other hand, the extra capacity may be viewed as a reserve against the uncertainties that make the best predictions go wrong. Therefore, in Example 11.16a the inherent extra 25% capacity of the oversize machine might be viewed as an irreducible advantage. Actually, it also appeared in the first cost of the machine, which we presume would have been lower if a unit of 100% capacity had been available, and in the operating cost, if the machine's efficiency had been higher by operating nearer to the rated capacity. If the analyst purposely suggests an oversize unit (reflecting a lack of confidence in his prediction?), his annual costs should be higher, even though operating disbursements will be computed for an output identical with that of the other alternatives.

The quantitative treatment of inherent extra capacity, however, is to compute operating costs based not on the units' rated capacity but on the job requirements—which are the same for all alternatives.

11.18 REPLACEMENT BY LEASING

Whether to own or lease equipment is a basic problem which has been given much attention by management. Leasing presents several advantages. By leasing we can avoid the responsibilities of ownership, including maintenance, repair, protection against loss and destruction, obsolescence, deterioration, and replacement of equipment. These become the worries of another party. It is also possible that the lessor will do a more efficient and more economical job if he specializes in handling that class of equipment.

Furthermore, by avoiding ownership through leasing, we do not have to finance the equipment. Assets that are leased will not appear on the books as assets or, if borrowing is necessary to finance the purchase, as funded debt. Leasing instead of owning warehouses, buildings, tools, and transportation equipment can make considerable differences in a company's debt position and balance sheet ratios.

The profit picture of leasing versus owning is determined by an economy comparison, as illustrated by the following example.

EXAMPLE 11.18 A 2-year-old truck has a net realizable value of $3,000 and is expected to have a salvage value of $900 after its remaining 3-year life. Its operating disbursements for taxes, insurance, and registration are $160 a year. Annual inspection, maintenance, and repair are estimated to be $150 for the first year and to increase $50 each year thereafter. An equivalent truck can be leased for 20 cents a mile plus $15 a day for every day that the customer keeps it, whether it is driven or not. The expected annual utilization is 3,000 miles and 30 days. It is presumed that the same employee will act as driver whether the company owns or leases. The minimum required rate of return is 15%.

SOLUTION:

$$\text{Own} \quad \underset{0}{\overset{3,000 \quad D = 310 + (t-1)(50) \quad L = 900}{\vdash\!\!-\!\!-\!\!-\!\!-\!\!-\!\!-\!\!-\!\!-\!\!-\!\!-\!\!-\!\!-\!\!\dashv}} \underset{3}{}$$

$$\text{Lease} \quad \underset{0}{\overset{0 \qquad\qquad D = 1,050}{\vdash\!\!-\!\!-\!\!-\!\!-\!\!-\!\!-\!\!-\!\!-\!\!-\!\!-\!\!-\!\!-\!\!\dashv}} \underset{3}{}$$

AC to own:

$$(3,000 - 900)\underset{0.43798}{(A/P, .15, 3)} + (900)(0.15) + 160 + 150 + 50\underset{0.9071}{(A/G, 3)} = \$1,410$$

AC to lease:

$$(3,000)(0.20) + (30)(15) = \$1,050$$

Here it is cheaper to lease than to own. It can be noted from this example how a high first cost coupled with low utilization creates a situation economically favorable to leasing. Consequently, contractors may find it more economical to rent bulldozers, power shovels, steam rollers, air compressors, and rock drills to meet special needs on a construction contract than to purchase the equipment.

The own-lease problem has been included because it frequently appears as a replacement problem, namely, whether to replace existing equipment by renting it or to replace leased equipment by owning it.

11.19 SECOND-HAND EQUIPMENT

It was noted in the last section that if utilization is low it may be more economical to rent than to continue ownership. Under similar circumstances the purchase of good second-hand equipment for jobs of short duration is often more economical than renting. It is frequently a method of providing construction machinery for use on a specific job or industrial machinery for use on a short contract, particularly the extra or the special machinery that will be needed on a given job. The equipment is often sold at the conclusion of the contract. The period is too short to justify the purchase of new equipment just for that job, and the period and utilization are too great to justify rental.

11.20 IMPROVING PRESENT EQUIPMENT

A decision to replace a piece of equipment is not complete unless one has considered the alternative possibility of improving the present equipment. This alternative is so often better that it gives rise to the principle, "Always improve what you have."

The areas of possible improvement should, of course, include repairing and overhauling the equipment to correct the effects of deterioration, but primarily improvement should include redesigning, as far as this may be feasible and economical, to overcome the effects of obsolescence. Redesigning will largely consist of incorporating the new technologies that were not originally built into the machine—possibly because they were not available at that time. Such improvements often take the form of labor-saving designs and attachments with the ultimate objective of automatically feeding and ejecting the pieces, the mechanizing of all operations, the increase of operating speeds, provision for mechanical holding devices, and so on. The objective is to increase the engineering efficiency of the old machine. The cost is the cost of planning, building, and installing the design changes. The savings will largely result from an increase in the productivity of labor by reducing the time required for makeready, putaway, machine operation, handling, inspecting, setup, supervision, maintenance, and repair. The savings may also result from savings in material, power, and perhaps items of overhead.

The principle of improving what you have is based on the fact that the increase in efficiency may be achieved more cheaply by improving the old machine than by constructing or buying a whole new one. This is particularly true where the technological advance incorporated in the new machine may be largely the result of an addition of a labor-saving device. This is illustrated in the following example.

EXAMPLE 11.20 A present machine appears to be as reliable as when it was purchased 5 years ago; however, a technologically improved machine has just appeared which costs $2,000 and has operating disbursements of $540 a year. It is expected to have a salvage of $1,000 at the end of its 5-year economic life. The present machine has a net realizable value of $1,000, annual operating disbursements of $800, and $500 salvage value at the end of a 5-year economic life. The present machine can be improved by the addition of an automatic hopper feeder and an automatic ejector of finished parts at a cost of $500. These additions are expected to increase the salvage value in 5 years to $750 and to reduce operating disbursements to $610. The minimum required rate of return is 10%.

SOLUTION:

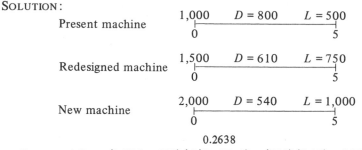

$$\overset{0.2638}{\text{Present, } AC_A = (1{,}000 - 500)(A/P, .10, 5) + (500)(0.10) + 800 = \$982}$$

$$\overset{0.2638}{\text{Redesigned, } AC_A = (1{,}500 - 750)(A/P, 5) + (750)(0.10) + 610 = \$883}$$

$$\overset{0.2638}{\text{New, } AC_B = (2{,}000 - 1{,}000)(A/P, 5) + (1{,}000)(0.10) + 540 = \$904}$$

Without improvement, the old machine would be replaced, but this is avoided by the more economical alternative of redesigning the machine.

It is not expected that the redesigned equipment will necessarily be as efficient as a new machine. What the creative designer is looking for is the more economic level of the added investment. He will find in many cases that adding investments sufficient to bring the old machine fully up to the engineering efficiency of the new machine will not be economical.

11.21 RETENTION FOR STANDBY

We have seen that replacement usually results in displacement instead of retirement but that, nevertheless, if any machine fails to win a contest for a degraded post, it should be retired. There is no justification in keeping a machine out of sentimentality. And there is no justification in keeping a unit on standby service unless it is economical to do so.

The alternative to the cost of owning a standby unit is the cost of a shutdown. The cost of "doing nothing," that is, continuing without a standby unit, is a real cost. It is the labor cost of idle employees (and, sometimes, extra shifts), material that may be wasted or destroyed, extra setup costs if they are occasioned by the shutdown, extra heat, light, and so on.

EXAMPLE 11.21 Shutdowns in the power supply to a glass-making process have occurred on an average of once every 4 years. Every shutdown costs $600, mostly for the labor of cleaning out the glass which has congealed in the molds. The company now owns an old steam-driven generator worth $150 scrap value whenever it is sold. It occupies space valued at $50 a year. The cost of inspecting, testing, and maintaining it so that it will be available when needed is $90 a year. The extra cost of operating it over the regular power supply during the short duration of a shutdown is considered to be negligible in spite of its low efficiency.

The minimum required rate of return is 15%.

SOLUTION: The probability of an occurrence in any year is 1 in 4, so the probable cost[1] in any year is 600/4 = $150. Therefore,

No standby, AC = $150

Standby, AC = (150)(0.15) + 50 + 90 = $162.50

In the given example it is more economic to suffer the damage then it is to do anything about it. Nevertheless, other alternatives may be more economic, such as designs to prevent the damage entirely, reduction of the extent of damage during the shutdown, or cheap restoration of the system after shutdown occurs. All the alternatives should be considered and tested.

Selection for standby service is the last opportunity for a piece of equipment to give service in the company, but its retention for that post is by no means assured. If the old generator unit fails to win an economic position in the company, then liquidation is desirable.

11.22 REPLACEMENT OF AN INCOME PROPERTY

Although the previous sections have illustrated cost-reduction investments, replacement situations also apply to income-expansion investments. Obviously, investment in one income-producing property can be replaced by investment in another; for example, a company can replace its investment in bonds with an

[1]For a complete explanation of these computations see Chapter 14.

investment in a new line of products. An income-expansion investment can re-place any status quo situation including a present policy not to invest. The fol-lowing example illustrates the general situation.

EXAMPLE 11.22 An investor feels he can fare better by selling his invest-ments in bonds currently yielding 5% for an estimated $100,000 and investing in income-producing real estate. He predicts that the property will be worth $120,000 in 10 years, that the gross income from rentals will be $22,000 a year, and that the cost of operation including maintenance, repairs, taxes, and oper-ation of the property will be $19,000. At maturity the bonds will be redeemed for $100,000.

SOLUTION:

$$\text{Real Estate} \quad \overset{100,000}{\underset{0}{\rule{0pt}{0pt}}} \quad \overset{I = 3,000}{\rule{0pt}{0pt}} \quad \overset{L = 120,000}{\underset{10}{\rule{0pt}{0pt}}}$$

Real Estate,

$$\text{PW} = (22,000 - 19,000)\overset{7.722}{(P/A, .05, 10)} + 120,000\overset{0.6139}{(P/F, 10)} = \$96,834$$

Bonds,

$$\text{PW} = \$100,000$$

Valued at the same rate of return as on the bonds, 5%, the real estate venture does not recover the entire $100,000 invested in it. The 20% appreciation in the property plus the small rental income are not enough to justify the investment quantitatively. Furthermore, the greater risk of not realizing the predicted in-comes turns the irreducible factors against the realty proposition.

11.23 FREQUENCY OF REPLACEMENT TESTS

The frequency of replacement tests ought to be guided by a general plan in-stead of a mere haphazard procedure. The need for initiative, and especially of a planned initiative, by management is necessary because no indication is received from equipment which should be replaced except in the rare instance of equip-ment which is so beyond repair that it cannot be made to provide further service (and in that case we do not need quantitative procedures to know that replace-ment is necessary). Some plans for replacement tests are also imperative because the lost profits caused by the rejection of savings by failing to replace on time are irretrievable and can be substantial.

Some guides to occasions for making replacement tests on a piece of equip-ment are

1. Whenever it appears that heavy obsolescence has occurred. This would be indicated by the appearance of new technological developments in replacement machines or processes, regardless of the age of the incumbent equipment.

2. Whenever it appears that heavy deterioration has occurred. This is indi-

cated by the necessity to overhaul or make more than routine repairs to a machine.

3. When the machine approaches the economic life that was originally forecast for it. If this does not result in replacement of the machine, it may appear judicious to test the machine every year thereafter.

PROBLEMS

11.1 A machine presently installed in a manufacturing plant can be sold for $1,500 "f.o.b. cars seller's factory." Disconnecting and dismounting it from its foundation will cost $100; boxing and loading it on the cars will cost $150. If the machine is kept for service elsewhere in the company, it can be moved and installed in a new department for $200 (after being disconnected and dismounted from its present location, of course).

1. What is the machine's investment value P for use in an economy analysis pertaining to (a) continuing the machine in its present task, (b) operating the machine on a new service in another department?

2. Compare these with the investment value of a machine that can be purchased from a second-hand dealer for $1,700 with freight allowed to the buyer's siding if the costs of removing it from the car and unboxing are negligible but the costs of inspection and testing are $50.

3. What is the investment value in case 1(b) immediately after the machine is installed in the department?

4. What is the investment value in case 1(a) and 1(b) if the machine must be reconditioned and overhauled for $300?

11.2 A 10-year-old machine has a $4,000 book value but only a $2,000 net realizable value. It is contending for its present job with a new machine costing $10,000 installed. The management insists that book value must be taken into account in the analysis. (a) Prove mathematically that book value is irrelevant to the choice. (b) Management maintains that replacement at this instant will show a loss in profit equal to the excess of book value over net realizable value. They propose to avoid this by continuing the unit in the present service. Comment on this policy.

11.3 Give examples of decisions in which the following costs will be relevant to the choice:

Indirect labor	Rework	Safety
Clerical labor	Subcontracting	Flexibility
Supervision	Floor space	Fringe benefits
Indirect materials	Tooling	Inventory
Scrap	Supplies	Down time

11.4 A new machine can be acquired for $25,800. Its economic life is predicted to be 8 years with a salvage of $6,000. Operating disbursements are expected to be $16,500 a year. The existing machine presently has a net salvage value of $3,000 and this is expected to decrease $500 a year. The annual disbursements of the present machine will be $21,000 and these are not expected to increase in the foreseeable future. The minimum required rate of return is 20%. Make an annual-cost comparison. Test the old machine for a 1-year life. What conclusion can be drawn from a 1-year test?

11.5   A new machine can be acquired for $25,800. Its operating disburse-
ments for the first year of operation are expected to be $16,500; there-
after they are expected to increase $692 a year as a result of deteri-
oration. The analyst predicts that the proposed machine will be replaced
in the future by "like" machines having the same first cost and operating
disbursements as the proposed new machine.   Replacements will be
necessary because of increasing operating disbursements.   The salvage
values of all the new machines in any year t are expected to conform to
the formula,

$$L = \left[\frac{(15 - t)(16 - t)}{15 \times 16} \right] (25,800)$$

The present machine has a net salvage value today of $3,000, and this is
expected to decrease $500 a year for every year that the machine is kept
by the company.   Its operating disbursements will be $22,728 for the
coming year, and these are expected to increase $650 a year thereafter.
The minimum required rate of return is 20%.   Should the present
machine be replaced?

11.6   Rework Problem 11.5 under the following revised conditions. The economic life of the proposed machine will be terminated as the result of
combined deterioration and obsolescence, which is presumed to increase
annually by an arithmetic gradient.   The differences between the next
year's disbursements of the two machines is $6,228, and this is presumed
to result entirely from deterioration and obsolescence. The same rate is
expected of new machines.   The old machine is currently 9 years old.
All other data are the same as in Problem 11.5.

11.7   Rework Problem 11.5 under the following revised conditions. The economic life of the proposed machine will be terminated as the result of
combined deterioration and obsolescence which is presumed to increase
annually by an unknown arithmetic gradient.   The economic life of the
proposed machine is predicted to be 7 years (i.e., the analyst predicts the
life, not the gradient).   The salvage value in year t in the life of the proposed machine or any future machine is presumed to vary by the formula,

$$L = \left[\frac{(15 - t)(16 - t)}{(15 \times 16)} \right] (25,800)$$

All other data are the same as in Problem 11.5.

11.8   A new machine can be acquired for $25,800. Its operating costs for the
first year of operations are expected to be $16,500, and they are ex-
pected to increase annually by an arithmetic gradient as the result of
combined deterioration and obsolescence. This increase is expected to
be $1,060 a year. The salvage value of the machine is expected to be
30% of the first cost whenever the machine is replaced. The minimum
required rate of return is 20%. What is the economic life and the comparative annual cost of the new machine?

11.9   Rework Problem 11.8 except that instead of predicting the gradient the
analyst predicts that the economic life will be 7 years. The combined
deterioration and obsolescence gradient will be arithmetic as before.

Compute the gradient and determine the comparative annual cost of the proposed machine.

11.10 Machine A costs $20,000 and its next year's operating disbursements are expected to be $12,000. The analyst estimates that the deterioration and obsolescence gradient will be 4% of the first year's operating disbursements and that it will increase arithmetically. Salvage will be 10% of the first cost whenever the equipment is retired. The present machine has a zero net realizable value and its operating cost for next year is predicted to be $18,000. The minimum required rate of return is 30%. Should the present machine be retained for 1 more year of service?

11.11 A machine costs $10,000. Its operating disbursements for the coming year are predicted to be $4,000. The deterioration and obsolescence of the machine are expected to increase by an arithmetic gradient throughout the life of the machine. The economic life is predicted to be 10 years. Assume that the machine is to have a constant salvage ratio of 0.865. Accordingly, the salvage value in any year will be 86.5% of the previous year's, or in any year t it will be $P(0.865)^t$ where P is the first cost. The net realizable value of the present machine is zero and its next year's operating disbursements total $7,000. The minimum required rate of return is 15%. Compute the gradient and the uniform equivalent annual cost.

11.12 Rework Problem 11.11 using the rate-of-return method of analysis.

11.13 A machine costing $20,000 is predicted to have an 8-year economic life with a salvage value at that time of $4,600. Its next-year operating disbursements are $15,000. The present machine on this job has a net realizable value of $2,500. This is expected to decrease $500 if the machine is kept another year. Its operating disbursements for the coming year are expected to be $19,000. The present machine is currently 10 years old. It is presumed that the difference in operating disbursements between the two machines for the coming year is the result of deterioration and obsolescence and that this difference has been accumulating annually by an arithmetic gradient. It is predicted that the proposed machine will have the same gradient as the old machine. The minimum required rate of return is 20%. Compare the two machines by the annual-cost method.

11.14 An existing compressor will supply only 60% of the predicted future compressed-air requirements of the plant. Its net realizable value is $2,000 with operating disbursements of $5,000 a year at that load. A new compressor that will just furnish the required 40% additional air can be purchased for $9,000. Its operating disbursements are $3,100 a year. A full-size machine can be purchased for $20,000 with operating disbursements of $7,600. The economic life of all three machines is estimated to be 10 years with salvage values equal to 10% of the present values. The minimum required rate of return is 20%. Compare the alternatives by the annual-cost method.

11.15 The machine currently installed on a job has a net realizable value of $3,000. In 5 years, according to predictions, an extensive overhaul will be required which will make it uneconomical to continue the unit in service; the salvage value at that date will be zero. Its annual operating disbursements are $4,000; however, this output is only half of the estimated future production requirements.

A new and improved machine of the same capacity as the existing machine can be purchased for $10,000. Its operating disbursements are expected to be $3,750, and its economic life is predicted to be 10 years with $1,250 salvage at that date.

A large machine is available for $18,000. At its full load it will provide 120% of the required capacity. The disbursements when operating at its full load are $8,400. The curve of the machine's engineering efficiency is essentially flat from 80% to 120% load. Its economic life is predicted to be 10 years with $2,250 salvage value at that date.

Ten years from now the present process and the equipment installed in the process are expected to be obsolete and will have to be replaced. It is also predicted that the salvage value of new equipment after 5 years of service will be 45% of the initial cost. The minimum required rate of return is 10%. Select the most economic alternative based on an annual-cost analysis.

11.16   A house can be purchased for $20,000. The prospective owner expects to occupy it for 12 years, at which time the salvage is expected to be $16,000. He estimates that the total annual operating disbursements—taxes, heat, insurance, maintenance, repairs—will be $1,200. He estimates that at the end of every 4 years, including the year he plans to sell it, the house will have to be painted at a cost of $300. He also estimates that maintenance and repairs will increase $10 a year after the first year. Alternatively, he can rent a house for $180 a month plus $15 for garage. This property will provide about the same facilities as the house he contemplates buying. He anticipates that his rent will be raised $15 a month 4 years from now and another $15 a month 8 years from now. He can invest his money elsewhere at 6% interest. Should he buy or rent, based on a rate-of-return analysis?

11.17   A machine was installed 2 years ago for $10,000. Its present net realizable value is $7,000. Disbursements on the required services are $1,500 a year. A second-hand machine can be purchased and installed for $2,500. Its disbursements on this service will be $2,000 a year. Economic lives for both machines are estimated to be 8 years with $1,000 salvage for the former machine and zero for the latter. The minimum required rate of return is 15%. Make a selection using the rate-of-return method.

11.18   A new machine can be purchased for $15,000 with an economic life of 10 years and salvage at that time of $3,000. Its operating disbursements are $8,000 a year. The present machine has a net realizable value of $3,000 and its operating disbursements are $10,000 a year. If the present machine is not displaced now, it is expected to continue on this service for 10 years. The salvage value will be zero. Alternatively, the present machine can be overhauled and modernized for $4,000, which will change the operating disbursements to $9,000 a year. In this case the economic life is also expected to be 10 years, but with $1,500 salvage at that date. The minimum required rate of return is 25%. Which machine should be selected, based on an annual-cost analysis?

11.19 Without standby equipment, a shutdown will cost $200 a day. It is estimated that an average of 2.5 days a year can be lost due to shutdowns. A standby machine can be purchased for $4,000 with an economic life of 10 years and $500 salvage at that date. Its annual disbursements, including 2.5 days of actual operation, would be $100. The minimum required rate of return is 20%. What decision is dictated by an annual-cost analysis?

11.20 An investor has $5,000 in a bank account at 4% interest compounded semi-annually. He can use this sum to finance the purchase of a town lot. He expects that in 10 years he will be able to sell it for 60% more than he paid for it. During that period he will have to pay $200 a year in property taxes and insurance. Should he make the purchase?

12

Economy of Variations in Operating Activities

12.1 VARIATIONS IN OUTPUT

Up to this point the text has been concerned with decisions for acquiring or replacing equipment based on a continuous picture of costs over the lifetime of the investment. Year-to-year variations in costs were, of course, included in the continuous picture if they could be predicted. However, certain problems exist which are concerned solely with the economic effects of variations alone. Despite the best efforts of management, businesses can rarely be run at a constant level throughout the year and, as might be expected, a number of operating decisions stem from variations in the activity of the firm.

Basically, these problems arise from the fact that variations in costs (i.e., the imputs to the system) are not proportional to variations in output. In the general case, the input-output curve does not pass through zero and it is not linear. This is explained by the fact that production costs consist of fixed costs, independent of output, and variable costs which, although they are a function of output, respond to the law of diminishing returns.

These variations in output are within the limits of design of the existing plant, so we are not concerned, as we have been, with the addition of equipment.

12.2 FIXED COSTS AND VARIABLE COSTS

Certain costs of an operation do not vary with changes in output; within limits they are independent of activity and of utilization of equipment. As may be expected, investment costs are readily classified as fixed costs. All "overhead" costs generally fit this classification because taxes, insurance, rent, heat, light, salaries of supervisory and administrative forces, and maintenance, do not vary for certain changes in output.

Costs cannot be classified as permanently fixed or variable because, in general, any cost can be altered by strong administrative action or, on the other hand, remain constant as the result of a failure to act. For example, supervisory costs may be considered constant regardless of output because the supervisory force is usually not reduced or increased with fluctuations in output. However, given a large enough or long enough decrease in output, the supervisory force may be intentionally reduced. Similarly, the ordinarily fixed costs of heat and light can be reduced by closing sections of the factory.

By the same reasoning, costs classified as variable may prove to be fixed in given situations. Although direct labor is considered a variable cost it is fixed in a situation where a cutback in output cannot, for some reason, be accompanied by a reduction in the direct labor force. In some instances, too, a cost may be partly fixed and variable; for example, part of the maintenance costs of a machine may be proportional to its hours of operation, whereas certain routine inspection and maintenance costs may continue regardless of reasonable changes in output.

The most unrealistic decisions can result from a rigid classification of fixed and variable costs without a careful examination of each situation. And, as we have seen, errors can also result from the assumption that variable costs are always directly proportional to changes in output.

12.3 INPUT-OUTPUT RELATIONSHIP

The input-output relationships of any operation can be ideally illustrated by the input-output of an electric motor. Generally the output of a system is expressed in the units produced by the system and the input is measured in dollars; however, for simplicity in the following example both the input and output are in units of horsepower.

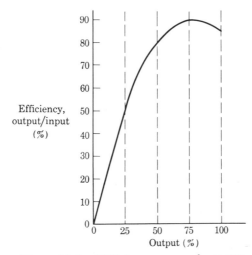

Figure 12.3a   Efficiency curve of a motor

Table 12.3a INPUT-OUTPUT RELATIONS OF AN ELECTRIC
MOTOR

Load (%)	Efficiency (%)	Input (hp)	Output (hp)
0	0	10	0
25	50	50	25
50	80	62.5	50
75	90	83.3	75
100	85	118	100

In practice, the input-output relations of a motor are usually expressed by an efficiency curve as shown in Fig. 12.3a. The curve is therefore a plot of Output/ Input, as the ordinate, versus Output, as the abscissa. The data from which the curve is constructed is given in Table 12.3a

The input-output relationship, plotted in Fig. 12.3b, depends on the shape of the efficiency curve of the operation. Inasmuch as the slope of the efficiency curve goes from positive to negative through zero, the input-output relationship is ideally ogee shaped, as shown in Fig. 12.3b. This figure illustrates that the input may increase at a faster or slower rate than the output, depending on the operating point, because the ratio of change in input to change in output is constant only if the curve is linear. Figure 12.3b represents the theoretical relationship of the inputs and outputs of any operation, although we frequently see only a straight-line approximation of this curve.

Figure 12.3b also illustrates that if the total input is viewed as the sum of fixed and variable components, a *change* in load is accomplished at an expense equal only to the *change* in the variable component.

The following example introduces some of the problems arising from variations in the operation of the preceding system.

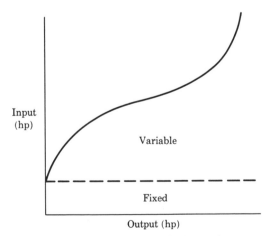

Figure 12.3b Input-output relations of a motor

EXAMPLE 12.3 The 100-hp motor described in Table 12.3a is operated 5,000 hours a year. Power costs 2 cents per horsepower-hour. The motor costs $1,510 with $500 salvage at the end of a 10-year life. For simplicity, insurance, taxes, maintenance, etc., are assumed to be zero. The minimum required rate of return is 10%. Show the input-output relationship of the system represented by the motor.

SOLUTION.

$$1,510 \quad D = \text{energy cost at specified loads} \quad L = 500$$
$$\begin{array}{cc} 0 & 10 \end{array}$$

Annual investment costs:

$$\overset{0.16275}{(1,510 - 500)(A/P, .10, 10)} + (500)(0.10) = \$214$$

$$\text{Annual energy cost} = \frac{(\text{bhp output}) (5,000 \text{ hr}) (0.02)}{\text{Efficiency}}$$

The energy and the costs are summarized in Table 12.3b, and the costs are plotted in Fig. 12.3c.

If we assume that the motor, like many other systems, will continue to run even if the operating point falls to zero, the $1,214 cost, consisting of $214 investment cost plus the $1,000 no-load power cost, may be regarded as a fixed cost. On the contrary, if operating practice dictates shutting down the motor,

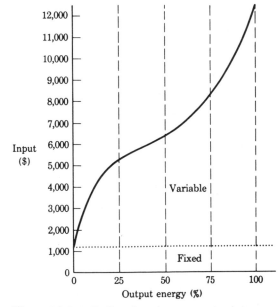

Figure 12.3c   Dollars input versus output energy

Table 12.3b   DOLLARS INPUT VERSUS ENERGY OUTPUT OF AN ELECTRIC
MOTOR

Load (%)	Output energy (hp-hr)	Annual power cost	Annual investment cost	Input (annual total cost)
0	0	$ 1,000	$214	$ 1,214
25	125,000	5,000	214	5,214
50	250,000	6,250	214	6,464
75	375,000	8,333	214	8,547
100	500,000	11,801	214	12,015

the fixed cost will be something else, which proves that fixed or variable costs cannot be classified in disregard of operating conditions.

This example illustrates the operation of any system at variable load (and therefore variable efficiency). This is typical of machinery operating at variable power, namely, at different rates of output. It is also broadly typical of a factory producing at various levels of output provided that management maintains adequate control over variable costs to assure their reduction with decreases in output.

We should observe that conditions may permit or require operating the motor at constant power (instead of variable power). Since the motor is running at constant load, the varying output requirements are met in this case by reducing or increasing the hours of operation. The advantage, of course, is that the system theoretically runs at constant efficiency. The input-output relation is therefore linear (but not through zero).

As an illustration of the two methods of operation, suppose a motor is driving a compressor supplying gas to a chemical process. A reduced demand for the product can be met (a) by operating the compressor at a reduced load to provide the required output over the regular work week or (b) by operating the compressor at a load representing *maximum* efficiency of the system and reducing the hours of operation. Method (a) requires the whole process to operate at a lower rate regardless of efficiency, whereas in (b) the process operates at optimum efficiency but for shorter periods of time.

Compare these two methods in the operation of a factory. A reduced demand for the product may be met (a) by operating at partial loads retaining a five-day week or (b) by reducing the work week and retaining the full work force. In the latter case, the efficiency is theoretically constant at a constant rate of output (assuming that efficiency will not be changed by reducing the length of the work week).

12.4 UNIT COSTS

Inasmuch as sales reports (and many statistical reports) are based on units of goods, management often deals with analyses involving unit costs and unit prices.

Unit cost is simply the total input cost divided by the number of units produced in the period.

Unit cost like total input cost, therefore, is composed of fixed cost and variable cost components, and many problems are based on the effect of changes in output on unit cost and its fixed and variable cost components. This is illustrated in the following example.

EXAMPLE 12.4 Compute the unit cost of energy delivered by the motor in Example 12.3a. The energy outputs and the total costs were listed in Table 12.3b and reproduced in Table 12.4

SOLUTION. The unit costs, computed from annual costs, are listed in the last three columns of Table 12.4. The unit cost at each level of production is plotted in Fig. 12.4.

Fixed cost per unit, as noted, continues to diminish as it is spread over more units of output. On the other hand, the total and the variable unit costs increase after reaching a minimum because they are images of the efficiency curve and

Table 12.4 THE VARIATION OF UNIT COST WITH OUTPUT

Load (%)	Output units (hp-hr)	Total cost	Fixed cost	Variable cost	Unit cost (¢)	Fixed cost/unit (¢)	Variable cost/unit (¢)
0	0	$ 1,214	$1,214	$ 0	∞	∞	∞
25	125,000	5,214	1,214	4,000	4.17	0.97	3.20
50	250,000	6,464	1,214	5,250	2.59	0.49	2.10
75	375,000	8,547	1,214	7,333	2.28	0.32	1.96
100	500,000	12,015	1,214	10,801	2.40	0.24	2.16

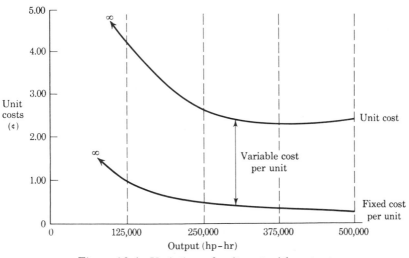

Figure 12.4   Variation of unit cost with output

reflect the law of diminishing returns. However, had the input-output curve been linear, the total and the variable unit costs would have continued to decrease with no upturn.

Example 12.4 shows that the unit cost of a product cannot be regarded as a firm figure, except at a given production rate (and, in practice, even that will change with daily conditions). As noted in the example, the unit cost of the product varies from 4.17 cents at 25% load through a low of 2.28 cents at 75% load up to 2.40 cents at 100% load. This pattern of input-output of a motor applies in general form to many systems, including a manufacturing plant. The situation can be summarized by noting that in most systems the cost to produce a unit of the product becomes a function of the plant load, and therefore unit cost is not constant.

12.5 MANAGEMENT ACTION TO MEET VARIATIONS IN OUTPUT

Although we have noted that unit cost is a function of the level of output of the system relative to its designed capacity, management action is usually required to secure the theoretical input-output relation. The reason is that many variable costs will not vary without management action. For example, executive control is required to reduce direct labor when the system's demand falls off. If such costs are not controlled, the unit cost at reduced output will be even higher. But in extreme circumstances this normal control may not be enough and extraordinary management action will be taken, as the following example suggests.

EXAMPLE 12.5 A factory has operating costs at the various outputs given in Table 12.5. The problem assumes that, in pursuance of normal management policy, variable costs such as direct labor will automatically remain variable, and therefore the input-output curve will take the general shape discussed earlier.

The fixed costs consist of overhead costs, including depreciation, insurance, taxes, heat, light, rent, supplies, certain maintenance, indirect labor, supervisory and management salaries, research and development, and so on. The variable costs consist of direct costs, including labor, materials, direct maintenance and

Table 12.5 EXPECTED INPUT-OUTPUT RELATIONS OF THE FACTORY

Load (%)	Units produced	Total cost	Fixed cost	Variable cost	Total unit cost	Unit fixed cost	Unit variable cost
0	$ 0	$ 8,000	$8,000	$ 0	$ ∞	$ ∞	$ ∞
20	2,000	20,000	8,000	12,000	10.00	4.00	6.00
40	4,000	24,100	8,000	16,100	6.03	2.00	4.03
60	6,000	26,850	8,000	18,850	4.47	1.33	3.14
80	8,000	32,500	8,000	24,550	4.07	1.00	3.07
100	10,000	39,400	8,000	31,400	3.94	0.80	3.14
120	12,000	49,500	8,000	41,500	4.13	0.67	3.46
140	14,000	70,000	8,000	62,000	5.00	0.57	4.43

repair charges, power and fuel—in short, all charges that can be specifically identified with the production of each additional item of goods.

Assume the product has been unit-priced at $5.75, which management regards as producing a reasonable profit on the unit cost of $3.94 at normal rated capacity. In a serious depression, however, the sales are expected to drop to 40% of plant capacity for an extended period. What will be the profit position and what can be done about it?

SOLUTION. At 40% output or 4,000 units, the gross income of 4,000 × 5.75 = $23,000 will be less than the total cost of $24,100, and the company will show a loss of $1,100. (On the other hand, if the unit costs were identical at all outputs, the company's profit would have been $7,240, i.e., 23,000 − 4,000 × 3.94, instead of a loss—quite a different story.)

Offhand, it would appear that the answer is that the company must suffer a loss of $1,100. However, by vigorous management action the input-output relationship can be changed and the break-even point can be relocated. The idea is to temporarily redesign the system toward a new operating point, keeping in mind the necessity of a reversal in the future. Actually, this is a procedure which is continuously followed by management as operations shrink or enlarge. The redesign is governed by the expected duration of the change in output and the extent of reversibility required.

In the given example the objective is to design for maximum efficiency at 40% output for a temporary term. Some of the possible actions are as follows:

1. Schedule work in those plants and departments or on those machines having the highest efficiency of the new loads and curtail operations on other machines. For example, the long setup times generally required for machines having high production rates may make them uneconomical on small production lots if machines having shorter setup times are available. The goal is to produce where the increment cost is lowest, even if it means closing sections of the plant.

2. Along the same line, substitute any methods which are more efficient at lower outputs than at higher outputs. A plant organized for mass production should examine its procedures, methods, policies, and designs for processing, assembling, inspecting, packaging, and handling the product on low production.

3. Reorganize the company for lower production. The reorganization may result in a reduction of the supervisory force; for example, a reduction in the number of assistant supervisors and reassignment to other jobs.

4. Introduce a program to reduce fixed costs (by converting them to variable costs). At the reduced output, the nominally fixed indirect expenses, such as heat, light, maintenance, and rent can be readjusted to the lower output.

5. Determine whether wages and salaries can be readjusted to the lower productivity of the individual.

6. Readjust economic lot sizes, etc., to the new level.

7. Determine whether new products or by-products can be introduced which will use the idle plant and equipment.

This example only illustrates that a stated input-output relation applies to a design of a plant of a specific capacity. Sometimes, as in the case of a factory, the design can be altered to meet a new operating point; in others, as in the case of a motor, redesign may be very expensive and uneconomical.

12.6 INCREMENT COST

Increment cost can be defined simply as the additional cost that will be incurred as the result of increasing the output one more unit. Conversely, it can be defined as the cost that will not be incurred if the output is reduced one unit. More technically, it is the variation in output resulting from a unit change in input. It is known as the marginal cost. It is the change in the variable cost for a unit change in output. It is the rate of change of output with input, and consequently increment cost is the slope of the input-output curve at a given operating point, namely,

$$\text{Increment cost} = \frac{\Delta \text{ input}}{\Delta \text{ output}} = \frac{\Delta \text{ input cost}}{\Delta \text{ output units}}$$

Increment cost is constant only for a linear curve or linear approximations of the curve.

The increment cost can be recognized as the cost which is relevant to the choice between producing one more unit and not producing it, as illustrated in the following example.

EXAMPLE 12.6 Compute the increment costs of the factory in Example 12.5 for each 2,000 units of output. Compare these with the fixed, variable, and total unit costs at all loads. If the plant is operating at 100% capacity and the company is offered an order for 2,000 more units at a special price of $4.50 each, should it be accepted?

SOLUTION. The costs of Example 12.5 are reproduced in the first six columns of Table 12.6, and the computed increment cost appears in the last column.

Table 12.6 INCREMENT COST OF THE FACTORY

Load (%)	Units produced	Total cost	Total unit cost	Unit fixed cost	Unit variable cost	Unit incremental cost
0	0	$ 8,000	$ ∞	$ ∞	$ ∞	$ 0
20	2,000	20,000	10.00	4.00	6.00	6.00
40	4,000	24,100	6.03	2.00	4.03	2.05
60	6,000	26,850	4.47	1.33	3.14	1.38
80	8,000	32,550	4.07	1.00	3.07	2.85
100	10,000	39,400	3.94	0.80	3.14	3.43
120	12,000	49,500	4.13	0.67	3.46	5.05
140	14,000	70,000	5.00	0.57	4.43	10.25

The disagreement between the increment cost and the variable cost emphasizes the change in efficiency at various operating points as expressed by the nonlinearity of the input-output curve. Only with a linear curve will variable and increment costs be alike. The increment cost, however, quantifies the *difference* between the choice of making or not making units at a given margin of production. Accepting an order for 2,000 more units at $4.50 may seem better than not accepting it, because this is higher than the variable cost, at 120% capacity, of $3.46. But the extra cost of producing these units is $5.05, the unit increment cost, so the company would be out of pocket. The total cost of $4.13, which would also seem to advocate acceptance of the order, is misleading because, as stated, the company would actually be out of pocket by accepting an order for 2,000 more units at the offered price.

The example, of course, tacitly assumes that acceptance of this order would have no other implications, such as injury to the price structure if sold at this price, that subsequent orders at higher prices will not be available, and that management cannot temporarily redesign the system to reduce the increment cost.

12.7 SUNK COST

A sunk cost in a given situation is one that will not be altered by future action. A sunk cost thereby becomes irrelevant to the choice. A good example is the book value of the present equipment in a replacement analysis—it is sunk because it must be written off regardless of the equipment selected. Generally speaking, therefore, past obligations to pay in the future are sunk.

In input-output operations the fixed costs are generally viewed as sunk costs but, as noted, must be reviewed in each prospective situation before positive classification. It is interesting to note in Example 12.6, for the situation relative to accepting 2,000 more units, that all costs except the increment costs were sunk costs! This means that the so-called variable costs can be sunk costs, too.

A rigid classification of a cost as a sunk cost is not generally possible, but there can be no question that the term eloquently describes the relationship of a cost to a decision.

12.8 PROBLEM OF SETTING UNIT COST

The analyst often uses accounting data for economy decisions, but he should always be sure that he understands the accounting procedures which established the data. This implies an adequate comprehension of accounting practices. We cannot attempt to teach accounting here, but nevertheless the analyst is warned against using accounting data blindly without a thorough understanding of its origin. In attempting to illustrate this problem we caution the reader that we admit to using a simplified accounting procedure for the purpose of illustration.

The accountant deals with unit costs in a number of ways, one purpose being to set unit prices. Where the output of a factory consists of several different kinds of products (as it invariably does) the computation of unit cost can no longer be the simple task of dividing the total annual factory cost by the total annual number of units produced. The first step in the attack on this complex problem consists of dividing all costs into two classes: direct costs and overhead costs.

Direct costs are those which can be reasonably allocated by the accountant to a specific unit of production. For example, the metal used to make a valve and the labor to form the metal are both direct costs. The direct costs are all variable costs. They are charged to the product when the labor or material is applied to product. If direct labor is idle due to reduced factory output and consequently cannot be fairly charged to the product, the cost of idle labor can be charged directly to the profit-and-loss statement as "idle-time expense" and not to the product.

The overhead costs are the indirect and the fixed costs. Typical examples are depreciation, insurance, property taxes, heat, power, rent, supervisory and clerical costs, maintenance, and the expense of staff departments like engineering, etc. These obviously are expenses that do not go directly into the product. On the other hand, some material or labor which goes directly into the product may be classified as indirect expense for accounting convenience. For example, nails and lumber for crating, although directly variable with output, may be classified as indirect expense if there is undue difficulty in allocating them to each product. Consequently, not all overhead costs are fixed costs, and overhead cost has both variable and fixed components.

Apportionment of overhead to the various products in the line must be according to the degree that each product is responsible for causing the overhead expense. Several methods of allocation of overhead are in use, but a common method is to distribute the burden according to the number of hours of direct labor to produce each unit of goods.

EXAMPLE 12.8 The overhead for the coming period is estimated to be $100,000. This includes all fixed and indirect costs necessary to run the factory at a normal output. The normal output of the factory is estimated to be 75% capacity and the hours of direct labor required to run the factory at this capacity is estimated to be 200,000. This company manufactures 10 sizes of valves. Compute the cost of manufacturing Valve A if the material cost is $2 and the direct labor is 3 hours at a labor rate of $1.50 per hour.

SOLUTION. The overhead rate, based on direct labor hours, is 100,000/200,000 = 50 cents per hour of direct labor. The unit cost of Valve A is

Direct material	$2.00
Direct labor, 3 × 1.50	4.50
Overhead, 3 × 0.50	1.50
Unit cost of Valve A	$8.00

In the ensuing period, if the plant operates at less than 75% capacity the accountant can charge the unallocated overhead to profit and loss as an expense called *underabsorbed burden* or, if it operates at excess capacity, credit the excess absorption as a profit to the financial statement.

The error, of course, is to regard the $8.00 unit cost as a constant. This confuses certain business and engineering economy decisions because it conceals the fact that unit costs may vary with output, and if this accounting data is adopted as valid under all circumstances it hides the true data relevant to the choice.

12.9 MAKE-OR-BUY DECISIONS

The background for make-or-buy decisions was developed in the two preceding sections. These decisions particularly emphasize the concept of sunk cost, as illustrated in the following example.

EXAMPLE 12.9 A manufacturer of valves has little demand for Valve *A*, one of the items in his line of products. This valve with a unit cost of $8 as computed in Example 12.8 can be purchased from an outside supplier for $7 in the required amount of 200 valves per year. Should Valve *A* be manufactured or purchased from the supplier?

SOLUTION. Offhand, it would appear to be cheaper by $1 per valve to purchase than to make valves. However, examination of the accounting data in Section 12.8 shows that $1.50 of the $8 unit cost is overhead and $6.50 is for direct material and labor. If this overhead will not be reduced as a result of not making the valves, then the entire $1.50 is a sunk cost and irrelevant to the choice. Therefore the increment cost of $6.50 compared with the $7 cost of buying indicates a $0.50 advantage in making the valve.

Another way of arriving at the same conclusion is that the $8 unit cost of making the valve is composed of $6.50 direct cost and $1.50 overhead, and the unit cost of buying is $8.50, composed of $7 direct purchase cost and $1.50 overhead—again a $0.50 advantage per valve for making over buying.

12.10 DUMPING

The variations in the output of a plant, usually caused by sales fluctuations, not only result in operations at less than optimum efficiency but also create an endless management task of adjusting or even redesigning the plant to the new point of output. Such tasks may include finding work for an excess direct labor force in order to avoid the "idle-time expense" (which is chargeable to management, not the product) or may include finding new methods to break bottlenecks resulting from operations at excess capacity, and so on. The examples are innumerable.

Many advantages can be derived by operating the plant at a constant output, and every method to achieve this should be considered, based, of course, on an economic test.

One of these devices is dumping the unsaleable production when the total output falls below the desired optimum operating level. The inference, of course, is that this excess production over the demands of the regular market can only be sold at reduced prices. These sales must be made in new markets, such as foreign markets, or even in domestic markets where the product appears unbranded or under a different brand name. This policy is based on the premise that the original market will not be disrupted by the low cost source created by dumping.

One question is how low the price must be to unload the required amount and how low a price the manufacturer can afford to offer. The latter is largely dictated by the increment cost, as shown in the following example.

EXAMPLE 12.10 The data in Table 12.6 shows the unit total cost, unit variable cost, and unit increment cost at various levels of operation of a given manufacturer. Assume that the price of the product, for various marketing considerations, is fixed at $5.75 but that not more than 8,000 units a year can be sold in a predicted period. What minimum price must be received for 2,000 units if they are dumped in a low-priced market?

SOLUTION. Referring to Table 12.6, the unit total cost is $3.94, the unit variable cost is $3.14, and the increment cost is $3.43. As we have seen, the variable cost, $3.14, is meaningless in a decision of this type, but if the increment cost of $3.43 is received, the company will recover its direct outlay and, at least, will not be out of pocket. Furthermore, any price above $3.43 brings income the company could not otherwise receive and will increase the net profit even though the price is less than $3.94, the total unit cost. The objective is to obtain the highest price above $3.43 that will dispose of the excess capacity. Under certain circumstances, it may even prove economic to be out of pocket, in order to secure other advantages.

The policy of dumping may become especially attractive in business recessions where the level of operation is so low that the gross income from sales is less than the total cost of operations. Any excess capacity that can be dumped at prices exceeding the increment cost will serve to reduce the overall loss of doing business.

12.11 OPERATIONS ABOVE NORMAL

It is easy for management to accept all the business it can get, but this is not always as profitable as it may seem. Like the policy of dumping to increase the output to the point of optimum efficiency, a policy of reducing output peaks merits consideration. Several methods are available, such as buying instead of making (through subcontracting) or taking orders on long shipments.

If pressed far enough, the diminishing efficiency can reduce the net profit to that which would have been received at a much lower level of output—in fact, the input-output curve can theoretically turn up sharply enough to have costs exceed sales income.

Furthermore, hidden dangers are attached to overtrading. The firm acquires abnormal amounts of inventory, operates on high accounts receivable, swollen liabilities, and low cash. The firm at that time is vulnerable to "unexpected" occurrences. For example, a sudden drop in the economy level can leave the firm with inventory which cannot be liquidated except at losses, with accounts receivable that can't be collected quickly (if at all, in some cases), and with many bills to be paid and little cash to weather the storm.

The price of overtrading, like any investment, should be measured on its returns, and many of these will be intangible. To keep a good customer a firm may have to take his order regardless of the level of plant operation or the loss that it may cause. To maintain sales relationships a company may not be able to refuse orders that will result in excessive operations. However, if the situation results from purposely overtrading, the cost can exceed the prospective reward.

12.12 JOINT COSTS, JOINT PRODUCTS, BY-PRODUCTS, AND DIVERSE PRODUCTS

The basic economics behind the development of joint products, by-products, or diverse products rests on the existence and utilization of waste. This may be waste material, waste labor, waste space, or waste machine time. Companies conduct programs to reduce waste; however, waste is inevitable in any plant, and the most economical procedure may be to utilize it in the production of new products.

EXAMPLE 12.12   The cost of disposal of a chemical waste is $2.50 a hundredweight. A by-product has been discovered containing equal weights of waste and a chemical costing $4.50 a hundredweight. The by-product can be made on existing plant equipment. The average plant load is about 90%, and management does not find it practicable to reduce the labor force for output variations that this represents. It is estimated that the existing labor force can process the new product during the periods when it is not assigned to other jobs. The cost of labor is $2.50 an hour, and overhead is $4.00 per direct labor-hour. The direct cost of power for making the by-product will be $0.60 per hour. The required time to produce 200 pounds of by-product is 20 minutes. What minimum selling price can be accepted?

SOLUTION.   Basing computations on a hundredweight of waste, the increment cost of making the new product is $4.50 + $0.20 = $4.70 and the increment cost of not making it is $2.50, or a net extra cost of $2.20 per hundredweight. The direct labor and the overhead costs are irrelevant in the decision for the conditions of the given program. From an accounting standpoint, the direct labor idle-time will undoubtedly be allocated to the by-product, but this does not alter the economic justification.

Any sale price above $1.10 per hundredweight of by-product (containing 50 pounds of waste) provides extra income for the firm. For example, if the normal waste is 500 tons a year and 1,000 tons of the by-product can be sold at $3.10 a hundredweight, $40,000 will be generated as additional profit not otherwise realized.

A by-product is also known as a joint product. J. M. Clark[1] says when "two products are complementary and can be produced more cheaply together than apart we have joint cost. Another way of putting it is that every added unit of product A makes it easier than it would otherwise be to produce added units of product B." A true joint product, therefore, results when by-products are made from waste material. For example, more pressboard (using sawdust) from more lumber milled, more hides from increased meat-packing operations, more lead from more silver mined, and so on.

In the broadest sense, joint products are complementary; one product does not have to be viewed as the main product and the other as the by-product, although they usually are. From this viewpoint the joint costs, namely, the costs other than the increment costs of the products, can be divided between the complementary products in whatever proportions the market will stand. Either one could be sold at the marginal cost with the other carrying all the joint cost.

From the standpoint of Clarke's definition, diverse or rival products are not joint if producing more of one does not help the other. For example, it may not make it easier to produce Valve B by producing more of Valve A. In many cases, and perhaps this is academic, it is difficult to draw a line showing that one product is not produced more easily by producing more of the other. For example, increased demand for Valve A may justify installing improvements that will also benefit the manufacture of B.

Obviously, the objective of developing joint products is to secure maximum economy, and the objective of setting a price policy for these products is to maximize profit. In general, a balance of the joint products, as in Example 12.12, where all the waste material and all the excess labor and equipment was utilized, is consistent with maximizing the profit.

12.13 PRICE CUTTING

Selling at or near marginal or incremental costs, as with dumping or perhaps with by-products, presumes that the sales cannot be made at prices which will recover the full cost plus a reasonable profit. These special pricing policies do not imply that strategies exist for conducting the main line of business at selling prices below the total cost of production plus a required profit. However, occasionally a manufacturer is faced with the decision to reduce or cut a regular price.

Price cutting is eschewed by reputable companies for a number of good reasons, but in certain situations it seems reasonable and ethical to do so. For example, the first machine of a new line requires the customer to accept a

---

[1]J. Maurice Clark, *Economy of Overhead Costs* (Chicago: University of Chicago Press, 1923), p. 80.

machine without a precedent; nevertheless, the installation of this machine may influence a large future sale in his plant or be the spark for immediate sales elsewhere. Both the customer and the manufacturer may feel the circumstances justify a special price on that machine without setting a precedent for future prices.

At this stage of production a number of unit costs can be conceived (which confuse the issue), such as the total unit cost at normal output when the new machines get into full production (and on which the selling price is based), the total unit cost at the present low production output, or the increment costs at each level. If, however, the sale can be made at a figure equal to or in excess of the present increment cost, the company will at least not be out of pocket. Consider, too, that *no* price might be too low to get the business, but it seems unreasonable for either party to expect to pass title to a valuable machine without valuable compensation, and a reasonable *minimum* can be justified at the present increment cost of production.

12.14 SHUTTING DOWN PLANTS

No company can remain in business for long which sells its output below its total cost of production; however, this may be the very thing to do in the short run. In such cases, it may be more economical to sell at a loss over a short period than not to sell at all.

EXAMPLE 12.14 In a depression only 25,000 units, representing 25% of normal plant output, can be sold at $50 each. The costs of the factory are:

Fixed costs not variable with output	$600,000
Variable costs at zero output	100,000
Variable costs at 25% output	900,000

Should the plant be operated at this output or be shut down for the duration of the depression, expected to last a year or two?

SOLUTION. At 25% output the gross income is $1,250,000, the cost is $1,500,000, and the loss is $250,000 a year. If the plant is temporarily shut down, certain functions costing $100,000 must be continued (protection, maintenance, top management, and so on) in anticipation of reopening. The total loss then becomes $700,000, so the smaller loss will result from continuing operations.

In this case the unit cost at 25% output is $60, the variable cost if $36, the increment cost is $32, and the selling price is $50. If the depression deepens, the company could lower its selling price to almost $32 (if increment cost remains constant) before it would be more economical to shut down the plant. From a more practical standpoint, the company should consider whether lowering its price at the present time would increase the demand and raise the level of output. For example, if a price of $40 will increase the demand to 50,000 units and if the total variable cost at this higher efficiency is assumed to be $1,600,000, the income will be $2,000,000, the total cost will be $2,200,000, and the loss $200,000 instead of $250,000 at 25% output.

This example also emphasizes that there are a number of predicted unit costs, unit variable costs, and increment costs depending on the level of operation as well as the point of reference. In the above example the increment cost at 25% operation relative to zero operation is $32, at 50% operation relative to zero is $30, and at 50% operation relative to 25% is $28. It is proof enough that the analyst has every right to doubt unit cost figures unless these are properly defined, but he also has the responsibility of employing the unit cost applicable to his situation.

12.15 BREAK-EVEN CHART

The break-even chart presents two curves: the input-output curve and a curve showing the income from sales. This theoretically indicates the points of maximum profit, maximum loss, and break-even, and thereby it suggests the optimum level of operation. Figure 12.15 has been constructed from the data in Example 12.5. The unit selling price as in that example is $5.75.

The data was purposely selected to show that maximum profit need not occur at the point of maximum plant efficiency. As seen in Table 12.5, the unit cost at 100% output is the lowest and the *profit per unit* is maximum, $5.75 – $3.94 = $1.81, giving a total profit on 10,000 units of $18,100. At 120% output, although the unit profit of $1,625 is lower, it occurs on more units, giving a higher total profit, $19,500.

At 140% output, the unit profit has dropped to only $0.75, which on 14,000 units gives a total profit of $10,500. The maximum profit, therefore, occurs at about 120% output.

The conclusion could also be established from the viewpoint of increment cost: if the sales price exceeds the cost of the next increment, the profit will be increased by the addition of that increment. The cost of the increment from 100% to 120% load is $5.05 per unit, but this increment can be sold at $5.75, so the total profit can be increased by operating at 120% load. However, the increment cost for the next 20% capacity is $10.25, so that it does not increase the profit to operate at 140% load.

Theoretically, there are two break-even points, as shown in Fig. 12.15, and it is only profitable to operate above one and below the other. In practice, the location of these points becomes flexible; for example, as business falls off toward the lower point, strong management action can generally move it lower by trimming the "fixed" costs or semivariable costs. In fact, the results of management action for any company can be seen by constructing break-even charts from the profit and loss statements of that company. The company's periodic statements illustrate the variations in the input-output relationship and the flexibility of the break-even point as a result of continuous management action.

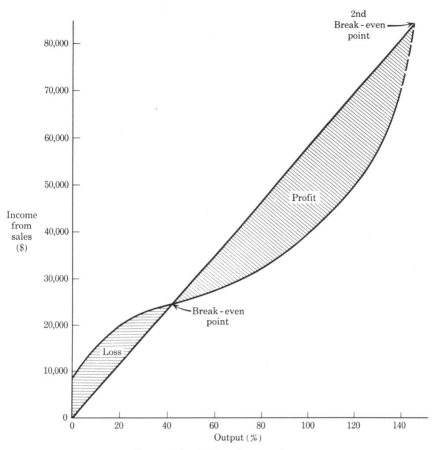

Figure 12.15   Break-even chart

12.16 CAPACITY AND DEMAND FACTORS

The *capacity factor* is the ratio of average load to the rated capacity. It indicates how close to rated design a system is operating based on the average load over a period of time. Depending on the type of system, this could be a month or even a 15-minute interval. The capacity factor shows only the average use of the facilities. A low capacity factor therefore does not reveal that at some instants the system may be vastly overloaded and, at these instants, could not be viewed as too large.

The *demand or load factor* is the ratio of average load to maximum load or maximum demand. This indicates the extent of the maximum variation in load from the average load.

Together, these two factors indicate the required capacity of a system to meet the calls on it. For example, a plant with a 50% capacity factor and 100% demand factor is operating steadily at 50% output (and very likely at low efficiency). The capacity factor will be varied if management can increase the sales to increase output to rated capacity either by sales stimulation or the introduction of joint products. An opposite approach which will also raise the capacity factor is to reduce the size of the plant. This raises interesting considerations, but it is a possible course of management action.

Taking another example, a plant with 100% capacity factor and 50% demand factor is operating irregularly at various load points and, in fact, is badly overloaded at certain times. Manggement's goal would be to smooth out the operation by increasing operations during the slack periods, such as storing in anticipation of the demand peaks or introducing policies that would transfer some of the demand to other periods—in order to achieve 100% demand factor.

As a third example, a plant with 50% capacity factor and 50% demand factor has problems similar to both previous cases. As noted from the factors, this plant runs well-loaded at certain intervals, but the average load is only 50% of rated. This general pattern is typical of many plants. The goal of management is to seek out policies that will raise the average output while not increasing the peaks of demand. Many approaches are possible, not the least of which is the addition of joint products.

12.17 PRICING TO RAISE CAPACITY AND DEMAND FACTORS

Sometimes the seller can offer a schedule of unit prices designed to increase the capacity and load factors of his plant or equipment. The objective of such a pricing system would be (a) to increase total output by incentives to purchase more of the product; (b) to eliminate periods of low demand by especially attractive prices during these periods; (c) to eliminate periods of high demand by high prices or long shipments to discourage sales at that time and convert them to other periods.

A schedule of prices that decrease with the customer's consumption enables the customer to justify new or additional uses of the product. An example is an electric power schedule employing an incremental rate which decreases as the customer's consumption increases. The power cost of a proposed equipment or appliance, priced at the consumer's lowest increment, increases the difficulty of justifying sources of energy other than electric, and this can intensify with each proposed capital expenditure as lower rate blocks are invaded. From the seller's standpoint, increasing his capacity factor with this system of pricing is a logical reflection of his own decrease in unit cost with increased output up to the point of maximum plant efficiency or maximized profit. The common sense of this system of pricing has been applied to electric energy and certain bulk items.

On the other hand, a schedule of prices that decrease in periods of low demand, despite high unit operating costs at these low operating points, has the economic advantage of raising the activity by transferring some load from the peak of the slack periods. A possible illustration of this is the store which is overloaded during certain hours but empty from 2 to 3 p.m. A price reduction of several percent on cash sales made during that period would tend to transfer some of the load. Pricing schedules of this type also serve to attract new consumers and increase the capacity factor, as well as the load factor. Other practical examples are the coal industry, with lower spring prices than fall or winter, transportation or hotel rates which are lower on certain slack days of the week, and electric rates which are lower during off-peak hours.

A schedule of prices that penalizes the customer's demands above his average rate of consumption is aimed solely at raising the producer's load factor. This schedule is basically different from the off-peak schedule in the previous paragraph which envisaged increment-cost pricing, if necessary, to encourage the transferral of customer's peaks or to entice new customers whose demands will conform to the producer's slack period. On the other hand, this schedule taxes the customer to encourage him to reduce his peak rates of usage, and proposes charging him for the excess capacity which the producer must maintain to meet the consumer's sudden demands. The demand charge in an electric rate schedule is a good example.

Many producers have an easier time with this problem because, unlike the electric companies, their solution is simply to cut off the supply. A transportation system can refuse loads beyond its capacity, stores can run out of goods, but utilities must satisfy all the demands that can result from the subscriber's equipment connected to their power lines.

Undoubtedly more can be done to design and employ these types of rate schedules in business following the lead of the electric utility companies which have excelled in their design and use. An economy analyst may find it profitable to follow some of their design patterns if his product can be priced in quantities. Every analyst should also understand his company's electrical rate schedule if he is to know the power cost of proposed equipment or the effect of procedures to cut the company's cost of electricity. In some cases, too, the company may have a choice of several schedules which should be analyzed and selected on an economy basis.

Electrical energy schedules may be the simple block type in which the rate decreases for additional blocks of consumption. Usually the simple block type is used for household rate schedules.

Another schedule employs a so-called "two-part rate" consisting of a block rate for the energy consumed plus a separate charge for the maximum demand.

A third and more sophisticated schedule employs blocks as before except that the size of each block is a function of the maximum demand. The following example illustrates this third type combined with a simple block rate.

EXAMPLE.12.17 A company operates under the following rate schedule for the purchase of its electrical energy.

First   500 kw-hr per month at 3.8 cents per kilowatt-hour
Next 1,000 kw-hr per month at 3.3 cents per kilowatt-hour

Next 2,500 kw-hr per month at 2.6 cents per kilowatt-hour
Next 5,000 kw-hr per month at 1.8 cents per kilowatt-hour

For all excess over 9,000 kw-hr per month:

First 50 kw-hr per kilowatt of maximum demand at 1.6 cents per kilowatt-hour.

Next 150 kw-hr per kilowatt of maximum demand, but not more than 90,000 kw-hr, at 1.3 cents per kilowatt-hour.

All excess at 0.8 cents per kilowatt-hour.

What is its power bill in a month in which the maximum demand was 500 kw and the energy used was 149,000 kw-hr?

SOLUTION. The cost of the first 9,000 kw-hr is based on a simple block rate computed below under Part 1:

$$\text{First 500 kw-hr} \quad = \quad (500)(0.038) = \$ \ 19.00$$
$$\text{Next 1,000 kw-hr} = (1,000)(0.033) = \quad 33.00$$
$$\text{Next 2,500 kw-hr} = (2,500)(0.026) = \quad 65.00$$
$$\text{Next 5,000 kw-hr} = (5,000)(0.018) = \quad 90.00$$
$$\text{Total of Part 1} \qquad\qquad\qquad \$207.00$$

The cost of the remaining 140,000 kw-hr is based on a block rate where the size of blocks is established by the demand. For example, the size of the first block is "50 kw-hr per kilowatt of maximum demand" or $50 \times 500 = 25,000$ kw-hr; the next block is $150 \times 500 = 75,000$ kw-hr; and so on. This cost of each block is computed as in Part 2 below.

$$\text{First } 50 \times 500 \text{ kw-hr} \ = 25,000 \text{ kw-hr at } 0.016 = \$ \ 400.00$$
$$\text{Next } 150 \times 500 \text{ kw-hr} = 75,000 \text{ kw-hr at } 0.013 = \quad 975.00$$
$$\text{Remainder} \qquad\qquad\quad = 40,000 \text{ kw-hr at } 0.008 = \quad 320.00$$
$$\text{Total of Part 2} \qquad\qquad\qquad\qquad\qquad \$1,695.00$$

Total monthly bill = $207 + \$1,695 = \$1,902.00$

As noted, the higher the demand the greater the power bill. A further refinement would be a schedule of low rates for the use of energy at off-peak hours. Refinements may be added for off-peak versus on-peak demands. The possible variations in schedules are many.

With a straight block type rate, the cost of power for added equipment, or the power savings by shutting down equipment, is at the increment rate. In the last example, if the monthly consumption had been only 9,000 kw-hr, the *average* cost of power would be $207 \div 9,000 = 2.3$ cents per kilowatt-hour. If a waste reduction program promises to save an average of 1,000 kw-hr a month, the saving is figured not at 2.3 cents but at the *increment* cost of 1.8 cents per kilowatt-hour.

Also, in the last example, if a machine is proposed which will add 10,000 kw-hr to the monthly consumption but by running at off-peak hours will not add to the maximum demand, its energy cost will be figured at 0.8 cents per kilowatt-hour, the incremental rate. If, however, this equipment will also add 100 kw to the maximum demand, the so-called increment must be computed by going back to the beginning of Part 2 as follows:

$$\begin{array}{lll}
\text{First } 50 \times 600 \text{ kw-hr} & = 30,000 \text{ kw-hr at } 0.016 = \$ & 480 \\
\text{Next } 150 \times 600 \text{ kw-hr} & = 90,000 \text{ kw-hr at } 0.013 = & 1,170 \\
\text{Remainder} & = 30,000 \text{ kw-hr at } 0.008 = & \underline{240} \\
\text{Total of Part 2} & & \$1,890
\end{array}$$

The monthly bill, therefore, increases $1,890 - 1,695 = \$195$. This incremental increase is the result of adding 10,000 kw-hr a month *and* 100 kw demand. If expressed as an incremental unit cost of energy it is 1.95 cents per kilowatt-hour. We should keep in mind that this figure consists of 0.8 cents per kilowatt-hour for the added block of energy and 1.15 cents per kilowatt-hour for the added demand.

12.18 SCHEDULING AND ASSIGNING LOADS

Scheduling or assigning loads among systems proceeds from the analysis of increment costs. Depending on the complexity of the system, the increment may be that above the existing load or the increment may have to be computed from the zero level, as noted in the last section. And, of course, all sunk costs are irrelevant. These points are illustrated in the following examples.

EXAMPLE 12.18a Systems C and D have the input-output patterns shown in Fig. 12.18a. Two simplifying assumptions have been made: the load will be added in 2,500-unit increments until both plants or systems are fully loaded, and the load can be added, dropped, or transferred between the systems with perfect flexibility.

SOLUTION. Based on total costs, the first 5,000 units would be cheaper if produced at C. However, the fixed costs will continue regardless of the loading, and the decision is solely based on increment costs. Each increment of 2,500 units costs less for D (the slope is less) and therefore it is more economical to keep C idle until D has been fully loaded.

EXAMPLE 12.18b The input-output relations for plants A and B are given in Fig. 12.18b and Table 12.18b.

SOLUTION. The total cost is not to be considered, because the fixed cost is irrelevant. In assigning each increment of production, consideration of the added cost of each increment may simplify the test. In this case, however, where first. B has the lower increment, then A, then B, and so on, the analyst

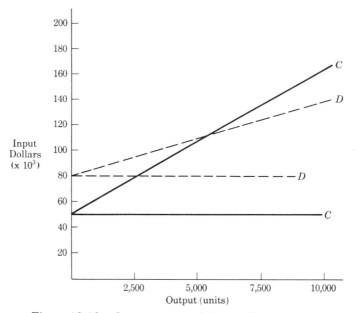

Figure 12.18a   Input-output relations of two systems

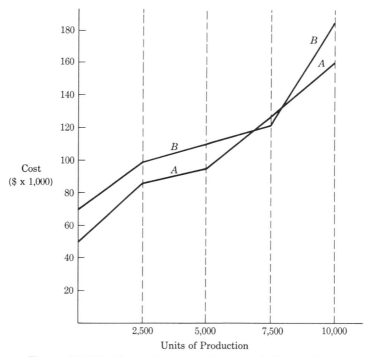

Figure 12.18b   Competing plants in a scheduling problem

Table 12.18b COSTS OF TWO PLANTS IN A SCHEDULING PROBLEM

		Plant A		
Load (units of production)	Total cost	Variable cost	Increment	Unit increment cost
0	$ 50,000	$ 0	$ 0	$ 0
2,500	86,000	36,000	36,000	14.40
5,000	95,000	45,000	9,000	3.60
7,500	127,000	77,000	32,000	12.80
10,000	160,000	110,000	33,000	13.20

		Plant B		
Load (units of production)	Total cost	Variable cost	Increment	Unit increment cost
0	$ 70,000	$ 0	$ 0	$ 0
2,500	99,000	29,000	29,000	11.60
5,000	109,000	39,000	10,000	4.00
7,500	121,000	51,000	12,000	4.80
10,000	185,000	115,000	64,000	25.60

must examine the "total increment from zero," namely, the variable cost of the total load—for every combination of assignments.

To illustrate, the first level is, of course, assigned to B with the lowest increment or variable cost of $29,000. The next level is more difficult, because if the next increment is also assigned to B at a cost of $10,000, we will have disregarded the fact that had the entire load been assigned to A we would have had the advantage of only a $9,000 increment at A. This must be solved by a test of the total increment of 5,000 units that gives $39,000 at B and $45,000 at A, which truly justifies scheduling the added increment at B.

The rule, typical of analyses of levels of investment, is that when an increment *stands out of line* it should be tested in combination with the proper adjacent increment or increments. In an analysis of the second load level, the $9,000 increment at B stands out, so it must be tested combined with the first increment at A.

In some cases in this example the load may be scheduled solely by examining the cost of the next increment, but where low increments have been or will be passed over, the analyst must compute the cost of the *total* increment at each level in every conceivable combination of assignments. For example, at the 10,000 unit level, the best schedule is to run each plant at 50% capacity. This gives the lowest variable cost compared to the other combinations of 0% at A and 100% at B, 25% at A and 75% at B, 75% at A and 25% at B, or 100% at A and 0% at B.

The most economic loading will follow the schedule in Table 12.18c.

Table 12.18c ECONOMIC LOAD SCHEDULE

Load	Units at A	Units at B	Variable cost
0	0	0	$ 0
2,500	0	2,500	29,000
5,000	0	5,000	39,000
7,500	0	7,500	51,000
10,000	5,000	5,000	84,000
12,500	5,000	7,500	96,000
15,000	7,500	7,500	128,000
17,500	10,000	7,500	161,000
20,000	10,000	10,000	225,000

PROBLEMS

12.1 Make a list of manufacturing costs and indicate which are fixed, F, and which are variable, V. Indicate with FV those that may be partly fixed and partly variable with output. Assuming a grave depression is expected, draw an arrow next to those fixed costs which you feel may be decreased.

12.2 Prepare a graph of Efficiency versus Output. The ordinate will be percent efficiency and the abscissa percent output. The points on the curve will be

Output (%)	Efficiency (%)
0	0
25	40
50	70
75	90
100	80
125	50

From the data on the graph construct an input-output curve (ordinate for input and abscissa for output). Assume that the input at zero load is 2,000 units and the output at 100% load is 25,000 units. Use data from the input-output curve to construct a table for each 10% increase in output, showing incremental increase in units of input, incremental increase in units of output, and ratio of incremental increase in input to incremental increase in output. How is it, as noted in the table, that at certain points in the system the increment of output is greater than the increment of input that produced it?

12.3 Using actual efficiency data published by the manufacturer of a motor, engine, or generator, plot the efficiency curve and the input-output curve. Inasmuch as your data will probably not state the input at no load, assume it to be 10% of full load output.

12.4 A 1,000-hp energy conversion system has the following efficiency; 125% load, 88%; full load, 92.2%; $\frac{3}{4}$ load, 89.9%; $\frac{1}{2}$ load, 75%; $\frac{1}{4}$ load,

52%. The no-load input horsepower is 110. Plot the efficiency curve and the input-output horsepower curve.

12.5 Select an input-output system from Problems 12.2, 12.3, or 12.4. Assume the unit cost is 2 cents per "unit"-hour (i.e., per horsepower-hour, etc., as the case may be). The "system" costs $100,000 with a 10-year life and $20,000 salvage. Insurance and taxes are 2% of first cost. Compute the total cost of operating 4,000 hours a year at zero, $\frac{1}{4}$, $\frac{1}{2}$, $\frac{3}{4}$, and full load, respectively. Assume the minimum required rate of return is 25%. Plot the Input Cost (ordinate) versus Percent Output (abscissa). Indicate which are fixed and which are variable costs.

12.6 Assume that the system in the previous problem operates at a constant 100% of rated capacity. In this case outputs at less than rated annual capacity will be obtained by shutting the unit down and, like a machine tool, its annual output will depend on its hours of utilization at full load. Consequently, at full output the system will run 4,000 hours; at half output it will run 2,000 hours and it will be shut down 2,000 hours, and so on. Plot the Input (cost) versus the Output (percent).

12.7 Compute the unit cost, the unit fixed-cost, and the unit variable-cost at all loads for the data in Problem 12.5. Plot this data on the following set of coordinates: Unit Cost versus Output (units).

12.8 Repeat Problem 12.7 using the data from Problem 12.6.

12.9 Compute the increment costs at all loads in Problems 12.5 and 12.6.

12.10 (a) A factory has a fixed cost of $500,000 a year. At the plant's rated output of 100,000 units a year, the total cost, including fixed charges, is $2,500,000. Variable costs are considered to vary directly with output. The unit sales price has been set at $35. Prepare a table showing the unit cost at rated, $\frac{3}{4}$, $\frac{1}{2}$, and $\frac{1}{4}$ plant capacity and also the annual profit or loss if the plant is operated for a year at each of these capacities.

(b) Compute the overhead rate per hour of direct labor for the data in (a) figured at an annual output of 75,000 pieces if the direct labor per piece is two hours. Using this burden rate and the variable cost from (a), compute the unit cost of each piece. Compare this with the true unit costs as computed in (a). What is the under- or over-absorbed burden at full, $\frac{3}{4}$, $\frac{1}{2}$, or $\frac{1}{4}$ plant capacity?

12.11 The cost of manufacturing a subcomponent is $20, consisting of $8 for labor, $5 for material, and $7 for overhead. (a) The piece can be purchased from a supplier for $15 delivered. Should the company buy or make this subcomponent? (b) During a depression, when the plant is running at one-half the output in (a), the same piece can be purchased from the supplier for $11. Assume the overhead cost is the same as in (a). Should the company buy or make the subcomponent? Discuss the irreducible considerations.

12.12 A company makes 250,000 units a year at its normal capacity. These sell at $10 each. The unit cost at this capacity is $6, of which $2.50 is labor, $1 is material, and $2.50 is overhead. During a recession, sales, which are entirely domestic, drop to 150,000 units a year. It is estimated that the material and labor costs will vary directly with output but fixed costs cannot be reduced. Examination of various foreign markets indicates that 20,000 units can be sold in one market at $4.50 each, 35,000 units in another market at $3.75 each, and 45,000 units in another at $2.50 each. Should the extra capacity be dumped in these markets? What will be the resultant effect on the profit and loss statement if the net loss from domestic sales is $30,000?

12.13 Plant waste amounting to 5,000 tons a year is carried away and dumped at a cost of $2 a ton. This waste could, alternatively, be processed into a marketable product. A process can be installed which will combine one pound of waste with one pound of new material costing $6 a ton. This will provide the company with 10,000 tons of new sales a year. The new process will require machinery costing $15,000, which is expected to have an economic life of 10 years and $3,000 salvage at that date. The annual cost of labor, maintenance, and power (exclusive of material) to process the 10,000 tons of product is $20,000. The minimum required rate of return is 10%. The fixed costs of the plant prorated to this operation would be $10,000.

At what price may the company sell the new product and (a) have as much profit as at present, i.e., when it has to dump the waste; (b) have more profit than at present?

12.14 A company division has a normal manufacturing capacity of 100,000 units which sell for $60 each. This price consists of profit $10; fixed cost $20; variable cost $30. During a depression only 20,000 units can be sold annually at $50 each. The total fixed cost can be reduced 15% below normal if the plant stays open and 30% below normal if it closes. The variable cost is directly proportional to output.

Disregarding irreducible considerations, should the plant remain open for the next year or two to produce 20,000 units a year or should it shut down and reopen when business improves?

At the 20,000 unit production rate, how low may the price be reduced during the depression before shutting down the plant becomes more economical than operating it?

12.15 The Capital City plant has a normal capacity of 80,000 units a year with a unit cost of $55. Each unit of product uses 10 pounds of material. The material is available from different locations at different costs as follows: 200,000 pounds at $2 a pound, 300,000 pounds at $2.50 a pound, and another 300,000 at $3 a pound. The fixed costs at the Capital City plant are $1,550,000 a year, and the other costs, except the aforementioned materials, vary in direct proportion to output.

The Queen City plant has a normal capacity of 100,000 units a year with a unit cost of $52. Each unit of product uses 10 pounds of material which can be obtained at the following prices: 300,000 pounds at $2.25 a pound, 400,000 pounds at $3 a pound, and 300,000 pounds at $3.25 a pound. Fixed costs not variable with production are $1,800,000, and variable costs except material are in direct proportion to output.

Draw up a schedule showing the load that should be maintained on each plant as the demand for the company's product varies from zero to 180,000 units.

12.16 The Omega process, designed to produce 10,000 units a year, has a fixed cost of $80,000 a year. The Gamma process with the same design capacity has a fixed cost of $60,000 a year. The Omega process produces the initial 4,000 units at a variable cost of $10 and the next 6,000 units at a variable cost of $7. The Gamma process produces the first 5,000 units at a variable cost of $9 each, and the next 5,000 at $8 each. Prepare a schedule giving the load that should be assigned to each plant if the demand for the product is varied from zero to 20,000 units. (At no load the fixed costs will continue at the stated amount.)

12.17 A plant with a rated output of 1,000 units has total costs of $120,000 a year, of which $50,000 represents fixed costs. The variable costs are directly proportional to output. The selling price per unit is $180. Assuming that the plant is operating at the rate of 800 units a year, how low may the price be cut if permitted to do so to get an order for one unit? If you suggest more than one price, discuss each.

12.18 A factory has a rated output of 100,000 units a year. In response to demand, its output for each 3-month period throughout the year was 12,000, 14,000, 18,000, and 20,000 units for the first through the last quarter, respectively. Compute the annual capacity factor and the annual demand factor. What might this company do to improve its position?

12.19 A company has a maximum production capacity of 4,000 units a year. The total cost of operation at various loads is as follows:

Units output	Operating cost
0	$ 20,000
1,000	58,000
2,000	70,000
3,000	80,000
4,000	105,000

The selling price of the product is $40. Draw a break-even chart showing the break-even cost and the profit and loss areas.

12.20 Select the annual profit-and-loss statements for the last 10 years of a company of your choice and reconstruct a break-even chart. The 10-year cost and income data when plotted will give a scattering through which you may be able to draw approximate break-even curves. Does the company appear to have a break-even point and what is its position relative to the operating points of the years you plotted? Does your chart seem to suggest that management action altered the possible location of the break-even point?

12.21 Compute the month's cost of electrical energy if the consumer's maximum demand in a given month is 700 kw and the energy used is 210,000 kw-hr. The schedule is as follows:

First 1,000 kw-hr per month at 4.0 cents per kilowatt-hour
Next 1,500 kw-hr per month at 3.5 cents per kilowatt-hour
Next 2,500 kw-hr per month at 3.0 cents per kilowatt-hour
Next 5,000 kw-hr per month at 2.5 cents per kilowatt-hour

For all in excess of 10,000 kw-hr per month:

First 100 kw-hr per kilowatt of maximum demand at 1.5 cents per kilowatt-hour

Next 150 kw-hr per kilowatt of maximum demand at 1.0 cents per kilowatt-hour

All excess at 0.8 cents per kilowatt-hour

12.22 A company has contracted for electric energy according to the following monthly rate schedule:

Demand Rate:

$1.50 per kilowatt of demand in excess of 5 kw

Normal Energy Rate:

First 20 kw-hr or less: $1.75

Next 130 kw-hr at 5.2 cents per kilowatt-hour

Next 850 kw-hr at 3.5 cents per kilowatt-hour

Next 1,500 kw-hr at 3.2 cents per kilowatt-hour

All over 2,500 kw-hr at 2.5 cents per kilowatt-hour

Inducement Energy Rate:

When not less than 1,000 kw-hr have been billed under the Normal Energy Rate, energy in excess of 300 kw-hr per kilowatt of maximum demand will be priced at the rate of 1.5 cents per kilowatt-hour

In a given month the company's maximum demand is 100 kw and the energy used is 140,000 kw-hr.

What is the bill for the given month under the foregoing rate schedule?

13

Minimum Cost Points

13.1 MINIMUM COSTS

In cost-reduction analyses, because the gross income is irrelevant to the choice, the decision rests solely on finding the alternative with the lowest cost, namely, the lowest total of present and future costs based on the accepted time value of money. (In income-expansion propositions the lowest total cost is not the criterion, it is the highest net profit.)[1] Since most alternatives are conceived singly, comparisons are made in pairs between the new alternative and that which preceded it. However, where several alternatives are generated at once, the various levels of investment can be analyzed together. In previous examples each level of investment was treated as a separate problem, but if the cost equation for the family of alternatives can be defined, the analysis can be treated as a single mathematical problem. Finding the equation of the total cost curve in terms of certain variables may prove to be a task, but then a *single* solution of that equation will indicate the alternative having the minimum annual cost.

Graphical representations of multiple-alternative problems are particularly worthwhile from the standpoint of showing the conclusions clearly and forcefully to top management. These graphs of the cost equations also develop comprehension of the underlying economic factors in the problem, an aid not only to analysis but to visualizing the paths to further design improvements.

13.2 LOCATING THE MINIMUM ANNUAL COST

As frequently noted, increasing the first cost of a design is intended to raise the engineering efficiency and lower the operating disbursements. Viewed mathematically, both the first cost and the operating cost are functions of the same design variables, the first cost increasing directly with some design param-

---

[1] The highest net profit is also the criterion for cost reduction; this occurs at the point of minimum cost.

eters and the operating cost inversely. If these costs can be quantitatively expressed as functions of these design variables, the minimum total annual cost can be determined by differentiation.

A simple introduction to this is found in the case where a change in a *single* design factor produces proportional changes in the first and future costs. For example, if the first cost of a transmission line, considering the line alone without the poles and hardware, is directly proportional to the area of the wire (within limits), and if the cost of lost energy caused by the resistance of the line is inversely proportional to the area, then

$$\text{Annual cost} = (a)\,(\text{area}) + \frac{b}{(\text{area})}$$

where a and b are constants.

If x represents the design variable, in this case, the area, the general equation of cost is

$$\text{Annual cost} = ax + \frac{b}{x}$$

It can be seen that the investment cost ax increases linearly with the design variable x, and the future costs b/x decrease hyperbolically with x.

It is now a simple matter of differentiation to locate the design factor which gives zero slope and minimum annual cost. In practice the analyst can justify considerable time and effort to determine the equation of the annual-cost curve if it is to be used repeatedly, as may be the case in the design of a vast project or in variations of basic designs repeated in the business (such as new machines economic lot sizes, etc.).

EXAMPLE 13.2a   A transmission line is to carry 45 amperes for 6,000 hours a year. For the sizes in question, wire costs $0.20 per pound and energy costs 1 cent per kilowatt-hour. The economic life is 20 years with zero salvage. Taxes and insurance on first cost are 2.5% and the minimum required rate of return is 10%. The areas and weights and resistances per 1,000 feet of wire are listed in Table 13.2. Determine the most economical size of transmission line.

SOLUTION.

```
P = cost of
wire of given          D = cost of energy loss for
cross section          wire of given cross section          L = 0
     |—————————————————————————————————————————————————————|
     0                                                      20
```

The annual investment cost includes the taxes and insurance at 2.5% of P, the cost of 1,000 feet of line. The energy loss, also for 1,000 feet of wire, is at the rate of $I^2R/1{,}000$ kilowatts for 6,000 hours at 1 cent per kilowatt-hour, where the current, I, is 45 amperes.

Table 13.2 ECONOMIC SIZE OF A TRANSMISSION LINE

Wire size, AWG number	3/0	2/0	1/0	1	2	3
Area (circular mils × 1,000)	167.8	133.1	105.5	83.7	66.4	52.6
Weight (lb)	507.9	402.8	319.5	253.3	200.9	159.3
Resistance (ohms)	0.06180	0.07793	0.09827	0.1239	0.1563	0.1970
First cost	$101.58	$80.56	$63.90	$50.66	$40.18	$31.86
Annual investment cost	$ 14.47	$11.48	$ 9.10	$ 7.22	$ 5.72	$ 4.54
Kilowatt-hour per year	[751]	[947]	[1,194]	[1,505]	[1,899]	[2,394]
Annual energy cost	7.51	9.47	11.94	15.05	18.99	23.94
Total annual cost	$ 21.98	$20.95	$21.04	$22.27	$24.71	$28.48

$$\text{Annual Cost} = P\,[(A/P, .10, 20) + \overset{0.11746}{0.025}] + \left(\frac{I^2R}{1{,}000}\right)(6{,}000)(0.01)$$

The computations, along with the original data, are summarized in Table 13.2. The results can be visualized in Fig. 13.2, which shows the variation of annual costs with cross-sectional area. As noted in the table, the minimum cost occurs

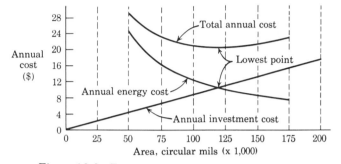

Figure 13.2   Economic size of a transmission line

with a size 2/0 AWG line. Actually, the lowest point occurs somewhere between 2/0 and 1/0 AWG, where no commercial size is available (this specific minimum is located by differentiating the annual-cost curve).

EXAMPLE 13.2b   Derive the annual-cost equation in terms of a design variable of the transmission line in Example 13.2a and solve for the minimum cost point.

SOLUTION. The annual-cost formula[1] for the given problem as derived in Example 13.2a is

$$AC = P\,[(A/P, .10, 20) + \overset{0.11746}{0.025}] + \left[\frac{I^2R}{1{,}000}\right](6{,}000)(0.01)$$

$$AC = 0.1425\,P + 121.5\,R$$

The design variable can be either the area A or the weight W, which is proportional to area for a fixed length of line. Then

$$\frac{R_1}{R_2} = \frac{A_2}{A_1} = \frac{W_2}{W_1}$$

The weight and resistance of size 3/0 wire is 508 pounds and 0.0618 ohms per 1,000 feet. The resistance, R_x, of any other weight of line is

$$R_x = \frac{(508)(0.0618)}{W_x} = \frac{31.39}{W_x}$$

---

[1]This is the symbolized annual-cost *formula*. It is not the *equation* of the annual-cost curve required for mathematical operations. It locates one point in terms of several independent variables, whereas the equation locates it in terms of one variable, the area of the wire.

And the annual cost as a function of weight is:

$$AC = (0.1425)(0.20W) + (121.5)\left[\frac{(508)(0.0618)}{W}\right]$$

$$AC = 0.0285W + \frac{3,814}{W}$$

which is in the form,

$$AC = aW + \frac{b}{W}$$

Then

$$\frac{d(AC)}{dW} = a - \frac{b}{W^2}$$

and if we equate this to zero,

$$W = \sqrt{\frac{b}{a}} = \sqrt{\frac{3,814}{0.0285}} = 366 \text{ pounds}$$

This is between size 2/0 and 1/0, but nearer the former, which is selected in the absence of in-between sizes.

It will be noted that the work of computing the cost of each alternative is transferred in part to the work of defining the cost as a function of a design parameter. The analyst must decide in given cases which method is easier.

13.3 MODEL FOR KELVIN'S LAW

In 1881 Sir William Thompson (Lord Kelvin) suggested that the most economic size of conductor is the one which results in annual waste-energy costs equal to annual investment costs. This rule will not be well understood by casual readers, because a study of it reveals that it is limited solely to the situation in which investment costs are directly proportional and energy costs are inversely proportional to area, as in Example 13.2. It does not apply, therefore, to situations where energy losses (corona, for example) are not indirectly proportional to area; it does not apply where first costs for suspension, for insulation, or for the wire itself are not directly proportional to conductor area. In those cases the minimum annual cost does not occur where the annual investment cost equals the waste-energy costs. Kelvin's case from a mathematical standpoint occurs only when two curves intersect at a point where the negative slope of one numerically equals the positive slope of the other. Only in this situation is the minimum cost directly above the intersection, as shown in Fig. 13.2. Linear variation of investment costs is not enough; for Kelvin's case the curve must originate at zero, as noted in Fig. 13.2. Although Kelvin's Law describes a limited situation, cost variations of this type can be found in designs other than the wire size of transmission lines.

Furthermore, we should remind the reader that transmission lines present more economic problems than wire size. As E. M. Strong[1] says, "For either interior or exterior lines, the choice of the material and fabrication of the conductor, of its insulation, design of supporting structure, protection equipment, etc., together with the weighing of cost of equipment against cost of installation; installed cost against cost of maintenance, cost of energy loss and value of reliability is no mere Kelvin's law problem but is a study in itself."

And an important point is that many of these problems do not conform to the special case, which is Kelvin's law, as the following section will illustrate.

13.4 GENERAL CASE OF MINIMUM ANNUAL COST

As a general rule, the minimum total annual cost cannot be expected to occur at the point where the investment costs and the operating costs are equal. The following example contrasts the more general case with Kelvin's special case.

EXAMPLE 13.4 The transmission line in Example 13.2 must be supported and insulated from ground. However, the cost of the insulators, crossarms, hardware, and supporting structure is not directly proportional to the wire size. The cost of these items and the cost of the line itself (which is the same as in Example 13.2) are given in Table 13.4. The economic life of all equipment is again 20 years with zero salvage. Compute the size of line to be installed.

SOLUTION. The investment cost of the line and the energy charges were computed in Example 13.2. These costs and the added cost of the insulating and suspension equipment are tabulated in Table 13.4. In this example, at the point of minimum cost, (size 1/0 wire), the annual investment cost and annual energy costs are not equal, although the linear variation of investment cost makes the situation deceptively similar to Kelvin's case. The minimum total cost

Table 13.4 ANNUAL COST OF TRANSMISSION LINE INCLUDING
POLE ACCESSORIES

Wire size, AWG number	3/0	2/0	1/0	1	2	3
Area (circular mils X 1,000)	167.8	133.1	105.5	83.7	66.4	52.6
Cost of pole accessories	$130.66	120.28	112.02	105.50	100.32	96.27
Annual investment cost of accessories	$ 18.61	17.14	15.96	15.03	14.29	13.71
Annual investment cost of wire	14.47	11.48	9.10	7.22	5.72	4.54
Total annual investment cost	$ 33.08	28.62	25.06	22.25	20.01	18.25
Annual energy cost	7.51	9.47	11.94	15.05	18.99	23.94
Total annual cost	$ 40.59	38.09	37.00	37.30	39.00	42.19

[1]Everett M. Strong, *Electrical Engineering* (New York: Wiley, 1943), p. 113.

occurs where the negative slope of one curve numerically equals the positive slope of the other, which in the general case does not occur at the point where the curves intersect. This can be verified by a detailed analysis of the mathematical logic of the process of differentiation. Kelvin's rule does not describe the case where the cost components are merely a function of a single design variable; his rule is a special case of that.

In fact, in the most general case the investment costs will not even be linear, probably as a result of diminishing design efficiency with added investment.

13.5 MINIMUM FIRST COST

The test of an investment is its financial efficiency, not engineering efficiency. High first cost generally produces high engineering efficiency, and low first cost low engineering efficiency; but engineering efficiency is not the criterion so equipment is not selected solely from its low first cost.

The criterion in income-expansion propositions is the selection of the alternative with the highest net income, and the criterion in cost-reduction propositions is the selection of the alternative with the lowest cost, both computed at a minimum acceptable time value of money. These amounts are, of course, the totals of the first costs and future costs and incomes. This may be summarized by stating that the selection of a piece of equipment is also the selection of the particular engineering efficiency which is most economical for *that* job.

The objective of finding the equipment with the lowest total annual cost does not preclude an independent search for low first cost; in fact it heightens it. The engineer is obliged to search for an alternative having lower first cost than another alternative with the same engineering efficiency. In this case he is permitted to concentrate entirely on finding low first cost.

Unfortunately, in too many cases, engineers have maintained only this search for low first cost without conducting an equally determined search for alternatives having higher or lower engineering efficiencies. But an even more unfortunate engineering procedure is the selection of the engineer's first design without searching for any alternatives.

Chronologically, the search for all the low first-cost designs for each level of engineering efficiency should be performed before the alternatives of different efficiency are compared; otherwise the comparison of total costs is without merit. However, even after the economic selection of a machine against all others, a reexamination of the design to ascertain that it does represent the lowest first cost for that efficiency generally justifies the effort.

Broadly stated, problems in finding minimum first cost are those in which future incomes or savings are fixed and will not be changed in an alternative with a lower first cost. It is natural that these cases should be called problems in present economy. Obviously here low first cost is the criterion; not so obvious is the fact that engineering efficiency is fixed or inconsequential.

A structure, system, machine, etc., can generally be designed in alternative ways to provide precisely the same efficiency. For example, to meet a maximum required floor loading in a wooden building, a floor can be designed with 2-inch by 8-inch joists on 12-inch centers or can be designed with 2-inch by 10-inch joists on wider centers. One can be expected to have a higher cost of material and lower cost of labor; consequently one or the other will have a lower first cost. With equal lives, maintenance, and liquidation values, the problem is solely one of first cost. This presumes, of course, that the 10-inch joists do not add to the height of the house or significantly decrease the interior space. Presumably, too, a separate decision has selected the type of building with the highest financial efficiency. This is a simple example, but it is typical of designing a bridge, an office building, a machine tool, a driving engine, and so on. Another illustration is given in the following example.

EXAMPLE 13.5[1]   Find the practical length of span for a steel bridge under the following conditions. The cost of steel in place is 9 cents per pound. The weight W of the superstructure in pounds may be found by the formula $W = 9.25$ $L^2 + 150L$, where L equals the length of span in feet. A pier or abutment is estimated to cost $15,500. The entire length of the bridge must be 1,550 feet and there are no navigational restrictions on the design of the bridge.

SOLUTION.   Let n = number of spans. Then $n + 1$ = number of piers plus abutments. The total first cost C of the bridge is the cost of superstructure plus the cost of piers and abutments.

$$C = 0.09W + (15,500)(n + 1)$$

$$C = (0.09)(9.25L^2 + 150L) + (15,500)(n + 1)$$

but the length L of a span is $1,550/n$, so

$$n = \frac{1,550}{L} \quad \text{and} \quad n + 1 = \frac{1,550}{L} + 1$$

The total first cost C is

$$C = (0.09)(9.25L^2 + 150L) + (15,500)\left(\frac{1,550}{L} + 1\right)$$

$$= 0.8325L^2 + 13.5L + \frac{24,025,000}{L} + 15,500$$

so

$$\frac{d(C)}{dL} = 1.665L + 13.5 - \frac{24,025,000}{L^2} = 0$$

---

[1]This example appeared on the February 1944 New York State examination for professional engineers.

$$1.665 = \frac{48,050,000}{L^3}$$

Table 13.5 MINIMUM FIRST COST OF A STRUCTURE

Number of spans, n	Number of supports, $n + 1$	Span length, L (ft)	Cost of superstructure	Cost of piers and abutments	Total first cost
4	5	387.50	$130,236	$ 77,500	$207,736
5	6	310.00	84,188	93,000	177,188
6	7	248.33	59,043	108,500	167,543
7	8	221.43	43,807	124,000	167,807
8	9	193.75	33,867	139,500	173,367

From this, L equals 241 feet, or 6.43 spans. The least cost will occur for 6 equal spans of 258 feet. The comparison of first costs of various numbers of spans is given in Table 13.5 and Fig. 13.5. A mathematical examination of the cost equations of the superstructure and substructures indicates that they are not expected to cross where the slopes are equal. The rules proposed for the economic determination of substructures and superstructures make interesting history in engineering economy. In 1890, J. A. L. Wadell of the ASCE said, "For any crossing, the greatest economy will be attained when the cost per lineal foot of the substructure is equal to the cost per lineal foot of the trusses and lateral systems."

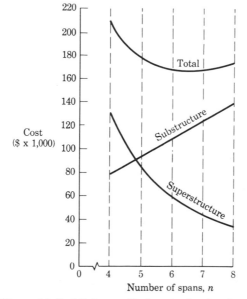

Figure 13.5   Minimum first cost of a structure

In 1911 H. P. Gillette disputed this[1] on the grounds that the formula disregarded the maintenance and renewals of the superstructure (namely, disregarded future costs), a very interesting point in light of the comments in the next section. Mr. Gillette, however, agreed that if there is "no annual expense for maintenance and depreciation" the most economic point occurs where both costs are equal. These earlier formulas presumed that the cost of the piers and abutments is directly proportional to the number of spans n; later thinking observed that this cost is proportional to $n + 1$ so that, as in Example 13.5, the minimum first cost does not occur where the cost of the substructure and superstructure are equal.

All formulas held that the cost of flooring mounted at the superstructure was irrelevant because it was the same regardless of the span length.

Economic analyses of a number of steel viaducts after their construction were reported in the *Handbook of Construction Costs*[2] with the comment that "many of them fall wide of the economic mark, so wide, in fact, that it is quite clear that the designers made little or no advance study of the cost of the foundations and pedestals."

In the previous example the entire family of bridges has the same engineering efficiency, that is, they will carry the same traffic load at the given location. A separate study of the economic location of the bridge must consider the problem of future economy and determine what location will maximize net profit (if it is a toll bridge, otherwise what location will maximize "benefit" to the public[3]). Conceivably, such an analysis could show that the most economic location is at the widest and deepest point on the river. In Example 13.5, however, all future cost and income considerations, although they exist, are irrelevant, because they are presumed to be the same for all the first-cost alternatives erected at this point.

13.6 EXTENT OF PRESENT-ECONOMY PROBLEMS

Every problem in future economy implies that there is also a problem in present economy, and vice versa. Consider merely a tube of tooth paste as an example. The problem in future economy is whether to invest in paste and save the cost of tooth decay, a problem which must consider all types of paste, powder—and the alternatives of plain water or whether to brush at all. The problem in present economy is to acquire the paste at minimum first cost, considering all alternatives including purchasing the large economy size. To be a problem in present economy, future costs must be irrelevant. Significant inventory costs, deterioration, or loss of material can easily convert the problem to one in future economy.

Another and more practical example is the economy problem of whether to use screws, rivets, welding, or unit construction in a structure, considering first

---

[1] *Engineering and Contracting*, 4 January 1911.
[2] H. P. Gillette, *Handbook of Construction Costs* (New York: McGraw-Hill, 1922), p. 1116.
[3] See Chapter 18 for an explanation of the benefit-cost technique.

costs and the future costs of inspection, maintenance, and replacement. A present-economy aspect of such a problem from the standpoint of the manufacturer is whether to make brass or steel screws. This analysis hinges on the fact that the material cost is lower for steel than for brass but the cost of machining steel is higher. If the previous study reveals that all the *future* cost differences between steel and brass will be insignificant, then we have only a problem in present economy.

For another illustration consider that the cost of machining a piece may be reduced by heat-treating it. Suppose in a given case it costs 95 cents to machine a certain piece having a required hardness. The alternative is to draw the hardness, machine the piece when soft, then heat-treat it to the required hardness. This will be attractive if the cost of machining the soft piece is only 75 cents and the entire heat treating cost is 10 cents. As expected, the present economy problem implies a host of future economy problems, such as all the other methods of forming, other types of cutting tools, alternative methods of heat-treating, and so on.

The fact is that present-economy problems cannot be undertaken without consideration of the associated future-economy problems and vice versa. Executives should expect to give as much creative and judicial effort to searching for alternatives with different engineering efficiencies as for alternatives having low first cost and the same engineering efficiency. Where the designer concentrates on one without attending to the other it is very likely that a better conclusion has been overlooked.

It is not correct, either, to assume that problems in present economy are necessarily simple or that they require little mathematics because the time value of money is absent. The mathematical problems in linear and dynamic programming, game theory, and so on, are examples of the level of the mathematical tools employed in some present-economy problems. But, to begin with, the manager must visualize the problem, and before this he must recognize its existence. To achieve any of this he must understand the economic forces or elements that create the problem. He must, in short, have developed a managerial sense of economic awareness because without it these fine tools for evaluation will not be used. Most problems in this area go unsolved merely because management fails to visualize their existence.

13.7 ECONOMIC LOT SIZES IN MANUFACTURING

Problems in computing the economic size of manufacturing lots are nothing more than problems in finding the minimum annual cost as discussed in the first four sections of this chapter.

The economy of lot sizes arises from the fact that the component pieces of the end product are not in continuous production; if they were, the production rates of modern tools would often create more pieces than could be used in the final assembly. Consequently, during a production run, the excess produced beyond the daily needs of the factory goes to storage and, when a predetermined amount has been stored, production of the piece stops until its inventory has been depleted to a certain reorder level. In the interim the machine produces batches of other components. The economy relevant to the choice between producing the annual requirements in small lots versus large lots occurs because the former creates a higher annual cost of setups but a lower cost of inventory (including storage costs). The setup costs are the costs of make-ready, such as changing the tools, programming the machine, and running sufficient test pieces before approving the setup for a production run on a new piece. The inventory and storage charges are those costs relevant to the size of the lot, such as taxes and insurance on the inventory; storage space including maintenance, heat, and light; handling to and from storage; guarding, protecting, and recording inventory including the cost of records and paper work; thefts and disappearances; and the investment cost of the inventory consisting of interest on the investment and capital shrinkage from deterioration or obsolescence.

This problem has been recognized for a long time and mathematical models of annual cost have been suggested by many authorities; for example, the *Production Handbook*[1] suggests as many as four separate formulas (by Camp, Raymond, Lehoczky and Norton). The number of available lot-size formulas reflects the differences in each author's assumptions regarding the behavior and relevancy of certain cost factors. Since one formula fits one situation better than another, selection requires an understanding of all the available formulas and each author's assumptions. The user must also comprehend his own problem to know what factors must be included. In fact when the analyst knows what he should know about his problem, it will be easy enough to derive his own formula.

Another disadvantage of prepared formulas can be the diversity of symbols introduced by various authors. Rather than suggest new symbols, we favor those generally appearing in the *Production Handbook* and particularly in Norton's formula. The symbols employed here are defined in example 13.7. The objective of this example is to prepare the student to derive the formula, not to memorize it.

EXAMPLE 13.7 The annual requirement for a single component used in a product is 15,000 pieces. The production rate of the machine is 500 pieces a day. The factory works 300 days a year with a uniform output of the product. The piece has a total unit cost of $1.50 including factory overhead. The increment cost of the piece (labor, material, and variable indirect costs) is 95 cents. The cost for each setup of the machine is $20. Taxes and insurance are 2% of the cost of the inventory. The annual cost of storing a piece is 5 cents, which covers the cost of space, storeroom facilities, personnel, and records. The stock value lost in storage is zero. The reorder point is assumed to be zero. The minimum

[1]L. P. Alford and John R. Bangs, *Production Handbook* (New York: Ronald Press, 1949), p. 101.

required rate of return is 10%. What is the most economic manufacturing lot size?

SOLUTION. The symbols with definitions and values are listed below:

Q Lot size in number of pieces per lot.

n Number of lots produced per year (also equal to the number of esparate production runs).

S Setup cost for each lot—$20

P Production rate in pieces per day—500.

U Pieces used per day—50.

N Number of days per year that pieces are used—300.

A Annual storage cost per piece—5 cents.

B Taxes and insurance expressed as a percentage on the cost of inventory (not on its sale price)—2%.

C Increment cost of a piece going into storage (labor, material, and any burden costs resulting directly from production of the piece)—95 cents.

T The unit cost of the piece (total labor, material, and overhead charged to one piece)—$1.50.

I Minimum required rate of return—10%.

R Minimum number of pieces in storage (number in reserve at reorder point)—0.

L Percentage of the lot lost in storage (spoilage, deterioration)—0.

Then the amount which goes into stock every day during a production run is $P - U$.

The amount added to stock as the result of a single production run is the amount going to storage per day times the number of days in a production run:

$$(P - U) \left(\frac{Q}{P}\right) = Q\left(1 - \frac{U}{P}\right)$$

This quantity will equal the maximum number of pieces in storage if the reorder point is zero.

Assuming that the additions to storage and the withdrawals are uniform as well as continuous, the average number of pieces in storage over any number of cycles of making and using the product is

$$\left(\frac{Q}{2}\right) \left(1 - \frac{U}{P}\right)$$

Annual Cost of Storage: If storage space must be provided for the maximum number of units put in storage, as would be necessary if space were reserved for each piece (e.g., bins for each item), then the annual cost of storage is the cost of storage per piece times the maximum pieces in storage:

$$(AQ) \left(1 - \frac{U}{P}\right)$$

But if the storage space is shared with other pieces on an open floor or shelves, the annual cost of storage is more logically based on the average pieces in storage:

$$\left(\frac{AQ}{2}\right)\left(1 - \frac{U}{P}\right)$$

Annual Cost of Taxes and Insurance: The annual cost of taxes and insurance is the tax rate plus the insurance rate per dollar times the value of the average amount of inventory during the year:

$$\left(BT\frac{Q}{2}\right)\left(1 - \frac{U}{P}\right)$$

The value of the inventory for determining the cost of insurance and property taxes is based on its total cost, not on its increment cost or its sale price.

Annual Investment Cost: The amount of money tied up or foregone in one lot size compared to another is the difference in the increment costs of the lots. The fixed burden will be the same regardless of the size of these lots and is irrelevant to the choice between them. Interest on this investment is the sole investment cost as long as there is no capital shrinkage from deterioration, theft, and so on. The annual cost is

$$\left(IC\frac{Q}{2}\right)\left(1 - \frac{U}{P}\right)$$

Annual Cost of Setups: Annual cost of setups is the number of setups times S. The number of setups is the number of pieces used per year divided by Q:

$$\frac{UN}{Q}$$

The annual cost of setups is

$$\frac{UNS}{Q}$$

The Total Annual-Cost Equation: The annual-cost equation based on providing storage space for the *maximum* number of units that will be in storage is:

$$AC = \left(BT\frac{Q}{2}\right)\left(1 - \frac{U}{P}\right) + \left(CI\frac{Q}{2}\right)\left(1 - \frac{U}{P}\right) + (AQ)\left(1 - \frac{U}{P}\right) + \frac{UNS}{Q}$$

$$= (BT + CI + 2A)\left(\frac{Q}{2}\right)\left(1 - \frac{U}{P}\right) + \frac{UNS}{Q} \tag{13.7a}$$

which is in the form,

$$AC = aQ + \frac{b}{Q}$$

Differentiating and equating the result to zero:

$$\frac{d(AC)}{dQ} = a - \frac{b}{Q^2} = 0$$

whence

$$Q = \sqrt{b/a}$$

$$= \sqrt{\frac{2UNS}{(BT + CI + 2A)(1 - U/P)}} \qquad (13.7b)$$

Substituting the given values in Eq. 13.7b,

$$Q = \sqrt{\frac{(2)(20)(50)(300)}{(0.02)(1.50)(0.95)(0.10 + 2)(0.05)(1 - 50/500)}}$$

$$= 1,720 \text{ pieces in a lot}$$

The number of lots per year[1] is

$$\frac{NU}{Q} = \frac{(300)(50)}{1,720} = 8.7$$

The variation of the cost of setups and the cost of inventory with the number of lots is illustrated in Fig. 13.7. The curve of the annual costs (of course these are comparative annual costs) of the lots is typically flat and permits a wide latitude in the selection of lot size without much sacrifice in cost. The low cost in this example occurs where the setup and inventory costs are equal.

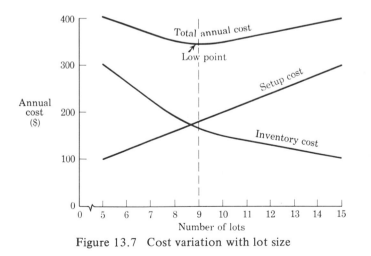

Figure 13.7   Cost variation with lot size

[1] Presumably the piece is in production year after year, so the number of lots in a calendar year need not be an integer. In fact, lot sizes will be altered at any time in the year when predicted requirements change.

Lot-size problems are perfect examples of problems of setting up and analyzing a family of annual-cost equations, although this does not seem to be immediately evident to most analysts, perhaps because the time period is only 1 year and the investment cost may be only interest. Consequently, instead of reliance on derivations of the annual-cost equations, we find an almost universal use of handbook formulas. No doubt these cost derivations are more complex than most, but on the other hand the task will be simpler if the analyst is aware that these are only annual-cost equations.

13.8 ECONOMIC LOT SIZES IN PURCHASING

Estimating lot sizes for purchase orders follows the procedure used in the Section 13.7. The same symbols can apply except that a few must be redefined. For example, S must now represent the cost of placing an order instead of the cost of setting up a machine.

Unlike manufacturing lots, when the purchase order lot, consisting of Q pieces, is received, the amount Q is immediately added to inventory, as shown in Fig. 13.8 (assuming the entire order is filled in one shipment). The symbol P, production rate of the machine, now has no significance (although its value might be considered infinite, inasmuch as the rate of units going to storage is infinite). The increment cost of the piece C is the purchase price plus any other costs directly incurred by the purchase. The total cost T includes the addition of any assignable factory burden.

The formulas of Eqs. 13.7a and 13.7b can be applied to purchase lots if P is considered infinite, and so we get

Comparative annual cost:

$$(BT + CI + 2A)\frac{Q}{2} + \frac{UNS}{Q} \tag{13.8a}$$

Economic purchase-order size:

$$Q = \sqrt{\frac{2UNS}{BT + CI + 2A}} \tag{13.8b}$$

Equations 13.8a and 13.8b apply where the cost of storage is based on providing space for the maximum number of pieces in storage; i.e., where bin space or shelf space is reserved solely for a given item.

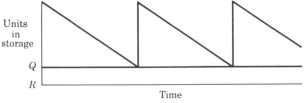

Figure 13.8   Variation in storage quantities

The analysis can be complicated by the addition of quantity discounts which may be available when ordering in large lots. Discounts may dictate ordering larger lots than would be justified without discounts. A guide to this lot size can be obtained by first computing the economic lot size disregarding discounts. Generally this is sufficient for locating the discount classification so that the annual cost of an economic lot at the available discount rate can be computed. This should then be compared with the annual cost of the minimum quantity that can be obtained at the next higher discount rate. This comparison provides the test of whether the added discount justified the higher inventory with the larger quantity.

13.9 OPTIMAL VERSUS SUBOPTIMAL SOLUTIONS

Most solutions have been approached from the suboptimal viewpoint, that is, from the viewpoint that the most economic inventory, for example, will result from the analysis of only the individual items that compose the entire inventory. Presumably if the annual cost of each item is minimized, the cost of the total inventory necessary to manufacture the product at a continuous rate throughout the year will also be minimized. This is similar to saying that analyzing a factory machine by machine and replacing each with the alternative having the lowest annual cost will maximize the company's overall profit picture. Needless to say, we are all sceptical of that conclusion. Broadly stated, the basic reason for the failure of such reasoning is the possible existence of a problem larger than the one that we have visualized. For example, selecting the best machine for job A and the best machine for job B without doubt gives the best economy for the performance of these two separate jobs. But, if viewed as a larger problem, namely the performance of jobs A and B together, a machine that will perform these two jobs together, not separately, will possibly have a better overall economy. Profit maximization requires consideration of combined processes: combinations of pairs of processes, of groups, or of departments; integration of systems into larger systems; and final consideration of the entire factory as a single machine. Obviously this requires seeing the problem that is bigger than the smaller problems,[1] and the guide to this is an economy analysis. These problems must be approached with ingenuity. For example, by visualizing and quantifying the potential advantages of combining units, one can compute the first cost that would be justified for such a machine. The question then is, "Can the designers build such a machine for that amount?" The fact is that the manager must have sufficient economic awareness to envision these larger areas even though the immediate and apparent problem is only a suboptimal one.

---

[1] The importance of this cannot be overstated. One of the major objectives of using operations research tools is to permit solutions of complex problems such as those in which the manager envisages the completely integrated problem in order to achieve the "overall optimum."

Inventory may also be viewed from a larger picture. Economy considerations would include the cost of making interchangeable parts to reduce setups, combining versus decentralizing storage areas, surplus inventory costs versus shortage and delay costs, and so on.

EXAMPLE 13.9 Machine *A* has been selected to replace an existing machine. The required extra investment is $10,000 and the prospective annual savings are $2,500 for a 10-year period with zero salvage at that date. In the same department machine *B* has been selected to replace another existing machine. Its extra cost is $20,000 with a prospective saving of $6,000 a year for 10 years with zero salvage. Machines *A* and *B* are performing successive processes: the piece is removed from *A*, deposited, transported, and fed to machine *B* by the respective machine operators. Engineers predict they can design a single machine to perform the two processes almost simultaneously and eliminate the manual handling between machines *A* and *B*. Furthermore they figure the extra investment in the machine would be only $25,000, with savings of $9,000 a year over the two existing machines for 10 years with zero salvage. The minimum required rate of return is 10%.

SOLUTION.

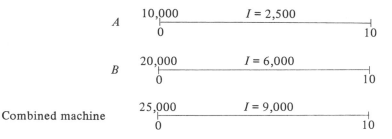

Machines *A* and *B*, as stated, had been approved. A check reveals that they have rates of return of 21% and 27%, respectively, which exceed the minimum required. However good this suboptimal viewpoint, it is not as good as using the combined machine which shows a return of 34%. A computation was not necessary, because we note that a reduction in the expenditure increases the savings, and, since these are mutually exclusive alternatives, we cannot justify spending additional money to reduce the amount of savings.

This example does not imply that this particular favorable pattern can be expected for all proposals to combine processes; in some situations it might be economical to divide processes. However, the economy of combining processes is a strong basis for extending the mechanization of a plant. The road to mechanization will proceed through improved individual machines, improved handling between machines leading eventually to automatic transfer devices, and ending in integrated designs for all machines and transfer systems. Full automation, as an immediate economic solution for most factories, is the exception rather than the rule, but it will develop by the evolution and integration of each of the processing units in the factory. Evolution of the product, too, through new materials and better product designs, makes fully automatic, integrated processes easier to adopt.

13.10 BEHAVIOR OF UNIT COST

Chapter 12 introduced the question of minimum unit cost. The point to be reminded of here is that the unit costs, like other costs considered in the present chapter, reach a minimum point. The slope of the unit-cost curve depends on the slope of the input-output relation. If it is linear, as in Fig. 13.10a, the minimum occurs at the maximum number of units produced as noted in Fig. 13.10b. The ogee curve, the result of diminishing returns, Fig. 13.10c, gives a minimum unit cost at the point of maximum engineering efficiency, as shown in Fig. 13.10d. The dotted curve in Fig. 13.10d is the efficiency curve, the reciprocal of the unit-cost curve, as noted from the following relationship.

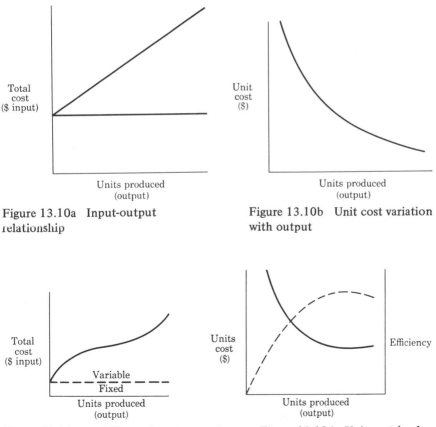

Figure 13.10a Input-output relationship

Figure 13.10b Unit cost variation with output

Figure 13.10c A different input-output relationship

Figure 13.10d Unit cost (and efficiency) variation with output

$$\text{Unit cost} = \frac{\text{input}}{\text{output}}$$

$$\text{Efficiency} = \frac{\text{output}}{\text{input}}$$

13.11 UNIT COST IN RELATION TO CAPACITY

Very similar to the discussion in the last section is the analysis of the unit cost of capacity. When a machine is built in several sizes, the price per unit of machine capacity generally decreases as the size of the machine increases. This is illustrated in Fig. 13.11, which shows the variation of the machine size rated in horsepower, with dollars per horsepower.

The decrease in unit cost is largely due to the existence of certain fixed costs which do not change materially as size is increased. For example, a shaft of a motor must have a certain strength of its own even though it is not called upon to support any exterior weight or load; therefore only a slight alteration in shaft size will permit considerable increase in load capacity. Based on this reasoning, the cost of many of the components in the machine will follow the curve in Fig. 13.11.

As a general rule, the first cost of two half-size machines is greater than one full-size machine (and generally, too, the efficiency of the large machine is higher). Since both first cost and operating disbursements are greater, this certainly precludes the installation of two units to do the work of one and justifies the combination of units. This is similar to the conclusion in Section 13.9.

There are, however, many situations where two half-size units will be selected over one large unit, based on the economics peculiar to that situation. One example, as we have seen, occurs in the case of deferred investments where it may be more economical to install one of the half-size units at a deferred interval instead of the large unit today.

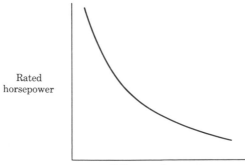

Rated
horsepower

Dollars per horsepower

Figure 13.11   Variation of price per horsepower with machine size

Another example occurs where the expense of a shutdown is prohibitive. In that case it may prove more economical to install three half-size units (two to run) instead of a large unit and a full standby, even though the efficiency of the half-size units is less.

A further example may be found in "scheduling" problems. If a plant has a low capacity factor, say 50%, two half-size units will prove more economical than one unit if the load can be scheduled so that the small units run fully loaded most of the time, since their full-load efficiency usually is higher than the half-load efficiency of the large unit. Some interesting scheduling problems are possible if the prospective load pattern can be reasonably predicted in advance.

In the decrease of unit cost with increased capacity we would expect, of course, that a point of diminishing returns would eventually be reached which is not shown in Fig. 13.11. As an illustration of this, recall that the first cost of a unit of space in a multistory building will increase when its design has been extended to a certain height.

An interesting way of reducing the first cost of a unit of capacity is to overload the equipment to get more units of output for the given first cost. But the final economy test in this case (and in all cases) is not first cost alone but whether overloading gives the lowest annual cost (or highest annual net profit). This problem, relative to overloading equipment, is discussed in Chapter 19.

13.12 EFFECT OF LOT SIZE ON SELECTION OF EQUIPMENT

In this chapter we have discussed three separate areas of minimum cost: (a) the minimum annual cost (i.e., the lowest total of first and future costs), (b) the minimum first cost for a given efficiency, (c) the minimum operating cost (i.e., 1-year costs as with lot sizes or operating disbursements alone). The search for alternatives must be conducted in all three of these areas. In a cost-reduction proposition, we expect to select the alternative with the lowest annual cost in which the first cost is the lowest for the engineering efficiency represented by that alternative and in which the operating cost is also the lowest as permitted by the engineering efficiency of that alternative. In an income-expansion proposition we expect to select the equipment with the highest net profit but, again, the first cost and the operating cost must be the lowest for the alternatives selected.

Attention must be given to determining the minimum operating costs of a machine of a certain engineering efficiency. In the past discussions we have simply envisioned a single operating cost for a given engineering efficiency. We have, in fact, assumed the simplest operating procedures. For example, we assumed that a machine would produce one item continuously until the annual requirements were filled. However, many machines run intermittently, producing different items in separate lots, the runs being punctuated by the necessity to set up the machine for each new run.

A closer look at this situation reveals that (a) a setup cost is incurred for each production lot, (b) each item should be produced in economic lot sizes, (c) the number of setups per item will equal the number of economic lots of that item, (d) the total number of setups is also a function of the number of items, and (e) producing equipment by lots incurs storage costs as well as setup costs.

The effect of production in lots on machine selection is illustrated in the following example:

EXAMPLE 13.12 Machine A has a higher production rate than machine B; it is more automated, its first cost is greater, and its setup cost on each production run is higher.

These machines are being considered for a job on which they must produce 6 separate items, and each item will require a new setup of the machine. Therefore a minimum of 6 setups a year will be required if the annual requirement for each item is produced in one production run and stored for the year. Carrying this inventory might be very expensive, and determination of the minimum total operating cost suggests an economic lot-size analysis.

The presentation of this example has been greatly simplified by assuming that, although each item requires a new machine setup, each item is required in the same quantity and uses the same amount of labor, material, and supervision. It assumes also that the overhead will be the same whether machine A or B is used.

The detailed costs for each alternative are tabulated below:

	Machine A	Machine B
First cost	$10,000	$ 6,000
Economic life, years	4	4
Salvage	0	0
Machine rate, pieces per day, P	400	240
Number of items being produced	6	6
Setup cost per setup	$125	$50
Pieces used per working day per item, U	40	40
Days worked per year, N	250	250
Pieces used per year per item, NU	10,000	10,000
Pieces used per year, all items	60,000	60,000
Days to produce 60,000 pieces	150	250
Annual cost of direct labor, all items	$3,000	$5,000
Annual cost of direct labor per item	$500	$833
Annual cost of material per item	$800	$800
Annual cost of storage per piece	$0.05	$0.05
Factory overhead per item	$600	$600
Increment cost per piece, C	$0.13	$0.163
Total cost per piece, T	$0.19	$0.223
Tax and insurance, B	2%	2%
Minimum required rate of return, I	10%	10%

SOLUTION. If storage space is required for the maximum number of pieces stored, the economic lot sizes are computed from Eq. 13.7a as follows:

For machine A:

$$Q = \sqrt{\frac{2SNU}{(BT + CI + 2A)(1 - U/P)}}$$

$$= \sqrt{\frac{(2)(125)(10,000)}{(0.02)(0.19) + (0.13)(0.10) + (2)(0.05)(1 - 40/400)}}$$

$$= 4,289 \text{ pieces}$$

or 2.33 lots per year per item, based on the annual requirement of 10,000 pieces. This is a total of 14 lots per year if machine A is used; a total of $1,750 per year just for setups of machine A.

For machine B:

$$Q = \sqrt{\frac{(2)(50)(10,000)}{(0.02)(0.223) + (0.163)(0.10) + (2)(0.05)(1 - 40/240)}}$$

$$= 3,152 \text{ pieces}$$

or 3.17 lots a year per item. This is a total of 19 lots per year if machine B is used; a total of $950 per year for setups alone.

The cost of each lot is not the cost of setups alone, but the cost of inventory which each lot creates. The annual cost of 14 lots produced on machine A is

$$(BT + CI + 2A)\left(1 - \frac{U}{P}\right)\left(\frac{Q}{2}\right) + \frac{SNU}{Q} \text{ per item}$$

$$= [(0.02)(0.19) + (0.13)(0.10 + (2)(0.05)]\left(1 - \frac{40}{400}\right)\left(\frac{4,289}{2}\right)$$

$$+ (125)\left(\frac{10,000}{4,289}\right) = \$517 \text{ per item}$$

$$= (517)(6) = \$3,102$$

And the annual cost of 19 lots produced on machine B is

$$[(0.02)(0.223) + (0.163)(0.10) + (2)(0.05)]\left(1 - \frac{40}{240}\right)\left(\frac{3,152}{2}\right)$$

$$+ (50)\left(\frac{10,000}{3,152}\right) = \$318 \text{ per item}$$

$$= (318)(6) = \$1,908$$

Most company data sheets used in an economy analysis include machine setups in the tabulation of operating disbursements. Rarely, however, is provision made for computing the annual cost in consideration of the number of economic lots for all the items produced and the inclusion of the comparative cost of the resulting inventory. It is interesting to observe the possible effects of these considerations on the decision between the two machines.

The comparative annual costs of the machine, therefore, are

$$AC_A = 10{,}000 \overset{0.31547}{(A/P, .10, 4)} + 3{,}000 + 3{,}102 = 6{,}155 + 3{,}102 = \$9{,}257$$

$$AC_B = 6{,}000 \overset{0.31547}{(A/P, .10, 4)} + 5{,}000 + 1{,}908 = 6{,}893 + 1{,}908 = \$8{,}801$$

In this case the cost of the lots is enough to reverse the selection that would be made if the machines were producing only one product continuously. The conclusion is not unreasonable. The general observation is that machines with low setup costs are selected for short production runs, for job shops where a variety of items go over the machines. The high-production machines which generally have the higher setup time are selected for the mass-production runs. The machines with high setup costs are generally not selected for work in shops where diversity necessitates many setups.

PROBLEMS

13.1 Make a case for the statement in Section 13.1 that "in income-expansion propositions the lowest total cost is not the criterion, it is the highest net profit."

13.2 Find the most economic size of a transmission line if its economic life is 15 years, the minimum acceptable rate of return is 15%, the wire costs 22 cents a pound, and the current averages 50 amperes for 5,000 hours a year with an energy cost of 1.5 cents a kw-hr. Weights and resistances of conductors may be found in Table 13.2.

Show how a change in utilization of the transmission line would affect your conclusion by assuming the hours of operation are alternately 3,000, 4,000, 6,000, 7,000, and 8,000 instead of 5,000.

13.3 If the pole accessories varied with the size of transmission line as follows, how would they alter your conclusion in Problem 13.2? Size 3/0, $400; size 2/0, $320; size 0, $260; size 1, $220; size 2, $200. These are the extra first costs of pole line accessories per 1,000 feet of line.

13.4 Discuss the effect on annual cost of varying a design factor and indicate whether or not the results would be expected to illustrate Kelvin's Law. For example, consider the effect of varying the thickness of insulation of a steam transmission line. Try other examples too.

13.5 In a certain design of steel bridge the weight of a span is W where $W = 10L^2 + 1{,}000L - 50{,}000$ and L is the span length. The steel in the span costs 20 cents a pound. The crossing is to be 1,500 feet long. The piers and abutments are each estimated to cost $C = 80{,}000 + 80L$. Find the number of spans to give minimum first cost.

13.6 Show how the following objects may be the basis of present-economy decisions; alternatively, show how they may also be future-economy problems: (a) a bridge; (b) a telephone pole; (c) a man's dress shirt; (d) a machine tool.

13.7 Find the economic lot size for a manufactured piece, 30,000 of which are used a year at the rate of 100 a day. The total cost including overhead to make one piece is $2.50. The increment cost to produce one piece is $2.00. Taxes and insurance on inventory cost are 3%. The annual storage cost per piece is $0.10. The pieces are stored in specially reserved bins. The machine on which the pieces are produced has an output of 750 per day. The setup cost of the machine is $50. The loss of inventory in storage is zero and the reorder point is approximately zero pieces. The minimum required rate of return is 15%.

13.8   Assume that 10% of a lot Q will be lost in storage due to spoilage, deterioration, or disappearance. Compute the economic lot size for the piece in the previous problem. Assume that insurance and taxes will be paid only on the "unspoiled" pieces. The storage space must be for the total number of pieces in a lot and the investment cost will be figured on the average of the total number going into storage.

13.9   An economic lot-size slide rule states that the economic lot size should be 2,600 for a setup cost of $50, a unit cost of $2.50, and a monthly usage of 2,500 pieces. The slide rule does not indicate what the other parameters were assumed to be, but we assume that the storage costs are based on the average number of pieces in storage, that the number of pieces used per day are insignificant relative to the pieces produced per day (i.e., the day's entire production will go into storage), that none of the inventory is lost in storage by spoilage, etc., that the total unit cost and increment cost are equal, that insurance and taxes are 4%, and that the minimum required rate of return is 10%. (a) What is the annual storage cost per piece? (b) If the minimum required rate of return is 25%, what is the storage cost per piece?

13.10 Three machines form the backbone of a manufacturer's business: one machine does the processing, another the assembling, and the third does the finishing. A proposition has been made to replace each of these with a new machine. The investment value P of the machines and the operating disbursements D are tabulated as follows:

	Present machines		Proposed machines	
	P	D	P	D
A Processing	$10,000	$8,000	$20,000	$6,000
B Assembling	5,000	4,000	12,000	2,000
C Finishing	4,000	3,000	10,000	1,000

A further alternative to this is a machine costing $55,000 that will do all three jobs at a total operating disbursement of $5,000 per year. The economic life of all machines is 10 years with zero salvage value. If the minimum required rate of return is 24%, which machines should or should not be used?

13.11 A certain component purchased from a supplier is presently ordered in 100-carton lots. Four cartons are used a day for 300 work days a year. It costs $25 to place a purchase order regardless of size, including receiving room costs. Each carton costs $20 delivered. Taxes and insurance on inventory are 3% based on the purchase price. The annual storage cost is 15 cents a carton. The reorder point is considered to be zero and there is no loss of inventory in storage. The minimum required rate of return is 15%. Is the company correct in ordering in 100-carton lots?

13.12 In the previous problem the supplier is now offering discounts according to the following schedule:

Number of cartons	Discount
1–100	3%
101–300	5%
301–500	10%
501 and over	15%

Will this alter the economic purchase order lot size?

13.13 Draw an assumed efficiency curve of Percent Efficiency versus Output. Assume the rated output is 1,000 units and the cost of each unit of input is $1. Compute and plot a curve of Unit Cost (Y-axis) versus Output units (X-axis).

13.14 From the pricebook of a manufacturer, select a family of machines, engines, or motors, and plot Rated Output (bhp, kw, gpm, cfm, etc.)[1] of each machine in the family versus Dollars per Unit Output.

Do some machines in the family appear to be too highly or lowly priced? Does it appear the equipments have been priced from a curve?

13.15 Machine A costs $27,000 and Machine B $10,000 with zero salvage for each. Each has a 10-year economic life. Machine A produces 500 pieces a day with an annual cost of $4,000 for labor and $1,000 for power. Machine B produces 250 pieces a day with a labor cost of $8,000 and a power cost of $700. These are the costs to make a year's supply of this part. The machine is not used for any other purpose.

The plant uses 45,000 pieces a year and works 300 days a year. The cost of material is 10 cents a piece. The setup cost of Machine A is $100 and that of Machine B $40. The cost of storage per piece is 15 cents a year. Taxes and insurance are 3% on machines and inventory. The factory burden rate is 50 cents per dollar of labor. The minimum required rate of return is 10%. Compare the alternatives with and without consideration of lot size.

---

[1] Brake horsepower, kilowatts, gallons per minute, cubic feet per minute.

14

Analysis of Risk and Uncertainty

14.1 CLASSES OF HAZARDS

Chapter 16 in its coverage of forecasting discusses the hazards of predicting costs, incomes, production levels, and economic lives, and recognizes the probability that all these predictions will be incorrect. Some will err greatly and others by only a few dollars and some will be favorable, others unfavorable to our prior decision. However, the present chapter will examine not the hazards of prediction but the prediction of hazards. This chapter will discuss the problem of predicting a special class of costs, the costs of disasters. No doubt it is a disaster if one week after installing a machine an economically superior machine appears; however, in the present chapter we will regard disasters primarily as the consequence of natural causes.

The risk of doing business must include all possible disasters regardless of their degree. The nature of the risk is defined by three questions: (1) what disasters are possible, even remotely; (2) what is the damage if the disaster occurs; and (3) what is the probability of occurrence?

In general, the disasters that could occur to an enterprise can be easily imagined. Examples of these are fire, flood, wind, hail, frost, freezing, icing, lightning, earthquake, collision, derailment, riot, theft, spoilage, breakage shut-down, outage, loss of service, collapse, explosion, overspeeding, and rotting.

Predicting the extent of damage is in a class with predicting operating disbursements, but predicting the frequency of damage occurrence is more difficult.

Disasters and their consequent costs suggest the possibility of investments to prevent them. The development of this economic picture will be the subject of the next section.

14.2 INVESTMENTS TO REDUCE RISK

The occurrence of loss can be reduced by investments in preventive designs. For example, investment in a sprinkler system reduces the occurrence and magnitude of fire loss. The test of this investment is the recovery of capital with a satisfactory return out of savings in predicted fire losses.

Other examples are investments in fire alarm systems, fire-fighting equipment, fire extinguishers, fireproof construction, and organizing and training fire-fighting personnel, all with the aim of reducing loss from fire. Investments to raise the height of a dam or levee, to increase the capacity of a spillway, or to create detention dams, reduce the occurrence of flood damage. Increased structural strength of electrical transmission lines reduces the probability of collapse and disruption of service from wind, snow, and ice. Investment in earthquake designs will prevent collapse or fire from shocks. Damage by frost and freezing can be reduced by insulation, heating plants, antifreeze solutions, and smudge pots. Certain fire disasters are reduced by installing lightning rods. Loss by theft is reduced by investigating prospective employees and by employing safes, alarms, guards, and burglar-proof procedures. Spoilage may be reduced by refrigeration, better packaging, and other preventive measures. Injury to personnel may be prevented by machine guards and various safety devices, by employing a safety engineer, and by educational programs and safety campaigns.

Investments to reduce the expected cost of damage will be analyzed in subsequent sections. The role of insurance in this investment picture will also be examined.

14.3 PROBABILITY OF OCCURRENCE OF DISASTERS: WEIGHTING OF UNCERTAINTY

As stated, we must predict the cost of damage in the event that a specific disaster occurs. This is primarily a prediction of the cost of replacement and, in addition, the cost of dislocation until replacement is accomplished.

We must also assess the probability of the occurrences of the specific disaster in a period of time. For example, we may predict the frequency that a flow intensity of 3,000 cubic feet per second (say, ± 100 cfs) will occur in 100 years or, we may predict the frequency of flood flow intensity *equal to or greater than* 3,000 cubic feet per second. We will see later how these predictions are used in economy analyses.

Simple illustrations of probability generally relate to throwing dice or tossing coins, because frequencies can be intuitively predicted without having to collect historical data. Intuitively we have no reason for preferring heads to tails in any future toss of the coin; therefore we are willing to say that these are equally probable. Since it is a law of probability that the sum of the probabilities of all the possible outcomes is 1.0, we can say that the probability of heads is $\frac{1}{2}$ and the probability of tails is also $\frac{1}{2}$. In practice we may also express this as a 1 in 2 chance of a head, a 50% probability of a head in a given throw, or, more precisely, we have assessed the probability of tossing a head in a given throw to be 0.50.

Another example in which the assignment of probabilities proceeds intuitively is the rolling of a die. Here we believe that each face is as likely to appear as any other face and as there are 6 faces the probability of the appearance of any given face in a roll is 1 in 6, a 1 in 6 chance, or a probability assessment of 0.16667.

Assessing the probability of the occurrence of disasters is far more difficult than predicting heads and tails because more complicated personal judgment is needed. An aid to this judgment is formal historical evidence, but even where historical data is plentiful, the assessment will still be guided by some degree of subjective, personal judgment, as later developments will suggest.

Although rational people will tend to agree in their assessments of the probability of heads on the toss of a coin, in dealing with complex situations in which there is uncertainty, they will differ in their probability assessments.

The reader is aware that this area of engineering economy is based on a knowledge of statistics and probability. The analysis of capital expenditures, as we have seen, requires a knowledge of accounting, taxation, equipment design and operation, costing, finance, and a sense of technological development. To this almost unlimited array of subjects we must now add statistics and probability theory. Here, too, adequate treatment would require another volume and cannot be undertaken. We must presume that the analyst will acquire the necessary knowledge or help when he needs it:

Time and space limit us to illustrations of economy analyses based on the assumption that the analyst has the statistical and probability background to make the necessary probability assessments. However, as far as possible we will introduce and explain some of the concepts on which the statistical approach to the probability assessments are based.

Suppose the analyst believes there are n possible outcomes, some of which may be favorable and some unfavorable, and suppose he assesses a cost $D_1 \ldots D_n$ (if the cost is favorable, let it be negative) and probabilities $p_1 \ldots p_n$, then the expected cost is

$$p_1 D_1 + p_2 D_2 + p_3 D_3 + \cdots + p_n D_d$$

Let us first consider the special case in which there are only two possible outcomes. Then $p_1 = p$ and $p_2 = 1 - p$, so the expected cost is

$$p D_1 + (1 - p) D_2$$

Consider, for example, a gambling game in which a player using a single die must pay $1,000 every time he rolls a six but wins $180 every time he rolls any other number. Then the expected value of each roll is

$$pD + (1 - p)D_2 = \left(\frac{1}{6}\right)(1,000) + \left(\frac{5}{6}\right)(-180) = 166.67 - 150 = \$16.67$$

This is a costly game, because on the average the player can expect to lose $16.67 a roll (although in any given roll he will either gain $180 or lose $1,000).

Many variations of this illustration are possible. For example, rolling "ones" or "sixes" may cost the player $1,500, and any other number may pay $360. In this case the expected value is

$$\left(\frac{2}{6}\right)(1,500) + \left(\frac{4}{6}\right)(-360) = 250 - 240 = \$10 \,(\text{a cost})$$

In many problems the cost or income from nonoccurrence of the disaster is zero, as in the following example.

EXAMPLE 14.3a   A flood of a certain intensity will overflow banks of a stream and cause general damage to the grounds and certain operations of an adjacent factory. Based on flood data, the analyst estimates a 1 in 6 chance of such a flood occurring in any one year. The damage on the condition that the flood occurs is estimated to be $12,000. A levee to prevent any overflow from the stream can be constructed at a cost of $19,000 and its economic life is expected to be 25 years with zero salvage. The minimum required rate of return is 15%. Should the levee be constructed?

SOLUTION.   The expected annual cost with no levee is

$$AC = pD_1 + (1 - p)D_2 = \left(\frac{1}{6}\right)(12,000) + 0 = \$2,000$$

The annual cost with a levee is
$$
\begin{array}{c}
0.1547 \\
AC = 19,000(A/P, .15, 25) = \$2,940
\end{array}
$$

With a levee, the cost of flooding is zero, because it is presumed to completely eliminate the disaster. Nevertheless, rather than install the levee, the most economical procedure is to let the damage occur.

This example suggests that $2,000 a year is a fair apportionment of the cost of disaster or a fair price to pay annually to avoid the disaster. Therefore, the expected annual cost of disaster, pD, can justifiably be regarded as a series of end-of-year costs on the time scale. We propose, in other words, to treat expected annual cost as a real cost and consequently to accept the year-end distribution as real. This resolves the problem arising from the fact that, not knowing when the $12,000 disasters will occur, we dare not give them time values by locating them on the time scale. A fair method, therefore, is to adopt the annual apportionment of the risk as in Example 14.3a.

We should be aware of the simplification inherent in our introductory example. In the first place we assumed that the damage is insensitive to flood intensities beyond a certain minimum intensity sufficient to overflow the banks. If damage becomes a function of flood flow, then we must assess the probability of occurrence of floods of various intensities and predict the conditional cost at each level. In the second place, the computation of annual cost is further simplified to some extent because flood disasters generally can occur only once a year as the waters rise in the spring.

A more complex problem on both counts occurs in computing the expected cost of a machine failure. For example, assume that a certain machine can fail an unlimited number of times during the year. Assume, too, that 24 hours will be required to restore a machine to operation after a failure. If the factory works only 250 days a year, the machine can fail at most 250 times a year or at the least, none. If the cost of one failure is D dollars and $p_1, p_2, \ldots, p_{250}$ are the probabilities of $1, 2, \ldots 250$ failures a year, then the expected annual cost due to failure is:

$$AC = p_1 D + (p_2)(2D) + (p_3)(3D) + \cdots + (p_{250})(250D)$$

The analyst will have to assess the probabilities of each occurrence (perhaps with the aid of an assumed probability distribution based on historical data, touched on later). However, he will likely find that many of these occurrences are so very improbable that coupled with the damages might not make a significant contribution to the total expected value. Therefore, in this case it is not necessary to assess probabilities for all possible outcomes.

EXAMPLE 14.3b   An executive of a costume jewelry concern proposes a new product that, on one hand, could create a fad for the coming summer season or, on the other, could completely fail. If it succeeds, the company will make a net profit of $200,000 in three months; if it fails the company will lose $50,000 at the end of three months. The executive feels there is a 3 to 2 chance of success[1]. The analysis will neglect the time value of money because of the short time period.

SOLUTION.   The executive's appraisement of this situation establishes a probability of 0.6 for success because odds of "r to s" can be translated as a probability of $r/(r + s)$. The expected value of offering the new product is

$$pI + (1 - p)(-D) = (0.6)(200,000) - (0.4)(50,000)$$

$$= 120,000 - 20,000 = \$100,000$$

The company can therefore value the proposal as a gain of $100,000.

Actually, the company will gain $200,000 or it will lose $50,000 if the product fails.

Suppose, on the other hand, that the probabilities had been different, say a 1 to 10 chance of success. Now the company would be advised not to offer the new product because the expected value of the enterprise would be:

---

[1] The difficulty of arriving at the probability of 3 to 2 is not to be underestimated. The reader can find more information on this in Robert Schlaifer, *Probability and Statistics for Business Decisions* (New York: McGraw-Hill, 1959).

$$pI + (1 - p)(-D) = (0.0909)(200,000) - (0.90909)(50,000)$$
$$= 18,182 - 45,455$$
$$= -\$27,273$$

In this case the company can value the proposal at a $27,273 loss.

The above example illustrates the process of weighting the alternatives according to their degree of uncertainty. The weights are the probability assessments. Uncertainty is one of the hazards of doing business and the approach to this problem is about the same as to any risk situation.

The reader's attention is strongly directed to other tools which present a different approach to the uncertainty of predictions. One very practical tool is the best-worst choice and another is the break-even analysis, both described in Chapter 16, "Forecasting." That chapter in many ways may be considered a continuation of the present subject.

14.4 COMPUTING ANNUAL COST OF DAMAGE FROM DISASTERS

In commenting on the simplicity of Example 14.3a we noted that in many cases the cost of damage will be a function of the intensity of the disaster. This is illustrated in the following example.

EXAMPLE 14.4 The lowest annual temperatures in a certain locality in the past 50 years are reported in the first two columns of Table 14.4a. The damage is held to be a function of the lowest temperature reached during the year. Specifically, this means that every time a new low is encountered some of the units will be destroyed but others will be strong enough to survive. It also means if that same low temperature is encountered the same units will survive—until a still lower temperature is encountered. It is further assumed that when the damage is created by a certain temperature the damage will not or cannot be repaired in that year. By this statement, subsequent occurrences of the same temperature will not or cannot repeat the same damage: increased damage can result only from subsequent occurrences of colder temperatures. For example, if the analogy of a farm crop is used, we assume that the annual damage will be established by the coldest temperature in the year and that subsequent lesser freezes will not increase the damages regardless of their frequency. (This may be only approximately true but may be sufficiently true to serve as a reasonable simplifying assumption.) The example also assumes that the duration of the freeze is immaterial or at least that the facts will permit this, too, to be a reasonable assumption (of course the duration of each of the recorded temperatures must be enough to cause the estimated damage). Column 4 of Table 14.4a lists the damages corresponding to each disaster intensity.

Table 14.4b, column 5, lists the prices of equipment which will give protection against the disaster down through the temperature listed on the same line. The life of the protection equipment is 15 years and the minimum required rate of return is 10%. The life of the system subject to damage is indefinitely long.

Table 14.4a COST OF DAMAGE WITH NO PROTECTION AGAINST FREEZING

(1) Minimum temperature in the year ($^\circ$F)	(2) Number of occurrences	(3) Relative frequency p	(4) Damage D	(5) Contribution to annual cost of damage pD
20	10	0.20	$ 8,000	$ 1,600
25	9	0.18	10,000	1,800
20	8	0.16	13,000	2,080
15	7	0.14	17,000	2,380
10	6	0.12	22,000	2,640
5	5	0.10	29,000	2,900
0	3	0.06	38,000	2,280
-5	2	0.04	50,000	2,000
	50	1.00		$17,680

SOLUTION. The historical data over the past 50 years listed in columns 1 and 2 of Table 14.4a indicates that in 10 of these years the temperature went no lower than 30°F. Expressed as a relative frequency, this happened 0.20 of the time. Column 3 summarizes the relative frequencies of all of these occurrences. Now, for the sake of this illustration, let us adopt the relaitve frequency of these past occurrences as the *probability* of their occurring in the future. In Section 14.6 we will examine the logic of this in detail, but for the present we will not question whether we should adjust the historical data. In this example, therefore, column 3 also gives the probability assessment p of that occurrence.

The conditional damages D caused by each intensity are listed in column 4, and the total expected value of damage in any year will be

$$p_1D_1 + p_2D_2 + p_3D_3 + \cdots + p_nD_n$$

$$= (0.20)(8,000) + (0.18)(10,000) + (0.16)(13,000) + \cdots + (0.04)(50,000)$$

$$= \$17,680$$

which is the total of column 5, Table 14.4a.

This expected value of damage will be less if equipment can be installed to prevent the occurrence of some of these low temperatures. Table 14.4b summarizes equipment which will keep the system above certain disaster temperatures. For example, equipment costing $9,130 will protect the system against moderate freezes down through 30°F, equipment costing $60,900 will protect against all temperatures down through 5°F, and equipment costing $110,200 will protect against any temperature recorded in the past.

With protective equipment installed, the expected annual cost will be the annual cost of the equipment[1] plus the expected value of the damage caused by

---

[1]For simplicity, operating disbursements have been disregarded.

Table 14.4b COST OF DAMAGE WITH SOME PROTECTION AGAINST FREEZING

(1)	(2)	(3)	(4)	(5)	(6)	(7)
			Annual cost of			
Minimum annual temperature ($^\circ$F)	*Proba- bility,* p	*Annual cost of damage,* pD	*damage from lower temperatures*	*First cost of equip- ment*	*Annual cost of equip- ment*	*Total annual cost* (4) + (6)
30	0.20	$ 1,600	$16,080	$ 9,130	$ 1,200	$17,280
25	0.18	1,800	14,280	15,200	1,998	16,278
20	0.16	2,080	12,200	21,300	2,800	15,000
15	0.14	2,380	9,820	31,200	4,102	13,922
10	0.12	2,640	7,180	44,900	5,903	13,083
5	0.10	2,900	4,280	60,900	8,007	12,287
0	0.06	2,280	2,000	83,700	11,004	13,004
-5	0.04	2,000	0	110,200	14,488	14,488
		$17,680				

temperatures below the temperature eliminated by the equipment. For example, if equipment is installed to protect the system against 30°F temperature.[1]

$$AC = 9,130\overset{0.13148}{(A/P, .10, 15)} + (0.18)(10,000) + (0.16)(13,000) + \cdots$$

$$+ (0.04)(50,000)$$

$$= 1,200 + 16,080 = \$17,280$$

The sum of $16,080 is the expected value from all disasters *below* 30°F. The expected costs of damage that will still occur if the protection is installed are listed in column 4 of Table 14.4b.

As noted, it does not pay, in the given example, to protect against all possible temperatures; the most economical decision is to protect down through only 5°F.

14.5 DAMAGE AS A CONTINUOUS INSTEAD OF DISCRETE FUNCTION OF DISASTER INTENSITY

Although the method in Example 14.4 for computing the expected cost of disasters is both simple and adequate, the reader will encounter variations and other viewpoints which it would be well to mention at this time. One of these is the concept of cumulative probability.

As noted in Section 14.3, the probability of an event occurring plus the proba- bility of its not occurring is 1.0. If the probability of a 30°F temperature is 0.20, the probability of its not occurring is 0.80. Because we have said in this problem

---

[1]For simplicity, we assume that the protection equipment does not give partial protection *below* its design temperature. For example, the $9,130 equipment has no effect at all on events at 25°F.

that the only possible minimum temperatures are those given in the table (we propose to question this in Section 14.5), the probability of a lower temperature than $30°F$ is $1 - 0.20 = 0.80$. This, we note, is the sum of all the probabilities below the given temperature, hence it is a cumulative probability. In Example 14.4 we cannot use the cumulative probability to compute the expected value of the damage below $30°F$ because the conditional damage D depends on *how low* the temperature goes in that year; we must therefore use the method outlined in Example 14.4. Nevertheless, the analyst will find that he must understand the viewpoints expressed by cumulative probabilities.

Various cumulative probabilities are summarized in Table 14.5. For example, column 5 gives the probabilities of temperature below the given temperature; column 3 gives the probability of temperatures equal to or higher than the given temperature; and column 4 gives the probability of temperatures equal to or lower than the given temperature.

Cumulative probabilities are often employed in graphical presentations or analyses of problems like the one illustrated by Example 14.4. Figure 14.5 shows that the sum of the areas of all the rectangles to the left of the probability of the temperature equalling or going below a given temperature is the expected annual cost of that possibility. For example, the expected annual cost of all temperatures equal to $30°F$ or lower is the sum of the areas of all the rectangles to the left of 1.0. This sum is $17,680, as we noted in Example 14.4. Similarly, the expected annual cost of all temperatures equal to or less than $25°F$ is the sum of the areas of all rectangles to the left of 0.80, the probability that all temperatures will be equal to or less than $25°F$. This sum is equal to $16,080, as noted in Table 14.4b.

Table 14.5 ILLUSTRATIONS OF CUMULATIVE PROBABILITIES

(1)	(2)	(3)	(4)	(5)
			Cumulative Probabilities	
Minimum annual temperature $(°F)$	Probability of the temperature occurring	Probability of an equal or higher temperature in any one year	Probability of an equal or lower temperature in any one year	Probability of a lower temperature in any one year
30	0.20	0.20	1.00	0.80
25	0.18	0.38	0.80	0.62
20	0.16	0.54	0.62	0.46
15	0.14	0.68	0.46	0.32
10	0.12	0.80	0.32	0.20
5	0.10	0.90	0.20	0.10
0	0.06	0.96	0.10	0.04
-5	0.04	1.00	0.04	0.00

The existence of such a graph can be helpful in analyzing the level of investment that should be proposed to reduce the annual cost of damage. For example, if equipment can be installed to eliminate freezing temperatures down
through 30°F, the damage from temperatures equal to or below 25°F, namely,
the areas to the left of 0.80 on the graph, must still be expected.

Another use of such a graph arises in connection with the observation that
continuous variation in damage with intensity is more appropriate to many
problems, including the last one, than the assumption of discrete variation.
Damage as a continuous function of intensity will be a smooth curve, as shown
by the dashed line in Fig. 14.5. The area under this curve, the expected annual
cost of damage from temperatures equal to or less than a given temperature, can
be found in a number of practical ways, such as by counting squares, by planim-
eter, or by calculus if the equation of the curve is determined.

The reader will find both the discrete and continuous methods in the engineering and business literature. The user of the discrete technique is, of course,
approaching the continuous method as he assesses the effects of minimum temperature for a finer range of temperature; for example, for every degree of temperature. He can even read these assessments from a smooth curve.

Example 14.4 serves to illustrate the general approach to the problem of risk
analysis, and among other things it illustrates that certain simplifying assumptions can avoid some very complex solutions at an acceptable sacrifice in accuracy. In computing a potential risk, the characteristics of the disaster must be

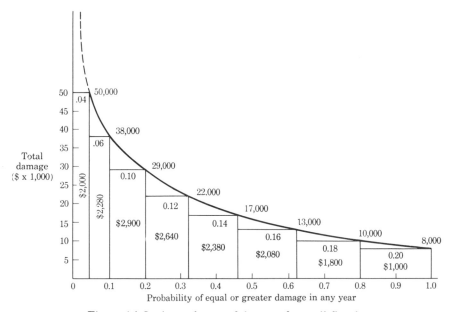

Figure 14.5   Annual cost of damage from all floods

studied as a prerequisite to quantifying the problem. The following are illustrations of various possible damage-characteristics:

(a) The total damage will be a function of the disaster intensity. For example, the loss depends on how low the temperature goes.

(b) Conversely, the total damage will not be a function of disaster intensity. For example, the loss results once a freezing temperature is reached; lower temperatures can do no more damage.

(c) Subsequent occurrences in the same year will not increase the damage, because the initial disaster leaves nothing to destroy. For example, the entire crop is destroyed by the initial disaster.

(d) Conversely, subsequent occurrences in the same year will repeat the damage. For example, a machine can be restored to service after each power failure and the cost of restoring it can recur as often as the failures occur.

(e) Subsequent disasters will increase the damage only if the intensity exceeds the intensity of the first disaster. For example, all structures that withstand the first tremor of an earthquake presumably are strong enough to withstand all subsequent tremors except greater ones.

This is not the place to classify the characteristics of damages. However, observations of this type will be necessary because simplifying assumptions may be essential to quantifying the problem.

14.6 COMMON SENSE OF PROBABILITIES

Possibly the reader has already observed in Example 14.4 that the same answer would have been obtained by simply averaging the historical costs. Column 4 of Table 14.4b is in fact nothing more than the *average* cost of the past 50 years because we adopted the historical relative frequencies as the probability distribution of future disasters. Let us, at this time, examine the logic of doing this by observing that if the next 50 years are held to be exact duplicates of the historical data of the past 50 years, as assumed in Example 14.4, we must adopt the following questionable conclusions.

1. The minimum temperature will *always* go below freezing. (But if in 10 of the years it went no lower than 30°F, isn't it logical that in some future years it might never be this low?)

2. The minimum temperature will never go below -5°F. (But if on two occasions it went to -5°F, isn't it logical to expect it can go lower?)

3. The historical frequency distribution is presumed to be the same as the distribution of the infinite sample. (But is it logical to accept a limited sample as an expression of the long run?)[1]

Obviously, we cannot simply equate probabilities to historical relative fre-

---

[1] Schlaifer says: "When the record contains only a very few observations, it is contrary to common sense to use the historical cumulative frequency of any value of a random variable as an estimate of the long-run cumulative frequency of that value." *Probability and Statistics for Business Decisions*, p. 111.

quencies without an examination of whether all the conclusions forced on us by that procedure are reasonable or whether common sense will develop better ones.

Let us first note that often the solution is not by collecting more data, for the simple reason that it may not be available. In flood-flows,[1] for example, we are very lucky if the experience covers 50 years, as it did in the last example. In many instances, we must work with extremely sparse data.

Adequate treatment of the necessary statistics and probability theory would require another volume but, at least, we can suggest why and to some extent how it should be applied to problems of this type. The first statistical analysis of data is concerned with the prediction of the certainty, ($p = 1.0$), that no temperature will be above 30°F and none will be below -5°F, questionable conclusions as we already noted. The statistical approach to this problem is to use 50 + 1 instead of 50 as the total occurrences in computing the long-run estimate of frequency, a suggestion which can be supported by proof.[2]

Column 3 of Table 14.6 shows the cumulative relative frequency computed from the historical data (reproduced from column 3 of Table 14.5. Any of the cumulative frequencies in Table 14.5 could have been used). Column 4 of Table 14.6, on the other hand, shows the long-run cumulative relative frequency computed from the historical data except that the occurrences are divided by 51 instead of 50. The values from column 4 are plotted in Fig. 14.6 and fitted with a smooth curve. If we now adopt these expected frequencies as the probabilities of future occurrences, we observe that the unreasonableness of our previous

Table 14.6 STATISTICAL TREATMENT OF HISTORICAL DATA

(1) Minimum annual temperature (°F)	(2) Number of occurrences	(3) Cumulative historical relative frequency (table 14.5, column 3)	(4) Estimated long-run cumulative relative frequency
30	10	0.20	0.196
25	9	0.38	0.373
20	8	0.54	0.529
15	7	0.68	0.667
10	6	0.80	0.784
5	5	0.90	0.882
0	3	0.96	0.941
-5	2	1.00	0.980
	50		

[1]Edgar E. Foster, "Evaluations of Flood Losses and Benefits," *Transactions of ASCE*, vol. 107 (1942), pp. 871–894.

[2]Consider that this sample of 50 events came out of a population of 51,000. It is most probable that these 50 events would be ranked in the population as follows: 1,000th, 2,000th, ... , 50,000th, or the 1/51, 2/51, ... , 50/51 fractiles–not the 1/50, 2/50, ... , 50/50.

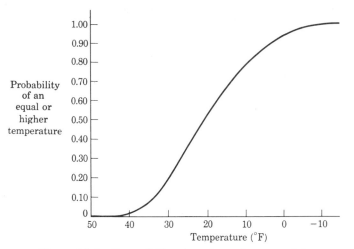

Figure 14.6   Curve fitting to extremely sparse data

probability assessments has been overcome; temperatures above 30°F and below −5°F are now possible, no matter how remotely.

In this illustration we have not tried to introduce too many concepts at once. For example, most sparse data will plot as scattered points. To put off a discussion of curve fitting, cursorily examined in the next section, we purposely selected data which will give a smooth trace through its points. We trust, however, that the selected illustration emphasizes the common sense of requiring probability techniques—even if the historical data itself happens to be smooth. Another serious objection to the use of straight historical frequencies is the inherent disregard of trends, cycles, and other information which would influence a future time series. Consideration of these other factors which should be considered prior to trying to smooth the data is beyond the scope of this book and has been avoided in our illustrations.

Common sense dictates that a technique for assessing probabilities must replace the mere adoption of historical frequencies. Consequently, Example 14.4 is incorrect to the extent that the probability assessments used in it are incorrect.

14.7 PROBABILITY DISTRIBUTIONS

We have noted that the analyst must have a technique for assessing probabilities. The method that we have illustrated in Fig. 14.6 is not the only one in use. A common practice is to fit a smooth curve to the historical relative frequency plotted against the random variable (temperature, in our example). The fitted curve must have a reasonable shape and the sum of the relative frequencies under the curve must, of course, equal 1.0. Graphs I and II of Fig. 14.7 present two such frequency distributions which we will examine.

Probability distributions of many shapes have been conceived and defined mathematically but the best known and most important is the normal, or

Gaussian, distribution, which has the familiar symmetrical inverted bell-shape as in Graph I. Asymmetrical or skewed distributions having longer tails on one side, as in Graph II, can be reasonably expected, however. For example, the probability of flood flows can be expected to show a skewed distribution because the relative frequency of low floods (on the left side of Graph II) is high but the relative frequency of great floods (on the right side of the graph) is low. A similar skew is shown by the data in Example 14.4, where the relative frequencies are high on one side of the distribution (warm temperatures) and low on the other side (cold temperatures). This immediately raises the question, "Is this a logical distribution? What would you expect the distribution to be?" Robert Schlaifer[1] says that the probability distribution should express "our considered judgment of the workings of the underlying mechanism of process." In this respect the analyst must temper his judgment with the further observation that a reasonable sample cannot, after all, be expected to be a complete denial of the larger population.

"Probability paper" may be used to assist in sketching cumulative distributions. For example, if the normal distribution is plotted on normal probability paper, cumulative probability becomes a straight line, as illustrated by line N in Fig. 14.7. The skewed distributions give almost straight lines except for the tails, as illustrated by line S. (If rectangular coordinate paper is used, the symmetrical and skewed distributions both produce S curves, as in Fig. 14.6.)

Special coordinate paper is also available, such as paper with logarithmic scales for the random variable (used in plotting flood-flows), which will give straight lines for certain types of probability distributions and make curve fitting easier.

With extremely sparse data, it may become impossible to fit a smooth curve to the relative-frequency distribution. This is illustrated in Table 14.7 by the fact that plot of the relative frequency in column 3 gives a flat distribution (except at

Table 14.7 TREATMENT OF EXTREMELY SPARSE DATA

(1) Minimum annual temperatures ($^\circ$F)	(2) Number of occurrences	(3) Historical relative frequency	(4) Fractiles of long-run probability distribution
32	1	0.1111	0.10
22	1	0.1111	0.20
17	2	0.2222	0.40
13	1	0.1111	0.50
8	1	0.1111	0.60
1	1	0.1111	0.70
-3	1	0.1111	0.80
-11	1	0.1111	0.90
	9		

[1] Schlaifer, *Probability and Statistics for Business Decisions*, p. 109.

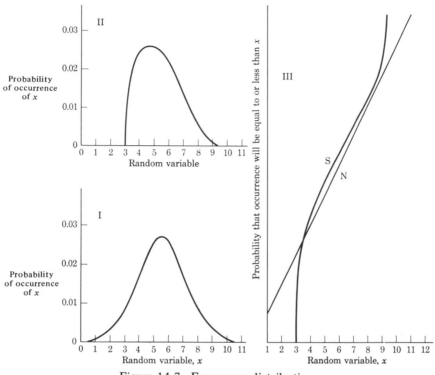

Figure 14.7 Frequency distributions

17°F). Instead, the analyst can plot the fractiles of the long-run probability distribution—computed from the cumulative relative frequency except that the occurrences are divided (for the reason described in the previous section) by 10 instead of 9. These values, listed in column 4, when plotted on probability paper and after judicious curve fitting, can suggest a smooth curve, as in Graph III, which reasonably reflects the judgment of the analyst. Having arrived at this curve, computation of cost can now proceed in the manner outlined in Example 14.4.

The information in this section is presented with some misgiving, because when so much must be left out, so much can be inferred that is not intended; but it is hoped that the reader will become aware of the knowledge that is available to assist him in the problem of establishing probabilities, and that he will also be aware that statistical and probability theory follows the path of common sense that would be developed if he reasoned his way, step by step, through the problem.

A great deal of advanced work is available to make this subject a valuable tool for the student. An example of this is the computation of confidence intervals to test the predicted probabilities. However, we hesitate to try to list these many valuable areas; in the final analysis these can only be discovered by a more complete study of the subject.[1]

14.8 WHY INSURE?

If the probability of a disaster is 0.01 in any year and the damage $50,000, it is reasonable to say that a fair cost of the loss or a fair price to pay to avoid the loss is $500 a year. Should one insure if the expected annual cost of this disaster is only $500? Neglecting the insurer's operating costs and profits, the expected annual cost is the same to the insured as to the insurer, so why pay one's expected annual costs of disaster through an insurance company?

The point is that, although the probability is only one occurrence in 100 years, the disaster may happen any time in the next 100 years, or, in fact, several times in that period. In determining whether to self-insure, the questions to ask are whether you can stand the shock (a) if the disaster occurs tomorrow, (b) if it occurs any time, (c) if it occurs several times in a row. Most people are self-insured for many hazards, but by purchasing insurance the insured has two major advantages. First, he is protected against the shock of a sudden loss by substituting a distributed one. He may be unable to finance the dislocation caused by the disaster, but he can avoid this and spread the cost of the disaster smoothly over a period of time by purchasing sufficient insurance.

Insurance transfers the financing of disasters to one who is better able to stand them. Presumably, the insurance company is engaging in enough trials, by having enough insurance accounts, so that its experience is approaching the limit as expressed by the long-run probability.

From a practical standpoint the transfer of risks from insured to insurance company succeeds because the insurance company has very large assets relative to the risks of any insured account; therefore, the insurer is more willing than the insured to use the expected monetary value of the disaster as a guide for his actual losses in any one year. Therefore, the fair price received from a great many insurance accounts should in any year pay for the disaster in that year (plus operating costs and a reasonable profit for the service).

14.9 BASING PROBABILITIES ON INSURANCE ASSESSMENTS

The insurance rate is an approximate assessment of the probability of a specific disaster. It is the insurance company's assessment adjusted by the operating expense and profit necessarily added by the company, but it nevertheless establishes a fair annual price in lieu of the cost of the disaster, as the following example illustrates.

EXAMPLE 14.9 A manufacturing plant is insured against fire for $100,000 at an annual premium of $550. If the company will install a sprinkler system,

[1] A condensed story of statistics applied to quality control is found in L. H. C. Tippett, *Technological Applications of Statistics* (New York: Wiley, 1950).

the insurance company offers to reduce the premium to $300. The cost of the sprinkler is $4,500 with an economic life of 15 years and zero salvage.

The management estimates that the uninsured loss if the plant is destroyed will be $50,000. This additional loss will be caused by the dislocation during reconstruction and will result in an extra cost of production, a loss of sales, and loss of profit.

If the minimum required rate of return is 10%, will it pay to install the sprinkler?

SOLUTION. The annual cost of loss is the probability of loss times the damage. In this case, for want of other information the assessment of the probability of loss is taken to be the quotient of the annual insurance cost divided by the damage, namely, 0.0055 with a sprinkler and 0.003 without it. Since the added $50,000 has the same risk of loss, the same probabilities exist and the annual cost of loss for the uninsured amount may be computed at the same rate as the insured amount, namely, $0.55 per hundred without and $0.30 per hundred with the sprinkler.

$$\text{AC without sprinkler} = \left(\frac{0.55}{100}\right)(100,000 + 50,000) = \$825.$$

$$\text{AC with sprinkler} \quad = 4,500 \underset{0.13147}{(A/P, .10, 15)} + \left(\frac{30}{100}\right)(100,000 + 50,000)$$

$$= \$1,042$$

In this case, it does not pay to install the sprinkler.

14.10 LEVELS OF INVESTMENT TO REDUCE RISK

In some instances the only acceptable level of design is one which completely eliminates the risk. Bridges, buildings, tunnels, towers, dams, grandstands, and similar structures are never built with collapse as a possibility. They are protected against all possible intensities of wind, snow, and ice as well as variations in the structural strength of building materials. This is largely dictated by economic factors, because not only will the cost for human injury be great, but the entire structure will be lost by collapse. Compare these, on the other hand, with devices where "breakdown" is possible without losing the entire value of the equipment. Certainly the reputation of the designer and the humanitarian considerations are very important, but nevertheless most examples seem to indicate that the economics primarily govern the situation. For example, highways are not designed to eliminate a loss of life in the same degree that buildings are. In highway construction, the economic factors[1] fail to justify the cost of a highway designed to completely eliminate the loss of life; however, an entirely different situation can be envisioned if the courts begin to assess a loss of life at $1,000,000 damage. Nevertheless, economic factors have not entirely dictated

[1] See the benefit-cost ratio in Chapter 18.

the present situation. The acceleration of technology has been so great in transportation devices, automobiles, planes, and now space vehicles, that man has often decided in favor of technological progress at the cost of safety. Man seems to believe that the danger to his safety is worth accelerating achievement of the goal, but even that viewpoint might be said to be economy-oriented.

In any of these examples we detect levels of investment. For example, there is a level of investment in designing roads to eliminate the more predictable accidents. At the other extreme, many situations exist in which it is more economical to let the damage occur without protection against it.

In many other situations the economics dictate a design between the two extremes. Machines are generally designed so that a piece will be spoiled if the operator is careless, or a machine will shut down from a failure of parts for which replacements are available, or an operator will be injured if he takes chances in operating the machine.

Levels of investment which increase the efficiency of this protection will continue to be invented and be tested by economic criteria. Example 14.4 was an illustration.

PROBLEMS

14.1 If two dice are thrown, what is the probability that in a single roll: (a) two 6's are thrown? (b) one 6 is thrown? (c) the sum of the dice is 5? (d) the sum of the dice is 12? (Hint: in throwing two dice there are 36 possible outcomes; what is the probability that two of these will be sixes?)

14.2 How much should a player pay as a fair price in a game in which he wins a number of dollars equal to the number of spots on the face that turns up each time he rolls one die? A fair price is one in which he will break even.

14.3 A chemical company estimates that in the manufacture of its products the probability of an explosion in any year is 0.025. The damage from this explosion is estimated at $1,000,000. (a) By spending $150,000 the safety of the process can be improved so that the probability of explosion is reduced to 0.001. The economic life of the expenditure is 10 years with zero salvage. The cost of damage if it should occur with the added protection equipment will be $1,100,000. The operating disbursements of the protection equipment are $5,000 a year. (b) Alternatively, the plant may be redesigned for $100,000 to restrict the explosions to limited areas and the loss will therefore be held to $100,000. The salvage of this extra investment will be zero at the end of a 10-year economic life. The probability of occurrence will still be 0.025, however. In either case the process is automatic and no damage to personnel can occur. The minimum required rate of return is 15%. Use the annual-cost method of analysis.

14.4 Every time a certain machine fails, the cost in idle labor and repairs is about $1,000. The outage time is 4 working hours and the plant works

2,000 hours a year, so the machine could theoretically fail as many as 250 times in a given year.

The probabilities of failure are assessed as follows: no failures, 0.050; 1, 0.113; 2, 0.209; 3, 0.333; 4, 0.201; 5, 0.080; 6, 0.009; 7, 0.003; 8, 0.001; 9, 0.0008, 10, 0.00008.

A standby machine with an expected life of 10 years can be procured for $10,000 with $2,000 salvage value. The annual disbursements to keep it ready to run are $500. The probability of its breaking down during a standby run are nil. The minimum required rate of return is 15%. Make an annual-cost comparison.

14.5 The directors of a company are faced with the decision of whether to continue a patent suit brought by a competitor. This is a vital patent and its loss would wipe out the business. The alternative to continuing the suit is to settle it out of court at terms which are very unfavorable to the company but, of course, better than those resulting from the loss of the suit. The company's lawyers estimate that the company has a 4 to 1 chance of winning the suit.

The directors estimate that if their company wins, the total market value of the stock will be $7,000,000 in 5 years. They estimate that if settlement is made, the market value of the stock which is $1,000,000 today will be worth $1,500,000 in 5 years.

Based on the values to the shareholders in 5 years, what course of action is recommended? Assume the legal cost of continuing the suit is negligible because the legal preparation has been completed.

14.6 In Problem 14.5, if the probability of winning the suit had been only 50%, what recommendation would you make?

14.7 The rainfall in a certain farming community recorded over the last 40 years, as reported below, has been insufficient to support the expected crop yield. The estimated damage resulting from a loss of crops and the level of rainfall at which this damage will occur are recorded on the same line in the following table.

Inches of rainfall	Number of occurrences	Annual loss	First cost of equipment
30	5	$ 5,000	$ 4,000
25	8	13,000	10,200
20	13	25,000	23,100
15	9	40,000	39,500
10	4	60,000	75,500
5	1	85,000	108,000
	40		

An irrigation system can be installed to protect the community against each degree of drought. For example, if a 20-inch rainfall occurs in any year, the loss in crops will be $25,000 in that year. However, at a first cost of $23,100 an irrigation system can be installed that will eliminate all losses from insufficient rain except in those years when the rainfall is below 20 inches. The life of the irrigation systems will be 25 years with zero salvage. The minimum required rate of return is 20%. Assume that the probabilities of future occurrences will be exactly the same as the historical relative frequencies (i.e., in the present problem do *not* adjust the relative frequencies). How much of an irrigation system should be installed, if any?

14.8 Using the same historical relative frequencies that you adopted as probabilities in Problem 14.7, what, then, are the probabilities of (a) an equal or greater rainfall occurring in any one year? (b) an equal or lower rainfall occurring in any one year? (c) a lower rainfall in any one year? (d) a higher rainfall in any one year? Make a table similar to Table 14.5 in the text.

14.9 Using the data in Problems 14.7 and 14.8, construct a graph similar to Fig. 14.5 in the text.

14.10 If we adopt the historical relative frequencies given in Problem 14.7 as the probabilities of future occurrences, (a) what illogical conclusions must we also adopt? (b) what adjustments should be made to correct them? (c) what probability assessments would be more logical to use in Problem 14.7?

14.11 Solve Problem 14.7 using the probability assessments which you suggested in part (c) of Problem 14.10. How does this solution compare with that obtained in Problem 14.7?

14.12 Solve Problem 14.9 using the probability assessments which you suggested in part (c) of Problem 14.10. How do these compare with the results obtained in Problem 14.9?

14.13 Assuming that your curve fitting in Problem 14.10 used rectangular coordinate paper, plot your adjusted data on normal-probability paper (if such is available). Would you make the same probability assessments as in Problem 14.10?

14.14 A factory and office is insured for $250,000. The rate is $8.50 a thousand a year. An automatic sprinkler system can be installed for $20,000 with an economic life of 15 years, zero salvage and $100 annual disbursements. If it is installed, the insurance company quotes an annual rate of $4.00 a thousand. It is estimated that a fire will cause an additional uninsured loss of $50,000. The minimum required rate of return is 10%. Use the annual-cost method to indicate whether to purchase the sprinkler.

14.15 A flood control commission has collected the following data from a hydrologic study of a certain flood basin.

Flood stage	Cubic feet per second	Probability of a greater flood occurring in any one year	Damage from a flood of that magnitude	Cost of protection (first cost)
A	0–1,500	0.060	$ 0	$ 0
B	1,501–2,000	0.020	300,000	50,000
C	2,001–2,500	0.010	410,000	90,000
D	2,501–3,000	0.004	525,000	120,000
E	3,001–3,500	0.001	750,000	200,000
F	3,501–4,000	0.000	1,500,000	350,000

The damage in the table is the cost of loss when a flow occurs equal to the magnitude shown on the same line. For example, if the peak flow in a given year is 3,200 cubic feet per second, the year's damage will be $750,000. In this problem the flow of water increases in the early spring until a peak flow occurs, an event which can occur only once a year.

The flood protection shown in the table will prevent all floods up through the peak flow shown on the same line. The life of this protection is estimated to be 25 years with zero salvage. If the minimum required rate of return is 10%, what level of protection should be provided?

14.16 If the insurance rates in the previous problem can be taken as fair assessments of the risk, (a) what are the probabilities of fire in the company's plant with and without a sprinkler system? (b) discuss whether the company should buy insurance or whether it should self-insure; (c) can you expect the insurance company to be any more reliable in paying the loss resulting from a total fire than the manufacturing company?

14.17 A factory building is insured against fire for $300,000 and the annual insurance cost is 1.5%. The factory is located in a town where the fire-fighting facilities are inadequate for a building of this type. Had the factory been located in a town having adequate facilities the insurance company indicates that the insurance rate would be 0.6%. The manufacturing firm estimates that additional losses from a fire will be 75% of the insured losses.

How much could the company afford to pay for its own fire-fighting equipment if the result was to lower the insurance rate to 0.6%? Assume that the equipment would have a 12-year life with zero salvage and annual operating disbursements of $1,000. The equipment would be operated by volunteers from an existing company organization at no extra labor cost. Assume the insurance rates are fair assessments of the risk. The company's minimum required rate of return is 20%.

14.18 A machine can be designed with various degrees of reliability. The cost of loss resulting from a failure is $25,000. At the extra costs shown below, various designs can be built to reduce the chance of failure. The higher cost designs will also create higher annual disbursements for insurance, property taxes, and certain maintenance and repair costs.

The economic life is 5 years with zero salvage and the minimum required rate of return is 20%.

Investment for reliability	Operating disbursements per year	Reliability of the machine
$ 0	$ 0	0.000
5,000	300	0.500
10,000	600	0.700
15,000	900	0.850
20,000	1,200	0.940
25,000	1,500	0.990
30,000	1,800	0.995
35,000	2,100	0.999

The reliability of the machine is defined in this case as the probability of not failing during a year's run. Which design should be selected?

14.19 An operator of a certain ski lift will lose $20,000 income if the patrons cannot ski between December 26 and January 2 for lack of snow. Records show that on five occasions in the past 25 years this ski area had no snow cover in this calendar period although it was cold enough to snow.

Equipment for making artificial snow can be installed for $25,000. Its life is expected to be 12 years with zero salvage and the annual operating disbursements are estimated to be $2,000. The process can be used to make snow only if the temperature is below freezing.

If the machine is installed, the operator estimates that not only will the loss be avoided but on each of these occasions he expects $5,000 extra income unless all other areas also have snow-making machinery. He estimates this advantage would last 4 years. His minimum required rate of return is 12%. Should he install the equipment?

14.20 (a) What odds should be given on a wager that the number six will occur in a single roll of a die? (b) A bettor is offering 5 to 2 odds that the Yankees will win the World Series. What is the probability of a Yankee victory based on these odds?

15

Taxes

15.1 PROPERTY TAXES

Realty, which includes the buildings affixed to the land, and trade fixtures, which include the machinery and equipment installed in the buildings, are universally taxed by the local governments under the taxing powers granted to them by the states. Such taxes depend on (1) the valuation of the property by the tax appraisers and (2) the established tax rate. Property taxes are always relevant in an economy study, but their effect on the results of the study is generally slight, because of the small relative magnitude of the tax disbursements. Property taxes are quite insignificant compared to the burden on new equipment caused by the income tax; for most corporations, it can be expected to reduce the prospective rate of return 50%.

Although rarely encountered in industrial analyses, another tax is the excise tax. This is a tax imposed upon the manufacture of certain articles such as tobacco and alcoholic products.

A broad spectrum of general taxes, such as sales tax, user's tax, unemployment, social security, and others may also be relevant in specific decisions. Knowledge of "all relevant costs" must mean a knowledge of all the taxes.

15.2 INCOME TAXES

Income taxes are levied by the Federal Government and by some of the state or city governments as well. Income taxes fall into two classes: levies on personal income and on corporate income. Both taxes are designed to have an increasingly higher rate of taxation on the higher incomes. They are based on net income, but with the understanding that the "expenses" used in computing net taxable income must be computed in accordance with tax regulations which are very carefully defined and outlined in the instructions to the taxpayer.

Consideration of the great detail of material pertaining to personal income taxes is not necessary for the analysis of most industrial problems. This information, when required, is adequately covered in the literature of the Internal Revenue Service prepared for the use of the taxpayer in computing his tax returns.

As stated, corporation income tax is levied as a percentage of the net earnings of the corporation. In economy analyses the percentage can in many cases be 55% of net taxable income resulting from the combined effect of federal and state tax on income. Many states maintain corporation income taxes, but these taxes are too diversified to be treated here. The federal tax rate established in 1967 is 22% normal tax on the first $25,000 of taxable income and a "surtax" of 26% on incomes above that. Thus the tax rate on that increment is 48%, and for all practical purposes this amounts to 48% as a base tax rate in economy computations for large corporations. This became 52.8% when a special surcharge of 10% was assessed in 1968 and 1969. This was reduced to 5%, and then abolished in 1970, but the reader is aware that rate modifications can be voted in any session of Congress. After adjustment for the effect of state taxes, the net tax rate can possibly lie between 48% and 55%, except for small corporations. Since state income taxes in the United States are deductible in computing income taxable by the federal government, the net rate assuming 48% federal tax and 6% state tax will be $6\% + (1 - .06)48\% = 51\%$. Examples in the text will therefore employ various tax rates[1] between 50% and 55%.

However, the tax rate is only one factor in determining what the tax may be. The taxpayer must also understand *what* expenses he will be permitted to deduct from income, and also *when* the expenses may be applied in reduction of taxable income.

Net taxable income is gross income minus all expenses, so the Internal Revenue Service strictly defines what costs may or may not be expensed and the extent to which depreciable assets may be expensed in the various years of their taxable lives.

The Internal Revenue Service has good reasons to regulate the rate of depreciation used by a company or to approve the items it "expenses" in computing its income tax. The amount of federal income tax paid by a corporation in any year depends upon the depreciation expense deducted in that year. If the accountant employs a short accounting life or if he writes off a "loss" between book value and salvage value in the year of disposal of the asset, he reduces the net earnings and therefore the amount of corporation income tax paid in that year. Because this conceivably could be used by the taxpayer as a device to reduce current tax payments, the Internal Revenue Service has restricted the minimum permissible life periods for tax computations. This restriction also applies

---

[1] According to MAPI, "The overwhelming majority of medium-sized and large corporations use a flat 50%." This is for state and federal income taxes combined, after allowance for mutual offsets. George Terborgh, *Business Investment Policy* (Washington, D.C.: Machinery and Allied Products Institute, 1958), p. 194.

to "expensing" which might be described as a special condition in which the tax life of the capital expenditure is zero.

15.3 ANALYSIS INCLUDING CORPORATION INCOME TAXES

Up to this point in the text there has been no serious attempt to introduce corporation income tax as a factor in the economic analysis of alternatives. In previous problems the income tax has been ignored or in some portions of this book the effect of income tax has been approximated by including income tax in the minimum required rate of return. The extent to which the latter method is only an approximation should be clearly understood, and we consider it appropriate for us to examine the problem in detail. No analyst can make confident conclusions without the experience of a detailed survey of income taxes, which we will attempt to do by a number of illustrative examples.

In introducing the subject, let us observe that the problem is often confused by conflicting statements regarding the part of income taxes in economy studies. One rather general viewpoint is that the exclusion of income tax disbursements will not affect the decision. A contrary viewpoint says, "The first question to ask is, what is the tax?" It is believed that the following analyses will show how these conflicting viewpoints arise and whether they can be reconciled subject to a number of restricting assumptions.

It will also be observed in the following sections that the inclusion of income taxes complicates the technique of analysis. Some of these complications arise from (a) the fact that the life for tax purposes as permitted by the Internal Revenue Service is not necessarily the economic life of the equipment; (b) the methods of accelerated depreciation permitted for computing the tax; (c) the tax effect of losses and gains on disposal. These points and others will be illustrated in the sections that follow.

15.4 COST OF GIFTS BY CORPORATIONS

The effect of corporate income taxes can be illustrated by the simple example of a corporate gift, a situation with which many of our readers are already familiar. This familiarity probably arises from statements by organizations soliciting gifts to the effect that the taxpayer can engage in charities at a cost considerably below the amount of the gift.

EXAMPLE 15.4 The Development Council of a certain college suggests to an industrial corporation a program of corporate gifts to the college amounting to $10,000 a year for the next 10 years, and indicates that the cost to the corporation will only be $4,800 a year over that period. The corporate tax on the company is 52%.

SOLUTION. The simple fact is that the corporation gives $10,000 but only loses $4,800 in *net profits* by making the gift. A step-by-step development of this fact is shown here.

Expense of the gift paid by the corporation	$10,000
Reduction of income as a result of the expense	$10,000
Reduction in income tax due to reduction in income, (10,000)(0.52)	$ 5,200
Net expense to the corporation after the tax saving, (10,000 − 5,200)	$ 4,800

The sum of $4,800 is the net cost of the gift because it is the net reduction in profit. This does not deny that the expense to the corporation *before* taxes is $10,000 a year. The reason for the seeming impossibility is that the before-tax expense of $10,000 results in a tax saving of $5,200. Therefore the disbursement after taxes consists of the aforesaid disbursement of $10,000 minus a $5,200 reduction in tax disbursements. The before and after tax on the time scales will then look like this:

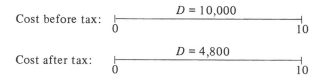

The concept of a tax saving also applies to any expense, not just a gift, and we will discover that it is a helpful concept in certain complex comparisons of alternatives as well as in computing certain types of taxes such as taxes on gains or losses on disposal.

The concept of a tax saving necessarily presumes that the corporation has other taxable income which produces a tax greater than the $5,200 saving. The magnitude of taxable income for the entire firm is so great that this seldom becomes a question in cost-reduction problems. In income-expansion problems the income must be predicted, so that the tax rather than the tax saving is computed anyway.

It is interesting to observe that the corporation and the government may be said to be partners in the gift. If the college in our example is receiving $10,000 a year and the corporation is incurring a net cost of only $4,800, someone must be standing the difference. Someone is: the government is contributing the amount equal to the tax saving—$5,200. The government gives up $5,200, the firm contributes a net sum of $4,800, and the college receives $10,000. This, of course, applies not only to gifts but to every corporate expense which the corporation is permitted to deduct from taxable income. Each of these expenses produces a tax savings indicative of the extent of the government's partnership in the operation.

This, of course, is not as illogical as it may seem, because if the recipient of the $10,000 had to pay a 52% tax on this income the initial tax loss to the government would be wiped out. If the new taxpayer's rate were less than 52% the government would still lose on the entire transaction, but if the new taxpayer's rate were higher, the government would gain. If the gift is tax exempt, as in the case of the college, then, of course, the government is a true partner to the extent of its overall loss in taxes.

15.5 CASH FLOW

Cash flowback, or merely "cash flow," is, as the term implies, the sum of the profit and the depreciation generated by operations. The financial executive generally describes the consequences of an investment in terms of its effect on the company's "cash flow." On the other hand, many managers and most engineers describe the consequence of an investment in an improved method or a machine in terms of the "savings" it produces. And, as the reader has observed, we have so far computed the "savings" resulting from a proposal. We did this because annual savings were simply the difference between the annual disbursements of the two alternatives being compared.

But let us now observe how we would describe an investment in terms of its effect on cash flow.

EXAMPLE 15.5 The annual disbursements for an assembly operation are $30,000. The net realizable value and the book value of the hand tools and fixtures used in that operation are zero.

The machine proposed to replace this will have total operating disbursements of $10,000, but will cost the company $100,000 to purchase and install. Its economic as well as its tax life is 10 years, at which time its salvage value is expected to be zero.

The company uses straight-line depreciation and its tax rate is 50%.

The present annual sales volume of $250,000 will be unaffected by the decision.

SOLUTION *A*. We have seen several proposals in which the financial analyst thought it necessary to make a brief profit-and-loss statement with and without the proposed acquisition as a basis for determining the cash flow generated by the proposal. The changes in the cost of the goods sold and the depreciation are solely the result of the proposed machine.

	Manual	*Machine*
Sales	$250,000	$250,000
Cost of goods sold	190,000	170,000
Profit before depreciation	$60,000	$80,000
Depreciation	40,000	50,000
Profit before tax	$20,000	$30,000
Tax @ 50%	10,000	15,000
Profit after tax	10,000	15,000
Cash flow after tax	50,000	65,000
Increase in cash flow after tax	——	15,000

SOLUTION *B*. Although the previous solution shows the effect on total profits, the work to determine the cash flows is unnecessary since the decision concerns only incremental cash flows. Even the following method involves extra and unnecessary steps.

Decreased operating expense = 30,000 – 10,000 = $20,000
Less increased depreciation = 100,000/10   = 10,000
Increased profit before tax   = $10,000
Tax @ 50% on increased profit   =   5,000
Increased profit after tax   =   5,000
Cash flow = increased profit + depreciation   = 15,000

SOLUTION C. For the same reason that cash flowback is profit + depreciation, it should be apparent that savings are also cash flowback. This can be quickly demonstrated because:

$$\text{savings} - \text{depreciation} = \text{profit}$$

whence   savings = profit + depreciation
but   cash flow = profit + depreciation
whence   savings = cash flow

In Solution C the savings are merely the difference in disbursements on the two time scales. Therefore:

1. Savings before tax = cash flow before tax = $20,000
2. Less extra depreciation = 100,000/10   = 10,000
3. Taxable income   = $10,000
4. Tax @ 50%   =   5,000
5. Savings after tax = cash flow after tax   = 15,000 (line 1 minus line 4)

The observation in Solution C proves that simply finding the difference in the disbursements on the time scales (namely, finding the savings) is the same as computing the cash flow. The results by this method and the cash-flow or discounted-cash-flow method will be the same. It also suggests that the cash flow can be found by easier procedures.

15.6 USEFUL LIVES

As noted in Chapter 11 the Internal Revenue Service requires equipment to be depreciated over its useful life for the computation of income taxes.

A guide to what these lives might be appears in *Depreciation Guidelines and Rules*.[1] This publication lists the guidelines for about 100 classes of assets. It lists 51 industry headings and in most of these the given guideline covers all the equipment used in that industry. In a few industry listings the industry is divided into categories. For example, the electric utility industry is divided into four types: hydraulic production plant (50 years); steam plant (28 years); nuclear plant (20 years); and transmission and distribution facilities (30 years). Each covers all the equipment in the plant or facility. In addition, the publication lists guidelines for 5 classes of assets used by all businesses such as office

---

[1]*Depreciation Guidelines and Rules* (Washington, D.C.: Superintendent of Documents, U.S. Government Printing Office).

furniture, fixtures, machines, and equipment (10 years); autos (3 years); and heavy trucks (6 years).

Some of the guidelines listed under the industry headings are:

Years

Metal cutting and forming	12
Refining metals	18
Manufacturing paper	16
Petroleum refining	16
Printing	11
Manufacturing railroad cars	12
Rubber manufacturing	14
Cement manufacturing	20
Manufacturing textiles	14
Aerospace	8
Electronic equipment manufacturing	8
Plastics products	11

The listings are of special interest since they are not only a guide to the tax lives but also imply the maximum length of the expected economic life. Where asset degradation is expected, the economic lives will be shorter than the guide-line lives.

The accountant's use of the guidelines is optional as he is privileged to prove the useful life he adopts in a given situation. However, to avoid disputes the Treasury Department has instituted the new ADR system (asset depreciation range). Although the rules are complex it permits a range of ±20% on the given guideline to establish upper and lower life periods. Also, in relation to depreciation, ADR establishes specific percentage repair allowances for each guideline class to determine whether certain repair costs may be deducted in the year incurred or capitalized (i.e., depreciated).

The permissible tax lives of depreciable assets are based on the average useful lives of the equipment. The tax view of the life period, much like the accountant's, is that it is the period of ownership of the equipment from the date of its acquisition until the date of its disposal. Obviously where functional degradation exists, the useful life is in reality the sum of all the economic lives on prime and degraded services up to its date of disposal by the one owner of the equipment.

The useful life, or tax life, then actually would be the result of a statistical study of the ownership period of a class of equipment. However, a company may present evidence that the average useful life of a type of machine in its plant is less than elsewhere in industry. Where a company has no evidence, the taxpayer may be guided by estimates of average useful life published by the Internal Revenue Service for a great many classes of depreciable assets. This discussion, of course, does not apply to nondepreciable assets like land.

15.7 ANALYSIS IF TAX LIFE EQUALS ECONOMIC LIFE

The simplest of economy analyses including income taxes occurs when the useful life for tax purposes equals the economic life of the equipment. An example of this exists when the Internal Revenue Service authorizes a fast write-off for industrial equipment employed in essential defense contracts. This, however, is a special case and an exception to the long write-off period required by the Service.

The type of problem illustrated here could occur in any case in which the useful life of the equipment equals its economic life, which does not necessarily limit the illustration to short write-off periods.

In the following example, three methods of solution are illustrated in order to prepare the analyst to apply whichever method may be the most efficient for a given problem. The first method of solution (generally more suitable to more complex examples) proceeds from the observation in the last section that an expense results in a tax saving equal to the amount of the expense times the tax rate. In such a case, tax savings will appear on the time scales as negative costs.

In order to compute income tax disbursements, the analyst must follow the same accounting procedures that the accountant will use when he computes the income tax. This means that he must compute taxable income on which the tax is based, (i.e., gross income less operating disbursements and depreciation expense according to the accepted accounting practice). Or if he approaches the problem by the use of tax savings, he must, in any event, arrive at the same tax effects.

In computing depreciation expense, the analyst must use the same depreciation rates and the same useful life (i.e., tax life) that the accountant will use in computing the corporation's taxes. He must also depreciate items that by law are not permitted to be expensed in one year. He must recognize all tax regulations and allow for all taxes and tax savings including, for example, those on gains or losses on disposal.

EXAMPLE 15.7 Conveyor system A for transporting powdered chemicals will cost $25,000 to install and $6,000 a year to operate. Conveyor system B, based on a different principle for transporting the powdered material, will cost $15,000 installed and $11,000 a year to operate. The required service period is 5 years. The company will also be permitted by the Internal Revenue Service to use a fast write-off of 5 years. The company employs straight-line depreciation for both tax and profit determination. The income tax is 50%. The salvage values on this special equipment are estimated to be zero for both conveyors.

SOLUTION.

Costs before tax:

Tax life: 5 years
Tax rate: 0.50
Deprecation: SLD

The effect of tax disbursements will be computed by three methods.
Method 1: By computing the tax savings.

	A	B
Operating disbursements	$ 6,000	$11,000
Depreciation expense	5,000	3,000
Total expense	$11,000	$14,000
Tax saving @ 50% tax rate	5,500	7,000
Net operating disbursements	$ 500	$ 4,000 (line 1 minus line 4)

Costs after tax:

$$A \quad \overset{25,000}{\underset{0}{\vdash}} \qquad D = 500 \qquad \dashv \atop 5$$

$$B \quad \overset{15,000}{\underset{0}{\vdash}} \qquad D = 4,000 \qquad \dashv \atop 5$$

$$AC_A = AC_B$$

$$25,000(A/P, i, 5) + 500 = 15,000(A/P, i, 5) + 4,000$$

$$10,000(A/P, i, 5) = 3,500$$

whence

$$i = 22.1\% \text{ after tax}$$

Method 2: By computing the extra income tax on the difference in profit.

	A	B
Operating disbursement	$ 6,000	$11,000
Depreciation expense	5,000	3,000
Total expense	$11,000	$14,000
Extra income, A over B	3,000	
Extra tax due to A	1,500	
Operating disbursement after tax	$ 7,500	$11,000

After tax:

$$A \quad \overset{25,000}{\underset{0}{\vdash}} \qquad D = 7,500 \qquad \dashv \atop 5$$

$$B \quad \overset{15,000}{\underset{0}{\vdash}} \qquad D = 11,000 \qquad \dashv \atop 5$$

$$AC_A = AC_B$$

$$25,000(A/P, i, 5) + 7,500 = 15,000(A/P, i, 5) + 11,000$$

$$10,000(A/P, i, 5) = 3,500$$

whence

$$i = 22.1\% \text{ after tax}$$

Although the time scales in Method 1 are different from those in Method 2, we must remember that these are comparative costs and only the differences between A and B must be the same in both methods.

Method 3: By computing the cash flow after taxes. By subtracting the time scales, we get the annual saving, or cash flow, resulting from the selection of A, the more efficient conveyor system.

Before tax if select A:

$$\begin{array}{c} 10{,}000 \quad \text{Cash flow} = 5{,}000/\text{yr} \\ \underset{0}{\vdash\!\!-\!\!-\!\!-\!\!-\!\!-\!\!-\!\!-\!\!-\!\!-\!\!\dashv} \\ 5 \end{array}$$

Cash flow before taxes	$5,000
Deduction for depreciation	2,000
Net profit before tax (i.e., taxable income)	$3,000
Income tax at 0.50	1,500
Cash flow after taxes	3,500

After tax if select A:

$$\begin{array}{c} 10{,}000 \quad \text{Cash flow} = 3{,}500/\text{yr} \\ \underset{0}{\vdash\!\!-\!\!-\!\!-\!\!-\!\!-\!\!-\!\!-\!\!-\!\!-\!\!\dashv} \\ 5 \end{array}$$

$$AC_{cost} = AW_{income}$$

$$10{,}000(A/P, i, 5) = 3{,}500$$

whence

$$i = 22.1\%$$

Inasmuch as all three methods are correct, the choice of method must rest on such advantages as ease, speed, fewer chances of error, and how readily it may be understood by those who use it as well as those who must approve the results. In this simple example, the advantage of Method 3 over the other methods is obvious, but in complicated problems (see Example 15.15) the extra work required in Method 1 may be justified.

Method 1 is generally easier if (a) the lives of the alternatives are different and (b) where the accountant employs different methods of depreciation for each of the assets. Also, it will be noticed that the cost equations set up by Method 1 are independent of each other, an advantage if multiple levels of investment are being compared or if future alternatives are likely to be added. Method 2 presents a slightly different viewpoint but seems to have no advantage over the other two methods. Method 3, as we have said, clearly is the easiest where the problems are not complex. This method is harder to handle with assets having different depreciation methods. It necessitates keeping positive and negative savings straight where they occur and may be a bit more difficult to understand where lives are different.

The three methods all give the same answer, and this means that they can all be reduced or simplified to the same mathematical model, in this case $(10{,}000) \cdot {}_{i-5}\text{crf} = 3{,}500$. The problem and the advantage of one method over the other is determined by (a) which is the simplest to set up and (b) which will be the most understandable. By knowing all the methods, the analyst is prepared to use the one best suited to his situation.

15.8 ANALYSIS IF TAX LIFE EXCEEDS ECONOMIC LIFE

A situation likely to confront the analyst is the disagreement between the useful life required for tax purposes and the shorter economic life of the equipment. This implies that much equipment will experience several degradations in service before the expiration of the useful life acceptable to the Internal Revenue Service. Each of these service periods represents an economic life starting with the prime service and probably ending with service on standby duty. The tax depreciation will nevertheless be based on the useful or service life.

EXAMPLE 15.8 A forming tool A in a fabricating plant has a first cost of $25,000 and an estimated salvage value of $6,500 at the end of its prime service life 10 years hence. Its annual operating disbursements are $6,000. Tool B has a first cost of $15,000 and an economic life of 10 years at which date its salvage is estimated to be $4,000. Operating disbursements are $9,000. The tax rate is 52% and the useful life for both alternatives is 20 years with zero salvage at that date. Depreciation is straight-line.

SOLUTION.[1]

Before tax:

A 25,000 $D = 6,000$ $L = 6,500$
       0   10

B 15,000 $D = 9,000$ $L = 4,000$
       0   10

Tax life: 20 years
Tax rate: 0.52
Depreciation: SLD

Method 3: By computing the tax on the cash flow.

Cash flow due to A, $(9,000 - 6,000)$	$= \$3,000$
Extra depreciation due to A, $(10,000/20) =$	500
Net profit before tax	$\$2,500$
Income tax at 0.52	1,300
Cash flow after tax	1,700

After tax: 10,000 $I = 1,700$ $L = 2,500$
              0   10

$$AC_{cost} = AW_{income}$$

$$(10,000 - 2,500)(A/P, i, 10) + 2,500i = 1,700$$

If $i = 12\%$, cost $<$ income by $73/yr

If $i = 13\%$, cost $>$ income by $7/yr

[1]The solution of Example 15.8 disregards any tax effects of gains or losses on disposal. This subject will be introduced in Section 15.17.

So,

$$i = 12.9\%$$

If either of these tools is purchased, the analyst feels that it will have a *useful* life with the company for 20 years. Evidence of this opinion is supported by the adoption of the 20-year tax life. Therefore, after the first 10 years, the company will continue to pay taxes on the income or savings generated by the tool until the date of its disposal. However, these taxes, like other disbursements incurred during subsequent life periods, are chargeable to those periods. They are relevant to the analyses of future contests with other equipment for continued employment in the company.

15.9 WHY USE ACCELERATED DEPRECIATION?

No matter which method of depreciation is used, whether decelerated, in which the write-off is less in the early years, or straight-line, in which the amount is the same each year, or accelerated, in which the amount is greater in the early years, it should be apparent that the total amount of depreciation, and therefore the tax disbursements, will be the same for all methods.

Although the total write-off and the total taxes are the same, the time value of money establishes an advantage for the rapid compared to the slow write-off.

EXAMPLE 15.9 In an income-expansion situation, the gross income and operating disbursements are expected to be the same in each of the 5 years of the project's life. The only question is whether to use slow, uniform, or accelerated write-off of the equipment.

SOLUTION. With a slow write-off of depreciation, the net taxable income, and consequently the tax, will be greatest in the first year and will decrease each year; with uniform write-off, the net taxable income and the tax will be the same each year; with rapid write-off the net taxable income and the tax will be the smallest in the first year but will increase each year thereafter. Since the total depreciation must be the same for all three alternatives, the total taxes will be the same but they will be distributed differently in time. Let us assume for the sake of illustration that the tax disbursements, totaling $15,000 in each case, are distributed as follows:

Tax Disbursements:

	5000	4000	3000	2000	1000
Slow write-off					
0	1	2	3	4	5

	3000	3000	3000	3000	3000
Uniform write-off					
0	1	2	3	4	5

	1000	2000	3000	4000	5000
Rapid write-off					
0	1	2	3	4	5

We can see from inspection that at *any* minimum required rate of return, other than zero, the present worth of the tax disbursements produced by the rapid write-off will be the lowest and therefore the most economic choice. It can be observed that *any* rapid write-off is more economic than any slow write-off or that any *more* rapid write-off is more economic than any less rapid write-off. This, of course, disregards irreducible considerations. It disregards, for example, that a rapid write-off also means reporting less profit at the outset (a short-run versus long-run consideration). It also disregards the question of a rise or fall in future tax rates.

15.10 ANALYSIS USING SUM-OF-THE-YEAR'S DIGITS DEPRECIATION

As may be inferred from the last section, the economic advantages of accelerated depreciation have influenced many companies to adopt a method of accelerated depreciation for tax purposes. One of these methods is the sum-of-the-year's digits.

By this method the depreciation expense in the first year[1] is

$$d_1 = \frac{2N}{N(N+1)}(P-S) \qquad (15.10a)$$

where N = the tax life and S = salvage at the end of the tax life. For example, if the tax life is ten years, the first year's depreciation is:

$$d_1 = \frac{2(10)}{(10)(11)}(P-S) = \frac{10}{55}(P-S)$$

and the depreciation in subsequent years will be 9/55, 8/55, 7/55, etc. to 1/55 $(P-S)$ in the tenth and last year. It will be noted that 55 is the sum of the years one through ten, namely, the sum-of-the year's digits in the tax life.

The annual decrease in depreciation is by an arithmetic gradient, $\frac{2}{N(N+1)}(P-S)$, which in the given example is $\frac{1}{55}(P-S)$

Also, the depreciation in any year, t,

$$d_t = \frac{2(N-t+1)}{N(N+1)}(P-S) \qquad (15.10b)$$

And the book value[2] in any year, t,

$$BKV_t = \frac{(N-t)(N-t+1)}{N(N+1)}(P-S) + S \qquad (15.10c)$$

[1] It will help to note that the sum of all the digits is $\frac{N(N+1)}{2}$.

[2] Note from Footnote 1 that the sum of the digits through any year, t, is $\frac{N(N+1)}{2} - \frac{(N-t)^2 + (N-t)}{2}$.

EXAMPLE 15.10 Cutting tool A costs \$25,000 with \$6,550 salvage value at the end of a 10-year economic life and operating disbursements of \$6,000. Tool B costs \$15,000 with a salvage of \$3,930 at the end of its 10-year economic life. Its operating disbursement will be \$9,000. The tax rate is 52% and the tax lives are 20 years for both with zero salvage values at that date. Depreciation is sum-of-the-year's digits.

SOLUTION.

Before tax:

A 25,000 $D = 6,000$ $L = 6,550$ Tax lives: 20 years
     0   10   Tax salvage: zero

B 15,000 $D = 9,000$ $L = 3,930$ Tax rate: 0.52
     0   10   Tax depreciation: SYD

Method 1: Computing the tax savings.

Since both alternatives have 20-year tax lives, the depreciation for each will be $\frac{20}{210}P$ in the first year and will decrease each year by $\frac{1}{210}P$. Therefore, the depreciation for A will be $\frac{20}{210}(25,000) = \$2,380$, which will decrease by $\frac{1}{210}(25,000) = \$119$ a year. For B, the first year's depreciation will be $\frac{20}{210}(15,000) = \$1,428$ with an annual decrease of $\frac{1}{210}(15,000) = \$72$. The annual decrease in depreciation will increase the taxable income and increase A's tax payments $119(0.52) = \$62$ each year and B's $72(0.52) = \$37$ each year. These annual increases in tax disbursements are gradient increases.

SUMMARY

	First Year			Each Subsequent Year	
	A	B		A	B
Operating disbursement	\$6,000	\$ 9,000			
Depreciation expense	2,380	1,428	Depreciation decrease	\$119	\$72
Total expense	\$8,380	\$10,428	Expense decrease	\$119	\$72
Tax saving at 0.52	4,358	5,423	Tax increase at 0.52	62	37
Operating disbursement	\$1,642	\$ 3,577	Disbursement increase	\$ 62	\$37

$$AC_A = AC_B$$

$$(25,000 - 6,550)(A/P, 10) + 6,550i + 1,642 + 62(A/G, 10)$$

$$= (15,000 - 3,930)(A/P, 10) + 3,930i + 3,577$$

$$+ 37(A/G, 10)$$

which reduces to

$$7,380(A/P, 10) + 2,620i + 25(A/G, 10) = 1,935$$

If $i = 14\%$, cost $<$ income by $67/yr

If $i = 15\%$, cost $>$ income by $13/yr

so,
$$i = 14.8\%$$

With some experience the analyst can write a *uniform equivalent annual series* for each element of each disbursement and expense instead of the year-by-year analysis in the previous example. For example, the after-tax operating disbursements of tool A could have been computed as follows:

Operating disbursements before tax   = \$6,000
Depreciation expense

$$= \left(\frac{20}{210}\right)(25,000) - \left(\frac{1}{210}\right)(25,000)(A/G, i, 10) = 2,380 - 119(A/G, i, 10)$$

Total expense   = \$8,380 - 119(A/G, i, 10)
Tax saving at 0.52   =   4,358 - 62(A/G, i, 10)
Operating disbursement after tax   = \$1,642 + 62(A/G, i, 10)

which checks the previous computation of A's operating disbursements.

A similar procedure could be used to compute B's after-tax operating disbursements. The results obviously are the same as before but for the experienced operator are easier to obtain. On the other hand, if the annual before-tax operating disbursements do not conform to a model which can be readily converted to a uniform equivalent annual series, a year-by-year analysis based on a table of annual disbursements and expenses will be easier and more accurate.

Method 3: By computing the tax on the cash flow.

                 10,000   Savings = 3,000/yr $L = 2,620$
Before tax: 0   10

Computing the *uniform equivalent annual series* of the cash flows and expenses:

Cash flow before tax   = \$3,000
Extra depreciation expense

$$= \left(\frac{20}{210}\right)(10,000) - \left(\frac{1}{210}\right)(10,000)(A/G, i, 10) = 952 - 48(A/G, i, 10)$$

Taxable income   = \$2,048 + 48(A/G, i, 10)
Tax at 0.52   =   1,065 + 25(A/G, i, 10)
Cash Flow   = \$1,935 - 25(A/G, i, 10)

$$AC = AW$$

$$7,380(A/P, i, 10) + 2,620i + 25(A/G, 10) = 1,935$$

This is the same equation as in Method 1, so

$$i = 14.8\%$$

15.11 ANALYSIS USING DOUBLE-RATE DECLINING-BALANCE DEPRECIATION

Another technique for accelerating depreciation is the double-rate declining-balance method. In this method the depreciation expense in any year is a constant ratio of the book value at the beginning of that year. Therefore, the book value or balance of the unamortized cost of the asset and the depreciation expense each decline at a constant rate. The 1954 tax laws permitted a declining-balance rate numerically equal to double the straight-line rate. For example, if the useful life is N years, the straight-line depreciation rate is $1/N$ and the double-rate declining-balance rate is $2(1/N)$. According to the tax rules, the depreciation expense is computed by multiplying the unamortized value at the beginning of each year by this rate (consequently the salvage value does not enter into the computation).

The book value at the end of any year is derived as follows:

$$B_1 = \text{BKV at end of yr 1} = P - P\left(\frac{2}{N}\right) = P\left(1 - \frac{2}{N}\right)$$

$$B_2 = \text{BKV at end of yr 2} = P\left(1 - \frac{2}{N}\right) - P\left(1 - \frac{2}{N}\right)\left(\frac{2}{N}\right) = P\left(1 - \frac{2}{N}\right)^2$$

$$B_t = \text{BKV at end of yr } t = P\left(1 - \frac{2}{N}\right)^t \tag{15.11a}$$

The depreciation expense in any year t is $2/N$ times the book value at the beginning of year t, as follows:

$$\text{Depreciation expense in year } t = B_{t-1}\left(\frac{2}{N}\right) = \left(\frac{2P}{N}\right)\left(1 - \frac{2}{N}\right)^{t-1}$$

$$\tag{15.11b}$$

As an illustration, if the useful life of an asset costing \$5,000 is 10 years, the straight-line rate is 0.1; the double rate is 0.2; the book values will decline at the rate of 0.2 a year; and the year-end balances will have a constant ratio of 0.8, which can be noted by examination of Table 15.11a. Any of the values in the table may be verified from Eqs. 15.11a and 15.11b as follows:

Book value in year 10:

$$P\left(1 - \frac{2}{N}\right)^t = (5,000)\,(0.8)^{10} = (5,000)\,(0.10736) = \$537$$

Expense in year 10:

$$\left(\frac{2P}{N}\right)\left(1 - \frac{2}{N}\right)^{t-1} = (500)\,(0.2)\,(0.8)^9 = \$134$$

Table 15.11a DECLINE IN VALUES WITH THE DOUBLE-RATE
DECLINING-BALANCE METHOD

Year	Cost	Book value at end of year	Depreciation expense in that year
0	$5,000	$ —	$ —
1		4,000	1,000
2		3,200	800
3		2,560	640
4		2,048	512
5		1,638	410
6		1,311	327
7		1,049	262
8		839	210
9		671	168
10		537	134

It can be observed from Eq. 15.11a that the book value with the double-rate declining-balance method can never become zero (except for a 2-year life which is not permitted by the IRS; a test of the formula will show why).

The computation of income taxes using DRDB depreciation is illustrated in the following example.

EXAMPLE 15.11 Compare the alternatives shown on the following time scales using double-rate declining-balance depreciation. The tax life is 20 years with zero salvage at that date.

Before tax:

$$
A \quad \overset{20{,}000}{\underset{0}{\vdash}} \quad \overset{D = 5{,}000/\text{yr}}{\rule{6em}{0.4pt}} \quad \overset{L = 6{,}975}{\underset{10}{\dashv}}
$$

Tax life: 20 years
Tax salvage: zero

$$
B \quad \overset{10{,}000}{\underset{0}{\vdash}} \quad \overset{D = 8{,}000/\text{yr}}{\rule{6em}{0.4pt}} \quad \overset{L = 3{,}490}{\underset{10}{\dashv}}
$$

Tax rate: 0.52
Depreciation: DRDB

SOLUTION. (This solution disregards consideration of the tax effects of gains or losses on disposal, which will be introduced in Section 15.17.)

Method 3: By computing the cash-flow.

$$
\text{The depreciation rate} = 2\left(\frac{1}{N}\right) = 2\left(\frac{1}{20}\right) = 0.1
$$

Before tax if select A:

$$
\overset{\text{Cost}}{\underset{0}{\overset{10{,}000}{\vdash}}} \quad \overset{\text{Savings}}{\overset{3{,}000/\text{yr}}{\rule{6em}{0.4pt}}} \quad \overset{L = 3{,}485}{\underset{10}{\dashv}}
$$

$$
AC_{\text{cost}} = AW_{\text{income}}
$$

See Table 15.11b for computation of cash flows after tax.

Table 15.11b COMPUTATION OF CASH FLOWS FOR EXAMPLE 15.11

Year	1	2	3	4	5	6	7	8	9	10
Cash flow before tax	$3,000	3,000	3,000	3,000	3,000	3,000	3,000	3,000	3,000	3,000
Depreciation expense	1,000	900	810	729	656	590	531	478	430	387
Taxable income	$2,000	2,100	2,190	2,271	2,344	2,410	2,469	2,522	2,570	2,613
Tax @ 52%	1,040	1,092	1,139	1,181	1,219	1,253	1,284	1,311	1,336	1,359
Cash flow after tax	$1,960	1,908	1,861	1,819	1,781	1,747	1,716	1,689	1,664	1,641

$$6{,}515(A/P, i, 10) + 3{,}485i = [1{,}960(P/F, 1) + 1{,}908(P/F, 2) + \cdots$$

$$+ 1{,}641(P/F, 10)](A/P, 10)$$

If $i = 14\%$, cost $<$ income by $79/\text{yr}$

If $i = 15\%$, cost $>$ income by $2/\text{yr}$

whence

$$i \cong 15.0\%$$

15.12 SWITCHPOINT IN THE DOUBLE-RATE DECLINING-BALANCE METHOD

In the double-rate declining-balance method we have noted that the book value at the end of the tax life, N, cannot become zero nor (as we will show) can it ever go above 13.53% of first cost. This maximum would occur if the tax life, N, were infinitely long, since the highest book value results from the greatest value of N.

Because the computed book value at the end of the tax life is independent of S, the salvage value at that date, the user of the DRDB method must contemplate a terminal tax effect from either a gain or loss on disposal. As an alternative to this, the tax regulations permit the taxpayer to adopt a switch from double-rate declining-balance to straight-line depreciation at any point in the tax life. The election of a switchpoint may prove advantageous to the taxpayer. For example, if the predicted salvage, S, is zero and the taxpayer does not switch at all, a tax saving will occur at the end of the tax life due to the write-off in depreciation at that date. However, by switching to straight-line depreciation before the end of the tax life, the final book value can be made equal to the predicted salvage. Of course, by either method the total write-off will be the same (and the tax savings will be equal) but as the time distribution will be different it is to the advantage of the taxpayer to select the method which gives the earlier tax savings, namely, the one with the switchpoint. From this reasoning, it is advantageous to make the switch whenever the terminal book value using DRDB depreciation alone exceeds the predicted terminal salvage. The tax advantage will begin in the year that the annual depreciation charge using the SLD method becomes greater than it would be for the DRDB method. This means that the switch is recommended in the year when

$$\frac{\text{Undepreciated balance} - \text{Predicted tax salvage}}{\text{Remaining tax life}} \geqslant \text{DRDB depreciation}$$

Therefore if t is the end of the year in which the switch occurs and S is the tax salvage at the end of year N:

$$\frac{P\left(1 - \dfrac{2}{N}\right)^{t-1} - S}{N - (t - 1)} \geqslant P\left(\frac{2}{N}\right)\left(1 - \frac{2}{N}\right)^{t-1}$$

Solving this for the ratio S/P, we get

$$\frac{S}{P} \leqslant \left(\frac{2t}{N} - \frac{2}{N} - 1\right)\left(1 - \frac{2}{N}\right)^{t-1} \tag{15.12a}$$

Given tax life N and predicted salvage S, Eq. 15.12a permits computing the year *t in which* it will pay to make a switch.

To avoid the trial-and-error procedures required by Eq. 15.12a the following observations[1] are helpful in locating the switchpoint.

Condition A. If by chance S is predicted to be equal to the DRDB book value, then:

$$\frac{S}{P} = \left(1 - \frac{2}{N}\right)^{N} \tag{15.12b}$$

From Eq. 15.12a it can be shown that this will occur when $t = N$, whence the switch can be made in the last year. But there will be no tax advantage in doing so. The reason is that by switching *in* the last year, N, the depreciation expense by SLD at time N equals the depreciation expense by DRDB plus the loss-on-disposal, both of which occur (in the discrete convention) at time N. Neither method will have a tax advantage, since the tax rate is the same on depreciation expense as on loss on disposal. Therefore Eq. 15.12b is taken to be a signal for no switch.

Condition B. If by chance $\frac{S}{P} \geqslant 13.53\%$ there will be no switch. This follows from Condition A because whatever the value of N, the DRDB book value at year N can never exceed $0.1353\,P$:

$$\lim_{N \to \infty} \left(1 - \frac{2}{N}\right)^{N} = e^{-2} = 0.1353$$

Therefore for a switchpoint to occur $\frac{S}{P}$ must be less than 0.1353. Figure 15.12 shows the limits of $\frac{S}{P}$ for all values of N.

Condition C. If there is a switchpoint, it will occur after the first half-life of the asset, that is, when $t > \frac{N}{2}$.

It can be shown from Eq. 15.12a that the earliest year in which a switch may occur is year $\left(\frac{N}{2} + 1\right)$. Therefore, depending on $\frac{S}{P}$, the switch can occur in any

---

[1] Sidney Davidson and David F. Drake, "Capital Budgeting and the Best Tax Depreciation Method," *Journal of Business*, vol. 34, no. 4 (October 1961), p. 442.

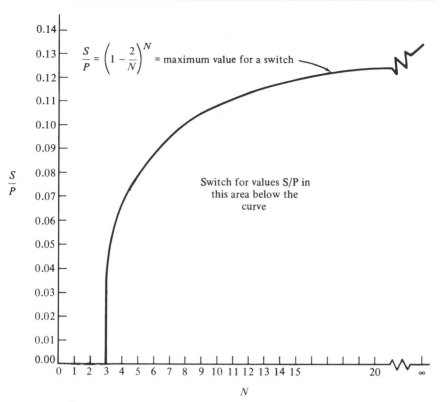

Figure 15.12   Values of salvage that justify switchpoints

year when

$$t \geqslant \left(\frac{N}{2} + 1\right)$$

The ratio $\dfrac{S}{P}$ must be in the range $0 < \dfrac{S}{P} < 0.1353$, as illustrated[1] in Tables 15.12a and b, for a switch to occur for $3 < N < \infty$.

Table 15.12a from Eq. 15.12a shows the limits for $\dfrac{S}{P}$ which call for a switch in the stated year, t, for an asset with a 10-year tax life, N. For example, if $\dfrac{S}{P}$ is equal to or less than 10.7% but greater than 10.1%, a switch can occur in the 10th and final year of the tax life (but without any tax advantage, as noted above). If $\dfrac{S}{P}$ is equal or less than 10.1% but greater than 8.39%, it will pay to

---

[1]If N is odd, switch at the smallest integer greater than the fractional t. For example, if $N = 9$, then $t = \frac{9}{2} + 1 = 5.5$, and so $t = 6$ is used.

Table 15.12a SWITCHPOINTS FOR VARIOUS SALVAGE VALUES IF
TAX LIFE IS 10 YEARS

N	To switch in year t	S/P must not exceed	Range of S/P to switch in year t
10	(5)	0	no switch
10	6	0	$S/P = 0$
10	7	5.24%	$0 < S/P \leqslant 5.24\%$
10	8	8.39%	$5.24\% < S/P \leqslant 8.39\%$
10	9	10.1%	$8.39\% < S/P \leqslant 10.1\%$
10	10	10.7%	$10.1\% < S/P \leqslant 10.7\%$

switch *in* the 9th year, and so on. The earliest switch is in the 6th year, but
only if the salvage is zero.

EXAMPLE 15.12 Using the data given in Table 15.11a, compute the depreciation expense using a switch point if the expected tax salvage S is 5.0% and compare the results with the DRDB method without a switch. The data in Table
15.11a are based on a 10-year tax life and $5,000 first cost.

SOLUTION. DRDB book values (always computed without regard to salvage
values) and the DRDB depreciation expenses without a switch are reprinted
from Table 15.11a in Table 15.12b. The previous discussion suggests testing for
the switch to occur *in* the 7th year. Substituting $t = 7$ in Eq. 15.12a verifies this

Table 15.12b COMPARISON OF DRDB WITH AND WITHOUT SWITCH

Year	Cost P	DRDB Book value at end of year	DRDB Depreciation expense in that year	DRDB with switch Book value at end of year	DRDB with switch Depreciation expense in that year	SLD Book value at end of year	SLD Depreciation expense in that year
0	5,000	—	—	—	—	—	—
1		4,000	1,000	4,000	1,000	4,525	475
2		3,200	800	3,200	800	4,050	475
3		2,560	640	2,560	640	3,575	475
4		2,048	572	2,048	572	3,100	475
5		1,638[a]	410	1,638	410	2,625[a]	475
6		1,311	327	1,311	327	2,150	475
7		1,049	262	1,045	265	1,675	475
8		839	210	780	265	1,200	475
9		671	168	515	265	725	475
10		537	134	250	265	250	475

[a]By DRDB 66% of the asset was written off by the end of the half-life, compared with
48% by SLD.

by showing that

$$.05 \leqslant .0524$$

The DRDB book value at the beginning of year 7 (i.e., end of year 6) is \$1311 and the remaining annual depreciation by SLD is $(1311 - 250)/4 = \$265$ as summarized in Table 15.12b.

15.13 DERIVATION OF THE GEOMETRIC-SERIES FACTOR

The annual depreciation expense by the DRDB method constitutes a geometric series represented by the following time scale:

where d is the first year's depreciation, and $a = 1 - \dfrac{2}{N}$, as noted below,[1] and m is the date of the last term in the geometric series—namely, the last term of the series computed by DRDB depreciation. For example, if a switch to SLD is justified *in* year t prior to the end of the tax life N, then m is the date of the last DRDB term, whence $m = t - 1$. If no switch is justified, then, of course, $m = N$.

The compound amount of this series is:

$$S = d(1 + i)^{m-1} + ad(1 + i)^{m-2} + a^2 d(1 + i)^{m-3} + \cdots$$

$$+ a^{m-3}d(1 + i)^2 + a^{m-2}d(1 + i) + a^{m-1}d \quad (15.13a)$$

Multiply Eq. 151.3a by $(1 + i)/a$

$$S\frac{(1 + i)}{a} = \left(\frac{d}{a}\right)(1 + i)^m + d(1 + i)^{m-1} + ad(1 + i)^{m-2} + \cdots$$

$$+ a^{m-4}d(1 + i)^3 + a^{m-3}d(1 + i)^2 + a^{m-2}d(1 + i) \quad (15.13b)$$

Subtract Eq. 15.13b from Eq. 15.13a.

$$S - \frac{S(1 + i)}{a} = -\left(\frac{d}{a}\right)(1 + i)^m + a^{m-1}D$$

$$S\left[\frac{a - (1 + i)}{a}\right] = d\left[a^{m-1} - \frac{(1 + i)^m}{a}\right]$$

$$S[a - (1 + i)] = d[a^m - (1 + i)^m]$$

$$S = d\left[\frac{a^m - (1 + i)^m}{a - (1 + i)}\right] \quad (15.13c)$$

[1]$d_2 = ad_1$, whence

$$a = \frac{d_2}{d_1} = \left(\frac{2P}{N}\right)\left(1 - \frac{2}{N}\right)^{2-1} \div \left(\frac{2P}{N}\right)\left(1 - \frac{2}{N}\right)^{1-1} = 1 - \frac{2}{N}$$

Equation 15.13c can be rewritten

$$S = d \left[\frac{a^m - (F/P, i, m)}{a - (F/P, i, 1)} \right]_{i-m} = d(\text{gscaf}) = d(F/g, i, m) \qquad (15.13d)^1$$

The bracketed member in the above equation can be mnemonically designated the "geometric-series compound-amount factor" for m periods at rate of return i.

Of course, S can be converted to a present sum or to a uniform series by multiplying by the appropriate factors, $(P/F, m)$ or $(A/F, m)$.

In Eq. 15.13c and 15.13d $a < 1$ since the depreciation series decreases with time. But the same equations could also be applied to series resulting from rising costs or deterioration in which $a > 1$ and where 1 is the first-year costs.

Although using Eq. 15.13c is not without effort, it is easier than computing 10 or 15 terms of a DRDB series. Unfortunately the equation cannot be satisfied by a simple set of tables, because with each value of N there may be several values of m over the whole range of interest rates. The factor in Eq. 15.13c may be quickly evaluated by computer or reasonably fast by hand by using the following conversion of Eq. 15.13c.

$$\text{gscaf} = (F/g, i, m) = \frac{I - (P/F, m) - (F/P, m)}{I - (P/F, 1) - (F/P, m)} \qquad (15.13e)^2$$

where $I = \dfrac{2}{N-2}$ and as noted, $m = t - 1$.

For example, if $N = 10$ and $t = 7$ then, $a = 1 - \dfrac{2}{N} = 0.8$ and $a^8 = 0.2621$.

Alternatively $I = \dfrac{2}{N-2}$ (100%) = 25%, and in the 25% table (P/F) for 6 periods (the value of m) is 0.2621, and for 1 period is 0.8, which checks the above calculation.

15.14 APPLICATION OF THE GEOMETRIC-SERIES FACTOR

In applying the geometric-series factor to DRDB computations we must remember that, as with all income tax computations, we are endeavoring to compute the tax as the *accountant* would compute it so that we may include the correct tax disbursements in our economic evaluation.

In our first illustration, therefore, let us assume that the accountant uses a tax life N and a switch point t but the economic life, n, of the asset is less than t. Where degradation of the asset over several service lines is expected this situation can very likely occur. Example 15.14a illustrates this.

---

[1]ASEE standards do not include a symbol for a geometric gradient or mnemonic and functional factors for geometric series. We therefore take the liberty of using "g" (compared to G) for the geometric symbol and $(F/g, i, m)$ for the functional compound-amount factor of a geometric series (gscaf).

[2]It can be shown easily that $a = \dfrac{1}{1+I} = (P/F, I, 1)$ if $I = \dfrac{2}{N-2}$

EXAMPLE 15.14a. Solve Example 15.11 using the geometric-series factor. The time scale in that example was:

	Cost	Savings		$N = 20$ yrs.
	10,000	3,000/yr	$L = 3,485$	$S = 0$
Before tax if select A:	0		10	rate 50%
				DRDB

From Eq. 15.12a we determine that there will be no switchpoint during the 10-year economic life. In fact, our discussions revealed that if a switch occurred it would have to be later than $\dfrac{N}{2}$ years. Therefore in this instance, if not in most, $m = n$.

SOLUTION. We note that the first year's depreciation is $\left(\dfrac{2}{20}\right)(10{,}000)$. Let us compute the uniform equivalent annual cost of the cash flow and the expense:

1. Cash flow before tax $= \$3{,}000$
2. Depreciation expense[1]

$$= \left(\frac{2}{20}\right)(10{,}000)(F/g, m)(A/F, m) = 1{,}000(F/g, m)(A/F, m)$$

3. Taxable income (line 1 minus line 2) $= 3{,}000 - 1{,}000(F/g, m)(A/F, m)$
4. Tax at 0.52 $= 1{,}560 - 520(F/g, m)(A/F, m)$
5. Cash flow after tax (line 1 minus line 4) $= 1{,}440 + 520(F/g, m)(A/F, m)$

$$AC = AW$$

$$6.515(A/P, i, 10) + 3{,}485i = 1{,}440 + 520(F/g, i, m)(A/F, m)$$

$$\text{If } i = 14\%, \text{ cost} < \text{income by } \$79/\text{yr}$$

$$\text{If } i = 15\%, \text{ cost} > \text{income by } \$2/\text{yr}$$

so,

$$i \cong 15\%$$

which checks the results of Example 15.11.

EXAMPLE 15.14b. Use the same accounting data summarized in Table 15.12b in which the accountant's tax life N was 10 years and the salvage at that date was $250. Assume that the cash flow resulting from the investment of $5,000 is $2,000 a year, the tax rate is 50%, and the economic life, n, is 10 years—the same as the tax life. Use the geometric-series factor and compute the present worth of the proposal with a switch, if there is one, at a minimum required rate of return of 15%.

[1] $i{-}m\text{gscaf} = \left[\dfrac{0.9^{10} - (F/P, i, 10)}{0.9 - (F/P, 1)}\right]$

SOLUTION.

	Cost	Cash flow		Tax life = 10 yr
If select the proposal	5,000	2,000/yr	L = 250	S = L = $250
	0		10	Tax rate: 0.50
				DRDB

Since $\dfrac{S}{P} = \dfrac{250}{5,000} = 0.05$ the switch will occur in year 7.

This conclusion follows from Eq. 15.12a and is verified in Table 15.12a. Thus the last term in the DRDB series is at the end of year 6, whence $m = 6$. Observe that $m = t - 1$ if a switch exists.

The following statements give the present worth of each line.

1. Cash flow before tax = $2,000 \overset{5.0188}{(P/A, .15, 10)} = \$10,038$

2. Depreciation expense[1]

$$= \frac{2}{10}\,(5,000)(F/g, 6)(P/F, 6) + \left(\frac{BKV_6 - 250}{4}\right)(P/A, 4)(P/F, 6)$$

$$= 1,000\overset{0.43233}{(5.86)(P/F, 6)} + \left(\frac{1,311 - 250}{4}\right)\overset{2.8550\ \ 0.43233}{(P/A, 4)(P/F, 6)}$$

$$= \$2,861$$

3. Taxable income (line 1 minus line 2) = 10,038 − 2,861 = $7,177
4. Tax @ 50% = (0.5) (7,177) = $3,589
5. Cash flow after tax (line 1 minus line 4) = 10,038 − 3,589 = $6,449
6. Present worth of the proposal = 6,449 + 250(P/F, 10) − 5,000 = $1,511

15.15 RELEVANCE OF BOOK VALUE

A statement often encountered in this subject is that book value is irrelevant. This refers to the fact that the investment value P of an incumbent machine is its net realizable value, not its book value. However, book value is relevant to the choice because it is the basis for computing the income tax savings and disbursements. For example, the difference between book value and net realizable value establishes the taxes paid on a gain on disposal or saved on a loss on disposal and, since book value is the basis of computing depreciation expense, it has a direct effect on annual tax disbursements.

EXAMPLE 15.15 A new grinder can be purchased for $10,000 installed. Operating disbursements are expected to be $6,000 a year over the machine's economic life of 10 years. The analyst is convinced that the equipment will have

---

[1] In this:

$$(F/g, .15, 6) = \frac{(0.8)^6 - \overset{2.3131}{(F/P, 6)}}{\underset{0.8 - (F/P, 1)}{1.15}} = 5.86 \ \ \text{(from Eq. 15.13c)}$$

and $BKV_6 = \$1,311$ (from Table 15.12b or Eq. 15.11a).

a net salvage at that date of $3940. Useful life is expected to be 20 years with zero salvage at that date.

The present tool is second-hand equipment purchased 2 years ago. Its book value is $5,000, although its present net realizable value is only $3,000. The machine can be rebuilt for $1,500, which will make it suitable for continued service on this job and will extend its useful life (tax life) for 4 years from the present. Its tax salvage will be zero at that time. After rebuilding, the operating disbursements will be $7,500 a year.

Tax depreciation for the new unit is sum-of-the-year's digits whereas the present unit is depreciated by the straight-line method. The tax rate is 50%.

SOLUTION.

A   10,000 $D = 6,000/\text{yr}$ $L = 3,940$ Tax life: 20 years
       0   10   Tax salvage: zero
                                                           Depreciation: SYD
                                                           Tax rate: 0.50

Before tax:

          Rebuild 1,500
          NRV 3,000

B $D = 7,500$ 0   Tax life: 4 years
          0   4   Tax salvage: zero
                                       Depreciation: SL
                                       BKV: $5,000

The investment in the present tool is computed as follows:

1.	BKV	$5,000	
2.	NRV	3,000	
3.	Loss on disposal	$2,000	
4.	Tax saving at 0.50	1,000	
5.	NRV after tax	4,000	line 2 plus line 4
6.	Cost to rebuild	1,500	
7.	Investment	$5,500	line 5 plus line 6

As noted in Chapter 11 on replacement, the investment in the present equipment is the amount of money the owner foregoes to continue it in its present service. In the present example the owner, of course, foregoes the net realizable value of $3,000 but also foregoes the tax saving of $1,000 by continuing the unit in service. He also foregoes $1,500 if he elects to rebuild the unit. In fact, he foregoes a total of $5,500.

The book value of A 10 years hence is $\dfrac{(10)\,(11)}{(20)\,(21)}\,(10,000)$, or $2,620$, which, compared with the analyst's firm conviction of a $3,940 salvage, gives the following tax effect:

Salvage	$3,940
BKV	2,620
Gain on disposal	$1,320
Tax on gain[1] at 50%	660
Net salvage	$3,280

Allowing for tax effects on distant future salvage values as computed above for A is far more the exception than usual. It is more likely to be found where asset lives are short and the analyst predicts market conditions producing wide variances between the liquidating value and the write-off value—conditions which may even permit tax strategies. For the conditions illustrated above the slight variance in market and book values 10 years hence despite the analyst's "firm conviction" of the variances could justifiably be disregarded considering the time value of money that far away.

Now examine the income tax resulting from operations. Depreciation expense for A is $\left(\dfrac{20}{210}\right)$ (10,000) = \$952 in the first year and this will decrease $\left(\dfrac{1}{210}\right)$ (10,000) = \$48 a year. The straight-line depreciation on B will be $\left(\dfrac{1}{4}\right)$ (5,000 + 1,500) = \$1,625 a year.

Method 1: By computing the tax saving.

First Year	A	B	Each Subsequent Year	A	B
Operating disbursement	$6,000	$7,500			
Depreciation expense	952	1,625	Depreciation decrease	$48	0
Total expense	$6,952	$9,125	Extra profit	$48	0
Tax saving at 0.50	3,476	4,563	Extra tax	24	0
Operating disbursement	$2,524	$2,937	Extra disbursement	$24	0

$$A \quad \begin{array}{c} 10{,}000 \\ \vdash \\ 0 \end{array} \quad\quad D = 2{,}524 + (t-1)\,24 \quad\quad \begin{array}{c} L = 3{,}280 \\ \dashv \\ 10 \end{array}$$

After tax:

$$B \quad \begin{array}{c} 5{,}500 \\ \vdash \\ 0 \end{array} \quad D = 2{,}937 \quad L = 0 \quad \begin{array}{c} \\ \dashv \\ 4 \end{array}$$

$$AC_A = AC_B$$

$$(10{,}000 - 3{,}280)(A/P, i, 10) + 3{,}280i + 2{,}524 + 24(A/G, i, 10)$$

$$= 5{,}500(A/P, 4) + 2{,}937$$

$$6{,}720(A/P, i, 10) + 3{,}280i + 24(A/G, i, 10) = 5{,}500(A/P, 4) + 413$$

[1]See section 15.17 for tax rates on gains or losses.

If i = 24%, $AC_A < AC_B$ by \$20

If i = 25%, $AC_A > AC_B$ by \$27

so,

$$i = 24.4\%$$

Method 2: By computing the extra income tax.

	First Year			Each Subsequent Year	
	A	B		A	B
Operating disbursement	\$6,000	\$7,500			
Depreciation expense	952	1,625	Depreciation decrease	\$48	0
Total expense	\$6,952	\$9,125	Profit due to A	\$48	0
Income due to A	2,173	–	Tax due to A	24	0
Tax due to A at 0.5	1,087	–	Disbursement due to A	\$24	0
Operating disbursement	\$7,087	\$7,500			

$$
\begin{array}{ccc}
 & 10,000 & D = 7,087 + (t - 1)\,24 & L = 3,280 \\
A & \vdash\!\dashv & \\
 & 0 & & 10
\end{array}
$$

After tax:

$$
\begin{array}{ccc}
 & 5,500 & D = 7,500 \quad L = 0 \\
B & \vdash\!\dashv \\
 & 0 & 4
\end{array}
$$

$$AC_A = AC_B$$

$$(10{,}000 - 3{,}280)(A/P, i, 10) + 3{,}280i + 7{,}087 + 24(A/G, 10) = 5{,}500(A/P, 4)$$
$$+ 7{,}500$$

$$6{,}270(A/P, i, 10) + 3{,}280i + 24(A/G, 10) = 5{,}500(A/P, 4) + 413$$

This is the same as the equation in Method 1, so i = 24.4%.

Method 3: By computing the tax on the cash flow.

	Year 1		Year 2
Cash flow before tax	\$1,500		\$1,500
Extra depreciation[1] due to A	*negative* 673	*negative*	721
Extra profit	\$2,173		\$2,221
Extra tax due to A at 0.5	1,087		1,111
Cash flow after tax	413		389

whence the gradient decrease in the cash flow is \$24 a year.

As in the *discounted cash-flow method*, compare the assets by discounting the stream of cash flows and, since the lives are different, make the comparison over the least common multiple of their lives as frequently practiced in that method.

[1] In year 1, extra depreciation due to A is −\$1,625 + \$952 = −\$673. In year 2, extra depreciation due to B is −\$1,625 + \$952 − \$48 = −\$721, which agrees with the other two methods.

$$10,000$$

$$10,000 \qquad L = 3,280 \qquad L = 3,280$$

A $\qquad$ | $\quad D = -413 + (t - 1)\,24$ $\quad$ | $\quad D = -413 + (t - 1)\,24$ $\quad$ |

$\qquad 0 \qquad\qquad\qquad\qquad 10 \qquad\qquad\qquad\qquad 20$

After tax:

$$5{,}500 \qquad 5{,}500 \qquad 5{,}500 \qquad 5{,}500 \qquad 5{,}500 \qquad L = 0$$

B $\quad$ | $\; D = 0 \;$ | $\; D = 0 \;$ | $\; D = 0 \;$ | $\; D = 0 \;$ | $\; D = 0 \;$ |

$\qquad 0 \qquad\quad 4 \qquad\quad 8 \qquad\quad 12 \qquad\quad 16 \qquad\quad 20$

Select A (Note: costs are positive, incomes negative.)

$$+4{,}500 \quad -5{,}500 \quad -5{,}500 \quad +6{,}720 \; -5{,}500 \quad -5{,}500 \qquad -3{,}280$$

| $\; D = -413 + (t - 1)\,24 \;$ | $\quad D = -413 + (t - 1)\,24 \quad$ |

$\qquad 0 \qquad\quad 4 \qquad\quad 8 \quad 10 \quad 12 \qquad\quad 16 \qquad\quad 20$

PW of costs = PW of incomes

$$4{,}500 + 6{,}720\,(P/F, 10) = 413 - 24\,(A/G, 10) + 5{,}500\,(A/P, 4)(P/A, 16)(P/F, 4)$$

$$+ 3{,}280\,(P/F, 20)$$

If $i = 24\%$, cost $<$ income by \$82/yr

If $i = 25\%$, cost $>$ income by \$107/yr

so,

$$i = 24.4\%$$

A comparison of the foregoing three methods of computing tax is given in the next section.

15.16 COMPARISON OF THREE METHODS OF COMPUTING TAX AND THE DCF METHOD

What can we observe about the three methods of computation used in the previous section although all give identical answers?

Method 1 computes the tax saving on each asset independent of the other. It is therefore preferable in comparisons involving more than two alternatives.

Method 1 also sets up an annual cost equivalence of alternatives which is simpler than a present-worth set up over the least common multiple (LCM) of the lives of the assets.

Method 2 computes the extra tax on the extra profits and, where the lives are different, equates the annual costs of the assets as in Method 1. It is equal in simplicity to Method 1 and also is easier than a present worth comparison over the LCM. As stated, it is harder to use than Method 1 in comparing multiple levels of investment. But the "tax on extra incomes" may be easier to comprehend by the uninitiated than "tax savings."

Method 3 illustrates the *discounted-cash-flow method*. As the name implies, the DCF method computes the rate of return from a present-worth equivalence and all the DCF work sheets we have seen make the comparison over the LCM as in Method 3. If so, this adds much extra work, complicated by the need for a consistent bookkeeping of plus and minus for cash and incomes. The same answer would result from equating the present worths over a 4-year study period or equating the annual costs of the cash flows instead of their present worths as illustrated in the next paragraph. Either of these alternative techniques requires a deeper knowledge of the subject than implied by the illustrations we have seen on the DCF method.

In Method 3, if we had equated annual costs, we would have written

$$(10,000 - 3,280)(A/P, i, 10) + 3,280i - 413 + 24(A/G, 10) = 5,500(A/P, 4)$$

which the reader will observe is the same equation as resulted from Methods 1 and 2.

A further observation on the procedures which have been used to illustrate the DCF method is that the cash flow is computed as the sum of the extra depreciation plus the extra profit, as noted in Section 15.5. In Method 3 we used a shortcut to find cash flows by recognizing that the difference between disbursements (i.e., the savings) is also the cash flow.

Additional comments and illustrations of the DCF method are given in Chapter 17.

15.17 GAIN OR LOSS ON DISPOSAL AND TRADE-IN ALLOWANCE

The books of the company must account for gains or losses on disposal of an asset. This means that when an asset is sold at more or less than the value recorded in the books, the accounts will show a gain in income in the first instance and a loss in the second. For example, land purchased at $100,000 will be carried on the books, at that value until the land is sold. This is so because first, land is not depreciable, and second, because during the period of ownership, assets on the books generally are not adjusted for market value. So if the land is sold for $120,000 a gain in income of $20,000 is shown on the books in the year of disposal, or if sold for $70,000, a loss of $30,000 is shown.

Depreciable assets are handled in the same way except the value of the asset is carried on the books at cost less the amount the accountant has depreciated it since the date of acquisition; in other words at its current book value.

Since these gains or losses in income affect profits in the years in which they occur, they are subject to tax considerations. However, the amount and method of taxing depend upon very technical and complex rules. While the following will give the analyst a broad idea of these rules, they cannot be used in lieu of the detailed and correct knowledge of tax law required for accuracy.

The tax rules on gains and losses fall into two general categories:

1. Depreciable assets used in trade or business.
2. Capital assets.

Gains or losses on "depreciable assets used in the trade or business" are taxed as a gain or loss in ordinary income in the year of occurrence. Obviously this defines the treatment for machines, production equipment, and real estate. Such assets generate ordinary gains and losses, compared to "capital" gains and losses which qualify for the special tax treatment explained below.

The reason for treating gains on depreciable property as increases in regular income seems equitable because if the depreciation in previous years had been more or less, the profits in those years would have been affected by those same amounts.

Gains on "capital" assets are taxed at lower rates than ordinary income, for example at 30%, compared to 48% or 50% for ordinary income, and capital losses on these assets could be used to offset capital gains. A study of the law reveals that "capital" assets are *generally* intangible and nondepreciable. For example, stocks and bonds held by a manufacturing company in other firms meet this definition. Patents are capital assets, although they are depreciable and, in personal income tax laws, jewels are capital assets although they are tangible. (Obviously a firm whose stock in trade is stocks and bonds or jewels must treat their sale as ordinary income.)

Some significant limitations of the foregoing general rules are as follows:

1. They envisage item accounting—not multiple asset depreciation accounting where the rules for disposal of depreciable assets do not result in "gains" or "losses."

2. A depreciable asset used in trade or business may qualify partly under capital gains and partly under ordinary gains. For example a machine purchased at $100,000, depreciated since the date of purchase to $70,000, with a current market value of $115,000 represents a capital gain on disposal of $15,000 at the 30% tax rate and ordinary gain of $30,000 at the tax rate on ordinary income, such as 48%.

3. On a trade-in compared to a purchase without trade-in, a "gain" or "loss" is not computed on personal or business assets, but is presumed to be resolved by the following special computation of the tax "basis" (book value) of the new asset established by the following rule: When property is traded as partial payment for the new asset, the "basis" is the current book value of the asset traded plus the additional amount paid to acquire the new asset. For example, if the BKV of the old car is $1,000, the new car lists at $5,500 without trade-in, and an $1,800 trade-in allowance is given, the cash price is therefore $3,700. The book value on the new car for tax purposes under the rule is $4,700, i.e., what the buyer paid ($3,700), plus the BKV of the old car ($1,000). The tax basis for depreciation of the new car is therefore $4,700. Without the rule the tax basis would have been $5,500, the value of the car established by its list price, namely its BKV. A time-scale comparison of operating with and without the rule will show that under the rule the buyer avoids paying the tax on the gain at time zero but pays that tax distributed over the tax life of the car. This produces a tax advantage due to the time value of money.

Problems at the end of the chapter enable the reader to examine other situations for himself.

15.18 EXPENSING

As stated, not all capital expenditures must be depreciated for tax purposes. Certain proposed expenditures may be "expensed" and the tax effects will result in immediate tax savings. Considering the time value of money, these tax savings are more valuable than the same tax savings distributed over the tax life— the result of depreciating the expenditures.

Expenditures are expensible if they represent normal maintenance or repair, normal overhaul, or even if they cover costs of relocating equipment. However, any costs of rebuilding the equipment that would prolong life or increase original efficiency would logically be viewed as capital expenditures which must be depreciated.

It is appropriate to remind the reader that remarks in the text are not offered as interpretations of tax laws, but only as illustrations of the rules of economic decision-making. A point-by-point interpretation of the tax laws would require very many volumes and a study undertaken independently of this text. To obtain these tax details, the student is referred to the tax laws themselves.

EXAMPLE 15.18   Use the data in Example 15.15, but assume the cost of re-conditioning the present equipment can be regarded as normal maintenance and repair and can be expensed for tax purposes. The remaining tax life before and after the maintenance is 4 years. Example 15.15 is summarized as follows:

$$A \quad \overset{\displaystyle 10,000 \qquad\qquad D = 6,000 \qquad\qquad L = 3,940}{\underset{0 \qquad\qquad\qquad\qquad\qquad\qquad\qquad\qquad 10}{\vdash\!\!\!-\!\!\!-\!\!\!-\!\!\!-\!\!\!-\!\!\!-\!\!\!-\!\!\!-\!\!\!-\!\!\!-\dashv}}$$

Tax life: 20 years
Tax salvage: zero
Depreciation: SYD
Tax rate: 0.50

Before tax:

NRV 3,000
Reconditioning 1,500

$$B \quad \overset{\displaystyle D = 7,500 \qquad 0}{\underset{0 \qquad\qquad\qquad 4}{\vdash\!\!\!-\!\!\!-\!\!\!-\!\!\!-\!\!\!-\!\!\!-\dashv}}$$

BKV: $5,000
Tax life: 4 years
Tax salvage: zero
Depreciation: SL

SOLUTION.   The depreciation expense for A will be $\dfrac{20}{210}(10,000) = \$952$ the first year, decreasing by $\dfrac{1}{210}(1,000) = \$48$ a year. The depreciation expense for B will be $\dfrac{1}{4}(5,000) = \$1,250$ every year.

The investment value for B after tax will be as follows:

1. BKV	$5,000
2. NRV	3,000
3. Loss on disposal	$2,000
4. Tax saving on loss at 50%	1,000
5. NRV plus tax saving on loss on disposal	$4,000 line 2 plus line 4

6. M and R expense — 1,500
7. Tax saving on M and R at 0.5 — 750
8. M and R expense after tax — $ 750
9. Total investment in B — $4,750 line 5 plus line 8

By continuing the unit in service, the owner foregoes receiving the NRV of $3,000, the tax saving due to loss on disposal of $1,000, and the money he will invest in M and R after tax of $750—a total of $4,750. As would be expected, the immediate tax saving of $750 on the M and R expense reduces the investment value of $5,500 in Example 15.15 to $4,750.

The after-tax salvage of A, as computed in Example 15.15, is $3,280.

	First year		Each subsequent year		
	A	B		A	B
Operating disbursement	$6,000	$7,500			
Depreciation expense	952	1,250	Depreciation decrease	$48	0
Total expense	$6,952	$8,750	Increase in profits	$48	0
Total saving at 0.50	3,476	4,375	Extra tax	24	0
Operating disbursement	$2,524	$3,125	Disbursement gradient	$24	0

After tax:

$$
\begin{array}{l}
A \quad \begin{array}{l} 10{,}000 \\ \hline 0 \end{array} \qquad D = 2{,}524 + (t-1)(24) \qquad \begin{array}{l} L = 3{,}280 \\ \hline 10 \end{array} \\[2em]
B \quad \begin{array}{l} 4{,}750 \quad D = 3{,}125 \quad\quad 0 \\ \hline 0 \qquad\qquad\qquad\qquad 4 \end{array}
\end{array}
$$

$$AC_A = AC_B$$

$$6{,}720(A/P, 10) + 3{,}280i + 24(A/G, 10) + 2{,}524 = 4{,}750(A/P, 4) + 3{,}125$$

$$6{,}720(A/P, 10) + 3{,}280i + 24(A/G, 10) = 4{,}750(A/P, 4) + 601$$

whence

$$i = 22.0\%$$

The difference between 22.0% and 24.4% in Example 15.15 is due entirely to the tax effect of expensing instead of capitalizing the $1,500. It will be noted that, logically, the analysis favors keeping the present unit, the unit which benefits tax-wise by the expensing procedure.

15.19 INVESTMENT TAX CREDIT

The allowance for an investment tax credit since its inception in 1962 has been suspended, reinstated, repealed, temporarily restored, and during its existence altered repeatedly. Regardless of its status, we believe an analyst would want to understand the economics of a tax credit as it relates to the subject of the text.

The rule allows for a special investment tax credit of up to 7% of the value of the property that qualifies. This credit applies after the tax has been computed without it. For example the tax credit of 7% on an asset costing $10,000 applies a reduction of $700 in the taxpayer's total income tax in the year of the purchase of the asset. While the credit is computed as a percentage of the first cost of the asset, this does not affect the depreciable value of the asset, which remains at $10,000–not $9,300. If the year's tax is reduced $700, it is a direct tax saving in the year of acquisition.

EXAMPLE 15.19 Using the data in Example 15.8 compute the effect of a 7% tax credit on the rate of return on the extra investment.

SOLUTION. In the solution for Example 15.8 the after-tax time scale was shown to be:

$$
\begin{array}{ccc}
& \text{Cash flow} & \\
10{,}000 & 1{,}700/\text{yr} & L = 2{,}500 \\
\hline
0 & & 10
\end{array}
$$

and i was computed to be 12.9%.

As noted the investment tax saving of 7%(10,000) = $700 is in the year of acquisition, namely at time zero. Hence

Extra investment in new equipment =	$10,000
Less tax saving	700
Net outlay after tax saving	$ 9,300

Since the "investment" still is $10,000, the depreciation and the cash flow are the same as computed in Example 15.8. However the new time scale is:

$$
\begin{array}{ccc}
& \text{Cash flow} & \\
9{,}300 & 1{,}700/\text{yr} & L = 2{,}500 \\
\hline
0 & & 10
\end{array}
$$

$$AC = AW$$

$$(9{,}300 - 2{,}500)(A/P,\, i,\, 10) + 2{,}500i = 1{,}700$$

whence $i = 14.6\%$ compared to 12.9% without the tax credit.

The problem assumes that each of the assets, A costing $25,000, and B costing $15,000, in Example 15.8 is new equipment to deserve the tax credit. If B is currently owned by the taxpayer it is not an *investment* and does not qualify for the tax credit. If only A qualifies, the tax saving is 7%(25,000) = $1,750 instead of $700 and produces a still higher rate of return.

The rules for the tax credit are many and technical, for example:

1. Broadly, it applies only to depreciable manufacturing and related property.

2. It applies to purchases of new equipment and to limited purchases of used equipment.

3. The amount of tax credit allowed in a year is a function of that year's tax

liability with a maximum limit usually less than that amount but with carry back and carry over of unused credits.

4. If the useful life is less than 7 years, the amount of the *investment* allowed in the credit computation is reduced on a scale that becomes zero for a life less than 3 years. The rule includes a recapture of credits clause for premature disposal of the asset.

It is not our purpose to teach tax rules in this text. Such explanations would fill many volumes. The analyst must know the tax rules or be advised by a tax specialist the same as he must know or be advised on engineering, production, electrical rates, or transportation rates as they apply to computing time-scale disbursements or incomes.

15.20 TIMING OF INCOMES AND DISBURSEMENTS

At one time tax regulations permitted a corporation to pay 50% of the tax in the first half of the year after the income was earned after payment of the other 50% in the year it was earned. This difference in the time distribution of income and disbursements obviously had an appreciable effect on the rate of return in an economy study, and gave rise to a use of a center-of-year convention.

Current IRS regulations, however, require that corporations pay their estimated income tax in the year the income is earned. Whenever a situation arises, whether due to taxes or otherwise, which advances or retards significant sums in regard to the usual year-end convention the analyst must be aware of the potential consequences.

EXAMPLE 15.20 An investment of $10,000 produces savings of $2,000 a year for 8 years. Compare the rates of return if these are discrete year-end receipts versus discrete center-of-year receipts versus quarterly receipts.

SOLUTION. Year-end receipts:

$$10,000(A/P, i, 8) = 2,000, \text{ whence } i = 11.8\%$$

Center-of-year receipts:

$$10,000(A/P, i, 16) = 2,000(A/P, 2)(P/F, 1)$$

whence $i = 6.6\%$ per period and 13.7% effective interest per year.

Quarterly receipts:

$$10,000(A/P, i, 32) = 500$$

whence $i = 3.14\%$ per period, or 13.2% effective interest per year.

The center-year convention will closely approximate continuous cash flow with continuous interest.

The foregoing example demonstrates that on any occasion where we can foresee or predict the precise occurrence of a sum, especially if it is near the present, we should acknowledge this on the time scale rather than blindly assume a year-end convention. The present and almost universal practice of using year-end convention unquestionably saves labor and by treating all appropriations requests in the same manner, probably does not affect the overall accuracy too seriously. But the analyst should be aware of this situation and avoid selecting a convention which is contrary to the facts.

15.21 CARRY-BACK AND CARRY-OVER OF LOSSES

All previous computations of tax savings assumed that the total income tax in a given year would exceed the tax savings. This must be so in order to have tax savings, because savings exist only as a reduction on the gross tax payment. But now let us suppose expenses exceed income and the company has a deficit for the year. If there are no tax savings, how do we proceed with the computation of tax effects?

Tax regulations will permit the company to use the loss to offset profit in another year, or years, if necessary. The 1958 law permits the corporation to carry a loss back to the third preceding year. If the losses still exceed profits after application of all the profits in that year, the excess can be carried over to the second preceding year and then to the first preceding year and so on, if necessary, through the fifth *succeeding* year from the date of the loss. In summary, the loss may be carried back 3 years and carried forward 5 years if necessary. If this procedure is followed, it seems that there will always be tax payments against which these computed tax savings can be applied.

The equity of the carry-back, carry-over provision is that without it a corporation which has a constant profit each year will pay less taxes than a corporation which has the same total profit in an equal span of years composed of profitable years and loss years. The reason, of course, is that the first company will be able to apply all its tax savings against tax payments, whereas the second company will have nothing against which to apply its tax savings in the loss years. The 1958 tax law permits this company to carry its losses back and over and apply them against a profitable year providing that year occurs in the permissible span of the carry-back carry-over period.

15.22 INCOME TAX EFFECTS ON BORROWING

The volume of tax regulations is too great to illustrate every aspect of the tax effects on economy comparisons.[1] As a result simplifications have been favored and complexities avoided. For example, we have used only item depreciation because the tax regulations which cover group or multiple-asset depreciation are too extensive to be covered here. Nevertheless, where aspects of the tax laws create differences in alternatives the analyst must be aware of

---

[1]For details the analyst can refer to the IRS "Income Tax Regulations," available through the Superintendent of Documents; to the "Income Tax Bulletins" periodically issued by the IRS; and to publications of various private organizations such as "Code and Regulations of Federal Taxes," published by the Commerce Clearing House, Hillside, N.J.

the economic consequences. This is typical of the fact that he must be capable of an appreciation of all the differences between alternatives—tax differences as well as engineering differences. This is illustrated in the following example.

EXAMPLE 15.22 Machinery replacement projects totaling $50,000 can be financed from retained earnings or from borrowing. The after-tax "cost" of the retained equity is estimated to be 8%. The effective interest on the debt capital is 8% payable annually. Compare the alternative methods of financing if
  A : the loan can be repaid in a lump sum at the end of 10 years;
  B : the loan can be repaid in 10 equal year-end installments.
The tax rate is 50%.

SOLUTION A. Using stockholders' money the *company* will finance the projects by paying $50,000 at time zero for the replacement machinery. Using borrowed funds with lump-sum repayment, the lender will provide the payment at time zero but the company will pay $4,000 a year in interest plus $50,000 for the principal at the end of year ten.

The tax saving on the $4,000 annual interest payment is $2,000. The after-tax costs are as follows:

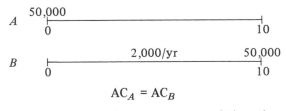

$$AC_A = AC_B$$

$$50,000(A/P, i, 10) = 2,000 + 50,000(A/F, 10)$$

whence $i = 4\%$ after tax (compared to 8% before tax).

SOLUTION B. The company's installment payments will consist of $5,000 for principal plus $4,000 for interest at the end of the first year. Thereafter the payments on principal will continue at $5,000 but the interest will be on the declining balance. The interest payments therefore will decrease by $400 a year. Each interest payment results in a 50% tax saving. As before, the company's alternative to borrowing is a present payment of $50,000 using its own funds.

The after-tax comparison of the alternatives is as follows:

$$A$$
50,000
0 ——————————————————————————————— 10

```
        2,000 1,800 1,600 1,400 1,200 1,000  800   600   400   200
          +     +     +     +     +     +     +     +     +     +
        5,000 5,000 5,000 5,000 5,000 5,000 5,000 5,000 5,000 5,000
B   ├─────┼─────┼─────┼─────┼─────┼─────┼─────┼─────┼─────┼─────┤
    0     1     2     3     4     5     6     7     8     9    10
```

$$50,000(A/P, 10) = 7,000 - 200(A/G, 10)$$

Again, $i = 4\%$ after tax.

This proves that the cost of debt capital is only 4% after tax, not 8%, and it also seems to show that we can save 4% cost of debt capital by using equity. This would be true if equity capital were free, but, as it is not, we may only conclude in the given example that while the cost of debt is 4% the cost of equity if 8%; i.e., the debt capital is cheaper.

The example illustrates the differences created by tax effects: whereas both alternatives cost 8% before tax, the debt capital costs only 4% after tax. The difference arises from the fact that interest is a deductible expense from taxable income whereas payments to shareholders are not.

The example also illustrates the importance of irreducible considerations. The quantitative analysis suggests borrowing but, in spite of this, management may have many reasons to reject the suggestion of incurring such liability. Depending on irreducible considerations, debt capital may prove to be very expensive: the effects may be far-reaching even to the extent of causing a change in the cost of both debt and equity capital. On the other hand, the irreducibles may concur with the suggestion that the company should introduce some debt into its capital structure.

15.23 CHOOSING A METHOD OF DEPRECIATION

The tax effects of accelerated depreciation were already noted in Section 15.9. It is not surprising therefore that industry has established a trend toward the use of accelerated depreciation. This has been evidenced by the large majority of corporations using sum-of-the-year's digits or double-rate declining-balance compared to the straight-line method.[1]

The economic advantage is not the only merit of a rapid write-off. Among the irreducible advantages is the fact that the uncertainty of the future generally favors paying less tax now. A very important advantage from the standpoint of the national economy is that accelerated depreciation rates decrease the payback periods,[2] increase industry's readiness to finance new projects, and in turn stimulate the market for technological improvements.

The tax law revisions of 1954 lowered the barriers to rapid write-off by authorizing the use of sum-of-the-year's digits and the double-rate declining-balance method for assets acquired in that year or after, if the useful lives were 3 or more years. Straight-line depreciation continues as a requirement for certain equipment; in particular it is required on acquisitions of second-hand equipment. Of course, it is also used after the switchpoint with the DRDB method.

The simple mechanics of the double-rate declining-balance method make it easy and economical to use as an accounting procedure and, of course, its

---

[1] Some firms maintain two systems: one accelerated for computing tax, and another for reporting to stockholders.

[2] Because (1) the savings after taxes will be higher in the earlier years, and (2) payback period = extra investment ÷ savings after taxes.

application in group accounting is another of its merits. In spite of the extra work of applying SYD depreciation to item accounting, SYD accounting may, in certain cases, have overall economic advantages as an accounting procedure. However, there is no simple rule for the economic selection of DRDB against SYD depreciation. The choice of method for accounting purposes depends on three parameters: the allowable tax life, the minimum required rate of return, and the terminal or tax salvage value.

The expected results of varying one of these parameters can be anticipated. In the first place, the characteristics of the two methods are such that the DRDB method always has the higher depreciation in the first year—$P\left(\dfrac{2}{N}\right)$ versus $P\left(\dfrac{2}{N+1}\right)$—and therefore the higher tax saving in the first year. A test of this distribution shows that the higher cutoff rates will be favorable to the use of the DRDB procedure.

Secondly, we note that DRDB factor is applied to full cost but that SYD is applied to full cost minus tax salvage, causing the SYD method to have even less depreciation in the first year. This change in the time distribution makes a high tax salvage unfavorable to SYD.

Thirdly, the shorter tax life favors DRDB because this increases the DRDB depreciation rate relative to SYD. For example, in the first year, $P\dfrac{2}{N}$ is greater in proportion to $P\dfrac{2}{N+1}$ if N is smaller.

The economic advantage of DRDB with a short tax life and high salvage is illustrated in the following example.

EXAMPLE 15.23a A truck costing \$7,000 will be kept for 4 years with a predicted salvage at that time of \$1,400. Operating disbursements are expected to be \$4,500 a year. The tax rate is 55%. Is it advantageous to use SYD or DRDB depreciation if the minimum required rate of return is 10%?

SOLUTION.

```
7,000            D = 4,500/yr        L = 1,400    Tax life: 4 years
├─────────────────────────────────────┤           Tax salvage: $1,400
0                                      4           Tax rate: 0.55
```

The first question is to locate the switchpoint or, in fact, to find whether any exists in view of the high tax salvage. The test can be made in two ways: the first is to note that if the book value is less than the salvage no switchpoint advantage exists. The second is to solve for the maximum salvage ratio with various assumed switch years using Eq. 15.12a. In this case we suspect that the salvage is high enough to recommend no switch so we can use the first method.

$$\text{BKV}_4 = (7,000)\left(1 - \frac{2}{4}\right)^4 = \$437.50$$

Therefore the company should pay a tax on the gain on disposal rather than use a switchpoint.

The tax on the gain is $(1,400 - 437.50)(0.55) = \$529.38$.

With DRDB the depreciation expense at the end of the first year is $P(2/N) = (7,000)(2/4) = \$3,500$, and the tax saving due to depreciation alone will be $3,500(0.55) = \$1,925$. This will decrease annually in a geometric series in which the ratio is 0.5.

The PW of the tax saving is

$$\overset{2.3360}{} \qquad \overset{0.68301}{}$$
$$[1,925(F/g, .10, 4) - 529](P/F, 4) = 2,710$$

in which

$$(F/g, .10, 4) = \left[\frac{(0.5)^4 - (F/P, 4)}{0.5 - (F/P, 1)}\right] = 2.3360$$

With SYD the first year's depreciation will be $\frac{4}{10}(7,000 - 1,400) = \$2,240$. As this will decrease by \$560 a year, the present worth of the tax saving is

$$\overset{1.38}{} \qquad \overset{3.16987}{}$$
$$[2,240(0.55) - 560(0.55)(A/G, .10, 4)](P/A, 4) = 2,558$$

So the DRDB method results in greater tax savings in this case.

At longer lives, lower tax salvages, and low minimum required rates of return, the SYD method is more economical, as the following example will illustrate.

EXAMPLE 15.23b A machine costing \$20,000 is expected to have a salvage of \$1,000 in 9 years. The economic and tax lives are equal. The minimum required rate of return is 20%. Which method of depreciation is more economical?

SOLUTION.

```
20,000                              L = 1,000
|-----------------------------------|
0                                   9
```

Tax life: 9 years
Tax salvage: \$1,000
Depreciation: SYD or DRDB
Tax rate: 0.50

With SYD: the first year's depreciation is $\left(\frac{9}{45}\right)(19,000) = \$3,800$, and the subsequent year's depreciation will decrease by $\left(\frac{1}{45}\right)(19,000) = \$422.22$. The tax savings will be half of these.

$$\text{PW of tax saving} = [1,900 - 211.11(A/G, i, 9)](P/A, 9)$$

With DRDB: the first year's depreciation is $(20,000)\left(\frac{2}{9}\right) = \$4,444.44$, and the subsequent year's depreciation will be in the ratio $a = \left(1 - \frac{2}{9}\right) = \frac{7}{9}$.

A switchpoint will probably be advantageous, so we will test for the year using Eq. 15.12a and guessing that it will occur in year 7, one year later than if $S = 0$. So

$$\frac{S}{P} = \left(1 - \frac{2}{9}\right)^6 \left[\frac{(2)(7)}{9} - \frac{2}{9} - 1\right] = \left(\frac{7}{9}\right)^6 \frac{1}{3} = 7.38\%$$

Therefore a seventh-year switchpoint is satisfactory if S is not over 7.38%. And just to make sure, a test for $t = 6$ shows that S cannot be greater than 3.15%. Therefore the switch to straight-line is in year 7. The book value at the end of year 6 will be $\left(1 - \frac{2}{9}\right)^6 20,000 = \$4,427.54$, and the SL depreciation will be $(4,427.54 - 1,000)/3 = \$1,142.51$. The tax savings will be half of the depreciation expenses.

$$\text{PW of tax saving} = \left\{ \left[\frac{a^6 - (F/P, 6)}{a - (F/P, 1)}\right] (2,222.22) + 571.26(P/A, 3) \right\} (P/F, 6)$$

Present Worth of Tax Savings

R of R	SYD	DRDB
10%	\$6,842.08	\$6,836.61
12	6,459.60	6,460.07
14	6,112.63	6,120.39

At 12% the methods are about equivalent, at lower minimum required rates of return the advantage is with SYD depreciation, and above it with DRDB.

The reader will also note that in these situations we also have dual rates of return, one at about 12% as shown and another at zero (because for either method the tax savings must be equal at zero interest). If we subtract the time distributed tax savings caused by SYD depreciation from those caused by DRDB depreciation we note a pattern in which savings precede costs followed by savings, a pattern that predicts the possibility of dual rates of return.

Be that as it may, we should be aware that this discussion primarily concerns the accounting decision relative to selecting the most economic method of depreciation. However, once the policy is established, the analyst, if he wishes to be precise, must use the same depreciation method as the accountant to compute the tax.

In an economy analysis the equivalent for SYD depreciation is easy to compute but, obviously, this is not so of the DRDB method.[1] When the salvage is not zero or when the economic life is less than the tax life, the analyst must lay out the detailed depreciation pattern over the economic life period, on the time scale if necessary. At the very worst this can be no more difficult than the procedure often used in the *discounted cash flow method* of bringing back each item with the single-payment present-worth factor. At best the procedure illustrated in Example 15.23b can be used to save time. But even at best it is a lot of work.

---

[1]In the special case where $S = 0$ and the economic life equals the tax life, tables are available which make DRDB as easy to use as SYD. See Harold Bierman, Jr., and Seymour Smidt, *The Capital Budgeting Decision* 3rd ed. (New York: Macmillan, 1971), p. 232.

For those who do not intend to go to all this trouble, we may observe that the SYD method generally gives final results which are reasonably acceptable, even though the DRDB method will be actually used in the accounting system. The MAPI system does just this and, based on a test of their system, Terborgh states that "the differentials are insignificant."[1]

However, where the analyst is suspicious of the results, as he might be when the parameters favoring one method or the other are extreme, the long way out is the safer one. Example 15.23a is an illustration of the differences that can result.

15.24 EFFECT OF LONG WRITE-OFF PERIOD

A reduction in the tax life achieves the effects of accelerated depreciation. Therefore it is to be expected that the tax regulations prohibit using a tax life shorter than the provable useful life. (However, the regulations do permit a short write-off for equipment used in connection with the national defense.) The objective of the accountant, therefore, would be to favor the use of the shortest life permitted by the tax laws. This is illustrated in the following example.

EXAMPLE 15.24 A special machine A costing $25,000 is proposed for primary service lasting 5 years, at which date the net realizable value will be zero. Operating costs will be $4,000 a year. Another special machine, B, can be purchased for $15,000 and will also have zero salvage at the end of the 5-year service period. Its operating costs will be $7,950. Both machines will likely be retained after the fifth year for use on degraded service; if so the total useful life will be 20 years. The company is permitted to write off the machine in 5 years for tax purposes because the service is related to national defense or if it elects can write off the machine in 20 years. Compare the results of using the long or short write-off periods if the tax rate is 55% and sum-of-the-year's digits depreciation is used.

SOLUTION.

Before tax:

A 25,000 $D = 4,000$ $L = 0$ Tax life: 5 years or 20 years
       0   5   Tax salvage: zero

B 15,000 $D = 7,950$ $L = 0$ Tax rate: 0.55
       0   5   Depreciation: SYD

If the 20-year tax life is used, the depreciation the first year will be $\left(\dfrac{20}{210}\right)(10,000) = \$952$ which will decrease by $\left(\dfrac{1}{210}\right)(10,000) = \$48$ a year. The book value at the end of the economic life, year 5, will therefore be

---

[1] George Terborgh, *Business Investment Policy* (Washington, D.C.: Machinery and Allied Products Institute, 1958), p. 242.

$\dfrac{(15)(16)}{(20)(21)}$ (10,000) = \$5,714 and will result in a tax saving from the loss on disposal as computed in the right-hand column below.

Cash flow	\$3,950	BKV	\$5,714
Depreciation first year	952	Salvage	0
Taxable income	\$2,998	Loss	\$5,714
Tax at 0.55	1,649	Tax saving	3,143
Cash flow after tax	\$2,301	Net salvage	\$3,143

The decrease in depreciation will result in an increase in taxable income of \$48 and therefore an increase in tax of $(48)(0.55) = \$26$ a year.

After tax,   10,000   Savings = $2{,}301 - (t - 1)(26)$ $L = 3{,}143$
20-year tax life   0   5

The rate of return after tax will be

$$\left|(10{,}000 - 3{,}143)(A/P, 5) + 3{,}143i + 26(A/G, 5) = 2{,}301\right.$$

At 11%, cost $<$ income by \$53/yr

At 12%, cost $>$ income by \$24/yr

whence

$$i = 11.7\%$$

On the other hand, using a 5-year tax life, the first year's depreciation will be $\dfrac{(2)(5)}{(5)(6)}$ (10,000) = \$3,333 which will decrease by $\left(\dfrac{1}{15}\right)$ (10,000) = \$666 a year. The book value and salvage will both be zero at year 5. Then

Cash flow	\$3,950
Depreciation first year	3,333
Taxable income	\$ 617
Tax at 0.55	339
Cash flow after tax	\$3,611

The taxable income will increase \$666 a year, which will increase the tax $666(0.55) = \$367$ a year.

After tax,   10,000   Savings = $3{,}611 - (t - 1)(367)$ $L = 0$
5-year tax life   0   5

The rate of return will be

$$10{,}000(A/P, 5) + 367(A/G, 5) = 3{,}611$$

whence

$$i = 15.0\%$$

Therefore, if permitted to elect the short tax write-off period, the taxpayer can earn 15% instead of 11.7%. Note that this is not because of any differences in the amount of taxes paid; the total of the taxes is the same under both plans but the timing is different.

15.25 ANALYSES DISREGARDING TAX DISBURSEMENT

What degree of error is introduced by multiplying the rate of return before tax by the factor (1 - tax rate) to get the approximate rate of return after tax? First, we should note that this method is an approximation; only the inclusion of the actual disbursements can give an exact result. But the question is, how approximate is the method?

Table 15.25a shows the results of using this method in examples from this chapter. Column 4, "Approximate Rate of Return After Tax," was obtained by multiplying the "Rate of Return Before Tax" in column 3 by the factor (1 - tax rate). The "Exact Rate of Return After Taxes" in column 5 was computed earlier in the specified example. The percentage errors of the approximate method listed in the final column can be positive as well as negative. This table indicates the possibility of considerable error in using the approximate method. On the other hand, the errors may be insignificant.

The variations in Table 15.25a are largely attributable to the fact that the approximate method makes no allowance for the effects of accelerated depreciation, no allowances for the effect of book value on taxes (i.e., no allowances for gains or losses on disposal or for the amount still to be amortized on existing machines), and no allowance for the tax effects of expensing versus capitalizing costs.

Will the tax situations mentioned above reverse the decision to accept or reject a proposal? They can reverse the conclusion if the computed rate is near the minimum required rate of return. This is illustrated in Table 15.25b in which we have assumed a 30% rate of return before tax in the first example and 40% in the second example. The after-tax cutoff rates are derived by multiplying each by $(i - t)$.

While the after-tax "estimated rate of return" is multiplied by the same factor $(i - t)$, it errs by disregarding the actual taxes occurring in a given situa-

Table 15.25a COMPARISON OF EXACT AND APPROXIMATE METHODS

Example	Tax rate	Rate of return before tax (%)	Approximate rate of return after tax (%)	Exact rate of return after tax (%)	Percentage error (%)
15.10	0.52	28.1	13.5	14.8	- 8.8
15.11	0.52	28.3	13.6	15.0	- 9.3
15.15	0.50	37.3	18.7	24.4	-23.4

Table 15.25b REVERSALS IN DECISIONS DUE TO TAX EFFECTS

Example	Before tax			Estimated after-tax			Actual after-tax		
	Computed rate of return	Minimum required rate of return	Decision	Estimated rate of return	Minimum required rate of return	Decision	Computed rate of return	Minimum required rate of return	Decision
15.11	28.3%	30%	Reject	13.6%	14.4%	Reject	15.0%	14.4%	Accept
15.15	37.3%	40%	Reject	18.7%	20%	Reject	24.4%	20%	Accept

tion as well as their time distribution. The error is enough to cause reversals in each of the situations in the table below.

The conclusion is that the analyst must know the tax rules in order to know how they may affect his conclusion. Then he must decide if approximate solutions will be acceptable for justifying or rejecting the specific proposal.

PROBLEMS

15.1 A company has a program of student aid in which each award is worth $2,500. The company's tax rate is 50%. (a) If these are tax deductible, what is the cost to the company of each award? (b) If these are ruled nondeductible, in what way must the company "account" for them and what is the cost to the company? (c) If the student pays no taxes, under what circumstances does the government become a partner and to what extent? (d) Answer part (c) if the student must pay personal income taxes on all gifts and if his tax rate for that increment of income is 15%.

15.2 A company wishes to compare two special-purpose tools for use on a government defense contract. One tool has a first cost of $40,000 and operating disbursements of $15,000 a year.   The other tool costs $25,000 and, requiring more manual operations, has annual operating disbursements of $22,000. The economic life of the equipment for use on the intended job is 5 years, a period which, in this case, may also be used for tax depreciation.   The salvage value at the end of this period will be zero.   The company's income tax is 50% and the method of depreciation is straight-line.

Compute the rate of return after taxes by three alternative methods: (a) by computing the tax on the cash flow; (b) by computing the tax on the extra profit; (c) by computing the tax savings on the expenditures.

15.3 Assume in Problem 15.2 that the tax rules permit the $40,000 machine to be depreciated more rapidly than by straight-line and that the following depreciation expense in each of the 5 years will be allowed: $12,000; $12,000; $8,000; $4,000; $4,000.   Assume the $25,000 machine must still be depreciated by the straight-line method.   Rework Problem 15.2 based on these assumptions.

15.4 Show why the savings, namely, the difference between the annual operating disbursements of alternative proposals, will be the cash flowback into the firm in the event that the alternative with the extra investment is selected.   To get cash flowback, why is it not necessary to adjust the savings to allow for recovery of the extra investment?

15.5 A heat-treating process can be installed for $30,000. The operating disbursements will be $12,000 and the economic life is expected to be 8 years, with $10,000 salvage at that time. An alternative process can be installed for $21,000.   Its operating disbursements will be $15,000 and its economic life is also expected to be 8 years with $7,000 salvage. The tax life is required to be not less than 12 years.   Salvage at that date is expected to be zero.   The company's income tax rate is 50% and its method of depreciation is straight-line.   Compute the rate of return after taxes.

15.6 A certain machine which can be installed at an extra cost of $7,500 will bring annual savings of $5,000 and zero salvage at the end of a 5-year economic life. Assume that the company can use a rapid system of depreciation in which the annual depreciation expense from the first to the fifth year is $2,500, $2,000, $1,500, $1,000, $500; or the company can use a decelerated system in which the annual depreciation expense from the first to the fifth year is $500, $1,000, $1,500, $2,000, $2,500. The company's tax rate is 50%. For each system of depreciation, compute the stream of annual taxes, profits after taxes, and cash-flow after taxes.

Note that the tax stream using the accelerated write-off is low in the early years compared to that using a slow write-off. This time distribution obviously favors using a fast write-off. However, the *profit* after tax using rapid write-off is also low in the early years compared with the after-tax profit using the slow write-off. What, then, if any, is the advantage of a rapid write-off? (Hint: consider the cash flow after tax.)

15.7 A company proposes to install printing and marking equipment having a first cost of $48,000 and operating disbursements of $22,000 a year. The economic life is estimated to be 10 years with a salvage value of $5,400 at that date.

The company is considering alternative equipment for this job costing $38,000 with operating disbursements of $25,000 a year. The economic life is also estimated to be 10 years with a salvage of $4,275 at that date.

The method of depreciation for tax and profit computation is sum-of-the-year's digits, and the company is permitted to use the same tax lives as the economic lives listed above as well as the same salvage values. The company's tax rate is 50%.

Using the method in which you compute the tax savings, find the rate of return on the extra investment.

15.8 What is the rate of return in the previous problem if the allowable tax life is 15 years with 10% salvage value at that date? The other data will remain the same, including the 10-year economic lives and salvage values at 10 years. In this solution use the method of computing the cash flow after taxes.

15.9 A company is considering alternative methods of contour shaping. The first method costs $63,000 and is expected to have an 8-year life with $21,600 salvage at that date. Its operating disbursements are expected to be $31,500 a year. The other method the company is considering costs $48,000 with an expected economic life of 8 years and $16,500 salvage. Its annual operating disbursements are expected to be $35,000. The required tax life is 16 years with 5% salvage at that date. The tax rate is 50% and the company uses the double-rate declining-balance method of depreciation. Make an annual-cost analysis if the minimum required rate of return is 15%.

15.10 Supposing in Problem 15.9 that the economic life and the tax life are equal to 16 years, what are the switchpoints, if any, for each of the following salvage values expressed as a percentage of the first cost P: 0, 2, 5, 7, 9, 12?

15.11 Find the uniform equivalent of a geometric series of five end-of-year terms. The first term is $400 and (a) each subsequent term is 60% of the preceding term; (b) each subsequent term is twice the preceding term. Use 10% interest.

15.12 Solve Problem 15.9 if the economic life is 16 years, the same as the tax life, and the salvage value at that date is 5%.

15.13 In order to show the advantage of using a switchpoint, compare the solution obtained in Problem 15.12, which used a switchpoint, to one in which the double-rate declining-balance is used without a switch. As before, use the annual-cost method with a minimum required rate of return of 15%.

15.14 A new machine can be installed for $25,000. The analyst predicts a 10-year life and is convinced that the salvage value at that date will be $5,000, regardless of the depreciation method used in accounting. Its operating disbursements are $7,000 a year.

The present machine on this job has a net realizable value of $1,500 but cannot be continued without overhauling and rebuilding at a cost of $4,000. It is estimated that this will extend the life 3 years, at which time extensive repairs required on other parts of the machine are expected to prohibit its further use. Salvage at that time will be zero. Its operating disbursements are $12,000 a year.

The proposed machine will have a tax life of 15 years with 5% salvage at that date. Depreciation will follow the sum-of-the-year's digits method. The present machine currently has a $3,000 book value. If rebuilt, it will have a 3-year tax life with zero salvage at that date. Depreciation will be by the straight-line method.

If the tax rate is 50% and the minimum required rate of return is 20%, make an annual-cost analysis.

15.15 Solve Problem 15.14 if the analyst is certain that the salvage value of the new machine at year 10 will be its net junk value, $1,250.

15.16 How much will the annual cost of the new machine change if the analyst in Problem 15.14 had decided to accept the SYD book value at year 10 as a reasonable prediction of the salvage value at that date (instead of his conviction in Problem 15.14 that it would be $5,000)?

15.17 Use the data in Problem 15.14 except assume that the $4,000 cost of overhauling the present machine is regarded as a normal maintenance and repair cost and may be immediately expensed for tax purposes. What is the advantage, on an annual-cost basis, of expensing the $4,000 compared to depreciating it over 3 years as was done in Problem 15.14?

15.18 An investment of $10,000 in a new tool is expected to result in after-tax savings of $2,800 a year for 8 years with zero salvage at that date. (a) Compute and compare the results of using a center-of-year convention for the occurrence of the savings instead of the year-end convention. Use the rate-of-return method of comparison. (b) Compare the results in part (a) with a 6-month convention in which half of the annual savings are assumed to occur twice a year, that is, at the end of every 6 months beginning 6 months from time zero. (c) Comment on which you think should be used.

15.19 Over a 5-year period two companies have the same total net earnings of $50,000 prior to depreciation and prior to income taxes. In the case of Company A these earnings are distributed uniformly over the 5-year period, that is, $10,000 at the end of each year. However, Company B's earnings occur only in the first 2 years, that is, $25,000 at the end of years 1 and 2 with no income in the last 3 years.

The depreciation expense for both companies is $4,000 a year. Each company has the same tax rate of 40%.

Demonstrate the need for carry-back and carry-forward provisions in the tax law by showing that the taxes paid by these two companies, if such provisions do not exist, are unequal although the earnings of both companies are equal.

15.20 Use the data in Example 15.23a (in Section 15.23 in the text) except assume the salvage value at the end of the 4-year economic life (and tax life) is zero instead of $1,400. What, now, is the advantage of the double-rate declining-balance method of depreciation compared to the sum-of-the-year's digits method? Does a high salvage value favor the DRDB or the SYD method?

15.21 Use the data in Example 15.23a (in Section 15.23 of the text) except adopt a 6-year life (economic and tax life) with $350 salvage value at that date. (a) What, now, is the advantage of the double-rate declining-balance method compared to the sum-of-the-year's digits method? Does a long life favor the DRDB or the SYD method? (b) Suppose the cutoff rate is 30% instead of 10%, what is the advantage of the double-rate declining-balance method compared to the sum-of-the-year's digits method? Does a high cutoff rate favor the DRDB or the SYD method?

15.22 Solve Problem 15.7 using double-rate declining-balance depreciation instead of sum-of-the-year's digits. In this case, what is the percentage error if SYD is substituted for DRDB depreciation merely to save labor in making an analysis?

15.23 Solve Problem 15.8 using double-rate declining-balance depreciation instead of sum-of-the-year's digits. What would be the percentage error if SYD is substituted for DRDB depreciation merely to save labor in an analysis?

15.24 Solve Problem 15.9 if SYD depreciation is used instead of DRDB depreciation. What is the error introduced by assuming that SYD depreciation will give the same answer as DRDB?

15.25 Solve Problem 15.12 if SYD depreciation is used instead of DRDB. What percentage error will be introduced by assuming that SYD depreciation will give the same answer as DRDB in order to make the work of the analyst easier?

15.26 Regardless of using a long or short write-off, we expect the same total tax payments. As a matter of proof, show that the tax paid in Example 15.24 (in Section 15.24 in the text) is the same for the short as for the long write-off.

15.27 In Problem 15.2, compute the after-tax rate of return by the approximate method, i.e., adjustment of the rate of return before taxes by the factor (1 − tax rate) and compute the percentage error.

15.28 Prove that the cash flow after tax is equal to the following: the cash flow before tax, minus the tax on this cash flow, *plus* the tax savings on the depreciation expense.

15.29 A company trades in an executive car for a new one which lists at $6,000. The dealer's allowance on the old car is $2,400. On the company's books its BKV is $1,000. The tax rate is 50% and the tax life of the new car is 3 years. Find the tax advantage using the trade-in rule described in Section 15.17 compared with not using the rule. Assume SLD.

15.30 Compute the rate of return if a 7% tax credit is allowed on the new machine in Example 15.15 in Section 15.15.

16

Forecasting

16.1 INCLUSION OF ALL RELEVANT ITEMS

The objective of the forecast is to predict the performance of the machine on the intended job. Knowledge of the intended job sets the boundaries for making the prediction. The prediction covers only the costs on the job for which the machine is being considered, not the costs on subsequent degraded services and, in such cases, therefore, not the costs over the entire service life.

Predicting this performance requires forecasts of

1. First cost installed and ready to run (or net realizable value).
2. Insurance and property tax (investment costs).
3. The life period of the machine until displaced from the proposed job.
4. The salvage value at the date of displacement.
5. The degree and the pattern of utilization; that is, the percent of capacity at which the machine will operate on the intended job with allowances for possible future changes in utilization.
6. Routine maintenance and repair costs.
7. Major repair items or periodic overhauls.
8. Direct operating costs, including, operating labor, fuel or power, scrap material and rework.
9. Indirect costs (when relevant to the choice): indirect labor, tooling, supplies, floor space, inventory.
10. Fringe benefits.
11. Hazards and losses relative to equipment, material, and labor time.
12. Changes in sales volume or price resulting from the choice.
13. Changes in unit cost of labor, power, supplies, etc., resulting in changes in operating costs.

The prediction of data must be preceded by a reasonably clear knowledge of the specific job for which the machine is intended. Once this job has been defined the task of the estimator becomes much clearer but, nevertheless, the service of a good cost estimator is necessary. It is surprising what a competent job can be done by an experienced cost engineer in producing the relevant cost estimates.

The job is somewhat simplified, we will remember, by the fact that only cost differences are relevant and are the only costs that need be computed. But the scope of the operation must be sufficiently envisioned by an experienced cost estimator so that none of these relevant costs will be overlooked.

16.2 EXPECTING NONUNIFORM COSTS

An experienced estimator will look for the unusual costs. For example, he will not treat the lifetime cost pattern as a steady state condition but will expect, among other variables, an initial transient condition. He will anticipate that the predicted savings in a cost-reduction proposition or the net income in an income-expansion proposition may not be attained in the first year or possibly even in the first few years.

This is illustrated by the company that engaged in a major cost-reduction activity by the installation of semiautomated processes throughout most of its plant. These processes were paced by a new conveyor system. In the first year the operating costs were higher than they had been under the old system due to the fact that normal production routines were interrupted by the installation and switchover, production labor had in many cases been used to install, transfer, and adjust new equipment, and the labor force during part of that period did not learn to operate the new equipment as productively as the old.

The full savings will not begin at the date when the machine first turns over. A period must certainly be allowed for testing and adjusting the machine and establishing and standardizing a method. In addition, the expected savings should not be counted until the required learning time, using the standard method, has occurred.

Some of these "initial costs" are more accurately located at time zero and others are adjusted operating costs located at the end of the period. Where the costs of installation extend over several years, as they may with large income-expansion projects, they will be viewed as "costs before zero," and the total investment at year zero will be the compound amount of these costs.

Other events that destroy cost uniformity are those that may occur infrequently as the equipment ages; for example, replacements of clutches, bearings, pumps, electron tubes, and so on occur at less certain intervals than costs like labor and power. These unusual costs will be anticipated by the experienced estimator.

Other nonuniform occurrences are the result of hazards such as fire, explosion, wind, and so on, but more often these items are covered by the insurance cost included in the estimate, provided, of course, that the insurance covers the full cost of the loss.

The risks of shutdown will also be carefully scrutinized by the cost estimator, but if the hazard—such as a breakdown in equipment—will result in the same expense for either alternative, it may be ignored as irrelevant to the choice. Cost differences may in some cases result from differences in frequency of the occurrence (based on the difference in design, age, etc.) although the cost of damage for each occurrence may be the same. The cost of a hazard should also be all-inclusive; for example, the dislocation costs of a fire, not just the insurance costs, should be included.

Prediction of events in the distant future, such as the life period, the salvage, a sudden increase in deterioration, increased obsolescence due to the appearance of new machines, obsolescence due to a change in demand for the product will be considered later. The present point is to focus the estimator's attention on the uniform costs, the unusual costs, versus the steady-state costs throughout the life of the equipment.

16.3 AIDS TO FORECASTING

The first step in predicting costs, familiarity with the equipment, invariably calls for an engineering background. This requires a sufficient understanding of the equipment and its operation and of the input requirements in men, material, and time for the required service.

The second step is a familiarity with unit costs in order to convert the input of men, material, and time into dollars.

Maintenance of and access to records is, of course, a third important step. Cost records of the past will give clues to such costs as maintenance, repair, overhauls, spoilage, deterioration gradients, and so on. Much forecasting of future data can proceed from a knowledge of past data. This requires setting up costing points in the accounting system to collect the required data. Unfortunately, few firms are scientifically collecting this data but with the advent of automatic data-processing the collection of such data will eventually become feasible. In fact, management will, in time, learn to apply automatic data-processing equipment to uses not conceived at present. One of these uses is bound to be the collection of data needed in the economic evaluation of equipment.

Research, of course, will remain a major step in the forecasting of data. We must recall how Frederick W. Taylor experimented with alternative methods and scientifically collected data to permit him to select the best alternative. It is not very likely that an estimator will fall heir to much research data or even to a research organization, and the chances are that he will have to organize and direct a research program of his own.

Data from the equipment manufacturer may also be a primary source. A reputable manufacturer will give reliable data on inputs and outputs and in most cases back up its estimates with guarantees. In many cases the sales organization will be glad to initiate some research on a customer's specific problem.

As stated earlier, one of the first steps in forecasting is a familiarity with the equipment in an engineering sense. This, of course, extends to a familiarity with production processes so that costs will be conceived from a realistic environment and will be based on what might happen in actual practice.

Predictions should also be based on a familiarity of installation and construction practices so that allowances will be made for delays, extra costs, incidental costs, expenses for adjustment, and so on.

Familiarity with design development and the state of the art is also necessary to assist in predicting the date when a process might be displaced.

Familiarity with the strengths and weaknesses of the machine's design helps in the prediction of major overhauls and replacement of components. This should be coupled with a knowledge of maintenance and repair practices.

And, of course, a knowledge of management's outlook is necessary. It will not be satisfactory to predict an 8-year life based on the expected appearance at that date of a superior machine when management believes that a major change in the product in 4 years will probably eliminate the need for that machine.

An experienced estimator will be familiar with most of these areas. Obviously, it is not something that can be taught in a single course. In fact, no estimator, regardless of his experience, should attempt to make all the forecasts by himself. The more experience he has the more he will consult the specialists in his firm in the fields of: production, installation, design, maintenance and repair, top management. Whenever he can he will get their estimates of standard costs, unusual costs, time periods, hazards, and so on.

Very often the responsibility for setting up an investment procedure and for judging capital expenditures has originated in the finance department of the company. It is not unusual, therefore, to find the financially trained individual dispirited by the absence of data. The subject of this text is obviously a *bridge* between the financial function and the engineering and manufacturing functions. It is expected that the financial executives would be at a loss for data without the participation of these other departments. The financial executives will be surprised to find what a good job of predicting data an experienced engineering estimator can do.

Another thing must be kept in mind: this subject is the *common ground* of the finance department, the operating departments, and the engineering staff departments. It provides them, for the first time, with a common goal and a common language. However, the executives on both sides must be mutually educated to understand the subject and to learn what cost data, time data, and so on are needed and are relevant to the analyses. The finance executives who set up the financial procedures cannot expect the operating executives or the staff engineers to supply adequate data until they, too, understand the procedures by which the equipment investments will be tested.

Participation of all the executives whose functions enable them to contribute an insight into the future performance of the machine or process being analyzed will develop more accurate forecasts. To secure useful and valuable participation from these executives they must receive competent education in the principals of investment analysis. Without education the ability to forecast can be grossly misdirected.

Another aid to forecasting is the post-audit, because it provides the estimator with an opportunity to compare his predictions with actual occurrences. Over a period of time this should make for wiser estimates.

16.4 FORECASTING LIFE PERIODS

The purpose of classifying equipment as in Chapter 10 is to improve life predictions by identifying the factors that establish the life of a piece of equipment. Where physical life is the determinant, as in one-horse shay equipment or where annual deterioration establishes the life, statistical data from past equipment can become the basis of future predictions. In the absence of such data, reliance must be placed on the judgment of the people who may know: the engineers and designers, maintenance and plant people, and those who have operated such equipment.

Where obsolescence is the factor as in the military aircraft type or in MAPI's annual obsolescence approach, judgment is the sole aid in prediction. The best judges of economic life will be the persons familiar with the history of the design and development of such equipment and particularly with the trend of its design and development. Who are the executives in the firm who can provide the most capable answers to, "How rapidly are these machines being improved?" or, "At this rate, how long before this trend in improvement will provide a machine sufficiently better than the proposed machine to displace it?" The best guess-work involves the participation of those who should know.

If new machines have not appeared in some time it is prima facie evidence that development in that field is currently stagnant. However, infrequent appearances of new machines does not preclude the possibility that a vastly improved machine may be just around the corner. The analyst should consider this possibility too.

Another point in the prediction of life is that the need for the service may be altered by factors that have nothing to do with its physical life, deterioration, or with the development of improved machines. Top management must, therefore, have the opportunity and responsibility of predicting whether the need for that service will continue. A service might be terminated by a change in company policy, buying habits, inevitable legislation, competitive pressures, and so on.

Top management should not interfere with the judgment of the executives who are in a position to make these predictions of life periods. This interference often takes the form of an arbitrary decree that the life period of all equipment without regard to type or function may not exceed a figure established by the decree, for example, 3 years. This, of course, is the exact approach adopted in the payout method. This procedure not only substitutes an incorrect life period for a correct one—usually on the mistaken assumption that the procedure is setting up a factor of safety—but it also tends to destroy the whole process of prediction by taking the authority from those who might be qualified to predict. This destroys confidence, removes opportunities to learn how to predict, and lowers—not raises—the competence of those who initiate these propositions. All suggestions involve predictions, and the fact to face is that executives must therefore be called on to make them and must be educated to make them.

At some point, therefore, someone must say, "We believe the proposed equipment will continue on the intended job for 8 years." This definite statement can be wrong, but it must be made by someone and it must be made as intelligently as possible based on an understanding of all the factors that determine it. A fault as big as any in this subject is the failure of executives to face up to the fact that predictions must be made. Many executives fail to appreciate that predictions of this type are not greatly different from the predictions implied in their daily decisions, all of which concern future action.

A fortunate aspect of making predictions in the distant future is that they can be wrong often without serious consequence because of the time value of money. This will be examined in the next section.

16.5 RESULT OF INCORRECTLY PREDICTING THE LIFE PERIOD

As a result of the time value of money, errors in predictions in the distant future are not as serious as those in the present. This means that the accuracy of the computation will not be greatly altered as a result of inaccurate predictions in the dim future where predictions are made with difficulty. This is illustrated for a prediction of physical life in the following example.

EXAMPLE 16.5a A lining for a container used in a chemical process costs $20,000 and will have zero salvage whenever it is replaced. Replacement will be necessitated at the end of its physical life, which the analyst predicts to be 15 years. A less expensive lining can be installed for $10,000, but it will cost $2,000 a year to maintain although its physical life is also expected to be 15 years. Salvage in both cases is expected to be zero. Compare errors in the prediction of physical life with the resulting errors in the computed rate of return before taxes.

SOLUTION. The computed data is listed in Table 16.5a. The rate of return for the 15-year life is 18.4% (from the solution for i in $10,000(A/P, 15) = 2,000$). If the forecaster had incorrectly predicted a 21-year life, he would have computed a rate of return of 19.5%. This 40% error in the life prediction would have resulted in only a 6% error in the computed rate of return.

It can be seen in Table 16.5a and in Fig. 16.5 that the more distant the error the less effect it has. For example, a 40% error in the prediction of the life at year 21 produces a smaller error than an equal error at year 9. For a similar reason, had the life been longer, say 25 years, the errors resulting from incorrect predictions of the life period would be even less.

Table 16.5a RESULTS OF ERRORS IN PREDICTING THE LIFE PERIOD FOR
EQUIPMENT WITH NO SALVAGE VALUE

Years life	Error in life prediction (%)	Rate of return (%)	Error in rate of return (%)
9	−40.0	13.7	−25.5
10	−33.3	15.1	−17.9
11	−26.7	16.1	−12.5
12	−20.0	16.9	− 8.2
13	−13.3	17.6	− 4.3
14	− 6.7	18.0	− 2.2
15	0	18.4	0
16	+ 6.7	18.7	+ 1.6
17	+13.3	19.0	+ 3.3
18	+20.0	19.1	+ 3.8
19	+26.7	19.3	+ 4.9
20	+33.3	19.4	+ 5.4
21	+40.0	19.5	+ 6.0

EXAMPLE 16.5b Machine A costs $30,000 installed with an operating cost
of $6,000 a year; machine B costs $20,000 with an operating cost of $8,000 a
year.   The useful life of each machine is expected to be 20 years with zero
salvage at that date but the economic life on the intended service is expected to
be 8 years.   The net realizable value of either machine is expected to vary in
accordance with the sum-of-the-year's digits.   Assuming the economic life is

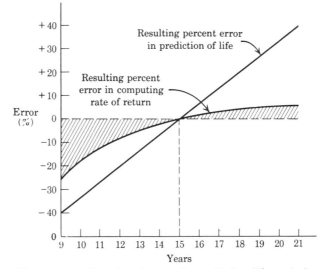

Figure 16.5   Results of errors in predicting life periods

really 8 years, compare the percent errors in predicting other life periods with the resulting errors in the rate of return before taxes.

SOLUTION. The salvage values in Table 16.5b are computed by the sum-of-the-year's digits method because, as stated in the problem, the analyst feels that this pattern closely approximates actual salvages. At the end of year 8, the salvage, based on a 20-year useful life and zero terminal salvage, would be

$$L = \frac{(N - t)(N - t + 1)P}{N(N + 1)} = \frac{12 \times 13}{20 \times 21}(10{,}000) = \$3{,}714$$

The rate of return would be computed as follows:

$$(10{,}000 - 3{,}714)(A/P, i, 8) + 3{,}714i = 2{,}000$$

which, by trial and error, gives 15.5%.

Table 16.5b RESULTS OF ERRORS IN PREDICTING ECONOMIC LIFE FOR EQUIPMENT WITH SALVAGE VALUES

Years life	Error in predicting life (%)	Salvage value	Computed rate of return (%)	Error in rate of return (%)
4	-50	$6,476	12.7	-18.1
5	-38	5,714	13.4	-13.6
6	-25	5,000	14.2	- 8.4
7	-13	4,333	14.9	- 3.9
8	0	3,714	15.5	0
9	+13	3,143	16.1	+ 3.9
10	+25	2,619	16.6	+ 7.1
11	+38	2,143	17.1	+10.3
12	+50	1,714	17.6	+13.6

Table 16.5b shows that an incorrect prediction of a 4-year life instead of the 8-year life, an incorrect prediction in the life period of 50%, results in an error in the rate of return of only 18.1%. And the longer the life, the less this error will be. Judging the life period is uncertain business at best, but because the event is usually well into the future, the consequences are softened by the time value of money. On the other hand, the prediction of a short life should stem from the availability of more reliable information.

Unfortunately, the pressure on a forecaster encourages him to predict a short life rather than a long life. He knows that predicting a short life distributes the investment costs over only a short period. This opposes the installation of the proposed equipment, and if it is never installed it is not around to embarrass him. On the other hand, a prediction of a long life promotes the installation of the unit, and if the life is grossly in error so that the unit is replaced long before the predicted date it can be embarrassing.

16.6 FORECASTING SALVAGE VALUE

In some cases a clue to salvage value can be obtained from dealers. For example, a real estate dealer may give opinions on future land and factory values or a second-hand machinery dealer may help predict the net realizable value of a marketable item at a future age. If life is not expected to be long, the analyst can look to this source of information with reasonable accuracy.

On longer lives the information may not be available or, if it is, it may be far less reliable. Due to the time value of money, small error results from mistakes in distant salvage values, as Example 16.6 shows. In cases where statistical sources of information may not be available to the forecaster he may have to resort to patterns of depreciation which he thinks might reasonably fit the actual decline in salvage value. Here again, assumptions which only approximate the truth will not produce too serious errors.

The forecaster's fear of distant predictions should be considerably relieved by the knowledge that errors at that point in time are not very serious. The possibility of an error in the present or in the near future should be more frightening to the analyst, because the effects on his conclusion are greater; on the other hand, these predictions can be made more accurately.

EXAMPLE 16.6 Examine the result of incorrectly predicting the salvage value at the end of the 8-year economic life period in Example 16.5b. In that example the analyst had predicted that it would be $3,714. Suppose now that the analyst had erred in his prediction by various amounts up to 50%. Compare these errors with the resulting error in the rate of return after taxes. It will be remembered that the extra investment in Example 16.5 was $10,000 and the savings $2,000 a year.

SOLUTION. Table 16.6 examines the consequence of errors in predicting the salvage value. For the given conditions it will be noted that a 50% error in

Table 16.6   RESULTS OF ERRORS IN PREDICTING SALVAGE VALUE

Salvage value	Error in salvage (%)	P − L	Computed rate of return (%)	Error in rate of return (%)
$1,857	−50	$8,143	13.8	−11.0
2,228	−40	7,772	14.2	− 8.4
2,600	−30	7,400	14.3	− 7.7
2,971	−20	7,029	14.9	− 3.9
3,348	−10	6,652	15.2	− 1.9
3,714	0	6,286	15.5	0
4,085	+10	5,905	15.9	+ 2.6
4,457	+20	5,543	16.1	+ 3.9
4,828	+30	5,172	16.4	+ 5.8
5,200	+40	4,800	16.7	+ 7.7
5,571	+50	4,429	17.0	+ 9.7

salvage value produces a maximum error in the rate of return of 11%. (Although not shown in the table, even a 100% error in prediction, such as a prediction of zero salvage, will give a rate of return of 11.8%, an error of just 23.9% in the rate of return.)

All returns in the table were computed from

$$(10,000 - L)(A/P, i, 8) + Li = 2,000$$

16.7 FORECASTING UTILIZATION

Prediction of the degree of utilization of the equipment on the intended job is important because it affects immediate costs, costs that begin as soon as the equipment is installed. An error in the degree of utilization of the equipment is therefore serious, and predictions of utilization should be given the best attention, as the following example illustrates.

EXAMPLE 16.7a The machine comparisons in Examples 16.5b and 16.6 consisted of an extra investment of $10,000 and annual savings of $2,000 with a salvage of $3,714 at the end of the 8-year economic life. How serious would an error in the prediction of the utilization of the equipment be, assuming that the disbursements of each machine, and therefore the savings, will decrease directly as the utilization?

SOLUTION. If the forecaster erroneously predicts a utilization 50% greater than it should be, the savings will be $3,000 a year, the resulting rate of return will be 27.1% instead of 15.5%, an error of 74.8% and a serious one.

The computations are based on

$$6,286(A/P, i, 8) + 3,714i = \text{savings}$$

and the results are summarized in Table 16.7.

The error in the prediction of savings in Table 16.7 could also result from incorrect prediction of disbursements as well as utilization. However, if the

Table 16.7 RESULTS OF ERRORS IN PREDICTING UTILIZATION

Annual savings	Error in utilization (%)	Computed rate of return (%)	Error in rate of return (%)
$1,000	-50	2.9	-81.3
1,200	-40	5.5	-64.5
1,400	-30	8.1	-47.7
1,600	-20	10.6	-31.6
1,800	-10	13.1	-15.5
2,000	0	15.5	0
2,200	+10	17.9	+15.5
2,400	+20	20.2	+30.3
2,600	+30	22.5	+45.2
2,800	+40	24.8	+60.0
3,000	+50	27.1	+74.8

utilization is known, the cost engineer should be reasonably expected to predict the associated cost. The more elusive prediction may well be the utilization.

The previous example presumes that the utilization will be constant through-out the life but, of course, the analyst must consider that it may increase with the growth of the firm or, conversely, that it may decrease, perhaps from a drop in product demand. If the change in utilization is limited to the distant future, the error in failing to predict it will not be as serious as the failure to predict next year's utilization or those in the near future. It is not the average savings that count but the time distribution of them.

EXAMPLE 16.7b   Compute that rate of return for the investments represented by time scales A, B, and C. For the sake of illustration consider that A represents the analyst's prediction but that B represents the actual occurrence, in which the analyst failed to predict a falling off in savings in the later years of service. Then, alternatively, assume that C represents the actual occurrence in which the analyst failed to predict a low utilization of equipment during the early years of service.

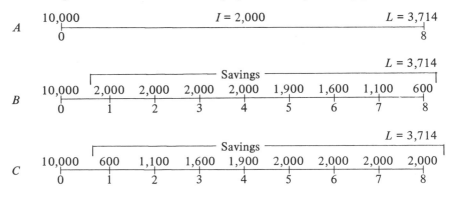

SOLUTION A.

The rate of return is 15.5% as previously computed.

SOLUTION B.

$6,286(A/P, i, 8) + 3,741i$
$= 2,000 - [100(P/F, 5) + 400(P/F, 6) + 900(P/F, 7) + 1,400(P/F, 8)](A/P, 8)$

Solving for i gives a rate of return of 12.5%.

SOLUTION C.

$6,286(A/P, i, 8) + 3,741i$
$= 2,000 - [100(P/F, 4) + 400(P/F, 3) + 900(P/F, 2) + 1,400(P/F, 1)](A/P, 8)$

Solving for i gives a rate of return of 10.0%.

In the first case, in which B proves to be the correct prediction over A, the error in the rate of return is $3.0/12.5 = 24.0\%$. In the second case, in which C proves to be the correct prediction over A, the error in the rate of return jumps to $5.5/10.0 = 55.0\%$, or more than twice as much. In each case, the magnitude of the error is the same, that is, the analyst estimated his savings to be $16,000 instead of $13,200 over the 8-year period, an error in magnitude of 2,800/13,200 = 21.2%. However, with the time value of money, the effect of this error on the error in the computed rate of return is only 24.0% if the prediction errs late in the life period but becomes 55.0% if the prediction errs early in the life period. Although savings in *B* and *C* and the same, we see again the effect of the time distribution on the conclusion, the importance of correct predictions in the early years, and the small effect of errors in the distant future.

16.8 USING FACTORS OF SAFETY

It is good practice in engineering to use factors of safety so that machines and structures will be operated below the point at which failure is predicted to occur. Is it possible that factors of safety can be adopted relative to the predicted data in engineering and business economy?

Although factors of safety have not been directly introduced in practice, procedures have been used apparently with the thought that they accomplished the same result. One such procedure involves the use of a "payout period." Many variations of the payout method will be found, but in general the idea is that the extra investment must be recovered, assuming zero salvage, in an arbitrary period unrelated to the economic life.[1] This arbitrary period is set by top management and is usually very short; the one that most generally seems to be selected for production equipment is 3 years. If there is a deviation from this, it is generally on the short side.

A close examination of the payout period reveals that

1. It disregards all savings after the payout period.
2. It disregards the economic life of the equipment.
3. It disregards the time value of money.
4. It disregards the rate of return on the investment.
5. It disregards the minimum required rate of return or cutoff rate.

As a result it not only fails as a test of an investment but actively favors the selection of incorrect equipment, as the following example illustrates.

EXAMPLE 16.8   The cutoff rate is 25% before taxes. Which of the following projects (A) through (E) will be correctly accepted or rejected by a 3-year payout period?   In each case the extra investment is $9,000, salvage is zero, and the annual savings are $3,000 (i.e., the payout period is 9,000 ÷ 3,000 = 3). The one exception is project (E) which has a salvage of $4,500 and a savings of $2,800 a year. The economic life of each project is expected to be as follows: (A) 3 years, (B) 4 years, (C) 5 years, (D) 6 years, and (E) 6 years.

---

[1] Some payout methods compute the payout on the *total* first cost, not on the extra investment! Most payout methods disregard salvage value. Other methods are discussed in Section 17.7.

SOLUTION. The computed rate of return for each project is (A) zero %, (B) 12%, (C) 20%, (D) 24%, and (E) 27%.

The first four projects should be rejected, as the rates of return of all are less than 25%—however, they will all be accepted by the payout method. This is to be expected because the method accepts or rejects a proposal without any regard to its profitability.

For project (E), however, the payout method would reject this proposal because the payout period is greater than 3, namely, $9,000 \div 2,800 = 3.2$. However, of all the projects, this is the only one that should be accepted because it is the only one with an acceptable rate of return.

This example illustrates that the payout method, instead of serving as a barrier to all poor projects, can be the very means of admitting them. The example also illustrates that the payout technique can, in addition, be an effective barrier to the good projects. In the above example any project with an annual saving of less than $3,000 will be rejected regardless of the rate of return on the investment.

The obvious conclusion, since the payout method gives approvals without regard to the rate of return, is that it is not a test of an investment. The payout test is only a calculation of how soon the investor will get his money back. If the only reason for "investing" money is to get it back without earnings, then the payout method is the best to use. But the idea of investing is to make a profit, and the way to test a proposed investment is to compute the prospective profit or rate of return.

Nor can the payout method be visualized in the light of a factor of safety; not when it admits the four unsatisfactory proposals and rejects the one acceptable proposal as it did in Example 16.8. In order to employ a factor of safety, we must make predictions, such as predictions of the expected load or predictions of the expected life. The payout method fails in this because it contains no prediction of economic life; in fact it proceeds in complete ignorance and utter disregard of the life period.

The next section will indicate how a factor of safety can be visualized relative to predictions in economy problems.

16.9 BREAK-EVEN ANALYSIS

The payout period is actually a computation of the break-even period if the salvage and the rate of return are zero. Purposely omitting some of the cost elements is, however, not a recommended approach to computing a break-even point, so the payout computation must be recognized as a unique break-even analysis. In general, a break-even analysis proceeds from a computation of the value of one of the cost factors to break-even if all of the other cost factors are included.

EXAMPLE 16.9 A project requiring an extra investment of $10,000 is expected to produce a saving of $2,800 a year for 8 years with $3,340 salvage at that date. The minimum required rate of return is 15% before tax. What is the break-even of each factor in the analysis?

SOLUTION.

$$10,000 \qquad I = 2,800 \qquad L = 3,340$$
$$0 \qquad\qquad\qquad\qquad\qquad\qquad 8$$

With a cost of capital of 15%, the savings to break even would be

$$6,660(A/P, .15, 8) + (3,340)(0.15) = \$1,986$$
$$\overset{0.2229}{}$$

and the salvage to break even would be

$$L(A/F, .15, 8) = 10,000(A/P, .15, 8) - 2,800 = -\$571 \text{ (a cost)}$$
$$\overset{0.2229}{}$$

In an analysis for the break-even of the life period, we can hold the salvage value constant along with all other cost factors. This is conservative, if anything, because the salvages will at least be higher if the life is shorter. The alternative, of course, is to predict the new salvage at each life period. In the following computation the salvage was assumed to be constant.

$$6,660(A/P, .15, n) + (3,340)(0.15) = \$2,800$$

whence n will be 4.1 years.

These analyses show how much each of the predicted values can be in error before break-even occurs, that is, before the selected course of action should be reversed.[1] From this it is possible to compute a factor which expresses this spread, and such a factor is clearly a factor of safety. In the present example the factors would be:

	Predicted value	Break-Even point	Computed factor of safety
Savings	$2,800	$1,986	1.41
Salvage	$3,340	-$571	—
Life (years)	8.0	4.1	1.95

Unlike an engineering structure, each factor of safety is computed with the assumption that all other elements will be correct as predicted. The analysis merely shows how much one of the elements can be off, assuming all the others are correct, before the decision will be reversed. Each analysis is therefore limited to a test of the safety or margin of error of a single prediction.

In conclusion it should be noted again that a factor of safety relates a predicted value to the value at the point of failure, the break-even point, and the advocates of the payout method have overlooked this if they tend to view their method as a test of safety.

---

[1] This is not exactly true. At the given break-even points we would still select the alternative with the extra investment. However, at any lower rate of return we would not.

16.10 BEST-WORST CHOICE

The break-even method provides an excellent test of any one of the variables, assuming that the other variables have been correctly predicted. However, the probability is that all of the variables are incorrect even if only by a small amount. A practical way to meet this situation is by the "best-worst choice" approach. In this method all the variables can be adjusted simultaneously to present (a) the least favorable picture, namely, the worst choice; (b) the optimum picture, namely, the best choice; and (c) the most reasonable picture.

EXAMPLE 16.10   Assume that the data in Example 16.9 represents the most reasonable choice, make a best-worst analysis based on the following data. The extra investment is expected to be $10,000, but it could be as high as $10,300 or as low as $9,800. The savings are expected to be $2,800 but could be as high as $3,000 or as low as $2,100. The expected salvage of $3,340 could be as high as $4,000 or as low as $2,400. The expected life could be as high as 10 years or as low as 5 years. The minimum required rate of return, as before, is 15%.

SOLUTION.   It will be observed that under the worst conditions the rate of return of 7.1% falls below the minimum required rate of return of 15%, although even the worst predictions indicate that the investment will be recovered with some return.

The worst choice is the result of the least favorable predictions for each element of cost and therefore represents the viewpoint that all the unfavorable predictions will occur simultaneously. If so, the worst choice is the lowest level that the forecasters can reasonably conceive. In reviewing a worst-choice analysis management must consider not only the probability of experiencing the stated degree of variance but the probability that the variances in each element will coincide. For example, may the prediction of the best first cost, $9,800, occur

Table 16.10   RESULTS OF A BEST-WORST CHOICE ANALYSIS

	Worst choice	Most reasonable choice	Best choice
Investment	$10,300	$10,000	$9,800
variation (%)	+3.0	0	-2.0
Savings	$ 2,100	$ 2,800	$3,000
variation (%)	-25.0	0	+7.1
Salvage	$ 2,400	$ 3,340	$4,000
variation (%)	-28.1	0	+19.8
Life (years)	5	8	10
variation (%)	-37.5	0	+25.0
Computed rate of return (%)	7.1	24.6	29.2
Payout period (years)	4.9	3.6	3.3

along with the prediction of the worst saving, $2,100? The method permits anyone charged with approving an appropriation request to substitute his own predictions of amounts and coincidence.

On the other side of the coin, if the rate of return computed for the worst choice exceeds the minimum required rate of return, there is no doubt about recommending the expenditure.

This approach tends to view a prediction as a band or spectrum in which the forecaster says, "I estimate the savings may be between $2,100 and $3,000, although I strongly feel they will be close to $2,800." This is not an unusual procedure, in fact it is more natural to see a prediction in terms of the highest, lowest, and best notion. This approach also lends itself to participation by a number of people in predicting future values and in establishing extreme limits from which best and worst choices or probability distributions may be selected.

16.11 QUANTITATIVE TREATMENT OF IRREDUCIBLES

An "irreducible" element is one that cannot be quantified; however, the analyst may discover to his surprise how many items, which he first viewed as irreducibles, can actually be quantified. In some cases he may find that due to the extreme difficulty of predicting numbers that the best he can do is to predict the worst extremity, the minimum savings, for example. This figure is better than none and, in fact, may prove to be sufficient if it serves to prove-in the proposal.

With a little thought he may find some quantitative approach to the problem which may sufficiently demonstrate the logic of the proposal. For example, the installation of a superior lighting system, the installation of music in a factory, the redecoration of a clerical office, the construction and operation of an employees' club house, and so on—the benefits of these investments are generally considered irreducible. The analyst probably cannot produce any data by which he can predict how much increase in productivity will result from better lighting and he probably cannot even guess what the very minimum increase might be.

EXAMPLE 16.11   A new lighting system can be installed in a factory department for an extra investment of $10,000. This modernization will improve the appearance of the shop interior and, in accordance with present recommended practice, double the light at the working surfaces. The extra annual cost of power and maintenance with the new system will be $500 a year. The annual labor cost of all the people in the department whose work places will be affected by the improved lighting system is $250,000. The life of the system is predicted to be 10 years with zero salvage. The minimum required rate of return, neglecting taxes, is 15%.

SOLUTION. The expenditure of $10,000 is justified if the savings are
$$10,000(A/P, .15, 10) \overset{0.19925}{} \text{ or } \$1,993,$$ making a total of $2,493 to cover the added cost of power and maintenance. To justify the installation, the annual savings

must be almost 1% of the annual labor cost. This means that improved lighting must cause an increase in productivity of almost 1%. Will this result from better vision as well as a better environment? Will the operations of selecting, inspecting, positioning, grasping, and so on be easier and quicker? Will fewer mistakes, less rework, fewer hazards result? Is it a fair guess that productivity will increase at least 1%?

Because all such decisions are investments, all the benefits and costs of the investment should be listed and studied. Some may remain irreducible but, in many cases, study may reveal some satisfactory quantitative approach.

Strategic decisions are generally viewed as irreducibles because the benefits are too indefinite to quantify. Nevertheless, even these must promise a reduction in cost or increase in profit. As in Example 16.11 it may be possible to test these expenditures by weighing the possibility of achieving the savings necessary to break even.

16.12 PRICE CHANGES

The analyst must look beyond the initial cost and the first year's operating cost. Will the future bring a change in the number of units required, an increase in maintenance and repair, a decrease in machine efficiency? Even if these items are expected to be constant, will the net savings be altered by a change in unit prices? Consequently, all prospective changes in real costs should be included if they can be predicted.

EXAMPLE 16.12 Machine A has a prospective first cost of $1,000, annual operating disbursements of $800, and an economic life of 5 years. Machine B costs $1,500 with $750 in annual disbursements and a 10-year economic life. Salvage values are zero. It is expected that a new machine will be available in 5 years which, as a result of the technological improvements, will cost only $500 a year to operate. The cost of the improved machine is expected to be $1,250 with zero salvage at the end of a 5-year economic life. The minimum required rate of return before taxes is 20%.

SOLUTION.

$$PW_A = 1,000 + 500(P/A, .20, 10) + 300(P/A, 5) + 1,250(P/F, 5) = \$4,496$$

$$PW_B = 1,500 + 750(P/A, 10) = \$4,644$$

Further computation will show that without the price change machine B would have been selected, but the prospects of a more efficient machine in the future favored the selection of the short-lived equipment.

16.13 INFLATION

The foregoing illustration applies to changes in real costs. A *real* cost may be described as a cost expressed in terms of the goods and services that it will buy. If a real cost increases, its equivalent in goods and services will increase, but if the equivalent in goods and services remains the same after the change, it is not a change in real cost but an inflationary effect.

A change in real cost can be produced by the introduction of better methods. For example, the labor cost of a new machine may be lower the second year than the first, for the same output, because the operators will have acquired better methods through practice. A machine of higher engineering efficiency will have lower labor costs because the operation is based on better methods. These costs are real costs. A change in real costs may also result from shortages. A shortage of electronic repair men to service automated processes may cause an increase in the real costs of maintenance and repair. A shortage of automobiles during wartime may cause the salvage value to exceed the original cost. As stated in Section 16.12, changes in real cost or in real incomes should be included in the analysis.

On the other hand *costs or incomes* may increase without a corresponding decreasing in the *goods or services* available to the buyer or produced by the seller. For the purpose of this text we will call these inflationary costs or incomes.[1] By some reasoning shortages could also be called inflationary but we feel this is not the place to discuss national or international inflationary terms arising from supply and demand. The economist using this text is aiming only to predict the real cost or real incomes in the *specific problem* he is analyzing.

The following three examples will attempt to illustrate how to treat inflationary or real-cost changes.

EXAMPLE 16.13a If inflation is expected to increase at the rate of 5% a year for the next 5 years, compare investing $1,000 today in a savings account for 5 years earnings 3% interest with investing $1,000 today in a supply of coal needed 5 years hence (assuming for simplicity that all taxes, insurances, storage costs, and so on are zero).

SOLUTION: As a result of inflation, $1,000 5 years from now will not purchase the same goods and services as $1,000 today. In fact, at a 5% inflationary rate, $1,276 will have the same purchasing power as $1,000 today.

$$1,000 \overset{1.276}{(F/P, .05, 5)} = \$1,276$$

Therefore, the supply of coal can be sold for $1,276 5 years hence or conversely, this sum would be required to purchase it.

On the other hand, the bank deposit will have accumulated to only

$$1,000 \overset{1.159}{(F/P, .03, 5)} = \$1,159$$

The effect of inflation is a loss in purchasing power of $\left(1 - \dfrac{1,159}{1,276}\right) = 9.2\%$ if

---

[1] In terms of national or international economy, writers may employ "inflationary" to describe any and all increases in costs or incomes, these being the sum effect of all *increases* namely in real costs as well as inflationary.

the money is deposited in the bank.

If all the dollars for both alternatives are expressed in the purchasing power of today's dollar, then the investment in the coal can be described as an investment of $1,000 today which will have a real value of $1,000 in 5 years. The real costs or values are the same, so there is no loss on the transaction; the status quo has been maintained. However, the bank investment has lost 9.2% purchasing power; in real dollars it is worth only $908 at the end of 5 years. This investor has not maintained his status quo, because the increase in the principal has not matched the decrease in its purchasing power.

If an investment is defined as a transaction which increases the *real* wealth of the investor, we see that the bank deposit was not an investment, because it resulted in a loss of real wealth. But the purchase of the coal is not an investment either, because measured in real dollars the investor gained nothing, no more than if he had put $1,000 under a mattress during a period of constant purchasing power. Its only advantage relative to the bank deposit is the avoidance of a loss in purchasing power.

Now examine the effect of inflation on a proposed equipment expenditure as presented in the following example.

EXAMPLE 16.13b An income-expansion proposition can be procured for $10,000 which will bring a gross income of $8,000 and require an annual disbursement of $3,000 at the end of next year. In subsequent years inflation is predicted at the rate of 5% a year. The proposition is expected to last 4 years with zero salvage. What is the effect of inflation on this decision?

SOLUTION. With a predicted inflationary trend of 5%, cost and incomes are presumed to be subject to the same influence. For example, gross income at the end of year 2 will be inflated to $8,400 and the company will pay an inflated price of $3,150 at that time for the same services and materials it received in the first year. On the time scale the actual dollar amounts will be

$$
\begin{array}{ccccc}
& I = 8{,}000 & I = 8{,}400 & I = 8{,}820 & I = 9{,}261 \\
10{,}000 & D = 3{,}000 & D = 3{,}150 & D = 3{,}308 & D = 3{,}473 \\
\vdash & \vdash & \vdash & \vdash & \vdash \\
0 & 1 & 2 & 3 & 4
\end{array}
$$

However, each of these dollars in terms of today's purchasing power will be:

$$
\begin{array}{ccccc}
& I = 8{,}000 & I = 8{,}000 & I = 8{,}000 & I = 8{,}000 \\
10{,}000 & D = 3{,}000 & D = 3{,}000 & D = 3{,}000 & D = 3{,}000 \\
\vdash & \vdash & \vdash & \vdash & \vdash \\
0 & 1 & 2 & 3 & 4
\end{array}
$$

Alternatively, from the viewpoint of the cash flow the time scale will be

$$
\begin{array}{ccccc}
10{,}000 & I - D = 5{,}000 & I - D = 5{,}250 & I - D = 5{,}512 & I - D = 5{,}788 \\
\vdash & \vdash & \vdash & \vdash & \vdash \\
0 & 1 & 2 & 3 & 4
\end{array}
$$

But expressing the cash flow in terms of today's purchasing power,

$$
\begin{array}{ccccc}
10{,}000 & 5{,}000 & 5{,}000 & 5{,}000 & 5{,}000 \\
\vdash & \vdash & \vdash & \vdash & \vdash \\
0 & 1 & 2 & 3 & 4
\end{array}
$$

By either of the above approaches, it is obvious that inflation should be disregarded. The same conclusion applies to a cost-reduction investment, as can be seen in the following example.

EXAMPLE 16.13c Machine A costs $30,000 with annual disbursements for next year of $10,000. Machine B costs $20,000 with $15,000 in disbursements for next year. Annual inflationary increases of 5% are expected to occur after next year over the 4-year life of the project. Salvages will be zero.

SOLUTION. If the savings are computed from the inflated costs, the time scale of savings will be

```
            Cost  ┌─────────── Savings ───────────┐
           10,000   5,000   5,250   5,512   5,788
  A - B    ├───────┼───────┼───────┼───────┤
              0       1       2       3       4
```

But expressed in dollars of today's purchasing power, the savings will be

```
            Cost  ┌─────────── Savings ───────────┐
           10,000   5,000   5,000   5,000   5,000
  A - B    ├───────┼───────┼───────┼───────┤
              0       1       2       3       4
```

Therefore in cost reduction, as in income expansion, inflation may be neglected. In cost-reduction projects, the company's gross income I also increases at the inflationary rate, but this item is, of course, irrelevant to the choice, because it is the same regardless of the alternates selected.

The rule is that all sums must be expressed in terms of dollars of the same purchasing power. It is also immaterial what year is chosen to serve as the base of purchasing power.

The previous conclusions rest on the assumption that *incomes and costs are inflating at the same rate.* Of course, if incomes and costs, in an income-expansion problem, are inflating at different rates, and if these differences can be predicted, inflation is not irrelevant. For example, if incomes will inflate faster than costs, the net profit after the payment of costs out of income will represent an increase in real savings.

However, if certain costs inflate faster than other costs, the problem becomes very complex. In that case, however, it is questionable whether the forecaster can predict differences in the inflation between classes of expenditures.

Consider a situation in which it seems reasonable that the parties, the seller in this instance, predict and estimate an inflationary trend and compute the effect.

EXAMPLE 16.13d A manufacturer receives an order for an automatic machine tool for which he will be paid $300,000 as follows: $100,000 on signing the order, $100,000 at the end of 1 year, and $100,000 on delivery at the end of 2 years. Inflation is estimated to be 10% a year. The bid was based on normal profit. What is the effect of inflation?

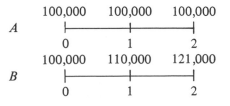

```
                                         100,000    100,000    100,000
Income according to the contract    A    ├──────────┼──────────┤
                                         0          1          2

                                         100,000    110,000    121,000
Income required to maintain constant B   ├──────────┼──────────┤
purchasing power                         0          1          2
```

SOLUTION. The contract intended to give the seller three time-payments equal to the purchasing power of $300,000 but due to the declining purchasing power of the dollar the payments shown on time scale *A* do not conform to this intention. An income of $110,000 at the end of year one will be required to equal the purchasing power of $100,000 conceived at the time of the contract, and $121,000 at the end of year two. Time scale *B* therefore correctly represents incomes that should be received in payment of today's $300,000 price of the machine because all payments are of equal purchasing power, that is each equals the purchasing power of $100,000 at time zero, the date of the contract. However, please realize that these payments are only intended to maintain the income value of the agreement--they are not profits.

The loss due to inflation is:

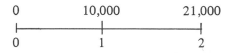

and therefore the time payments should have been higher by at least these amounts in years 1 and 2. Expressed another way these are actual losses as distributed in time or by their equivalent present worth. It is clear that this will be a direct loss in the profit expected by the seller because not only will his costs of material, labor, and overhead be inflating during this two-year period but his net profit and his surplus to net worth will therefore be squeezed.

It will result in less retained earnings for investment in improvements which are now also at inflated costs, and it will result in less ability to pay increased dividends which will be expected by the shareholders as counter inflationary measures.

Although this discussion has centered on inflation, the same type of analysis can be applied to deflationary trends.

16.14 SENSITIVITY AND SENSITIVITY ANALYSIS

The term *sensitivity* refers to the effect that changes in one or more parameters will have on the conclusion. A sensitivity analysis will consist of purposely changing conditions between possible limits and recording the resultant rates of return. A sensitivity analysis implies uncertainty and is designed to address uncertainty by recognizing that any parameter is merely a prediction and can likely be different when the date arrives. A sensitivity analysis displays, by assuming various degrees of difference, how sensitive the economic situation is to changes in various conditions.

In the previous sections we noted that the rate of return is very sensitive to variations in the first cost and very insensitive to salvage values or other predictions in the distant future. We have also noticed the sensitivity to variations in the utilization of equipment, especially in the immediate future. Effects similar to capacity utilization can be caused by changes in market predictions in quantity and selling price.

The situation is less sensitive to reasonable changes in economic life. Exceptional variations in economic life can, of course, result from unpredicted changes in technology. This may be caused by the sudden appearance of new equipment or a disappearance of product demand in the market place.

The break-even analysis is merely another display of a sensitivity analysis by showing the extent of variation in various parameters until the point at which costs and incomes break even.

The best-worst choice is a special application of a sensitivity analysis. Like the break-even analysis the point of view is to predict the parameters at specific points: the worst the analyst believes can occur, the best, and the most likely. This is a predictive procedure which tests selected limits within the range of a sensitivity analysis.

The best-worst choice, like a break-even analysis, also introduces the idea of testing combinations of parameters, inasmuch as the cause of variations in one parameter in a sensitivity analysis may affect other variations.

16.15 POST-AUDIT

Predicting future events without comparing the predictions to the events as they unfold is like playing baseball with no players in the field except a pitcher. In either case no one will know what the score might really be. Like a game, forecasting loses its zest unless the forecaster can observe the results of his predictions. Not only will the challenge be lost but the responsibility for correct forecasts will largely disappear. The answer is to keep score by the use of a post-audit.

A post-audit also helps the forecaster to gain experience by noting the variation between events and his predictions and by looking for assignable causes in the variations.

Furthermore, post-auditing helps to eliminate irresponsible predictions. The obligation to face future comparisons is a strong deterrent to making offhand predictions.

Assuming a new machine was installed, the post-audit can being with an analysis of first cost by comparing the actual installed cost and the predicted cost and investigating the reasons for a variance. Next the actual operating disbursements, totaled for the first year, can be compared with the predicted costs and the variances can be investigated. If labor cost was high, was it the result of an increase in the predicted production, a reduction in operator efficiency during the learning period, change in real cost, inflationary change which should be disregarded? Through a year-by-year post-audit, all the actual disbursements over the life of the equipment can be compared with predicted values. This can be continued right down through the date when the machine is displaced and its net realizable value established.

The post-audit can be applied only to the machine that is installed. This may be a machine newly installed on the service or it may be the incumbent machine if it is retained on its present service. In either case it is only a question of comparing actual costs with predicted costs.

Note that a post-audit cannot verify the savings; it can verify only the costs of the machine that has been installed on the intended job. The predicted savings will be correct only if the predicted costs of the machine that was *not* selected for the job would also have been correct as predicted. Because of the fact that the displaced machine is no longer on the job to permit an audit of its cost, the audit is not a complete check on the correctness of the decision.

The collection of data for an audit will also provide information that might be extended in the analysis of the installed machine when its replacement test is made. The collected data will also permit the construction of lifetime cost models that might be extended into models of future machines.

Few firms have collected such data to guide their forecasts, but the effort can become economical in the future with the development of data-processing machines. As the manager learns that he can demand information that previously was unavailable because of the expense and time to collect it, we can expect that the area of quantitative decision-making will benefit.

The auditing process, in any event, requires setting up the accounting system for the purpose, particularly establishing cost-accounting points around which the data is to be collected. Where items are evidently too small to justify the effort, they will be omitted from the audit, but as long as forecasting is being done, the expense of providing the accounting figures needed for an audit is in itself a good investment.

PROBLEMS

16.1 List some of the factors to look for that can create nonuniform costs.

16.2 A new machine which can be installed for an extra investment of $10,000 will produce annual savings of $4,000 a year. The useful life of the equipment is expected to be 15 years with zero salvage value at that time. The analyst *predicts* the economic life will be 9 years. What is the percentage error in the computed rate of return on the extra increment if the *correct* economic life is 7 years? 5 years? Assume that the salvage values at these times will be equal to the book value resulting from sum-of-the-years' digits depreciation.

16.3 An extra investment of $10,000 is expected to have an economic life of 10 years with $2,620 salvage value at that time. The savings resulting from the investment are expected to be $3,000 a year over that period. What will be the percentage error in the rate of return on the investment if the correct salvage value is 15% less than this? 30% less?

16.4 An extra investment of $10,000 is expected to have an economic life of 10 years with $2,620 salvage at that date. The savings resulting from the investment are expected to be $3,000 a year over that period. What will be the percentage error in the rate of return on the investment if the analyst erred in predicting the first 2-years' savings as follows: (a) they should have been $1,000 and $2,000 for the first and second year, respectively; (b) they should have been zero and $1,500, respectively.

16.5 Three cost-reduction opportunities are available in a certain plant and each requires an extra investment of $10,000. The first has annual savings of $3,400, the second $3,007, and the third $2,888. The salvage values are all estimated to be zero. (a) Which of these will be selected by a test of payout periods if the period may not exceed 3 years? (b) Which of these will be selected by a rate-of-return analysis if the economic lives are, first project 3 years, second 6 years, and third 9 years? The minimum required rate of return is 15%.

16.6 An existing machine produces the company's annual requirement of 5,000 motor endshields. It has a net realizable value of $8,000 and an expected life of 5 years with zero salvage at that date. The operating disbursements for this annual output are $12,000. Of these, $2,000 are for fixed costs, regardless of output, such as property taxes, insurance, routine inspection, and so on. The other disbursements are expected to vary directly with output. A new machine can be installed for $20,000 and its life is expected to be 15 years with 10% salvage. Its operating disbursement for the output of 5,000 units will be $9,000, of which $3,000 will be fixed and $6,000 will vary directly with output. If the company's minimum required rate of return is 15%, what is the company's annual requirement in endshields to break even?

16.7 A durable paint can be purchased for $8 a gallon while a less durable paint costs $3.50 a gallon. The labor cost of applying a gallon of paint is $6. Both paints are equally easy to apply and will cover the same area per gallon. The less durable paint is expected to last 30 months. How long should the more durable paint last to break even if the minimum required rate of return is 1% a month? At the break-even point would you make any choice?

16.8 An airline is considering two types of engines for use in its planes. Each has the same life, same power, and same maintenance and repair record. Engine A costs $8,000 and uses 40,000 gallons per 1,000 hours of operation at the average load encountered in passenger service. Engine B costs $10,000 and uses 32,000 gallons per 1,000 hours of operation at the same load. Both engines have 3-year lives with 10% salvage values.

If gasoline costs 25 cents a gallon and if the minimum required rate of return is 20%, how many hours of passenger service a year must be available to justify the use of the more expensive engine?

16.9 A fruit-picking machine can be purchased for $10,000. It is expected to have an 8-year life with $500 salvage. Annual operating cost for items such as insurance, taxes, inspection, and so on will be fixed, regardless of utilization, at $2,000. The variable operating costs will be fuel at $8 a day and two laborers at $14 a day each. The working day is 8 hours.

With this machine a tree can be picked in 1.5 hours. With manual labor as at present the tree can be picked in 5 hours. This requires four laborers who receive $10 a day each.

What is the minimum number of fruit trees a grower must have in his orchard to justify the machine if the minimum required rate of return is 10%?

16.10 An economy analyst gives the following as his most reasonable estimate of a prospective investment: An extra investment of $10,000 in a certain project will result in $2,500 savings a year for 10 years with $1,200 salvage value at that time. His worst or most pessimistic prediction is a saving of $2,000 and a life of 7 years instead of 10. At the end of this shorter life he predicts a salvage value of $2,000. He also estimates that at the worst the required extra investment will be 10% higher. His best or most optimistic prediction is a saving of $2,750 and a 12-year life with $600 salvage at that time. He also estimates that the extra investment might be 5% less. Compute the rate of return on his best, worst, and most reasonable predictions.

16.11 Suppose in the previous problem the analyst assigns the following probabilities to the occurrences of (a) the worst cost (b) the most reasonable cost, and (c) the best or most favorable cost.

| | | Occurrence | |
Item	Worst Cost (a)	Most Reasonable Cost (b)	Best Cost (c)
First cost, P	0.30	0.50	0.20
Savings	0.20	0.70	0.10
Economic life	0.15	0.65	0.20
Salvage, L	0.08	0.90	0.02

What is the probable rate of return on the extra investment?

16.12 A company is considering installing a system to play music in its factory at intervals during the day. As a result of the employees' favorable reaction to the music, production is expected to rise. The system will cost $7,500 installed and the annual operating disbursements will be $1,500. The factory labor force consists of 50 people on direct labor and 10 on indirect. The average pay of this group is $3 an hour. They work 40 hours a week for 50 weeks a year. If the company's minimum required rate of return is 20%, should they install the system?

16.13 A labor contract has 4 years to run. Management estimates that when this contract expires a new one will call for a 5% increase in labor costs. Management believes this will stabilize labor costs for an indefinite period. A present machine has a net realizable value of $3,000, but this will be zero 4 years hence. Its operating disbursements are $8,000 a year. A new machine can be obtained for $10,000 with an economic life of 10 years and zero salvage at that time. Its operating disbursements, essentially all for labor, will be $6,000 a year under the present labor rates.

Management expects that at the end of 4 years an improved machine will be available at a first cost of $10,500, or 5% higher than today's new machine. However, the improved efficiency of this machine will reduce the required hours of labor by 10%. The economic life of this machine is expected also to be 10 years with zero salvage. If the firm's minimum required rate of return is 20%, should the present machine be replaced now or deferred until the improved machine appears? Use a 10-year study period.

16.14 Solve Example 16.13b in the text if the company makes its price increases 1 year ahead of inflationary cost increases. For example, assume that the gross income is $8,000 at the end of year 1 as given, but the company is able to increase its prices to $8,820 at the end of year 2 or 5% over the increase necessary to nullify the inflation of disbursements. Thereafter the costs and incomes will inflate at the assumed rate of 5% a year. What will be the percentage gain in the annual cash flow, expressed in real dollars, resulting from this pricing policy?

16.15 Solve Example 16.13b in the text if the company cannot time its price increases to match the inflationary increases in disbursements but continually lags 1 year behind. For example, suppose the disbursements inflate as shown in Example 16.13b but the company does not raise its income to $8,400 until the end of year 3. Thereafter the company raises its prices 5% to keep pace with the rising disbursement (note that the income at end of year 2 will be $8,000 as in year 1). What is the percentage loss in the annual cash flow resulting from this situation if the cash flow is expressed in real dollars?

17

Industrial Methods, Techniques, and Formulas

17.1 TWO CLASSES OF SPENDING DECISIONS

All spending decisions can be divided into two classes. The first class relates to expenditures for long-lived items, namely, fixed assets such as machinery and real property. A characteristic of this class is its stream of future cost commitments and the depreciation of the first cost over the life period of the equipment. (Land is an exception.)

The second class of decisions pertains to expenditures which are entirely in the present. Examples of these are increment cost, make or buy, dumping, division of loads between existing production facilities, and the many problems of economic lot sizes in production and purchasing.

Most of industry's attention has been focused on the first class. It is in this class that the greatest confusion exists and the poorest decisions are made. In many cases the decisions are based solely on intuition with no attempt at a scientific approach—usually because of a lack of understanding of the basic theory. Nevertheless, attention will continue to be focused on these decisions because of their magnitude. These decisions are so great they are responsible for the entire production facility, they determine the entire capital budget, they are responsible for total fixed assets shown on the firm's balance sheet.

The second class, the present-economy decisions, occur less frequently in industry. These are the easier of the two and are generally handled with much greater ability by management. A certain lack of basic knowledge nevertheless haunts management in this area, too; for example, in economic lot-size decisions and make-or-buy decisions.

In placing all expenditures into two classes of decisions we are sometimes asked, "If I have a $50,000 payroll to meet next Friday, tell me how to make the decision so I don't have to pay it." The answer is that this decision was made years ago when it was decided to install the equipment that would require this labor force instead of some other one. Similarly, decisions today to expend money for new production methods will avoid paying this same payroll in the future. Any Friday's payroll is the result of decision-making which occurred in the past or will occur in the future.

17.2 FOUR ESSENTIAL INVESTMENT DECISIONS

As we know, it can be readily shown that all capital expenditures are *investment* decisions. This is best illustrated by the following four investment decisions.

1. Investment in the mechanization of a process.
2. Investment in the replacement (and modernization) of equipment.
3. Investment in higher machine efficiency.
4. Investment in business expansion.

These are briefly illustrated by the following four examples.

EXAMPLE 17.2a A company proposes to mechanize an existing manual process by installing a machine costing $10,000. This will result in annual operating disbursements for labor, fuel, taxes, maintenance, and so on of $5,000. The machine will be required to perform this service for 10 years with estimated zero salvage at that date. The existing manual process, in which there is zero investment for equipment, costs $8,000 a year for labor. How is this treated as an investment decision?

SOLUTION. If $10,000 is spent now for a machine, only $5,000 a year must be spent instead of $8,000. This is a savings to the corporation of $3,000 a year; however, this increase in earnings is acquired only by spending $10,000 today for a new machine. The investment decisions is simply this: Is it profitable to invest $10,000 now in order to receive $3,000 a year for 10 years?

EXAMPLE 17.2b A company proposes to replace an existing machine with the latest automatic model costing $10,000. Annual disbursements will total $5,000, and operation on this service is expected to last 10 years with zero salvage at that time. The machine now performing the service would sell for $2,000 on the open market with an expected salvage of zero in 10 years. Its annual operating disbursements will be $7,000. How is this treated as an investment decision?

SOLUTION. With an investment of an additional $8,000 today, expenditures will be reduced by $2,000 a year for 10 years. The investment question is whether investing $8,000 is justified by the annual increase in earnings of $2,000.

EXAMPLE 17.2c A company needs a machine to process some material. A semiautomatic machine can be purchased and installed for $10,000 and its annual operating disbursements will be $6,000. Alternatively, a fully automatic machine that can be acquired for $14,000 will have annual operating disbursements of $4,000. Each is expected to provide 10 years of service on the intended job with zero salvage at that time. How is this treated as an investment decision?

SOLUTION. The investment decision here is simply whether to invest $4,000 today in order to receive $2,000 a year for 10 years. Note that in either case the company must have a machine for the processing job. The question is whether to buy the higher machine efficiency.

EXAMPLE 17.2d If a certain production facility is purchased for $15,000, its entire output can be sold for $10,000 a year. The total annual disbursements for the operation of the process, including all labor and materials as well as selling and distribution costs, are $7,000. The service is expected to last 10 years with zero salvage at that time. How is this treated as an investment decision?

SOLUTION. The investment decision clearly is whether to invest $15,000 in order to receive an income of $3,000 a year for 10 years.

Every businessman recognizes the investment concept in the last example but too many fail to see the investment concept in the first three examples of spending decisions. What they do not seem to realize is that all spending decisions are investments.

The four examples are interesting in other respects. The first example, whether to invest in a machine to mechanize a manual process, is, of course, a special case of a replacement decision. In fact, the implication is clear in these four examples that all spending decisions are replacement decisions. Applying this viewpoint to each example, we make the following observations.

Example 17.2a is the test to replace a manual process with a mechanized one.
Example 17.2b is the test to replace an old machine with a modern machine.
Example 17.2c is the test to replace a proposed machine with a more (or less) efficient proposed machine.
Example 17.2d is the test to replace an existing investment of funds with an investment in a proposed enterprise.

Example 17.2c also has special interest because it could be one of the decisions in a cost-reduction analysis or a decision in an income-expansion analysis. In the first case it may be the analysis to determine the best machine to propose in a cost-reduction proposition and, in the second case, the analysis to determine the best machine to propose in an income-expansion proposition.

17.3 THE DECISION IS ALWAYS BETWEEN ALTERNATIVES

One obstacle to the use of the investment concept in industry is the failure to see the proposed expenditure as an alternative to present expenditures. However, we can note in each of the examples in the last section that the investment depends on the existence of an alternative course of action. A bit of reflection should convince us that there can never be less than two alternatives. At the very minimum the decision reduces to, "Should I continue what I am doing now or should I make the proposed expenditure?" Even if it seems reasonable to define what you are doing as doing nothing, it is not hard to discover that doing nothing is a real alternative in an economic sense. Doing nothing can be very uneconomical; for instance, keeping money in a strong box instead of investing it can be a very expensive way of doing nothing.

Doing nothing is a course of action which represents maintenance of the status quo—like keeping the same policies, the same products, the same designs, the same methods of production.

Too often in industry the capital budget is presented and considered for approval without any mention of the alternatives to the proposed expenditures. Management should, at least, insist on knowing the alternative (and its cost pattern) that the proposed expenditure will replace. Management should in addition insist on knowing what other alternatives were considered beyond the proposed one.

17.4 IMPORTANCE OF COST OF CAPITAL

The obligation to pay for the capital it uses binds the business to its supplier of funds. Debt capital binds the company to the lenders with all the force of common and statutory law so that failure to pay interest or principal can mean a complete loss of equity. Plowback capital binds the company to its shareholders and failure to pay satisfactory dividends becomes cause for removal of the management through the vote of the shareholders. It is important, therefore, that the management judge every spending decision in the light of its ability to meet the obligations to the suppliers of debt and equity capital.

Every management decision creates a cost, every decision involves an alternative, and every decision can be evaluated as an investment. Every manager should treat every decision as an investment with the knowledge that the rate of return on the investment must at least meet the cost of the firm's capital. Obviously, this way of thinking provides the guide to all management action and is an absolutely indispensable test of correct management action. It is therefore amazing how few executives have had adequate training in the evaluation of capital expenditures. It is also very gratifying to see how it changes a manager's entire way of thinking once he understands the procedure and learns to use it as a tool. This way of thinking (generally described as economic awareness) is invariably regarded as a quality found in all successful managers.

17.5 IMPORTANCE OF THE CUTOFF RATE

If the demand for funds exceeds the supply, a company will not be meeting its profit potential if it invests at a return which will recover only its cost of capital. The firm will not be maximizing the earnings on its investments until it governs its expenditures by a cutoff rate.

The economic reason for a cutoff rate arises when the demand for funds for capital expenditures exceeds the supply, because then the funds should be used to satisfy only the investments that promise the very best rates of return. Whenever a dollar is spent on a project returning only the cost of capital, a better investment at a higher rate of return will be denied because not enough money exists to saturate all the investments down through the cost of capital. Good management recognizes that it is not enough to meet the rates of return established by the obligations on debt and equity but that every dollar must be invested at its highest possible rate of return.

The cutoff rate is the theoretical rate of return of the poorest investment opportunity which will be financed by the last dollar available from the firm's supply for capital investment.

In general, we expect that the demands will exceed the supply of funds. In any company where the demands do not exceed the supply, the situation is prima facie evidence that the management is falling down on its obligations to find profitable investments within the firm—that it is failing to suggest better methods, processes, and equipment, failing to replace old and obsolete equipment, failing, in short, to be creative. It is management's duty to suggest expenditures, not to avoid them.

It is also management's duty to supply the funds necessary to finance the good investments that are available. When the amount of plowback capital is more or less fixed, as it usually is, management faces the problem of whether to increase the supply by adding to the firm's funded debt or by adding to its equity capital.

The forces that generate the supply also bring the cutoff rate closer to the cost of capital. On the other hand, the drive of management that causes the demand to exceed the supply bring the cutoff rate farther from the cost of capital. It is clearly the duty of all management to increase these demands by a never-ending search for better investments, and it is the duty of financial management to supply the capital for these demands subject to the restrictions arising from debt limits, loss of control by granting new equity, and so on.

17.6 THREE ESSENTIAL REASONS FOR SCIENTIFICALLY ANALYZING SPENDING DECISIONS

The magnitude of the firm's spending decisions is sufficient reason for giving time and effort to their analysis. To appreciate this let us see how these decisions are reflected, both in magnitude and quality, in the firm's financial statements.

Beginning with the balance sheet, we note that the expenditures represented by the fixed assets account, which in some companies can amount to nearly three-fourths of the net worth, are all the direct result of previous spending decisions. Furthermore, since the year-by-year sources of funds for these spending decisions are largely from the earned capital, the depreciation reserve, and the funded debt accounts, the amounts of these accounts also reflect the magnitude of these decisions.

The profit and loss statement, also, reflects both the magnitude and the quality of the firm's spending decisions. All the costs, the disbursements for labor, materials, power—even the expenses for depreciation—are the results of prior investment decisions which would determine today's costs. Similarly, the gross income is basically the result of a spending decision made years ago to engage in this enterprise and to produce this product. The profit and loss statement reflects the company's previous long-term spending decisions which established the standard incomes and the standard costs for a long time to come. Unless new spending decisions are made, the most that efficient management can do is to vary the incomes and costs around the norm established by these standards. The mere fact that the present profit and loss statement and the balance sheet are the image of all these decisions should be sufficient reason for adopting the most scientific approach possible.

The second major reason for adopting a scientific approach is that there is no place to hide from spending decisions. It is often implied by a manager's action that he hopes to escape the responsibility by just not making a decision to spend money. But the question is, "Can an executive hide from these decisions by refusing to make expenditures?" Obviously, refusing to spend the money is a decision, and the mere fact that one is not aware of the consequences does not mean that he can escape them. For example, if an opportunity exists to spend $10,000 for a new machine that will result in annual savings of $2,500 for 12 years, no one is forced to spend the $10,000. If he doesn't spend the $10,000 he *must* spend the $2,500 a year in extra disbursements. A decision not to spend money is therefore a decision to continue to pay for the operation of the present machine no matter how uneconomical. In the present example, deciding not to buy the new machine is a positive decision to spend $2,500 a year for 12 years instead of $10,000. Whoever thought he could hide from the decision to spend $10,000 will spend it and more in the long run.

This has given rise to the statement, "The man who needs a new machine is already paying for it." We might add that he will pay for the machine without obtaining it. The consequences of avoiding decisions by refusing to spend money is a rejection of savings, a rejection of the most economic equipment, a rejection of the best investments. It results in the gradual narrowing of profits relative to competition, and, if continued, degradation of the operating plant to the point where it becomes too deteriorated and too obsolete to continue in business. The fact is there is *no* place to hide from spending decisions.

If the entire business is the result of management's spending decisions and if management can adopt no way to hide from these decisions, somebody in the organization will be especially plagued with the thought that these decisions should be good ones. This often is the president of the company. We are reminded of one president who reported he had spent a rather sleepless night because every dollar approved the day before in the biggest capital budget in the company's history had not been tested by anything stronger than hunches. Having lost confidence in the profitability of ideas that had never been tested, he required his management to hold up all projects that had been approved until some degree of confidence had been restored.

Many a financial executive has wished for some system which would permit him to approve requests in good conscience as well as turn them down with a good defense. However, financial executives should realize that as long as they and other members of top management who have the authority to reject proposals continue to approve them without requiring them to be evaluated as investments, the operating divisions who originate these requests are not very likely to go to the trouble to make these evaluations. The introduction of a policy to require evaluation of proposals must usually be at the initiative of the top financial officers, if not the president himself.

In setting up a system, the financial officer will discover that this subject bridges the gap between finance and engineering and operations and provides these functions with a common goal and a common language. The engineering and operating departments can generally be expected to give the system their enthusiastic support because it welcomes their requests for expenditures, if they are good ones, and because it enables top management to rate executive for the value of their suggestions.

If these procedures are followed, the president of our earlier story could have concluded that the company's largest capital budget represented the company's finest step forward, one that would ensure success in the competitive years ahead.

17.7 COMMENTS ON SOME POPULAR METHODS

Perhaps every executive has a method for evaluating expenditure proposals. The main criterion, however, is whether the method is sound. Let us examine some of the most popular methods from this standpoint.

Probably the most frequently used unscientific approach to the approval of appropriations requests is the *intuitive method*. This method substitutes management hunches for mathematical analyses. The danger from hunch decisions is that the collection of data and the quantification of ideas becomes unnecessary. No degree of common sense can make up for the absence of data or for incomplete and incorrect data.

Another technique of approval (that probably works nearly every time it is applied) is the *squeaky wheel method*, which takes its name from the fact that the squeaky wheel gets the grease. Here the proposition is judged by the volume of sound that accompanies it. Its users are smart enough to use it only when they need it, but when they do, it works. The reason it works is that management usually has no way of refusing the request, because it is unable to show whether the project will have a return commensurate with the noise or no return at all.

And then there's the *necessity method*, which consists of waiting until the existing equipment must be replaced or the plant will shut down. This, of course, saves wear and tear on the analyst, because it doesn't require glasses or a mathematical analysis to see that replacement is absolutely necessary. This method is the most insidious, because while no one can deny that replacement is absolutely necessary, adherence to the method completely protects high operating costs and thoroughly minimizes the profits. (This is illustrated in detail in Section 19.7.)

In Section 16.8 we saw the payout method and why it is not a test of an investment. If management applies this method under the mistaken impression that it is a test, it can expect to get answers unrelated to the investment concept. We noted how it approved five investments that should have been rejected, and rejected the sixth, which should have been approved. Any agreement between the correct answer and that given by the payout method is the result of chance.

17.8 SCIENTIFIC METHODS IN PRACTICE

As we know, the scientific techniques can take the form of (1) an annual-cost comparison, (2) a present-worth comparison, and (3) a rate-of-return comparison.

Each of these approaches may be found in use today, but each has also had its day in history. In the days of railroad expansion the present-worth approach, in the form of capitalized-cost analyses, was favored because the lives of railroad lines were for all practical purposes infinite.[1]

As engineers in all fields, especially in mechanical engineering, began to use scientific analyses, the relatively shorter economic life period of mechanical and and electrical equipment favored the use of the annual-cost method. Annual-cost comparisons avoided the least-common multiple technique being used with present-worth comparisons when lives were finite and different. Instruction in the subject was primarily intended for engineers and, as these men seemed more interested in costs than returns, the texts generally favored the annual-cost method even though other methods were also covered.[2]

In the late 1950's a general switch to the rate-of-return method occurred. This was largely due to the growing interest of top management and the financial executives in this scientific tool for the analyses of expenditures. The use of the rate-of-return approach was stimulated by Joel Dean's work.[3] The rate-of-return techniques have been made available since the middle 1950's to all executives attending the writer's Executive Decision-Making seminars at Dartmouth. In general, most articles in professional magazines at that time were suggesting the rate-of-return method in one form or another. Additional momentum was added when the MAPI formula was revised in 1958 to give the "urgency rating" instead of the "adverse minimum," that is, to give a rate of return instead of an annual cost.

As a result, a majority of the scientific methods in use today are rate-of-return approaches. Nevertheless, the technique used in each method may be so different that the untrained observer may not readily recognize that each is designed to give a rate of return.

For example one method finds the rate of return that makes the present worth of costs equivalent to the present worth of income. It is based on the historically

[1] A. M. Wellington, *The Economic Theory of Railway Location* (New York: Wiley, 1887).
[2] John C. L. Fish, *Engineering Economics* (New York: McGraw-Hill, 1923).
[3] Joel Dean, *Capital Budgeting* (New York: Columbia University Press, 1951).

older present-worth setup and follows Joel Dean's writing in this respect. It is often known as the discounted cash-flow method.

An equivalent method finds the rate of return that makes the annual costs of the alternatives equivalent (or makes annual-cost differences equivalent to annual savings). It is based on the historically later use of annual costs, which, as we have noted, considerably simplified problems in which the lives of the alternatives might be different. We have had considerable success with this method in undergraduate and graduate courses, including the writer's executive programs. The MAPI method of 1958 for computing the urgency rating is also based on an annual-cost formulation.

These are two basic mathematical setups for computing the rate of return but they do not account for the entire differences between the scientific methods in use. These will be explained in detail in the following sections.

17.9 DISCOUNTED CASH-FLOW METHOD

The discounted cash-flow method is a rate-of-return method, although the name seems to imply a present-worth analysis. The essential factors usually employed in this method are as follows:

1. The use of continuous interest instead of discrete and continuous cash flow instead of end-of-year (based on the majority of the articles published on the DCF method);

2. The use of only one factor, the single-payment present-worth factor (based on the worksheets we have seen);

3. The equating of the extra investment to the present worth of the savings (i.e., cash flow). The savings, of course, may be positive or negative in certain years, and the signs must be maintained correctly.

The following two examples illustrate the worksheets and techniques generally employed in the discounted cash-flow method. The first example illustrates the technique applied to a fast write-off, and the second, to a more complex problem with different lives and a long tax write-off.

EXAMPLE 17.9a   A job, entirely manual, has a labor cost of $500 a year. A machine to do the job can be purchased for $1,000 and has a labor cost of $100 a year. A fast tax write-off equal to the economic life of 5 years is permitted and the income tax is 50%. Salvage is zero and straight-line depreciation is used.

SOLUTION.   The first step is to compute the "cash flow" resulting from the alternative having the extra investment. Cash flow from the profitable operation of a machine is the profit after tax caused by that machine plus the depreciation resulting from its selection. As will be noted in the Cash-Flow Worksheet I, the $300 cash flow is made up of the "Profit After Tax Due to A" of $100 plus the "Depreciation Expense" of A of $200. (Note: in the case of two

Worksheet I, Example 17.9a
COMPUTATION OF CASH FLOW

Time	Investment		Operating disbursements		Depreciation expense		Profit before tax due to A	Extra tax due to A	Profit after tax due to A	Cash flow tax due to A
	Higher A	Lower B	Higher B	Lower A	B	A				
0	1,000	0								
1			500	100	0	200	200	100	100	300
2			500	100	0	200	200	100	100	300
3			500	100	0	200	200	100	100	300
4			500	100	0	200	200	100	100	300
5			500	100	0	200	200	100	100	300
6										
7										
8										
9										
10										
11										
12										
13										
14										
15										
16										
17										
18										
19										
20										

Worksheet II, Example 17.9a
DISCOUNTED CASH FLOW

Timing	Trial 1 0%	Trial 2 10%		Trial 3 15%		Trial 4 25%		Trial 5 40%	
Period	Invest.	Factor	PW	Factor	PW	Factor	PW	Factor	PW
Start 2		1.221		1.350		1.649		2.225	
During 2		1.162		1.253		1.459		1.834	
Start 1		1.105		1.162		1.284		1.492	
During 1		1.052		1.079		1.136		1.230	
Zero	1,000	1.000	1,000	1.000	1,000	1.000	1,000	1.000	1,000
Total (Y)	1,000		1,000		1,000		1,000		1,000
Period	C. Flow	Factor	PW	Factor	PW	Factor	PW	Factor	PW
1	300	0.952	286	0.929	279	0.885	265	0.824	247
2	300	0.861	258	0.799	240	0.689	207	0.553	166
3	300	0.779	234	0.688	206	0.537	161	0.370	111
4	300	0.705	212	0.592	178	0.418	215	0.248	74
5	300	0.638	191	0.510	153	0.326	98	0.166	50
6		0.577		0.439		0.254		0.112	
7		0.522		0.378		0.167		0.075	
8		0.473		0.325		0.154		0.050	
9		0.428		0.280		0.120		0.034	
10		0.387		0.241		0.093		0.023	
11		0.350		0.207		0.073		0.015	
12		0.317		0.178		0.057		0.010	
13		0.287		0.154		0.044		0.007	
14		0.259		0.132		0.034		0.005	
15		0.235		0.114		0.027		0.003	
16		0.212		0.098		0.021		0.002	
17		0.192		0.084		0.016		0.001	
18		0.174		0.073		0.013		0.001	
19		0.157		0.062		0.010		0.001	
20		0.142		0.054		0.008			
Total (X)	1,500		1,181		1,056		856		648
Ratio X/Y	1.5		1.18		1.056		0.856		0.648

machines this must be the *extra* depreciation due to machine A; see Example 17.9b.)

As observed, the true rate of return is that which makes the first cost equivalent to the cash flow. This equality exists when the ratio of the present worth of the cash flow to the first cost is 1.0, which is between 15% (Trial 3) and 25% (Trial 4) on the Cash-Flow Worksheet II. The present-worth interest factors in the worksheets used with Examples 17.9a and 17.9b are those which generally appear in illustrations of the DCF method. They are for continuous interest and continuous cash flow, and the interest rate at the head of the column is the *nominal*[1] interest instead of the effective.

By interpolation between these two trials, i is found to be 17.8%.

Instead of interpolation, it is customary in the discounted cash-flow method to use the graphical method of solution illustrated in Fig. 17.9. As near as can be read from the curve in Fig. 17.9, the true rate of return is 17.5%.

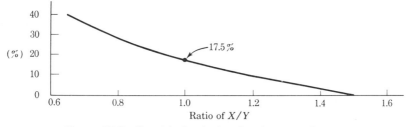

Figure 17.9   Graphical solution for the rate of return

EXAMPLE 17.9b   Machine A can be installed for $1,000. Its productive life[2] is 15 years but its tax life is required to be 20 years. Its annual operating disbursements are $100. Machine B costs $500 but its productive life and tax life are both 5 years. Its annual operating disbursements amount to $200. All salvage values are zero. Straight-line depreciation is used for tax purposes. Assume present prices will continue for future machines. Income tax is 50%.

SOLUTION.   Referring to Worksheet I of Example 17.9b, note that the cash flow due to A ($25) is the net profit after tax due to A ($75) plus the extra depreciation[3] of A over B (*minus* $50), except in the sixth and eleventh years, as explained in the next paragraph.

To compare alternatives over equal periods, it was persumed that machine B would be replaced every 5 years. This means replacement at the end of 5 years. Since the (sppwf)'s are for continuous cash flow, the DCF technique, based on the article in which this example was given, assigned the expenditure for a new machine to the cash flow in the sixth year and again in the eleventh.

---

[1]We have found these tables generally in use with the DCF method, unlike the tables in this text, which are indexed by effective interest.

[2]These two examples and the methods of solution are from examples in Ray I. Reul, "Newest Way to Figure Payoff," *Factory Management and Maintenance*, October 1955. The 15-year "productive life" undoubtedly means the "economic life," because the equipment will not be retired for 5 years after that, as indicated by the 20-year tax life.

[3]The depreciation expense of A is 1,000/20 = $50, and that of B is 500/5 = $100.

Worksheet I, Example 17.9b
COMPUTATION OF CASH FLOW

	(1)	(2)	(3)	(4)	(5)	(6)	(7)	(8)	(9)	(10)
Time	Investment		Operating disbursements		Depreciation expense		Profit before tax due to A	Extra tax due to A	Profit after tax due to A	Cash flow due to A
Year	Higher A	Lower B	Higher B	Lower A	B	A				
0	1,000	500								
1			200	100	100	50	150	75	75	25
2			200	100	100	50	150	75	75	25
3			200	100	100	50	150	75	75	25
4			200	100	100	50	150	75	75	25
5			200	100	100	50	150	75	75	25
6		500	200	100	100	50	150	75	75	525
7			200	100	100	50	150	75	75	25
8			200	100	100	50	150	75	75	25
9			200	100	100	50	150	75	75	25
10			200	100	100	50	150	75	75	25
11		500	200	100	100	50	150	75	75	525
12			200	100	100	50	150	75	75	25
13			200	100	100	50	150	75	75	25
14			200	100	100	50	150	75	75	25
15			200	100	100	50	150	75	75	25
16										
17										
18										
19										
20										

Worksheet II, Example 17.9b
DISCOUNTED CASH FLOW

Timing	Trial 1 0%	Trial 2 10%		Trial 3 15%		Trial 4 25%		Trial 5 40%	
Period	Invest.	Factor	PW	Factor	PW	Factor	PW	Factor	PW
Start 2		1.221		1.350		1.649		2.225	
During 2		1.162		1.253		1.459		1.834	
Start 1		1.105		1.162		1.284		1.492	
During 1		1.052		1.079		1.136		1.230	
Zero	500	1.000	500	1.000	500	1.000	500	1.000	500
Total (Y)	500								
Period	C. Flow	Factor	PW	Factor	PW	Factor	PW	Factor	PW
1	25	0.952	23.8	0.929	23.2	0.885		0.824	
2	25	0.861	21.5	0.799	20.0	0.689		0.553	
3	25	0.779	19.5	0.688	17.2	0.537		0.370	
4	25	0.705	17.6	0.592	14.8	0.418		0.248	
5	25	0.638	16.0	0.510	12.8	0.326		0.166	
6	525	0.577	302.9	0.439	230.5	0.254		0.112	
7	25	0.522	13.0	0.378	9.5	0.197		0.075	
8	25	0.473	11.8	0.325	8.1	0.154		0.050	
9	25	0.428	10.7	0.280	7.0	0.120		0.034	
10	25	0.387	9.7	0.241	6.0	0.093		0.023	
11	525	0.350	183.8	0.207	108.7	0.073		0.015	
12	25	0.317	7.9	0.178	4.5	0.057		0.010	
13	25	0.287	7.2	0.154	3.9	0.044		0.007	
14	25	0.259	6.5	0.132	3.3	0.034		0.005	
15	25	0.235	5.9	0.114	2.9	0.027		0.003	
16		0.212		0.098		0.021		0.002	
17		0.192		0.084		0.016		0.001	
18		0.174		0.073		0.013		0.001	
19		0.157		0.062		0.010		0.001	
20		0.142		0.054		0.008			
Total (X)	1.375		657.8		472.4				
Radio X/Y	2.75		1.32		0.945				

The example also illustrates the "round-about" method of computing cash flows and the extra work introduced by the LCM method. The reader should refer to Section 15.16 for a complete discussion on these two points in relation to DCF procedures.

It is seen on Worksheet II that the solution will fall between 10% and 15%. The rate of return by graphical solution or by interpolation is 14.4%.

17.10 ELEMENTS OF MAPI METHOD

The present MAPI method, published in 1958, is basically a rate of return analysis computed from the equivalence of annual costs. However, the basic concept is more complex than this simple statement would indicate. The following are the major elements which make up the MAPI method.

In the first place, the analysis is a one-more-year rate-or-return test. However, the cost of the proposed machine includes the cost of the disadvantages of installing the proposed machine now over waiting 1 year for the improved machine which will appear at that time. These disadvantages of not waiting 1 year are capitalized at 8.25% interest after taxes (the selection of this rate is explained later). Inasmuch as the time value of this stream of money is 8.25%, the rate of return computed by the MAPI method (the urgency rating) is not the rate of return on all dollars. "Urgency rating" is an appropriate name because, while it suggests that the computation gives a value to permit the numerical ranking of all projects, it does not imply that it gives the conventional rate of return on the extra investment.

The initial step in examining the theory of the MAPI method is to explain the computation of the disadvantage of installing the proposed unit A now versus deferring it 1 year to get the improved machine. If the *comparative* cost model developed in Section 10.11 is used, then the following time scales represent the stream of relative costs caused by future deterioration and obsolescence. It is assumed that the first cost of A and of all future machines will be the same, P. The incumbent machine shown on scale B has a 1-year life; an operating disbursement D_B for next year; for the sake of simplicity, a current net realizable value of zero; and salvage values that will be zero at all times.

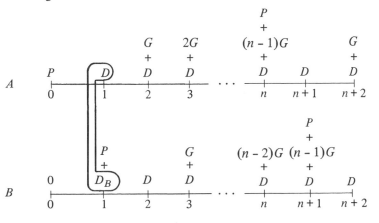

Now subtract B from A, except for the two terms within the loop:

$$A - B \quad \begin{array}{ccccccc} P & -P & G & G & & P & -P \\ | & | & + & + & \cdots & G & -(n-1)G & G \\ 0 & 1 & 2 & 3 & & n & n+1 & n+2 \end{array}$$

Now find the present worth at year 1 of the costs on the time scale:

$$\text{PW at year } 1 = \frac{G}{i} - \frac{nG}{i}(A/F, n) + [P(1+i) - P](A/P, n)\left(\frac{1}{i}\right)$$

$$= \frac{G}{i} - \frac{nG}{i}(A/F, n) + P(A/P, n) \tag{17.10a}$$

Equation 17.10a is the total disadvantage, measured at the end of year 1, of installing A now instead of waiting a year. The first term, G/i, is the disadvantage to infinity of A's inferiority over later, improved machines; the second term, $(nG/i)(A/F, n)$, being negative, is the advantage of A which occurs at n-year intervals, and $P(A/P, n)$ is the disadvantage to infinity of spending P dollars now instead of waiting 1 year.

In the MAPI method the entire expression, 17.10a, will be capitalized at 8.25% interest. The gradient G in this expression is unknown but can be evaluated if we predict the economic life n. Let us examine this problem next.

In Section 10.12 it was noted that A will be replaced when the cost of continuing it for one more year is greater than its uniform annual cost over its economic life. Inasmuch as these two costs approach each other as a limit, we can equate them, as we did in Section 10.12:

$$P(A/P, n) + D + \frac{G}{i} - \frac{nG}{i}(A/F, n) = D + nG$$

or

$$P(A/P, n) + \frac{G}{i} - \frac{nG}{i}(A/F, n) = nG \tag{17.10b}$$

From Eq. 17.10b, G can be computed if n is predicted. We also note that the left side of this equation is identical with the right side of Eq. 17.10a, so we can now write

$$\text{PW}_1 = nG \tag{17.10c}$$

If we examine the derivation of Eq. 17.10a we observe that P at time zero was included in PW_1. It must, however, be extracted from PW_1 and set up on the time scale in order that we may compute the rate of return on it. This is done simply by subtracting $P(1 + i)$ from PW_1 and replacing P on the time scale at time zero.[1] Remembering that as PW_1 is capitalized at 8.25%, then $P(1 + i)$ is 1.0825P.

[1] We of course could have kept P (at time zero) out of the initial derivation of Eq. 17.10a, but we chose the way we did it to better describe the pros and cons of installing A now.

The time scales can now be written as follows:

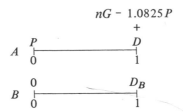

Everything on these scales is known except G, which can be computed as explained previously. Then, by equating the annual costs of A and B, the rate of return on the extra investment in A can be computed. The following example will be used to illustrate the foregoing theory.

EXAMPLE 17.10 A proposed machine costs $10,000 installed with zero salvage at the end of a predicted 20-year service life. Its prospective operating disbursements for the coming year are $3,000 compared to $6,000 for the existing machine. The existing machine has zero net realizable value. The proposed machine is expected to accumulate inferiority G by an arithmetic series. Compute the MAPI urgency rating.

SOLUTION. As noted in the previous discussion, gradient G must be computed. This can be done by equating the annual cost of A over n years to the annual cost for the $(n + 1)^{th}$ year as in Eq. 17.10b.

$$P(A/P, i, n) + \frac{G}{i} - \frac{nG}{i}(A/F, n) + 3{,}000 = nG + 3{,}000$$

where $n = 20$ years and $i = 8.25\%$, the capitalization rate.

$$(10{,}000)(0.1038) + \frac{G}{0.0825} - \frac{20G}{0.0825}(0.02127) = 20G$$

whence

$$G = 78.8$$

Now use this to compute the value of $nG - 1.0825P$ as follows:

$$nG - 1.0825P = (20)(78.8) - (1.0825)(10{,}000) = -\$9{,}249$$

Now the proposed and incumbent machines can be compared on a 1-year life as follows:

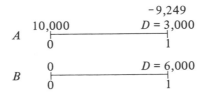

Since $-\$9,247$ is negative, it can be treated as, and can be shown to be, a hypothetical salvage value.

Now find the interest which makes the annual costs equivalent.

$$AC_A = AC_B$$

$$(10,000 - 9,249)(A/P,\ 1) + 9,249i + 3,000 = 6,000$$

$$(751)\,(1 + i) + 9,249i = 3,000$$

$$10,000i = 2,249$$

$$i = 0.2249 = 22.5\%$$

where i is the urgency rating.

The previous solution is intended solely to illustrate the MAPI assumptions. Actually, the MAPI method uses an entirely different formula and technique to obtain the foregoing answer. Before presenting the MAPI method itself we sum up the elements of the method as follows:

1. The life period for the proposed equipment is its service life, i.e., "the period for which you expect to keep the asset." This is the period of ownership; it is not defined as the economic life.

2. The prospective life period of the incumbent equipment is 1 year. The analysis is a one-more-year test. The MAPI forumla therefore is designed only as a test of equipment replacement.

3. The formula capitalizes future sums beyond that of the first year at 8.25%. This rate is derived from a 10% after-tax return on equity and a 25% debt ratio with 3% interest on debt. The resulting 8.25%, $[(0.75)\,(0.10) + (0.25)\,(0.03)]$, is a fixed rate, that is, each of its components—debt ratio, debt-interest rate, and after-tax equity return—is frozen.

4. The urgency rating is a percentage on the extra investment after recovery of all costs, allowing for the cost disadvantage, capitalized at 8.25%, of buying the proposed unit now rather than waiting a year for improved successors. Different dollars therefore have different time values within the formula.

5. The inferiority of the equipment is presumed to increase over the service life according to a predicted pattern or model. When the analyst predicts the service life he is predicting the year when the model will show a minimum annual cost. A specific gradient becomes implicit once the life period is predicted.

6. A choice of three rates of annual accumulation of inferiority is available in the MAPI method:

(a) *Standard projection*, in which the rate of accumulation of depreciation and obsolescence over the service life neither speeds up nor slows down. In this model the increase in inferiority will be an arithmetic series in which the gradient is g.

(b) *Variant A*, in which the rate of accumulation of inferiority is slower in early life than in later life. Mathematically, this is a geometric series in which the annual *differences* between the inferiority in adjacent years increases by the ratio a. For example, if the inferiority in any year t is $G + aG + a^2 G \ldots a^{t-2} G$, the *difference* in inferiority is increasing by the ratio a. For Variant A it is fixed by the relation $a^n = 4$, where n is the service life.

(c) *Variant B*, in which the rate of accumulation of inferiority is rapid in early life compared with later life. The annual cost of inferiority follows the formula for Variant A except that the ratio a is fixed by the relation $a^n = 0.25$. (Note in the standard projection that $a = 1$.)

17.11 THE MAPI FORMULA ITSELF

Now to examine the MAPI formula itself. There are three basic formulas but they differ only as to the assumed accumulation of inferiority, that is, whether Standard Projection, Variant A, or Variant B. Each formula is adjusted for the type of tax depreciation: sum-of-the-year's digits or straight-line. The same formula is used for double-rate declining-balance as for sum-of-the-year's digits because the differences are considered negligible.

The formula shown here[1] is for the standard projection with sum-of-the-year's digits tax depreciation. It is the simplest of the three.

$$C = \frac{n(Q^n - w^n)(Q - 1)^2 - (1 - b)P[(Q^n - 1) - n(Q - 1)]}{nQ^n(Q - 1) - (Q^n - 1)} - (Q - 1)$$

where

$$P = w^n \left[1 - w + py + \frac{(1 - p)z}{1 - b} \right]$$

$$Q = 1 + i - bpy$$

in which the symbols on the right stand for

n = service life
p = fixed debt ratio = 0.25
y = fixed interest rate on debt capital = 3%
z = fixed rate of return on equity after tax = 10%
b = fixed income-tax rate = 50%
i = fixed capitalization rate = 8.25%
w^n = salvage as a decimal of original cost
w = ratio of salvage in year $n + 1$ to salvage in year n.
C = next-year-capital consumption expressed as a ratio of the investment P.
In the preceding illustration it is

$$(10,000 - 9,249) \div 10,000 = 751 \div 10,000 = 0.0751$$

The formula is solved graphically by the use of prepared charts. See the MAPI Charts and Worksheet on the following pages.

---

[1] George Terborgh, *Business Investment Policy* (Washington, D.C.: Machinery and Allied Products Institute, 1958), p. 221.

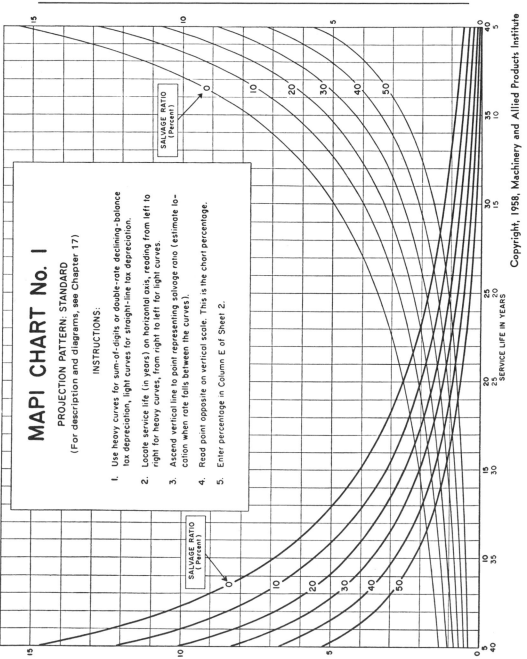

MAPI CHART No. I

PROJECTION PATTERN: STANDARD
(For description and diagrams, see Chapter 17)

INSTRUCTIONS:

1. Use heavy curves for sum-of-digits or double-rate declining-balance tax depreciation, light curves for straight-line tax depreciation.

2. Locate service life (in years) on horizontal axis, reading from left to right for heavy curves, from right to left for light curves.

3. Ascend vertical line to point representing salvage ratio (estimate location when rate falls between the curves).

4. Read point opposite on vertical scale. This is the chart percentage.

5. Enter percentage in Column E of Sheet 2.

SALVAGE RATIO
(Percent)

SALVAGE RATIO
(Percent)

SERVICE LIFE IN YEARS

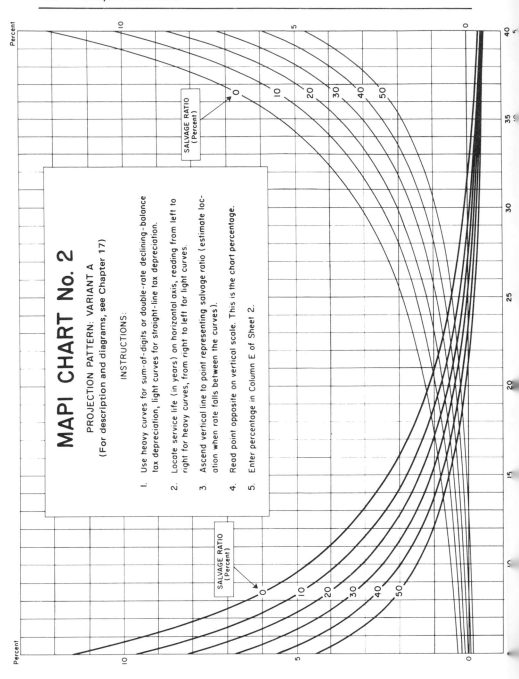

MAPI CHART No. 2

PROJECTION PATTERN: VARIANT A
(For description and diagrams, see Chapter 17)

INSTRUCTIONS:

1. Use heavy curves for sum-of-digits or double-rate declining-balance tax depreciation, light curves for straight-line tax depreciation.

2. Locate service life (in years) on horizontal axis, reading from left to right for heavy curves, from right to left for light curves.

3. Ascend vertical line to point representing salvage ratio (estimate location when rate falls between the curves).

4. Read point opposite on vertical scale. This is the chart percentage.

5. Enter percentage in Column E of Sheet 2.

SALVAGE RATIO
(Percent)

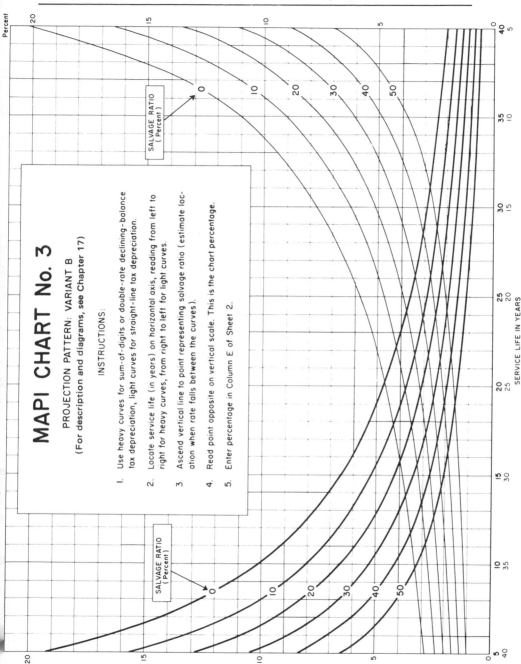

MAPI CHART No. 3

PROJECTION PATTERN: VARIANT B
(For description and diagrams, see Chapter 17)

INSTRUCTIONS:

1. Use heavy curves for sum-of-digits or double-rate declining-balance tax depreciation, light curves for straight-line tax depreciation.

2. Locate service life (in years) on horizontal axis, reading from left to right for heavy curves, from right to left for light curves.

3. Ascend vertical line to point representing salvage ratio (estimate location when rate falls between the curves).

4. Read point opposite on vertical scale. This is the chart percentage.

5. Enter percentage in Column E of Sheet 2.

SERVICE LIFE IN YEARS

SALVAGE RATIO
(Percent)

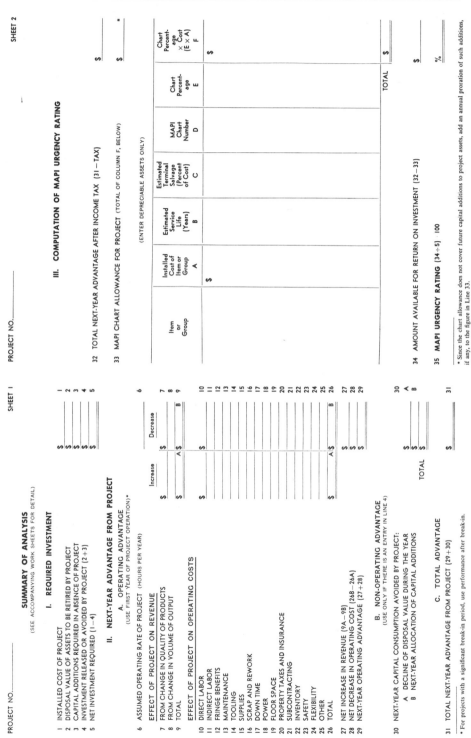

PROJECT NO. _____

SHEET 1

SUMMARY OF ANALYSIS
(SEE ACCOMPANYING WORK SHEETS FOR DETAIL)

I. REQUIRED INVESTMENT

1 INSTALLED COST OF PROJECT
2 DISPOSAL VALUE OF ASSETS TO BE RETIRED BY PROJECT
3 CAPITAL ADDITIONS REQUIRED IN ABSENCE OF PROJECT
4 INVESTMENT RELEASED OR AVOIDED BY PROJECT (2+3)
5 NET INVESTMENT REQUIRED (1-4)

II. NEXT-YEAR ADVANTAGE FROM PROJECT

A. OPERATING ADVANTAGE
(USE FIRST YEAR OF PROJECT OPERATION)*

6 ASSUMED OPERATING RATE OF PROJECT (HOURS PER YEAR)

EFFECT OF PROJECT ON REVENUE

	Increase	Decrease
7 FROM CHANGE IN QUALITY OF PRODUCTS		
8 FROM CHANGE IN VOLUME OF OUTPUT		
9 TOTAL	A	B

EFFECT OF PROJECT ON OPERATING COSTS

10 DIRECT LABOR
11 INDIRECT LABOR
12 FRINGE BENEFITS
13 MAINTENANCE
14 TOOLING
15 SUPPLIES
16 SCRAP AND REWORK
17 DOWN TIME
18 POWER
19 FLOOR SPACE
20 PROPERTY TAXES AND INSURANCE
21 SUBCONTRACTING
22 INVENTORY
23 SAFETY
24 FLEXIBILITY
25 OTHER
26 TOTAL   A B

27 NET INCREASE IN REVENUE (9A-9B)
28 NET DECREASE IN OPERATING COST (26B-26A)
29 NEXT-YEAR OPERATING ADVANTAGE (27+28)

B. NON-OPERATING ADVANTAGE
(USE ONLY IF THERE IS AN ENTRY IN LINE 4)

30 NEXT-YEAR CAPITAL CONSUMPTION AVOIDED BY PROJECT:
A DECLINE OF DISPOSAL VALUE DURING THE YEAR
B NEXT-YEAR ALLOCATION OF CAPITAL ADDITIONS
TOTAL

C. TOTAL ADVANTAGE
31 TOTAL NEXT-YEAR ADVANTAGE FROM PROJECT (29+30)

* For projects with a significant break-in period, use performance after break-in.

PROJECT NO. _____

SHEET 2

III. COMPUTATION OF MAPI URGENCY RATING

32 TOTAL NEXT-YEAR ADVANTAGE AFTER INCOME TAX (31-TAX)

33 MAPI CHART ALLOWANCE FOR PROJECT (TOTAL OF COLUMN F, BELOW)

(ENTER DEPRECIABLE ASSETS ONLY)

Item or Group	Installed Cost of Item or Group A	Estimated Service Life (Years) B	Estimated Terminal Salvage (Percent of Cost) C	MAPI Chart Number D	Chart Percentage E	Chart Percentage × Cost (E×A) F
	$					$
					TOTAL	$

34 AMOUNT AVAILABLE FOR RETURN ON INVESTMENT (32-33)

35 MAPI URGENCY RATING (34÷5) 100

* Since the chart allowance does not cover future capital additions to project assets, add an annual proration of such additions, if any, to the figure in Line 33.

17.12 MAPI WORKSHEETS

A knowledge of MAPI terminology is necessary to use the MAPI worksheets, which are conveniently made a part of the system. The simplest way to learn the terms and the system is to work an example from MAPI's *Business Investment Policy*. The following example is based on one which appears on page 153 of that book.

EXAMPLE 17.12 A grinder to operate 2,400 hours a year costs $6,124 installed and is predicted to have a 15-year service life at the end of which it can be sold for 7% of its initial price. Its predicted next-year savings over the present method of grinding is $2,255 in labor and $565 for fringe benefits. Maintenance on the present grinder has been costing $200 a year but for the new machine it will be only $50. The new grinder also has greater accuracy, an improvement valued at $500 a year in increased income. Additional insurance will run to $60 a year. The net realizable value of the present grinder is $400 and next year's salvage is estimated to be $200. Income tax is 50% and the double-rate declining-balance method of tax depreciation is used.

SOLUTION. The terminology in this solution has been taken from actual worksheets published by MAPI. After a little study, the meaning of MAPI's terms should become apparent.

In line 16, the MAPI allowance of 3.5% is found from Chart 1 (p. 482) using 15-year life, 7% salvage, and declining-balance depreciation. The amount of allowance will be 3.5% of $6,124, the installed cost.

I. *Required investment*

1. Installed cost of project	$6,124
2. Disposal value of assets to be retired by project; this is also the investment released or avoided by project.	400
3. Net investment required.	$5,724

II. *Next-year advantage from project*

A. OPERATING ADVANTAGE

	Increase	Decrease
Effect of Project on Revenue		
4. From change in quality	$500	
Effect of Project on Operating Costs		
5. Direct labor		$2,255
6. Fringe benefits		565
7. Maintenance		150
8. Insurance and property tax	60	
9. Total	$ 60	$2,970
10. Net increase in revenue (line 4)		500
11. Net decrease in operating cost (line 9)		2,910
12. Next-year operating advantage		3,410

B. NONOPERATING ADVANTAGE

13. Next-year capital consumption avoided by project:
decline of disposal value during year $200

C. TOTAL ADVANTAGE

14. Total next-year advantage from project $3,610
15. Total next-year advantage after income tax $1,805
16. MAPI Chart allowance for project   214
    (From MAPI Chart I using 15-year life, 7% salvage,
    and declining balance, the chart percentage is 3.5.
    The allowance is (6,124) (0.035) = 214.)
17. Amount available for return on investment, line
    15 minus line 16 $1,591
18. MAPI urgency rating, (line 17 ÷ line 3) × 100%   28%

17.13 NON-MAPI FORMULA SITUATIONS

A single formula can be built around just so many assumed situations. Additional situations may extend or contradict the basic assumptions to the extent that the formula no longer applies. The following non-MAPI formula situations are specified in *Business Investment Policy*.

1. Future capital additions during the lifetime of the proposed equipment.

2. Present capital additions to the existing equipment (because it extends the life period of the equipment beyond the 1-year test for which the formula is designed).

3. Existing equipment that for any reason has a more than 1-year economic life.

4. Predictable changes in the real cost of the project resulting in favorable or unfavorable future prices (not inflationary or deflationary changes).

5. Equipment not of the "deterioration and obsolescence" type, such as the one-horse shay class or the military aircraft class (termed by MAPI as "predictable total obsolescence").

6. The situation termed "predictable partial obsolescence," which occurs when a proposed machine of the deterioration and obsolescence type is expected to be replaced suddenly by one that is known to be under development (i.e., combined deterioration-obsolescence and military aircraft type).

The following are non-MAPI formula situations not specifically referred to in their publications:

7. The direct *comparison of new pieces* of equipment.

8. The comparison of income-expansion alternatives.

9. Equipment having discrete functional degradation, namely, discrete economic life periods.

MAPI does not pretend that the formula applies to all situations. MAPI's comments for some of these situations are to the effect that the MAPI formula is unsuited to such cases or that one may check it by non-formula solutions. For other non-MAPI formula situations, methods of approximating answers by averaging costs using zero time value of money are suggested.

A further and perhaps more important non-MAPI formula situation is referred to on Pages 12 and 13 of *Business Investment Policy* as follows: ". . . a formula has its main field of usefulness in the appraisal of minor investment projects . . . Major projects tend to be less amenable to formula solutions." Speaking again of major projects, we quote: "Since these projects represent a large investment, they are often subjected to elaborate and expensive investigative procedures . . . These tailor-made forecasts are naturally preferred to the standardized projections implied in an investment formula, useful as the latter may be for small projects."

The reader should not misconstrue these comments on specific limitations to the MAPI formula—MAPI readily points them out. On the contrary, we would prefer to suggest that the MAPI concept of deterioration and obsolescence was a realistic addition to the subject.

17.14 RATE-OF-RETURN METHOD

As stated earlier the rate-of-return method is merely the straightforward application of compound interest mathematics as taught in any basic text or handbook, to an investment situation. Its basic mathematical philosophy is the same as the discounted cash-flow method. In spite of this there are some fundamental differences in technique compared to the DCF method. For example, the rate-of-return method equates annual costs instead of present worths, a technique which avoids lengthy computations if the lives are different. The rate-of-return method expects that the analyst will use all six factors plus the gradient factors instead of only the (P/F) or (F/P) factors if they will simplify the effort. In the rate-of-return method the analyst may work in cash flows but may also treat each alternative as an independent cost stream, depending upon which is easier (whereas the DCF method must be worked in cash flows).

The interest rate is generally discrete in the rate-of-return method and continuous in the DCF method but, after all, this depends solely on which tables the analyst elects to use. In the MAPI method, discrete rates have been used since 1958.

Like the DCF method, and unlike the MAPI method, the rate-of-return method does not bind the analyst to a formula. He can analyze any stream of costs or incomes that he can conceive and quantify which, of course, necessitates his taking time to visualize each cost factor and to set up the problem. However, to require this of the person who proposes to commit the company to a long-term stream to expenditure is a strength, not a weakness, of a system. In order to use this system the analyst must find the facts by whatever degree of research necessary. Of course, he can still design formulas for repetitive use where they are suitable to the situation.

The rate-of-return method as we have used it is not a new approach, even though some of the techniques in the text may be. It is expected that this or other methods that permit financial executives to ladder appropriation requests will, for that reason, probably be the popular methods of analysis for years to come.

Whatever method is used, it can generally be simplified, as we have noticed, by the use of prepared worksheets. Those illustrated here might serve as the foundation for the analyst's own design, commensurate with the background and training of the people who will use them. In preparing sheets of this type even the words and terms employed must be considered in the light of past usage in the firm.

The attached worksheets are largely self-explanatory. The data have been taken from Example 17.9b, but it is apparent that the worksheets can be used for problems of much greater complexity.

It will be noted that we get a different rate of return than in Example 17.9b. This is because we are now using discrete instead of continuous interest, end-of-period instead of continuous payments, and effective instead of nominal interest tables.

Proposal No. _____   Sheet 1

Proposal for Capital Expenditure

Department _____ Prepared by _____ Date _____

	Proposed, A	Present (or Other), B
Name of equipment		
Manufacturer		
Model number		
Purchase price or present NRV	$ 1,000	$ 500
Added first cost	—	
Total investment cost P	$ 1,000	$ 500
Predicted economic life (years)	15	5
Predicted salvage at that time	$ 0	$ 0
Present annual production	100,000	100,000
Required annual production	100,000	100,000
Maximum available production	140,000	125,000
Present age of equipment (years)	0	10

Were other alternatives considered? _____

Briefly describe the nature of these alternatives.

Résumé: Extra investment: ___$500_____

Rate of return: _____15.6_____ % after tax

Payout period (Extra investment/Savings after tax): _____ years.

Discussion and irreducible considerations:

Approval: By _____ Date _____

Proposal No. ——————   Sheet 2

Capital Expenditure Proposal

COMPARATIVE FUTURE ANNUAL OPERATING DISBURSEMENTS

Year	First		Subsequent[a]	
Equipment	A	B	A	B
Annual production (units)				
Direct labor	$100	$200		
Indirect labor				
Material				
Fringe benefits				
Down time (idle labor)				
Rework				
Waste material				
Power and fuel				
Tooling				
Supplies				
Inventory				
Maintenance and repair				
Property taxes and insurance				
Floor space				
Safety				
Other				
Added income (negative cost)				
Total	$100	$200		

Basis for predicted economic lives of A and B

Basis for predicted salvage at that time for A and B

[a]Indicate whether changes are expected in the future. Use added sheets if needed.

Proposal No. _____   Sheet 3

Calculation of Income Tax Effects

Equipment	A	B	Equipment	A	B
Present net realizable value	$	$	Year life period		
Present book value			Operating disbursements	$100	$200
(Gain-loss) on disposal			Depreciation expense	50	100
Tax (expense-saving)			Total expense	150	300
NRV after tax			Tax (expense-saving)	75	150
Cost to overhaul . . . install[b]			Net disbursements	25	50
Investment P after tax[a]	1,000	500	Net savings		
Tax life	20	5	Year		
Investment (for taxes)[c]	$1,000	$500	Operating disbursements	$	$
Salvage at end of tax life	0	0	Depreciation expense		
Depreciation over tax life E	$1,000	$500	Total expense		
SYD First year's depreciation expense $= \dfrac{2N(E)}{N(N+1)}$			Tax (expense-savings)		
			Net disbursements		
			Net savings		
Gradient decrease in annual depreciation expense $= \dfrac{2(E)}{N(N+1)}$			Year		
			Operating disbursements	$	$
			Depreciation expense		
Resulting gradient increase in annual $tax = \dfrac{2(E)(t)}{N(N+1)}$			Total expense		
			Tax (expense-saving)		
Resulting gradient increase in annual savings			Net disbursements		
SLD Annual depreciation $expense = \dfrac{E}{N}$		50	Net savings		
		100	Use extra sheets if needed.		

[a] For new equipment, P is the purchase price plus cost to install.
[b] Excluding expensed items.
[c] The book value, including cost to overhaul, move, and install.

Proposal No. ――――――   Sheet 4

Rate-of-Return Calculation

Figures are (before-after) tax.

Trial 1, $i = 0\%$ (See footnotes a and b.)

$$AC_A \stackrel{\triangle}{=} AC_B$$

$1,000 \, (A/P, 15) + 25 \stackrel{\triangle}{=} 500 \, (A/P, 5) + 50$ whence $i \cong \left(\dfrac{58}{500}\right)(100) \cong 11.7\%$

$(1,000) \, (1/15) \stackrel{\triangle}{=} (500) \, (1/5) + 25$ $P > L$, so true $i > 11.7\%$

$67 \stackrel{\triangle}{=} 125$ Try $i = 15\%$

$0 \stackrel{\triangle}{=} 58$

$0.17102$0.29832

Trial 2, $i = 15\%$ $1,000 \, (A/P, 15) \stackrel{\triangle}{=} 500 \, (A/P, 5) + 25$

$171 \stackrel{\triangle}{=} 174$

$0 \stackrel{\triangle}{=} 3$

$0.21388$0.3344

Trial 3, $i = 20\%$ $1,000 \, (A/P, 15) \stackrel{\triangle}{=} 500 \, (A/P, 5) + 25$

$214 \stackrel{\triangle}{=} 192$

$22 \stackrel{\triangle}{=} 0$

Interpolation $i = 15 + \left(\dfrac{3}{25}\right)(5) = 15.6\%$

Rate of Return

(a) Computed R of R = ___% before tax $\cong$ ___% after tax; or
(b) Computed R of R = 15.6% after tax

[a] Strategic rates to use in the first trial are zero, or perhaps the cutoff rate.
[b] Set $AC_A = AC_B$; or AC of extra investment = AW (annual worth) of savings, whichever is easier.

PROBLEMS

17.1 Can you think of any decision in industry or business which cannot in any sense be described as an investment decision? Prepare to discuss this in class.

17.2 It has been shown that every *spending* decision must be an *investment* decision because the decision is always a comparison of alternatives. However, can you think of any spending decision in which there is no alternative to the expenditure? Are there any investment aspects to this decision? Prepare to discuss this in class.

17.3 Prepare to discuss the premise that the business will be an image of its previous spending decisions.

17.4 Prepare to discuss the contention that "there's no place to hide from a spending decision."

17.5 Prepare to discuss the economic disadvantages of the replacement technique known as the *necessity method*.

17.6 Solve Problem 15.5 by the discounted cash-flow method. Following the procedure illustrated in the text, organize your work by the use of worksheets. If you use the tables on Worksheet II, convert your answer from nominal to effective interest.

17.7 Solve Problem 15.8 by the discounted cash-flow method. Use worksheets where they may serve to simplify your work. If you use the tables on Worksheet II, convert your answer from nominal to effective interest.

17.8 Solve Problem 15.14 by the discounted cash-flow method. Use worksheets where they may serve to simplify your work. If you use the tables on Worksheet II, convert your answer from nominal to effective interest.

17.9 Solve Problem 15.14 by the rate-of-return method.

17.10 A proposed machine costs $15,000 and is expected to have a 20-year useful life with $1,500 salvage value at that time. Its next-year disbursements are $10,000 and its gradient is presumed to be established by the MAPI Standard Projection pattern. The present machine has a net realizable value of $3,000 and a next-year salvage of $2,000 (these values can be used for tax computation). The operating costs for the year are expected to be $13,000. (a) Compute the MAPI urgency rating using the MAPI worksheets and charts. (b) Solve part (a) by the method illustrated in Example 17.10 in the text. The tax is 50% and the depreciation is SYD.

17.11[1] A new method of degreasing parts prior to painting can be installed for $6,923. This equipment is predicted to have a 12-year service life with 5% salvage value at that time. The present degreasing equipment has a net realizable value of $260 and this will decline $100 during the coming year. The new method will save direct labor amounting to $4,150 plus $909 in fringe benefits. Rework totaling $100 a year will also be avoided. The new method employs a process which saves $6,255 in cleaning materials annually. On the other hand, the new equipment results in extra annual expenses of $98 for taxes and insurance, $150 for maintenance,

---

[1] This problem is composed from Terborgh, *Business Investment Policy*, p. 161.

and $910 for power. The tax depreciation method is sum-of-the-year's digits and the tax rate is 50%.

(a) Compute the MAPI urgency rating using the MAPI worksheets and charts. Assume that MAPI's Standard Projection pattern applies. (b) Solve part (a) by the method illustrated in Example 17.10 in the text.

17.12 Solve Problem 17.10 by the rate-of-return method except assume the gradient is zero. What is the percentage difference in the answers?

17.13 Solve Problem 17.11 by the rate-of-return method except assume the gradient is zero. What is the percentage difference in the answers?

17.14 (a) Find the capital consumption C by the MAPI formula (given in Section 17.11) if the useful life is 20 years, the tax is zero, the salvage value is zero at all times, and the minimum required rate of return is 10%. (b) Use you own method to compute the capital consumption C for the data in part (a).

17.15 Use the MAPI worksheets and charts to solve Example 17.10 in the text. MAPI's instruction for the case of zero income tax is to add 5.07% to the Chart 1 percentage.

17.16 Assuming a proposed machine has a next-year operating disbursement of $3,000, a 10-year useful life, and a gradient g of $100, draw the time scale of the comparative annual operating costs (neglecting taxes) for the following MAPI deterioration and obsolescence patterns; (a) Standard Projection; (b) Variant A; Variant B.

18

Public Economy

18.1 PROFIT MOTIVE IN PUBLIC ECONOMY

The motive for making economy analyses is profit maximization. All computations are designed to indicate which alternative, from a set of alternatives, contributes the maximum net profit at a certain time value of money. The general statement of philosophy is that no expenditure is justified unless it can be viewed as an acceptable investment.

Perhaps this goal of spending should be reexamined in the context of public economy. Certainly private organizations and corporations in general exist for profits; but how about public corporations created to carry out functions of the government[1] and eleemosynary corporations formed to conduct charitable functions? The problem seems simple enough: all these organizations spend money and the goal of spending is to create an advantage or benefit for the public or a segment of the public. For example, expenditures for highways should result in benefits to the public using the highways. Such benefits may consist of savings in time because speeds are higher, in distance because the route is more direct, in fuel because the elevations and depressions are levelled, in maintenance, repair, fuel, and time because the surface is smooth, in accidents because the highway is safe according to accepted standards, in waiting time because overpasses and cloverleaves are employed, and so on. Expenditures for highways, bridges, tunnels, waterworks, sanitary systems, airports, libraries, schools, flood controls, and public works of all kinds are "investments;" they are the cause of benefits to the public. The public may benefit directly as illustrated in the previous highway example or indirectly as in the example of a resort operator whose business is increased by improved highway systems.

The basic purpose of the public corporation and the private corporation is the same—to provide a benefit needed by mankind. In fact most public enterprises have been conducted privately at one time or another and, in some cases today,

---

[1] See section 18.10 for a discussion of public utilities.

429

the same services are provided by both types of organizations. Some enterprises are managed by a public organization solely because private enterprise was unable to meet the need at the moment. For example, the Interborough Rapid Transit system in New York City was privately owned like any other railroad, but the rapidly growing needs for additional subway transportation in this great city produced the city-owned subway system which now includes the IRT system.

In some instances the type of benefit provided under the title of "public economy" can result only through political or charitable organizations of the public. In the area of education, for example, the family can seek these benefits through private schools or even private tutors, or may even elect the most costly alternative of all, no education, but in many cases the benefits of education can be achieved only through state organization.

A major difference between public and private enterprises is that public expenditures often benefit those who do not make the expenditures! For example, funds for town road repairs may be supplied from taxes on town property although many who use the improved roads may come from other towns. Certain taxpayers may not even drive cars. The same is true of schools—the large family receives direct benefits from funds supplied by all taxpayers, many of whom have no children to send to the school. Naturally every taxpayer benefits directly or indirectly. Consider the loss to any town resident if his town lacks good roads, schools, or parks. Nevertheless the major difference peculiar to most public enterprises is that the quantifiable benefits may belong to a class of persons separate from those who supply the investment funds and stand the cost.

This doesn't, however, lessen the investment concept. As long as roads, schools, or parks are beneficial to society, a dollar of public funds should be spent only for an alternative, in a set of alternatives, which provides the maximum benefits.

As usual, funds are limited, although the demands for funds can be unlimited. When dollars are limited, they should be used only for investments that will maximize the benefits. At a given moment, for example, investment in a new fire engine may be selected over a proposed highway improvement because it contributes more benefits after costs—even though both would have been selected if more funds had been available.

18.2 COST OF CAPITAL

The tendency is to view capital acquired by the state or public body through its taxing power as free capital. Once before we noted the error in regarding capital retained in a private enterprise as cost free. Public money is no different. The moral obligation is to invest it profitably or let the individual retain it for investment in organizations of his own choice which will supply the intended benefits more economically.

The investment opportunities personally available to the taxpayers serve as the basic guide to the state's cost of capital. A specific expression of these opportunities is to be found in the rate of return on government bonds. These are, we must note, in direct competition with all other investment opportunities of the taxpayer and therefore provide a valid measure of the taxpayer's opportunity cost.

The investors' acceptance of the returns on government bonds, by the fact that they purchase these bonds, reflects their satisfaction with the return in competition with other investment opportunities. This not only establishes the state's cost of capital in projects financed by specific bond issues but it becomes a competent guide to the "cost of capital" in projects financed by the income from taxes. This cost of capital measures the moral obligation for the use of funds obtained through the government's taxing power. A good measure for the productive use of that capital is established by the expectations of the public when permitted freely to invest their capital in a unit of local, state, or federal government (hereafter referred to as the "state").

Again we observe that the cost of capital is not established by the opportunity cost of the organization but by the opportunity cost of the investors in that organization.

This is a broad treatment of the cost of capital; the next step is a consideration of the minimum required rate of return which, of course, is basically a capital budgeting decision, based on the supply and demand of funds. In this respect the basic obligation is to spend the limited funds only for those proposals that promise the highest return to the public. Before proceeding with a discussion of capital budgeting in public economy we should investigate one of the methods used in public economy for evaluating alternatives, namely, the method of computing the benefit-cost ratios explained in the following sections.

18.3 USER'S BENEFIT-COST RATIO

Engineering studies and proposals of public projects generally outline the benefits to be provided for the public by the proposed expenditure. For example, a proposed retention dam will benefit the public by eliminating certain flood damages. These "benefits," expressed in dollars, can be compared to the "cost" necessary to procure them. From this it is possible to compute the "rate of return" on the extra investment by making the annual cost equivalent to the annual worth of the benefits. However, a method that has had more acceptance in public economy is one which computes a benefit-cost ratio. Perhaps a disadvantage of computing the rate of return on the expenditure is the suggestion that the government is profiting on the public or is competing with private enterprise. Erroneous as these conclusions may be, the fact remains that a benefit-cost ratio does have the advantage of placing the emphasis on the *benefits* received by the public instead of on profitability. Another reason, and a very good one, for favoring the use of a benefit-cost ratio is that the benefits may accrue to a group different from the investors.

Perhaps a disadvantage of the rate-of-return method of evaluation, if it is used, is the implication that the rate of return is the return to the investors, which as we know is wrong because the direct beneficiaries, those who benefit from flood control for example, and the benefactors, the taxpayers, may be distinctly separate. In such circumstances the *user's benefit-cost ratio* described in this section may be the most appropriate method of evaluation.

This benefit-cost method computes the ratio of the "users'" dollar benefits to the state's cost of the project in which the time value of money is the cost of capital to the state, as follows:

$$\text{User's B-C ratio} = \frac{\text{AW (or PW) of Net Benefits to the Users}}{\text{AC (or PW) of Net Costs to the State}} \qquad (18.3a)$$

At a benefit-cost ratio of 1, the benefits are equivalent to the costs at an interest equal to the cost of capital, and this establishes the minimum justification for an expenditure, exclusive of irreducible considerations.

In quantifying the user's ratio, the analyst must be aware that "benefits" mean all the advantages, minus any disadvantages, to the *users* and that "costs" mean all the disbursements, minus any savings, that will be incurred by the *state*, namely the governmental body. A proposal with many valuable benefits may contain some inescapable disadvantages to the *user*. These must be treated as negative benefits and subtracted. It is therefore not to be implied that benefits are merely "benefits;" they are in fact the net accrual of the advantages to the user.

Similarly it is possible that the project will create some reduced or negative costs to the state as well as the expected extra costs. Savings in costs to the state are therefore not benefits to the users, but reductions in the denominator of the ratio, the cost. Improper accounting for benefits and for costs can cause considerable error in this ratio because adding a number to the numerator does not give the same ratio as subtracting the same number from the denominator.

The users are, of course, the public who receive benefits from the state's expenditures. "User" must therefore be broadly interpreted to include those who benefit either directly or indirectly.

EXAMPLE 18.3a Traffic lights control the flow of traffic across and between two major highways, Routes *A* and *B*. It is estimated that 50% of the traffic on each route is delayed; the average loss of time per car delayed is 1.0 minutes on Route *A* and 1.2 minutes on Route *B*. The traffic on Route *A* averages 5,000 cars a day, and on Route *B*, 4,000. Twenty percent of the cars are trucks and commercial vehicles; the rest are private. Whether on business or pleasure the occupants' time can be viewed as valuable. The cost of time for commercial vehicles is estimated at $5 an hour and private at $2. The cost of a stop and start is estimated to be 0.6 cents for commercial and 0.4 cents for private cars. Two fatal accidents due to failures to obey the traffic signals occurred in the last 4 years and the insurance settlements were $50,000 for each accident. Forty nonfatal accidents averaging $1,500 occurred in this same period. These accidents resulted from traffic light violations and will be eliminated by the new design.

An overpass with cloverleaves costing $750,000 is proposed to replace the intersection. The extra maintenance will be $2,500 a year. The cloverleaves will add $\frac{1}{4}$ mile to the distance of 15% of the total traffic. The operating cost (increment cost) for commercial vehicles is 25 cents a mile, and for noncommercial, 6 cents a mile.

The cost of operating the traffic lights is $500 a year and a patrolman earning $6,000 a year spends 2 hours a day at the crossing (he is paid to work 2,000 hours a year). No patrolman will be needed with the new structure.

The expected economic life is 25 years with zero salvage. The cost of capital is 7%. Compute the user's benefit-cost ratio.

SOLUTION.

BENEFITS TO USERS

1. Annual savings in delays

Route A = [(5,000) (365) (0.5) $(\frac{1.0}{60})$] [(0.2) ($5.00)

$\qquad\qquad\qquad\qquad + (0.8) ($2.00)] = \$ 39,500$

Route B = [(4,000) (365) (0.5) $(\frac{1.2}{60})$] [(0.2) ($5.00)

$\qquad\qquad\qquad\qquad + (0.8) ($2.00)] = \underline{\quad 38,000}$

Total $\qquad\qquad\qquad\qquad\qquad\qquad\qquad = \$ \ 77,500$

2. Cost of added distance

[(5,000 + 4,000) (365) (0.15) (0.25)] [(0.2) ($0.25)

$\qquad\qquad\qquad\qquad + (0.8) ($0.06)] = (12,070)$

3. Savings in stops and starts

[(5,000 + 4,000) (365) (0.5)] [(0.2) ($0.006) + (0.8) ($0.004)] $= \qquad 7,230$

4. Savings in accidents

$\qquad\qquad (\frac{2}{4})$ (50,000 + $(\frac{40}{4})$ (1,500) $\qquad\qquad = \qquad 40,000$

Total benefits: Item 1. + 3. + 4. – 2. $\qquad\qquad\qquad = \$112,660$

COST TO THE STATE

$\qquad\qquad\qquad\qquad 0.08581$

1. Investment cost: 750,000 $(A/P, .07, 25)$ $\qquad\qquad = \$ \ 64,400$

2. Maintenance $\qquad\qquad\qquad\qquad\qquad\qquad = \qquad 2,500$

3. Savings in operations: $500 + \dfrac{(2) (365) (6,000)}{2,000}$ $\qquad = \quad (2,690)$

Total $\qquad\qquad\qquad\qquad\qquad\qquad\qquad\qquad = \$ \ 64,210$

$$\text{User's B-C ratio} = \frac{112,660}{64,210} = 1.75$$

As illustrated in benefits to users, item 2, the disadvantages to the user must be accounted as negative benefits. And as illustrated in cost to the state, item 3, savings in costs to the state must not be accounted as benefits to the users.

The user's B-C technique supplements the rate-of-return method by emphasizing that the primary purpose of the state is to serve the people. The politician and the voters have another tool to measure the merit of public expenditures. The user's B-C ratio can be viewed as a cost-reduction or an income-expansion concept since it displays a reduction in the user's costs or an increase in the benefits from that service. Take, for example, a proposal to construct a bridge where no bridge now exists—that is, to add to the existing system of bridges. If it is properly located, it not only cuts the user's transportation costs but provides the user with expanded transportation services.

Nevertheless the user's ratio is not intended to replace the annual-cost, present-worth, or rate-of-return methods when public projects are to be evaluated. In fact we can already note that it does not apply to situations in which the only public advantage is a reduction in the state's cost. These topics will be covered in subsequent sections in this chapter.

Although we have a different frame of reference, the accumulation of benefits instead of profits from investments, we nevertheless proceed from a comparison of alternatives as before. In some instances the comparison is between the alternative of "doing" versus "not doing"; for example, a throughway versus none, an added bridge versus none.

In other instances the comparison may be between two similar alternatives of different engineering efficiency; for example, Route X versus Route Y between two points on the map. The extra cost to the state in one route location will provide extra benefits to the users. In this case the benefit-cost ratio will be

$$\text{User's B-C ratio} = \frac{\text{Extra Benefits to the Users}}{\text{Extra Cost to the State}} \qquad (18.3b)$$

This is illustrated in the following example.

EXAMPLE 18.3b Two alternative routes are being considered for a section of a state thruway; a river route and a mountain route. The river route is 20 miles in length and has a predicted first cost of $4,750,000. This is the complete cost of the highway itself plus such items as landscaping, fences, underpasses and entrances, acquisition of land, and so on. The annual cost of maintenance and operation will be $2,000 a mile. A major overhaul and surfacing will be required every 10 years at a cost of $850,000.

The mountain route needs to be only 15 miles long but will cost $6,375,000 because of the extra expense to establish acceptable grades, to bridge ravines, and so on. Major overhaul and surfacing will also be required every 10 years but will be only $650,000. The annual cost of maintenance will be $2,500 a mile, however.

The average speed on either highway will be 50 mph and the average daily traffic is predicted to be 5,000 cars of which 20% will be commercial. The cost of time for commercial traffic is estimated at $5.00 an hour, and for noncommercial, $2.00 an hour. The average cost of operating traffic on the grades of the river route is 25 cents a mile for commercial traffic and 6 cents for noncommercial, but each is estimated to be 15% higher on the grades of the mountain route. Both highways are estimated to have a 30-year life with zero salvage. The cost of capital to the state is 7%. Compute the user's benefit-cost ratio.

SOLUTION.

RIVER ROUTE

1. Cost to state
$$[4,750,000 + 850,000 \overset{0.5084}{\{}(P/F, .07, 10) \overset{0.2584}{+} (P/F, 20)\}] \overset{0.08059}{(A/P, 30)}$$
$$+ (2,000)(20) = \$ \ 475,323$$

2. Cost to users, time
$$[(5,000)(365)(\tfrac{20}{50})] \, [(0.2)(\$5.00) + (0.8)(\$2.00)] \qquad = \ 1,898,000$$

3. Cost to users, operations
$$[(5,000)(365)(20)] \, [(0.2)(\$0.25) + (0.8)(\$0.06)] \qquad = \ \underline{357,700}$$
$$\text{Total cost to users} \qquad\qquad\qquad\qquad\qquad = \$2,255,700$$

MOUNTAIN ROUTE

1. Cost to state
$$[6,375,000 + 650,000 \overset{0.5084}{\{}(P/F, 10) \overset{0.2589}{+} (P/F, 20)\}] \overset{0.08059}{(A/P, 30)}$$
$$+ (2,500)(15) = \$ \ 591,424$$

2. Cost to users, time
$$[(5,000)(365)(\tfrac{15}{50})] \, [(0.2)(\$5.00) + (0.8)(\$2.00)] \qquad = \ 1,423,500$$

3. Cost to users, operations
$$[(5,000)(365)(15)] \, [(0.2)(\$0.25) + (0.8)(\$0.06)] \, [1.15] \qquad = \ \underline{308,516}$$
$$\text{Total cost to users} \qquad\qquad\qquad\qquad\qquad = \$1,732,016$$

$$\text{User's B-C Ratio} = \frac{\text{Extra Benefits to Users}}{\text{Extra Cost to State}}$$

$$= \frac{2,255,700 - 1,732,016}{591,424 - 475,323} = 4.51$$

This method of evaluating projects based on their benefits to the users does not imply that projects of advantage primarily to the state do not exist; they do, and the state should seek them out diligently. These are generally cost-reduction projects (although income-expansion projects are possible) in which the state is the direct beneficiary.

Examples of cost-reduction projects for the advantage of the state would be a machine for faster marking of highway lanes, a machine for better snow removal, a more productive post-hole digger, or machine methods of data processing in the office of the tax collector. In such cases, the user's benefits may be so remote that they may be hard to trace. For example, replacement of old trucks used in highway maintenance may have only indirect and irreducible benefits to the users through the reflection of the savings on future gasoline taxes, road tolls, registration fees, and so on. (Of course, the state and the users may *both* benefit directly. In Example 18.3a benefits accrue to both.) When the state is the primary beneficiary, the user's benefit-cost ratio will not serve as a test, and the annual-cost, present-worth, or rate-of-return methods or the combined B-C ratio described in the next section must be used.

Projects for income expansion might be state-owned race tracks or state-owned liquor stores. The basic objective of establishing these income-expansion enterprises might be social, but one result is an added source of income, obtained from a limited group, to produce wider public benefits. Of course, income-expansion rests primarily on the state's taxing power, but in certain enterprises the state does charge the users for the benefits received, which creates the possibility that the state's investment can be recovered with a rate of return. This return becomes a source of capital for use in other public enterprises.

18.4 THE COMBINED BENEFIT-COST RATIO

The ratio formulated in the last section has been prescribed by the American Association of State Highway Officials. Another and different B-C ratio has been defined by the Bureau of Public Roads. The former is generally regarded as traditional and is reported to have more users. Both authorities call their formulation a benefit-cost ratio. In this text we distinguish them by calling the former the *user's B-C ratio* and the latter the *combined B-C ratio*.

As the term implies, the combined ratio lumps together all the benefits, whether accruing to the state or to the users. Thus:

$$\text{Combined B-C ratio} = \frac{\text{Benefits} + \text{Savings} - \text{Operating costs of users and state}}{\text{State's capital recovery cost}}$$

$$(18.4)$$

The difference between the two formulas results from placing the state's operating costs or savings in the denominator (Eq. 18.3a) or the numerator (Eq. 18.4). Clearly the numerical ratios will be different, as we shall see so are their philosophies, objectives, and conclusions.

A helpful observation is that the combined ratio comes in large part from a restatement of the annual cost, present worth, or rate of return methods, while the user's ratio is essentially different. We illustrate this with an example.

EXAMPLE 18.4 A state can install a new traffic pattern at an installed cost of $295,000. The pattern will cost $5,000 per year to maintain, but the method saves the labor of patrolmen amounting to $20,000 yearly. The motorist will save time valued at $35,000, but will incur extra gasoline and car operating costs of $8,000 yearly. The minimum required rate of return is 8%, and the economic life is 20 years with zero salvage value.

SOLUTION.

1. *Annual cost method:*

Advantage of savings = (Net savings) − (Capital recovery cost)

$$= [(35,000 - 8,000) + (20,000 - 5,000)]$$

$$0.10185$$

$$- 295,000 \, (A/P, .08, 20)$$

$$= 42,000 - 30,000$$

$$= \$12,000$$

The ratio of annual worth of savings to annual cost of capital recovery is thus

$$\frac{42,000}{30,000} = 1.4$$

2. *Combined ratio method:*

$$\text{Combined B-C ratio} = \frac{B_1}{C_1} = \frac{\text{Annual worth of net savings}}{\text{Capital recovery cost}} = \frac{42,000}{30,000} = 1.4$$

3. *Rate-of-return method:*

$$295,000 \, (A/P, i, 20) \stackrel{\wedge}{=} \text{savings of } 42,000$$

$$\text{whence } i = 13\%$$

4. *User's ratio method:*

$$\text{User's B-C ratio} = \frac{B}{C} = \frac{\text{User's net benefits}}{\text{Capital recovery cost} - \text{Net savings to state}}$$

$$= \frac{35,000 - 8,000}{30,000 - 20,000 + 5,000} = \frac{27,000}{15,000} = 1.8$$

While $\dfrac{B}{C} \neq \dfrac{B_1}{C_1}$ as in this example, it is always true that

$$B - C = B_1 - C_1$$

In this example $27,000 - 15,000 = 42,000 - 30,000$.

The example also illustrates that the combined ratio is another way of expressing the rate of return, annual cost, or present worth of the advantage in terms of a ratio, instead of as a sum or percentage.

The merits of each of these methods is examined in the following sections.

18.5 THE BENEFIT-COST PHILOSOPHY

The user's B-C ratio expresses the philosophy that the primary function of the state is to benefit the public with services authorized by the law of the given state. This is the same philosophy which guides the function of a private corporation: its chartered purpose and its ability to exist rest upon the benefits provided to the users of its products or services. Many services performed by the state were once performed by private enterprise—turnpikes, fire protection, education—so where these functions were transferred to the state, the act of authorization is based on the philosophy that the state should serve the public—not itself. The user's B-C ratio helps to emphasize and preserve this point of view.

Let us examine the economic rule of the private corporation that builds diesel engines and the state that provides roads. A new and better engine or a new and better road serves the primary purpose of either corporation. On the other hand, each might also reduce its costs through a more efficient production method or a lower-cost snow removal method. In the sense that these latter improvements do not provide direct benefits to the users, we must observe that the benefits accrue only to the company or to the state. In a private corporation these savings will in time and in some manner be distributed among the shareholders, the wage earners who also share in successes of new ideas, and the users through lower prices according to the dictates of competition.

In the public corporation cost-reduction proposals which contain no benefits for the users serve only the state—namely the taxpayers who pay the costs. For example a cost-reduction proposal for painting roadway dividing lanes affects only the taxpayer's costs, and not the costs and benefits of the users of the highway—unless the state charges the users for the total cost of using the facilities by the payment of tolls, permits, and so on. But a reduction in those fees is even doubtful because the state's monopoly places it under no competitive pressure to reduce its fees except perhaps in competition with another state for tourist trade. Furthermore these fees are seldom earmarked for the function which earned them and are regarded as general state income with little chance of reducing future fees.

Therefore in public economy where we more clearly identify and concern ourselves with benefits to two separate groups, the existence of a separate method to evaluate benefits to users seems especially important (but it does not preclude the need to evaluate the *other* aspects of the project). The user's B-C ratio should also stimulate political acceptance of a project compared to a rate-of-return method which implies profits at the taxpayer's or user's expense.

Although both ratios compute benefits, we should examine how the benefits may be divided between the state and the users.

18.6 SOME DIFFERENCES BETWEEN THE USER'S AND COMBINED B-C RATIOS

Differences between the two ratios can be illustrated most efficiently by examining some typical situations.

Situation 1: The savings (benefits) accrue only to the state, without affecting the users.

An example is an improved paperwork system for use in government offices. Clerical costs are reduced, and there is no effect on paper handled by the public.

This is strictly a cost-reduction proposal. The user's B-C ratio is easily seen to be zero, but the proposal should be accepted if the combined ratio is 1.0 or greater. Similarly, a rate-of-return analysis should indicate a yield at or above the minimum required. As previously noted, the analyst might prefer the combined ratio method to the rate-of-return method, although the results are the same.

Situation 2:   Savings accrue to the state while decreasing benefits to the users.

An example is a wider snow plow which requires less state labor, but which dumps more snow in the driveways of the residents, and thus adds to their time and effort in removing it.

While the combined ratio may be high, the user's ratio will in fact be negative. This is a cost reduction at the expense of the users which should not be justified solely by a high combined B-C ratio or high rate of return without recognizing the user's loss in direct benefits.

Contributions to cost reduction by the users may be desirable in many instances where the services reduced by the state can be handled easily or with little loss by the users, such as carrying litter home instead of dumping it on the highway or being satisfied with one mail delivery a day instead of two.

Carried to the extreme the potentials of this situation are disturbing. For example a public cost-reduction proposal might reduce police protection, fire protection, road maintenance, and so on, beyond the limits of the service delegated to the governmental body. In fact carried to the very extreme a police state can justify expenditures to increase the efficiency of its secret police to more effectively terrorize the public. The question this situation raises is whether every public proposal serves the primary function which the state was presumably empowered to serve.

The situation also finds its counterpart in private enterprise in which the company must examine whether its cost-reduction proposal also reduces the benefits to its clients by curtailing services or by providing a less reliable, more inefficient, or inferior product. In industry, however, such a situation becomes an income-expansion proposition since reducing services affects sales. Among the alternatives available to it, a company may reduce the price of a lower-quality, lower-cost product but expand its income by serving a larger market at the lower price. The market effect on income-expansion or contraction tells the company the services or products most in demand. However public corporations lacking such convenient profit guidelines may overlook the functions they are intended to serve. The user's ratio offers the voter and the politician a method of anticipating the consequences of the proposal.

Situation 3:   The benefits accrue only to the users with no effect on the state's operating costs.

An example is straightening curves on an existing highway to save time and accidents for the users but without effect on the state's costs of maintenance or policing of the highway.

This is the only situation in which the user's and the combined B-C ratios will be equal.

Unlike the first two situations, this expands the state's services to the users without any increase or reduction in the state's operating costs.

Situation 4: The benefits accrue to the users but with savings to the state as well.

This is typical of many highway proposals. Relocating a highway may reduce the state's maintenance costs because of improved construction and shorter length. In Example 18.3a the installation of a cloverleaf increased the state's cost of maintenance but decreased the cost of controlling traffic—resulting, however, in a net saving to the state. In this type of situation, the ratios will always be different except by coincidence.

In this situation we have not only an increase in service but a reduction in the cost of providing it, a situatic frequently encountered when modern technology makes it possible to provide a new product or service. In the given situation the cost reduction is an inseparable part of the expanded service—inseparable up to the point that the innovator may take a second look and find still lower-cost methods of providing the new service.

Situation 5: The benefits accrue to the users with extra operating costs to the state.

An example is a state park with annual costs to the state for its operation and maintenance.

Again the two ratios will be different—and oddly enough, the situation tends to make the combined B-C ratio higher than the users B-C ratio.

Table 18.6 displays the situations discussed earlier and gives the reader an opportunity to observe the effects on the two ratios.

The state's investment in each situation was assumed to be $100,000 with a 20 year life, 10% salvage, and minimum required rate of return of 10%. The annual capital recovery cost, therefore, is

$$P(A/P, .10, 20) + Li = \$12,746$$

The various annual savings are assumed merely to demonstrate the effect on the ratios.

Table 18.6 COMPARISON OF THE USER'S AND THE COMBINED B-C RATIOS

Line	Situation	Cost of capital recovery	Savings to state	User's net benefits	Combined benefits	User's B-C ratio	Combined B-C ratio	% Rate of return
1	#3	$12,746	0	$12,746	$12,746	1.00	1.00	10.0
2	#3	12,746	0	10,000	10,000	0.79	0.79	6.7
3	#3	12,746	0	17,000	17,000	1.33	1.33	14.5
4	#4	12,746	5,000	12,000	17,000	1.55	1.33	14.5
5	#4	12,746	12,000	5,000	17,000	6.70	1.33	14.5
6	#5	12,746	(12,000)	29,000	17,000	1.17	1.33	14.5
7	#5	12,746	(100,000)	117,000	17,000	1.038	1.33	14.5
8	#4	12,746	5,000	50,000	55,000	6.45	4.31	50.0
9	#1	12,746	17,000	0	17,000	0	1.33	14.5
10	#2	12,746	22,000	(5,000)	17,000	(zero) negative	1.33	14.5

It will be noted that the user's ratio can be greater, even much greater, than the combined ratio, and it may also vary, even though the combined ratio and the rate of return remain constant. This is so because the user's and combined ratios test different objectives.

18.7 THE RATE-OF-RETURN METHOD COMPARED WITH THE BENEFIT-COST METHOD

The rate of return is computed by equating the capital-recovery cost to the savings and solving for the i that makes the two equivalent.

$$P(A/P, i, n) = \text{Savings}$$

The combined B-C ratio is computed by dividing the total savings (the net savings to the state and the users) by the capital-recovery method calculated at the minimum required rate of return.

$$\text{Combined B-C ratio} = \frac{\text{Savings}}{P(A/P, i, n)}$$

The two methods therefore agree when the ratio is unity, so whatever the criterion for selection is, either the combined ratio or the rate-of-return method can be used for laddering. The only difference is that they increase at different rates—the combined ratio increases less: as the reader will observe in Table 18.6 the ratio increased 33% and the yield increased 45%.

The user's B-C ratio does not agree with the rate-of-return method. As noted in Table 18.6 the user's ratio increased or decreased, or even became zero or negative, even though the yield was constant. But, as we said, the user's ratio values different things.

18.8 AREAS OF PUBLIC ENTERPRISE

We have seen that benefits to the public may be enjoyed by those (a) who pay no taxes, (b) who are not taxpayers of the district standing the cost, or (c) who are not paying taxes in any proportion to the benefits received. This is both the nature of public enterprise in this country as well as a statement of its philosophy. This philosophy holds that the benefits must not be limited to those who can pay, and further holds that, by extending these benefits to those who cannot pay, society at large will maximize its total benefits.

These enterprises therefore cover areas not usually satisfied by private enterprise, in which the beneficiary is expected to pay for the value he receives. These enterprises cover extensive areas of man's life such as education, public health, police, fire protection, national defense, highways, waterways, coastal service, conservation, and so on.

In some of these cases the recipient presumably does pay for value received, for example a toll bridge which is operated entirely from fees. Nevertheless the enterprise itself may be one that private organizations cannot or would not engage in. The line in these cases may very well be a thin one.

But regardless of who pays for the benefits and who receives the benefits, the benefits should justify the cost or the expenditure should not be made. This is not saying that the investment should not be made if the benefits are not reducible; even irreducible situations can be judged to be meritorious investments.

A public awareness and particularly a legislative awareness of the investment concept and of the benefit-cost concept would do a lot for the generation of better suggestions for public spending. Injudicious spending for highways, bridges, military defense, and public projects to stimulate the economy or satisfy a pressure group can be combated only if the test for judging public spending decisions is better known.

In most cases the benefits from a proposed expenditure can be visualized and reasonably quantified. Examples 18.3a and 18.3b demonstrated the approach to this in highway construction. The same approach serves in the justification of a bridge or bridge location, railway overpasses, flood control, fire protection, water purification, and so on.

In some cases quantification of the benefit may not be required to prove the necessity of an improvement. For example, when an obsolete road deteriorates to the point of becoming almost impassable, the point is reached where something *must* be done about it. Where action is dictated by necessity and quantification is hardly necessary to prove the point, it generally is found that the decision is long overdue. In such cases the failure to make a decision at the proper time in the past has resulted in a loss of benefits over an extended period.

18.9 CUTOFF POINT IN PUBLIC ECONOMY

The supply of capital for public enterprises arises from (a) the taxing power of the state, (b) the state's power to borrow money, and (c) tolls and direct charges for services.

As expected, this supply may be inadequate to meet the demand for funds. Some means of establishing a cutoff point for expenditures is therefore necessary. If the cost of capital is the basis of the time-value calculations, then the appropriation of funds should be limited to those proposals with the highest benefit-cost ratios. Inasmuch as most prominent projects are reviewed in public hearings prior to approval and allotment of funds, opportunity exists to weed out all but those with the highest ratios.

However, in public economy two obstacles to efficient capital budgeting may exist. In the first place, if a benefit-cost *cutoff* ratio has not been established (one reason for this would be the absence of a State unified-budget authority), we can expect that some projects with B-C ratios of only 1.0 might be approved while others with much higher ratios are being rejected.

Complications arising from having two B-C ratios need not prevent using them as a basis of laddering. In the first place we have observed that the combined

B-C ratio provides a means of direct laddering since it corresponds to a rate-of-return laddering. On this we could superpose the laddering justified by the user's B-C ratio. Let us use Table 18.6 as an illustration. If the cutoff is set at a combined B-C ratio of 1.33 (corresponding to a 14.5% rate-of-return cutoff), then we must establish the user's B-C ratio cutoff which, let us say, we set at 1.50. Then only the projects on lines 4, 5, and 8 would be approved.

A second obstacle to efficient capital budgeting in public corporations is the independence of the sources of capital. This may occur if the law specifies the demands to which a given source may be applied. For example, highway tolls may be restricted for expenditures on that highway; or money collected from gasoline taxes may be restricted to road expenditures, not schools; or borrowed funds may be used to finance only the project stipulated in the bond issue. These independent sources of funds result in unequal satisfaction of the demands for different classes of projects. It is very possible that the supply of funds from gasoline taxes may more nearly meet the demands for highway expenditures than the supply of funds from general taxes meets the demands of the school system.

Strong arguments have been presented for and against establishing a common supply from the various sources, but the strongest argument in favor of it is the better opportunity to allocate funds to only the best demands, namely, those with highest benefit-cost ratios.

18.10 PUBLIC UTILITIES

What are some of the aspects of the philosophy of engineering economy pertaining to public utilities compared to the private or public corporations? For state enterprises, we have seen that profit implications are avoided; for public utilities, the profit implication is recognized but expressed as a "fair return." The limitation to a fair return is imposed by the state public utility commissions for intrastate utilities and by the Federal Power Commission, Federal Communications Commission, or the Interstate Commerce Commission for interstate activities. The concept of a "fair return" is commonly based on the rate of return necessary to satisfy the lenders of funded debt and to meet the expectations of the shareholders. Capital expenditures are not justified which do not anticipate meeting the expectations of the people who provide these sources of capital. The "fair return" concept therefore is an expression of the "cost" of capital.

Public utilities generally can meet the demands for capital. Where private corporations are reluctant to issue new equity or to increase the funded debt, the public utilities can generally sell more stock or issue new bonds to finance their needs for additional capital. Financing therefore is not the problem that it is in private corporations or even in public corporations where there is a resistance to raising taxes. The opportunity, therefore, is greater in utilities to saturate the demands down through the cost of capital.

The fact that the rates, fares, or service charges of utilities are regulated by the commissions suggests that profit maximization is not an acceptable term and that it does not apply in utilities. This point of view arises because whenever the prospective earnings exceed a conceived fair return, the utility will eventually be required to lower its charges to the public. But if this is interpreted to mean that profit-maximization is not the goal of every expenditure and the test of approval of every utility expenditure, then some other goal and some other test must be set up. The fact is, however, that utility expenditures are tested by the same basic methods used by private corporations, and profit maximization provides both the goal and the test for the expenditure of every capital dollar. For example, if the annual-cost analysis shows that extra investment in A over B is recovered with a "fair-return" of 7% plus $1,000 a year, A will be selected; but note that the rate of return is greater than 7%, possibly a lot greater. Furthermore, as long as the utility management maintains its search for the *best* alternative in each case, it is engaging in profit maximization. The fact is that the utilities are not rejecting cost-reduction alternatives just because the rate of return may be very high; they are, like private organizations, searching for and accepting the alternatives with the best financial efficiency.

Eventually the continuance of these profit-maximization decisions will produce prospective earnings which will exceed the conceived fair return and prices will be reduced by order of the commission. But note that the same effect occurs in private industry where prices under similar circumstances are reduced— except that they are reduced by the force of competition instead of a commission. This is no reason to conclude that profit maximization is not the goal and test of every expenditure in public utilities as in private industry.

Public utilities cannot afford to neglect a continued vigorous search for investments in new ideas, nor can they adopt philosophies or evaluation procedures that will select anything except the alternatives with the highest financial efficiencies. They are not completely shielded from competition and cannot depend on the commissions to protect their inefficiencies. High rates will introduce competitive alternatives to their products and services. High electrical energy rates permit the economic use of gas, coal, oil and private generating plants and also stimulate private research for substitute heat and energy sources.

High communications rates or poor service awakens competitive methods and provokes research to find economic substitutes. The telephone still competes with every imaginable method of communication. Its use can be affected by every device for faster letter writing, for transmitting the recorded voice on discs, for faster transmission of mails; in fact it competes with devices which increase man's ability to go in person, faster. It must also compete with every other dollar that the consumer spends to raise his standard of living.

Costly transportation resulting from slow, inefficient service and high rates introduces competitive means of transportation. If a railroad, for example, perpetuates obsolete roadbeds and rolling stock that limits the speed of passengers and freight to 30 or 40 miles an hour, it is inviting competition from buses, trucks, private or commercial autos and planes, all of which can exceed these rates of speed.

PROBLEMS

18.1 Describe the monetary benefits that will accrue to the public for the following public enterprises: (a) a highway bridge across the mouth of a bay in an industrial coastal region; (b) a highway tunnel through a hill on a major thruway; (c) a city sanitary system for waste and sewage disposal; (d) a city library; (e) a city airport.

18.2 Show how a taxpayer may benefit from a service for which he pays taxes but which he does not use—for example, a municipal airport—if the taxpayer never uses air transportation.

18.3 Name some enterprises which are conducted in some cases as public, and in other as private, enterprises. Discuss why this may be so.

18.4 Discuss a basis for establishing a "cost of capital" for state funds collected by taxation.

18.5 A bridge connects two main highways, Routes A and B, running parallel to a river. The bridge is also a connecting link in a main highway, Route C, running perpendicular to the river. At present a traffic light at the intersection of Routes A and C and another at the intersection of Routes B and C control the flow along and between these highways.

The traffic on Route A averages 10,000 cars a day, on Route B 3,000 cars, and on Route C 6,000 cars. Fifteen percent of the cars are trucks and commercial vehicles; the remainder are private.

The cost of time if commercial vehicles are delayed is estimated to be $5 an hour; private vehicles, $2 an hour. The cost of a stop-and-start is estimated to be 0.5 cents for trucks and commercial vehicles and 0.25 cents for private cars. It is estimated that 50% of the traffic on each route is delayed at the traffic lights and that the average loss of time on Route A is 0.78 minutes, on Route B 1.6 minutes, and on Route C 1.30 minutes.

The accident record at the intersection of Routes A and C for failure to abide by the traffic signal consists of 4 fatal accidents in the last 5 years and 75 nonfatal accidents. The record at the intersections of Routes B and C is 3 fatal accidents and 60 nonfatal ones. The insurance costs for fatal accidents have been $50,000 per accident and for nonfatal accidents $800 per occurrence.

The cost of operating each of the two traffic lights is $1,200 a year. In addition a patrolman is stationed at the junction of Routes A and C for a total of 8 hours a day for 365 days a year, and one is stationed at Routes B and C for 4 hours a day for every day of the year. A patrolman earns $5,000 a year and works the equivalent of 300 days at 8 hours a day.

A system of overpasses and underpasses, which will permit all traffic flows to proceed without stopping, can be constructed at each end of the bridge. The system at the A and C junction will cost $1,100,000 and that at the B and C junction, $1,200,000. At each of the new intersections, the added annual cost of road maintenance and repair will be $5,000, and each of the new intersections will also add 0.4 miles to the distance travelled by 35% of the traffic. The operating cost of commercial vehicles and trucks is estimated to be 24 cents a mile, and that of noncommercial vehicles, 6 cents. The new system will eliminate the traffic lights and the on-duty policemen, and it is presumed it will eliminate 90% of the accidents that occurred at the intersections. The first costs are based on the economy of installing the entire system.

The expected economic life is 20 years with zero salvage. The cost of capital is 6%. What action should be taken, based on the user's benefit-cost-ratio method of analysis?

18.6 A municipal ferry system across the bay of a coastal city handles an average daily volume of 2,000 cars, of which 20% are trucks and the remainder noncommercial. The crossing takes 15 minutes, but the average delay in waiting for the ferry is also 15 minutes. The annual operating disbursements for the ferry system—fuel, maintenance, repair, wages, and so on—is $450,000. The total book value of the ferries is $2,000,000. They can be sold, as is, to other communities for a total of $500,000. The remaining economic life (and accounting life) is 10 years with zero salvage value.

A toll of 50 cents per car is charged.

The waiting time of commercial vehicles is estimated to be $4.50 per hour and of noncommercial vehicles $2.25. The cost of each stop-and-start is estimated to be 0.5 cents for commercial and 0.25 cents for private cars.

A tunnel has been proposed to eliminate the ferry system. The cars can drive the one-mile crossing at 40 mph without any stops. The total traffic will be 4,000 cars, consisting of the 2,000 cars that use the ferry plus the 2,000 cars that presently avoid the ferry by driving 5 miles around the bay through the city at an average speed of 20 miles an hour, which includes an average of four stops for lights.

The cost of a stop-and-start is 0.5 cents for commercial and 0.25 cents for noncommercial cars. The operating cost of vehicles is 25 cents per mile for commercial and 5 cents for noncommercial cars.

The cost of the tunnel will be $20,000,000 dollars with a 30-year economic life and zero salvage value. The annual maintenance and repair will be $50,000, and the other operating disbursements, mostly for wages of operating personnel, will be $75,000. The toll charge for the tunnel will be 25 cents per car. If the cost of capital is 6%, what action should be taken based on the user's benefit-cost method of analysis?

18.7 An existing highway is 10 miles long and the average traffic speed is 40 miles an hour. The average daily traffic load for the next year is estimated to be 800 cars, of which 15% are commercial and the remainder private. The present net realizable value of the highway is zero and the remaining economic life is estimated to be 10 years.

The present highway can be replaced by a wider, straighter road. Also by rerouting sections of the highway, the distance will be shortened to 8.5 miles between the existing terminals. The average car speed on the improved highway is expected to be 50 miles an hour. The cost of the replacement is $2,400,000 with a 30-year economic life and zero salvage value.

At the present rate of traffic there are 8 accidents per year on the existing road at an average cost of $750. It is estimated that one fatal

accident will occur every 5 years at a cost of $50,000. It is estimated
that for every traffic increase of 100 cars, there will be one more nonfatal accident and the equivalent of $\frac{1}{5}$ of a fatal accident. The new road
will reduce accidents 30%. The daily traffic rate is expected to increase
100 cars a year; for example, 2 years hence it will be 900 cars a day.

Maintenance on the old road is $50,000 a year; on the new road it will
be $30,000 a year. The cost of time saved is at the rate of $4.50 per
hour for commercial and $2.00 for private vehicles. The cost of mileage
is 20 cents per mile for commercial vehicles and 5 cents for private automobiles. The cost of capital is 5%. Using a 10-year study period and the
user's benefit-cost technique, what course of action should be taken?

18.8 Alternative routes are being considered for a new highway between two
cities. Route S will be shorter but will have to be constructed over more
difficult terrain. It will cost $6,120,000 for a length of 15.3 miles.
Annual upkeep and operation will be $81,000. The life will be indefi-
nitely long except for reconstruction every 20 years at a cost of
$1,560,000.

Route L will be longer, but by following the contour of the land it will
be cheaper to construct. It will cost $3,750,000 for a length of 18.5
miles. Annual upkeep will be $98,000. Although its life will be indefi-
nitely long, reconstruction will be necessary every 20 years at
$1,880,000.

The average traffic is estimated to be 1,000 cars a day, 20% of this
being commercial vehicles. The average speed over the highway is expected to be 50 miles an hour. The operating cost for commercial
vehicles is 20 cents per mile and for private cars 5 cents per mile. The
cost of time is $5.00 per hour for commercial vehicles and $2.00 for
private cars. The frequency of accidents is expected to be the same for
either route.

If the cost of capital is 5%, which location should be selected, based on
the user's benefit-cost method of analysis?

18.9 A flood control district can build a system of retention dams to reduce
the annual damage from floods in the spring season. Each dam would be
located on one of the contributory streams to the flood basin. In case of
heavy flood, a gate in a dam is closed and the reservoir (behind the dam)
which is normally empty, begins to fill. The life of each dam is estimated
to be 75 years with zero salvage value. Any one, or none, of these dams
can be constructed.

Dam	Cost of construction	Annual maintenance of dam	Annual cost of damage
None	$ 0	$ 0	$2,400,000
A	11,200,000	280,000	1,500,000
B	8,800,000	210,000	1,700,000
C	7,200,000	180,000	2,000,000
D	4,800,000	120,000	2,150,000

The damages given in the last column are those that would occur if
only the corresponding dam is installed. If more than one dam is in-

stalled the total savings are assumed to be the sum of the savings that each would achieve by itself. If the cost of capital is 4%, what installations, if any, should be made? Use the user's benefit-cost method of analysis.

18.10   Suppose in Problem 18.9 that the total savings resulting from the installation of any 2 dams is 15% less than the sum of the savings resulting from the installation of each dam singly, the installation of any 3 dams is 35% less than the sum of their individual savings, and the installation of the 4 dams is 60% less than the sum of the individual savings. Based on the computations in Problem 18.9, which combinations would you test and why?

18.11   Refer to Table 8.5 in the text and assume that the annual gross income I is, instead, the value of the annual benefits to the public from the investment P and that the annual disbursement D is the cost to the state. If the cost of capital is 5%, make a benefit-cost analysis.

Assuming that the state has established a budget procedure to cut off the combined B-C ratio below 1.0 and the user's ratio below 1.25, what action should be taken? What if the user's ratio is cut off below 1.5? Below 1.35?

18.12   A state can obtain a special machine at a cost of $12,000 that will drill holes for guardrail posts along the highway. The machine will do 43 a day, with a daily labor and fuel cost of $55. Manually, 11 holes a day can be dug at a labor cost of $35. The highway department estimates that not less than 1,500 holes must be dug per year. The economic life is expected to be 10 years with 5% salvage value. If the state's cost of capital is 6%, what action should be taken?

18.13   Discuss the viewpoint of the executive who said, "The utilities' criteria for the selection of equipment is not the same as those in competitive industries, because the maximization of profit is not the objective of the public utility."

18.14   Relative to a proposition involving multiple levels of investment in a proposed ecology project, one analyst maintained that the state should select the level of investment with the highest benefit-cost ratio (assuming it is greater than one). Another analyst said that the state should "saturate the opportunity" by selecting the maximum level of investment which had a B-C ratio of not less than 1.0. How would you respond to this argument?

18.15   Compute the combined B-C ratio using the data in Problem 18.5.

18.16   Compute the combined B-C ratio using the data in Problem 18.6.

18.17   Compute the combined B-C ratio using the data in Problem 18.7.

18.18   Compute the combined B-C ratio using the data in Problem 18.8.

18.19   Compute the combined B-C ratio using the data in Problem 18.9.

19

Economic Difference Between Alternatives

19.1 SENSITIVITY TO ALTERNATIVES

I t would be unfortunate if the only achievement of instruction in this subject was to learn to compute the difference between two given alternatives. This, of course, may be no insignificant achievement, but if a person uses those techniques only to evaluate alternatives conceived by someone else, he is reduced to the status of a technician. Anyone who has developed his abilities to this point of technical competence should realize that the rewards of this knowledge result from its dynamic application to situations which he invents.

As a starting point, the administrator with this technical background can maximize his potential by developing his sensitivity to alternatives. By practice he can develop cognate powers of reasoning for the identification of alternatives.

A person's creativity may extend only to the point of suggesting the adoption of a process or a machine which is already in use elsewhere, or it may extend to the suggestion that a special tool having certain economic features should be put on the drawing boards. He should be in an enviable position to think of divergent methods of performing the company's goals because he knows the economic criteria by which these methods will be tested. His sensitivity has already been developed in a number of ways that he may not even realize at this point. For example, the fact that an executive realizes that machines deteriorate and are continually made obsolete by new technologies makes him aware of the economic advantages of replacing present machines, even those which still have the original coat of paint.

Sensitivity to alternatives is a factor in economic awareness because economic awareness is based on the observation of economic contrasts. The degree of economic awareness in some industrial leaders seems to indicate that they have come by it naturally, but there is no reason why economic awareness cannot be produced and highly developed by education, and the first step in this direction is to increase our awareness of alternatives.

Sensitivity to alternatives is heightened by the recognition of the *economic differences between alternatives*. These differences are in fact the forces that create the alternatives. For example, the executive—in engineering, production, finance, or sales—who senses in the makeready process of all the machines in his factory that there has to be an alternative to the lost machine time while the operator makes ready for the next run, has achieved a sensitivity. He is aware that a process that uses unproductive labor during part of its cycle can be challenged by a process designed to eliminate all or part of that unproductive labor.

Sensitivity to alternatives can be developed by systematically seeking alternatives. This should be done without waiting for instructions from above. It may have to be done alone if no one else is motivated to make the same search.

We believe that the executive must continually practice observing economic differences whenever he sees an operation. He should then attempt to identify the elements of cost and imagine how any important cost item might be reduced or eliminated by incurring another cost in its place—usually a different cost at a different time. We recommend that the executive practice this actively, even to the extent of keeping a book or file of these ideas for investigation and follow-up.

Meanwhile the present student, whether he is in industry or in college, can develop his sensitivity to alternatives by imagining hypothetical alternatives. To help him in this, the present chapter proposes to advance his awareness of differences and his ability to see alternative courses of action. In the following examples, the techniques are secondary, in fact, no attempt is being made to develop new techniques but only to apply those that the reader has now acquired.

We would like to point out also that this chapter should not be viewed as an illustration of the application of managerial and engineering economy. The main objective at present is to increase the student's awareness, not to serve up illustrations of engineering economy principles. We trust this will be a dynamic approach inasmuch as "application examples" can be a static educational experience, because the student will seldom experience a situation which duplicates the illustration in the text.

Einstein once said, "Imagination is more important than knowledge." We hope, therefore, that the student will practice an imaginative use of this management tool and that he will see in the following examples, not rigid applications, but examples of someone's economic awareness.

19.2 OVERRATING EQUIPMENT

The alternative to operating equipment as its nameplate rating is to overrate it, to exceed its nameplate specifications, as illustrated in the following example.

EXAMPLE 19.2 A proposed centrifugal machine for pulverizing coarse material has a nameplate rating of 120 rpm and 30 horsepower input to the motor.

The engineering department observes that the machine can be operated safely at a 25% increase in speed with satisfactory "fineness" of the ground material. The pounds of material ground by the machine and the labor hours to operate it will be proportional (directly or indirectly) to rotative speed. Since centrigural force is proportional to the square of the rotative speed, the horsepower, which is equal to force times speed, will be directly proportional to the cube of the speed. This is the power input to the material to reduce its coarseness. The power input to the motor must be adjusted to the efficiency of the system at each power level.

From the efficiency curve of the machine the following efficiencies are predicted at various speeds:

Rpm	Efficiency (%)
120	75
130	77
140	78
150	79
160	78
170	70
180	65

It is estimated that the life of the machine will be 12 years if it performs the required work load at 120 rpm, but that the life at any other speed will vary inversely as the square of the speed (i.e., inversely as the force). Maintenance, which is $1,000 a year at 120 rpm, is expected to vary directly as the square of the speed.

The machine costs $14,500, including a 30 horsepower motor. Higher first costs are shown in Table 19.2 to allow for the larger motors required at higher speeds. Salvage is presumed to be zero whenever the machine is retired. Power costs 3 cents per kilowatt-hour. At the rated speed of 120 rpm the machine is tended by two operators who work $1\frac{1}{2}$ shifts for the 250-day working year to produce the required output. The machine tenders earn $2.00 an hour. At other speeds two operators can still handle the machine's output.

What is the economy of overrating the machine if the minimum required rate of return is 25% before taxes?

SOLUTION. At 120 rpm:
Labor cost:

$$(250 \text{ days})(1.5 \text{ shifts})(8 \text{ hr/day})(\$2/\text{hr})(2 \text{ operators}) = \$12,000/\text{yr}$$

Energy cost:

$$(30 \text{ hp})(0.746 \text{ kw})(3,000 \text{ hr/yr})(\$0.03/\text{kwh}) = \$2,014/\text{yr}$$

Disbursements:

$$\text{labor} + \text{maintenance} + \text{energy} = 12,000 + 1,000 + 2,014 = \$15,014$$

Capital recovery:

$$14,500 \, (A/P, .25, 12) \overset{0.26845}{=} \$3,893$$

At other speeds the operating costs must be adjusted according to their relation to the speed. The input to the motor must also be adjusted according to the machine efficiency at that speed. The life periods are carried to the nearest integer in computing the capital recovery cost.

Based on this analysis, 140 rpm, a 16.7% increase in speed, is advocated despite the shortened physical life and despite the increase in horsepower and maintenance to produce the required output.

As noted, the point of most economic operation may or may not occur at the manufacturer's rating. In the given example the factors which determined this point were the labor rate, the required output or degree of utilization, the maintenance cost at a given rate of production, the expected life with a given work load, the degree of fineness required, and the minimum required rate of return. It is conceivable, as the next section will illustrate, that under-rating might also be an economic course of action.

If safety hazards are not created by the decision, it may pay to "overrate" equipment as long as some conditions exist which are favorable to "overrating." In some cases the only added cost is that due to the shortening of the equipment life. But this cost is far in the future and, in consideration of the time value of money, it is less significant than the earnings, which are in the immediate future.

The lives of certain pieces of equipment or their components may be shortened by impact forces as in the case of hammers, drivers, forges, and stamping machines. The lives of other pieces of equipment depend on temperature. In this class are electric motors or generators, in which the temperature rise of the winding accounts for the deterioration of the insulation. It is well known

Table 19.2 ANNUAL COST FOR VARIOUS DEGREES OF OVERLOADING A MACHINE

	Rpm			
	120	130	140	150
First cost	$14,500	$14,700	$14,900	$15,100
Life (yrs)	12.0	10.2	8.8	7.7
Labor (hr)	6,000	5,538	5,143	4,800
Labor cost	$12,000	$11,076	$10,286	$ 9,600
Maintenance cost	$ 1,000	$ 1,174	$ 1,361	$ 1,563
Output (hp)	22.5	28.6	35.7	43.9
Input (hp)	30.0	37.1	45.8	55.6
Energy cost	$ 2,014	$ 2,299	$ 2,636	$ 2,986
Disbursements	$15,014	$14,549	$14,283	$14,149
Capital recovery	$ 3,893	$ 4,117	$ 4,302	$ 4,536
Annual cost	$18,907	$18,666	$18,585	$18,695

that the life of incandescent electric light bulbs is a function of temperature. As stated earlier, the same factors that presently suggest overrating may, under other circumstances, lead to the conclusion that it is economic to underrate equipment.

19.3 UNDERRATING EQUIPMENT

Underrating has the advantage of increasing physical life. Therefore underrating is more likely to be economical in a situation experiencing high equipment cost relative to operating cost.

Underrating generally results in decreased operating efficiency and therefore for underrating to be economically feasible it is often necessary to have a situation in which there is low utilization and perhaps low unit-cost.

Underrating also has the advantage of reducing maintenance, and a situation where maintenance costs are very significant may be sufficient to justify it.

EXAMPLE 19.3 A mine uses 3,000 60-watt, 110-volt incandescent bulbs to light its shafts and its outdoor structures, elevators, and equipment. All power lines are 110-volt and well regulated from the mine's own power plant at the shaft head. Power costs 1 cent per kilowatt-hour and all lights burn continuously, day and night. The cost of a 60-watt bulb installed is 60 cents, largely due to the inaccessibility of the lighting fixtures. Consider the advantage or disadvantage of underrating 75-watt bulbs costing 65 cents installed.

SOLUTION. Three designs of light bulbs are available: 120-volt, 115-volt, and 110-volt. If 75-watt 120-volt lamps are used on the 110 volt lines the temperature of the filament decreases, causing an increase in life and a decrease in efficiency of the lamp. The efficiency of the lamp is expressed in lumens per watt; namely, the lumens output divided by the watts input. As expected, the lumens output will decrease with underrating. The 75-watt lamp operated at its design voltage has an average life of 1,000 hours, gives 1,100 lumens, and nominally takes 75 watts. The 60-watt lamp on rated voltage has an average life of 1,000 hours and gives 835 lumens for 60 watts.

On other than rated voltage, the variations in life, lumens output, and voltage input are nonlinear as follows[1] (in these formulas the uppercase letters represent the normal or design conditions):

$$\frac{\text{life}}{\text{LIFE}} = \left(\frac{\text{VOLTS}}{\text{volts}}\right)^{13.1}; \frac{\text{lumens}}{\text{LUMENS}} = \left(\frac{\text{volts}}{\text{VOLTS}}\right)^{3.38}; \frac{\text{watts}}{\text{WATTS}} = \left(\frac{\text{volts}}{\text{VOLTS}}\right)^{1.54}$$

Therefore, for the 75-watt, 120-volt lamp operated on 110-volts.

$$\text{life} = (1,000)\left(\frac{120}{110}\right)^{13.1} = (1,000)(3.126) = 3,126 \text{ hours}$$

---

[1] *McGraw-Hill Encyclopedia of Science and Technology*, 3rd ed., s.v. "incandescent lamp."

$$\text{lumens} = (1{,}100) \left(\frac{110}{120}\right)^{3.38} = (1{,}100)(0.745) = 820 \text{ lumens}$$

$$\text{watts} = \quad (75) \left(\frac{110}{120}\right)^{1.54} = \quad (75)(0.875) = 65.6 \text{ watts}$$

$$60 \text{ watt, AC} = \frac{(365)(24)(0.60)}{1{,}000} + \frac{(60)(8{,}760)(0.01)}{1{,}000} = 5.26 + 5.26 = \$10.52$$

$$75 \text{ watt, AC} = \frac{(365)(24)(0.65)}{3{,}126} + \frac{(65.6)(8{,}760)(0.01)}{1{,}000} = 1.82 + 5.75 = \underline{\quad 7.57}$$

$$\text{Annual advantage per socket } \$ \ 2.95$$

Total annual advantage of underrating for 3,000 bulbs = $8,850.

It will be noted that the underrated lamp gives 820 lumens compared to 835 for the 60-watt bulb, so that the saving is also accompanied by 2% loss in light. Actually, one cannot do anything about this drop in light other than decide (1) whether it is acceptable, (2) whether an annual saving of $8,850 justifies a 2% reduction in light.

As in all economy problems the comparison should be made on the same output. Although it may not be possible to adjust the voltage so that each lamp will give the same lumens, we can at least compare the results over equal lumen-hours.

$$60\text{-watt lamp, cost per million lumen hours} = \frac{(10.52)(10^6)}{(8{,}760)(835)} = \$1.44$$

$$75\text{-watt lamp, cost per million lumen hours} = \frac{(7.57)(10^6)}{(8{,}760)(820)} = \$1.06$$

Based on the same output, the underrated lamps are about 74% as expensive.

19.4 INDUSTRIAL RESEARCH TO ESTABLISH DIFFERENCES

Industrial research takes its direction from the economic factors in the company's activities—or it should. The best investment of the company's research time and expense will result if the research efforts are conducted in areas where the promise of financial rewards are the greatest. One cannot predict the results of research, but research must be presumed to be successful or companies would not engage in it. It is logical to outline in advance those areas where research, if successful, will produce the greatest savings or the greatest expansion of income. This presumes defined research objectives (compared to open-end research) and neglects chance discoveries unrelated to those objectives.

An illustration of this is research conducted with the objective of reducing the cost of cutting metal, a problem of major interest to a company whose most important costs are in this area. Specific problems of economic interest might be the frequency of sharpening tools, the speed as well as the depth of cut, the tool material, cooling the cutting tool, and so on.

One of the best known examples of industrial research to determine the economic differences between alternatives is the work of Frederick W. Taylor on the economic life of cutting tools. We will take this example to illustrate the necessity of research to establish the values of cost elements after economic awareness indicates their existence.

Taylor, who is acknowledged to be the father of scientific management, conducted many experiments in other fields to quantify the economic differences between the alternatives of which he was so keenly aware. Taylor set a good example for engineering economists by demonstrating the need for research and a scientific approach to produce the data required for an economy analysis.

The economics of tool life arise from the fact that high cutting speeds reduce labor cost but also reduce tool life and increase the number of sharpenings for a given amount of production.

We will define economic tool life as the most economic operating period until resharpening is necessary. This is not the total tool life, because the tool can be resharpened many times, but note that the number of sharpenings will be the same for each tool (just so much total steel can be removed).

The operating life of the tool between sharpenings is expressed by this empirical formula:[1]

$$T = \left(\frac{C}{V}\right)^{10}$$

where T is the cutting period in minutes until the tool must be sharpened again; V, velocity, is the cutting speed of the tool in feet per minute; and C is a constant depending on the material.

EXAMPLE 19.4 Compute the most economic tool life if any cutting speed can be selected and if the tool life varies according to the previous empirical formula. The machine rate is $1.50 an hour and the labor rate for tending it is $3.00 an hour. The tool costs $1.60 and can be resharpened nine times. The sharpening device has a machine rate of $0.40 and a labor rate of $3.05 an hour. It requires 6 minutes to sharpen the tool and the downtime of the machine for tool replacement is 3 minutes. Neglect tax effects. It is presumed that machine time saved cannot be put to other use. The required production is 100,000 pieces a year and the machine can produce 5.95 pieces per minute at 500 feet per minute cutting speed. The constant C is 500 for the given material.

Sufficient tools are kept in stock so that the cutting machine is delayed only for a change of tools. Also assume the salvage value of the tools is zero.

SOLUTION. The comparative cost of one sharpening is

$$\frac{1.60}{10} + (3.00)\left(\frac{3}{60}\right) + (3.05)\left(\frac{6}{60}\right) = \$0.62$$

[1] N. E. Woldman and R. C. Gibbons, *Machinability and Machining of Metals* (New York: McGraw-Hill, 1951), Fig. 14, p. 26.

Inasmuch as the tool can be used for 10 production runs (assume these equal to the number of sharpenings), the tool cost allocated to each sharpening is 1.60/10. The machine costs are sunk costs because, as stated in this particular example, savings in machine time cannot be applied elsewhere. On the other hand, it is presumed that labor savings can be realized by a reduction in the labor force.

From the formula $T = (C/V)^{10}$, in which C is 500, we can compute T for various assumed cutting speeds. The results are shown in Table 19.4.

The time to machine 100,000 pieces at 500 fpm is $(100,000)/(5.95)(60) = 280$ hours. The production time at any other tool velocity is inversely proportional to the cutting speed. All of these are summarized in the table.

At 500 fpm the number of production runs would be $(280)/(60)/(1.00) = 16,800$, because the tool would have to be changed every minute (for simplicity, let the number of sharpenings equal the number of production runs).

The labor cost of operating the machine at 500 fpm is $(\$3.00)(280) = \$840$ (again for simplicity, disregard the difference in power at various cutting speeds). The cost of sharpening at 500 fpm is $(16,800)(0.62) = \$10,400$.

Table 19.4 COMPUTATION OF ECONOMIC LIFE OF A CUTTING TOOL

Tool speed, V (fpm)	500	346	322	317	309	300	294
Tool life, T (min)	1	40	80	100	120	160	200
Total machining time (hr)	280	405	435	441	452	466	476
Number of runs	16,800	608	326	265	226	175	143
Labor cost of machining	$ 840	1,215	1,305	1,323	1,356	1,398	1,428
Comparative cost of sharpening	$10,400	377	202	164	140	109	89
Total cost	$11,240	1,592	1,507	1,487	1,496	1,507	1,517

Table 19.4 indicates that the economic tool life is approximately 100 minutes.

As stated in Section 19.1, the goal of this chapter is to create an awareness of differences. If this has been achieved, the next step is to quantify the differences by elaborate research if necessary. The limitations of space prevent us from presenting the complete and rigorous research data which apply to any of the illustrations in this chapter; to do so would require many books to adequately explain the data. A proper study of various information on maximum tool economy requires far more time than we have devoted to it here. Such expositions belong to other phases of engineering such as machine design, metallurgy, heat, light, and so on, over the entire field of engineering and the entire field of business, too.

19.5 WHAT ARE THE ALTERNATIVES?

Sometimes inability to analyze the economics of a situation is solely the result of not having defined the situation in the first place. Until a situation can be clearly visualized it is impossible to envisage the present economic model no less than various alternatives to it. The following example is a typical illustration of this. As a result of the failure of anyone to define the situation and establish an issue based upon the existence of some real alternatives, the argument continued endlessly and aimlessly.

EXAMPLE 19.5 The following news item covered an occurrence in a New England town meeting:

"Rivertown. Just before the Council meeting ended, Ellsworth questioned a figure of $18,400 used in the campaign statement of Jackson that indicated the local financial obligation in continued maintenance of the bridge. Ellsworth told the city council he felt the cost was too high.

"Jackson said the sentence Ellsworth challenged read: 'Continued maintenance of this bridge in the township involves an annual cost to Rivertown of about $18,400 including interest and depreciation.'

"According to Jackson this estimate was based upon the following factors: 'Painting cost is $2,000 and should be done every four years at a cost of about $8,000.

"Resurfacing costs $200 and should be done every 10 years at a cost of $2,000. Depreciation is about $5,400. This assumes a replacement value of about $270,000 and a 50-year life.

"Interest,' he continued, 'would be $10,800 and is based upon 4% for an investment of this size. The total annual cost is $18,400.

"Admittedly, the depreciation and interest charges are not current, direct, out-of-pocket expenses to Rivertown, but they do indicate the accrued liability which becomes Rivertown's responsibility with the continued maintenance of a bridge this size.'

"He concluded by stating, 'The replacement cost used in these estimates is definitely conservative as indicated by a rough figure of $500,000 supplied today by the Department of Public Works and Highways as the current cost of rebuilding a structure of this size, even with its present inadequate width.' "

SOLUTION. What was Jackson's purpose in presenting this statement in his campaign? We can undoubtedly rule out that his aim was to let the people know what they *have* been paying annually for the bridge, because without some implied action in the future his statement could not have been a campaign issue. Furthermore, the introduction of replacement costs suggests future action. If Jackson had intended to report on sunk costs he could have produced these with less trouble and greater accuracy. This statement, therefore, must imply future alternative courses of action such as the following sets:

Set 1. Keep the present bridge versus discontinue the bridge.
Set 2. Keep the present bridge versus replace the bridge.

Set 3. Keep the present bridge versus replace the bridge at a new site.

Set 4. Enlarge the present bridge versus build a larger bridge.

The number of alternatives will exceed this list because the types of replacements and the locations of these replacements are very great. However, for any of these alternatives, a clear argument necessitates a clear definition of the alternatives. If, for example, the problem had been recognized as Set 2, "Keep the present bridge versus replace the bridge at the same site," the annual cost of keeping the present bridge might be expressed by the following time scale:

```
25,000
 2,000
 8,000              8,000              L = 25,000
 ├──────────────────┼──────────────────┤
 0                  4                  8
```

The basic assumptions are that the bridge is currently due for painting and resurfacing, a conservative assumption which gives the highest annual cost. The present net realizable value of the bridge we have assumed to be its scrap value after demolition, which we estimated to be $25,000. The salvage at the end of the economic life will also be the scrap value, $25,000. The remaining economic life of the bridge is likely to be found in Jackson's observation of its "present inadequate width." We have assumed that this would become intolerable after 8 years. At 4% cost of capital the annual cost of keeping the bridge will be

$$[35,000 + 8,000 \underset{0.8548}{(P/F, .04, 4)} - 25,000 \underset{0.7307}{(P/F, 8)}] \underset{0.14853}{(A/P, 8)} = \$3,500$$

The annual cost can be lower than this if the painting and surfacing are not due at once, or it can be higher because comparative costs depend on the features of the proposed alternatives: for example, if the replacement bridge will have many safety features, including extra width, the present bridge can be charged with the annual cost of the probable extra accidents over those on the safer replacement.

Although the proposed analysis still leaves plenty of room for argument on items such as the economic life, net realizable value, and the amount and date of maintenance, the constituents of Rivertown can now argue on common issues.

19.6 THE NEED TO KEEP ALTERNATIVES SEPARATE

A mistake almost identical with the failure to define the alternatives illustrated in the last section, is the failure to keep alternatives separate. By not adequately defining the alternatives we may not observe that they are combinations of separate alternatives.

A very simple example of this is the comparison of a new machine with the proposed redesign and reconstruction of a present machine. The latter is, in effect, two separate alternatives, namely, the present machine "as is" and the proposed improvement of it. If the latter loses the contest with the proposed new machine, it is still possible that the old machine might win it without redesign.

Another example is the proposal to replace two machines with a single machine. In this case, assume that one of the existing machines, being less efficient than its teammate, is not assigned as much work. There are several alternatives within "the proposal to replace both machines with a single machine", and to overlook these invites the possibility of neglecting some potential winners. Here the combination of alternatives is very obvious but in some situations this may not be so apparent, as the following example illustrates.

EXAMPLE 19.6 A machine can be purchased for $40,000 cash or for $20,000 down and the balance in 6% notes requiring equal payments of the principal over the next 10 years. For example, the payment due at the end of year 1 is $2,000 + (0.06)(20,000) = \$3,200$. At the end of year 2 it is $2,000 + (0.06)(18,000) = \$3,080$, and so on.

The machine disbursements for labor, power, maintenance and so on will be $14,000 a year. The present method employs manual labor costing $25,000 a year. The economic life of the process is 10 years with zero salvage.

Based on a before-tax computation, discuss the recommended action.

SOLUTION. The time scales of the alternatives will be as follows:

Machine 20,000 14,000 14,000 14,000 every year
With   +   +   +
Time   3,200 3,080 2,960   and so on where $G = -120$ $L = 0$
Payments   0   1   2   3   10

Manual $\begin{matrix}0 \\ 0\end{matrix}$ $D = 25,200$ $\begin{matrix}L = 0 \\ 10\end{matrix}$

Let $AC = AC$

$$20,000 \, (A/P, i, 10) + 17,200 - 120 \, (A/G, 10) = 25,200$$

By trial and error,

$$i \cong 40\%$$

This appears to be a commendable proposition if, for example, the cost of debt capital is 6%, the cost of equity capital is 11%, and the cutoff rate is 30%. However, let us now observe that the proposition is really a combination of two independent alternative actions. One is whether to install a machine or continue with the present method; the other is whether to borrow money or self-finance the purchase. Let us examine each alternative separately.

First, whether to replace the manual method with a machine:

Machine
40,000 | 0 ——— D = 14,000 ——— L = 0 | 10

Manual
0 | 0 ——— D = 25,200 ——— L = 0 | 10

Let

$$AC = AC$$

$$40{,}000 \, (A/P, i, 10) + 14{,}000 = 25{,}200$$

which gives a rate of return of 25%.

Second, whether to borrow money or self-finance:

Self-finance
40,000 | 0 ————————— ··· ————— 0 | 10

Borrow
20,000 3,200 3,080 2,960 ——— where $G = -120$ ··· ———
0   1   2   3   10

Let

$$40{,}000 \, (A/P, i, 10) = 20{,}000 \, (A/P, 10) + 3{,}200 - 120 \, (A/G, 10)$$

This gives a rate of return of 6%. Of course we expected this, inasmuch as the loan was at 6%.

These last two analyses show that one question is whether to invest in a new machine which promises a rate of return of 25%. We will reject this proposition because the minimum required rate of return is 30%. The second question is whether to finance the machine, if it proves economical to buy it, by borrowing funds at 6%. These are two separate questions: Should we purchase the machine with our own funds for $40,000? Should we borrow funds at 6%?

The initial analysis shows that combining these separate propositions can result in a disproportionate and deceiving evaluation. Combining the independent propositions gives a 40% return versus a true return of 25% and 6% on the two separate propositions. Furthermore, the smaller the down payment the greater the combined return will be—for example, find the rate of return if the down payment is only $10,000.

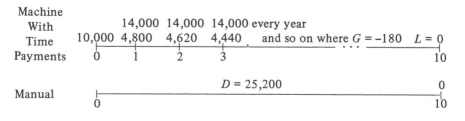

Machine With Time Payments
14,000 14,000 14,000 every year
10,000 4,800 4,620 4,440   and so on where $G = -180$ L = 0
0   1   2   3   ···   10

Manual
0 ——— D = 25,200 ——— 0 | 10

whence `   10,000 $(A/P, i, 10)$ + 18,800 − 180 $(A/G, 10)$ = 25,200

which, by trial and error, gives a return of 66%.

The rates of return on the separate propositions will be 25% and 6% as before but the rate of return on the combination has now become 66% instead of 40%. This is to be expected because the same savings which recovered $40,000 with 25% return will recover $10,000 with a much higher return. In fact, the rate of return will become infinite if *no* down payment is required!

19.7 THE CASE OF NO ALTERNATIVES

Too often we encounter a situation where there is no alternative course of action—for example, where the incumbent machine has reached the end of its physical life and if not replaced at once will leave us without a means of conducting the operation. Such a replacement is imperative and needs no mathematical analysis.

A comparable situation occurs where the incumbent machine is so old and the savings from a new machine are obviously so great that the need to make a computation of the rate of return seems ridiculous. When one of our graduate students was investigating industrial projects some years ago, he encountered one of these and was told by an executive, "You can use your mathematics to figure this one out if you want to, but any fool knows that it should be replaced." There was in truth no other alternative but to replace.

Each of these situations is a signal that replacement is generally long overdue and that the decision which dictated replacement was not made when it should have been. Whenever the engineer or the manufacturing manager sponsors such a replacement it is generally not advisable for him to point out that an analysis is ridiculous, but rather to anticipate the implication that a considerable amount of money has been lost by not replacing the machine on time. The following simple example in personal finance does some exploratory on this problem.

EXAMPLE 19.7a Suppose an investor purchased a mortgage for $10,000 which is to be repaid in annual year-end installments of $1,358.68 for 10 years.

The question is how to demonstrate the advantages of making this investment over (a) not making any; (b) making a less profitable investment.

SOLUTION. The only reality, of course, is that the investor has exchanged $10,000 for a stream of incomes of $1,358.68 a year for 10 years. But this is difficult to envisage beyond the fact that he will receive $1,358.68 distributed over 10 years compared to $10,000 at the outset.

A more effective comparison results from computing the return on the investment.

$$10,000 \, (A/P, i, 10) = 1,358.68$$

whence
$$i = 6\%$$

The advantage of making the investment versus not making it at all is an annual return of 6% after recovering the investment; and the advantage compared to a less profitable investment is the difference between 6% and the return on that investment.

By adopting certain assumptions we can demonstrate the advantages in other ways. For example, if by assuming that the investor would reinvest the returns and that these would have equal investment opportunities, the sum F that would be accumulated as the result of the investment and reinvestment would be

$$\overset{13.181}{F = 1{,}358.68\ (F/A, .06, 10) = \$17{,}909}$$

By investing $10,000 he has $17,909 today, a gain of $7,909. Had he not put the money to work he would have forgone $7,909. Or, by putting it to work at only 3%, he whould have forgone $17,909 − 15,576 = $2,333.

Suppose these comparisons are applied to the failure to purchase a machine at the proper time as in the following example.

EXAMPLE 19.7b   It is proposed to replace a machine which has performed the same job for 40 years with a machine costing $20,000. The analyst computes that the replacement will result in a rate of return of 50% over a 10-year economic life period. The minimum required rate of return is 15%.

Top management is convinced that replacement is long overdue and that the existing machine probably had a 15-year, not a 40-year, economic life. They believe that the machine would therefore have been replaced at that age based on a 15% minimum required rate of return. Other assumptions which seem reasonable are that the first cost of the replacement at that date would be $20,000 (the same as today's machine), that its economic life would be 15 years, and that salvage at the end of 15 years would be $4,000.

SOLUTION. On the basis of these conjectures we can compute what the savings would have had to be to justify replacement at the minimum required rate of return:

Extra Investment	Savings	Extra Salvage
16,000	x/yr	L = 4,000
15		30

The savings x will be
$$x = 16{,}000\ \overset{0.17102}{(A/P, .15, 15)} - 4{,}000\ \overset{0.02102}{(A/F, 15)}$$

$$= 2{,}736 - 84 = \$2{,}652 \text{ per year}$$

These are the savings that would have justified the replacement of the original machine 25 years ago. However, because replacement was not made, these savings have been rejected over that period.

If these savings had been invested at the minimum required rate of return of 15%, they would have accumulated at the present time to

$$2,652 \ \overset{212.79}{(F/A, .15, 25)} = \$564,320$$

In fact, it is more than likely that even the replacement machine should have been replaced before another 25 years elapsed, but this was not done either, so the accumulation of savings should be even greater.

If the $20,000 had not been invested at all the firm would have shown no increase on the $20,000 and would have rejected $564,320 − 20,000 = $544,320.

Of course, the $20,000 may have been invested elsewhere, perhaps in bonds at 3%, which over the 25-year period would have compounded to

$$20,000 \ \overset{2.094}{(F/P, .03, 25)} = \$41,880$$

The amount rejected still exceeds half a million dollars.

The replacement which is currently proposed shows a 50% rate of return using a 10-year economic life. If salvage is $5,000 at that date, the current savings x would have to be:

$$x = 20,000 \ \overset{0.5088}{(A/P, .50, 10)} - 5,000 \ \overset{0.0068}{(A/F, 10)} = \$10,132 \text{ per year}$$

These savings are considerably greater than before (i.e., $2,652) for the simple reason that the machine has now deteriorated for 40 years and is more obsolete relative to the machine available under today's technology. The truth about aging equipment, therefore, is this: the longer a machine is kept, the greater the savings relative to a new machine and the higher the rate of return on replacement. An executive, therefore, who keeps a machine too long can show a high rate of return on his long-overdue suggestion to replace. This rate of return may be even higher than on a timely and creative suggestion. Whereas the executive who makes the latter suggestion should be commended, the other should have to account for rejecting attainable savings by failing to replace on time. When a machine is very old, when savings are very large, when, in short, there is no alternative except replacement, these are prima-facie evidence of a failure in equipment investment policy.

The decline of British economy in the late 1940's was attributed to this cause. A study[1] revealed that as long as a machine was running and performing the job intended the British manager was not motivated to replace it. This, of course, is in complete disregard of the truth that replacement is dictated solely by economy considerations and not by the engineering ability of management to keep the machine running.

The economics of this is brought out by the statement that "The man who needs a new machine is paying for it anyhow." If the economics favor replacement, the savings which he rejects are equivalent to his paying for a new machine without getting it. (Additional comments on this topic appear in Section 17.6).

[1]George Terborgh, *Dynamic Equipment Policy* (New York: McGraw-Hill, 1949), p. 8.

19.8 DESIGNING FOR IMPERFECTION

There are times when the most economic answer is found in accepting the alternative with the lower engineering efficiency. This has been repeatedly illustrated throughout the text for the simple reason that the efficient, the more perfect machine, does not always win the contest. If it did, engineering efficiency, not financial efficiency, would be the criterion and no analysis would be necessary except to determine which alternative had the higher first cost, the barometer of high engineering efficiency.

Of course, certain imperfections in design should not be tolerated, particularly those which would result in a loss of life. Faulty engineering is not to be tolerated either. Reference is not to such cases but to the designs proposed by engineers and managers who realize that paying for waste may be more economical than paying to prevent it.

An inspection process illustrates this in a number of ways. The perfect design represented by inspection at every conceivable point may be less economical than paying for the extra work that will be performed on the few defective pieces that pass through a less perfect and less costly inspection system. The economics of inspection depends upon predicting the number of failures that will get by with partial instead of 100% inspection. This naturally implies the use of statistical methods and the theory of probability. Instruction in this area is beyond the scope of this book, but it is hoped that the need for these methods (and all the advanced mathematical techniques used in what has become known as Operations Research) will become apparent to the reader and lead him to investigate and use these techniques where they evidently apply to the solution of his problems.

Statistical quality control presents the economic advantage of inspecting only a fraction of a production lot according to sampling procedures. Through the systematic use of control charts it will also serve to predict, locate, and therefore prevent, the causes of rejection of the piece. Probability theory is used in statistical quality control to determine the size of the sample and how much of the sample must pass inspection if the entire lot is to have no more than a specified limit of defective pieces in it. If the defectives in a sample exceed the limit, the lot from which the sample was chosen should be rejected. By the use of proper techniques this point can be seen approaching and, by the identification of assignable causes, prevented. As stated, it is presumed that if the rejected pieces in a sample are below a certain limit the number of imperfect pieces in the lot will also be below a certain limit. This is only a prediction, and the certainty or reliability of this prediction is not 100%. This is a risk the user takes but, like all risks, he can reduce it at a cost, in this case at the cost of increasing the degree of inspection.

The reliability of the prediction of the limit of defective pieces that will be found in a lot can only be improved at the expense of increasing the size of the sample. (One hundred percent reliability of the knowledge of rejects

would, of course, require 100% inspection.) Obviously, the higher the reliability, the greater the sample and the higher the expense of inspection. This
in itself defines an economic problem: what is the extra cost of accepting extra
defective pieces versus the extra cost of detecting them?

19.9 DESIGNING FOR SHORT LIFE

Somewhat akin to designing for imperfection discussed in Section 19.8 is the
idea of designing for short life. This statement is amplified and modified by
the illustrations in the following examples.

EXAMPLE 19.9a A one-horse shay type of equipment can be procured for
$10,000 with a physical life of 10 years. By spending 50% more, the physical life
can be doubled, but the operating disbursements will be the same in either case.
Salvage values will be zero and replacement costs will be the same as the first
cost. The rate of return is 15% before taxes.

SOLUTION.

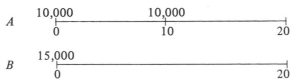

By inspection it can be seen that $10,000 ten years from now has a much lower
time value today. In fact, at 15% it is only worth $2,472 today:

$$\text{PW}_A = 10,000 + \overset{0.2472}{10,000\ (P/F, .15, 10)} = \$12,472$$

Therefore, at 15% interest, it is economical to invest only $2,472, or about
25% added first cost, to double the life. If it will cost more than this, it is
economical to adopt the design for short life.

From time to time we have heard executives complain, partly in jest, that
their product has been designed to last too long. These statements also imply
that it would be unethical to shorten the life in order to sell replacements.
This can be viewed in a new light, however, because the test of the ethics
in this case is entirely based on economics. It is proper for the manufacturer
to eliminate first costs that do not provide economic advantages. In fact,
designing for short life can be a boon to the economy if it can somehow prevent
the continuance of equipment in service long after economic replacement is due.

A certain degree of equipment reliability must be maintained by the designer, and this ruggedness of design may, in turn, increase the life period.
If the required level of reliability means designing to last forever, one cannot
argue for reducing the life, but the economic test in that case is based on the
cost of unreliability versus the extra cost to eliminate it. However, where
designing for reliability and designing for life are separable they can be
analyzed independently.

The following example illustrates that an economic alternative to designing for long life may be to extend the short-lived asset through replacement, not of the complete machine, but of some major wearing parts.

EXAMPLE 19.9b A machine can be built for $12,472 (see Example 19.9a) that will have a 20-year useful life without major overhaul or replacement of parts. An alternative machine can be built for $10,000 having equal operating efficiency but requiring replacement of major parts costing $4,000 at the end of year 10. The required rate of return is 15% before taxes.

SOLUTION.

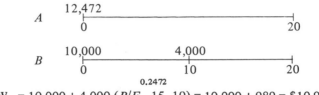

$$PW_B = 10,000 + 4,000 \, (P/F, \, .15, 10) = 10,000 + 989 = \$10,989.$$

Here, replacement of major parts is more economical than designing the entire system for long life.

The economics of designing for short life is based on the fact that a future advantage—like extended life—is worth much less today due to the time value of money. Would it not, therefore, be more strategic in many cases to put today's extra cost into improving the efficiency of the product where the returns are more immediate?

Example 19.9a concerned one-horse shay type equipment, but on the other hand, many pieces of equipment will not be permitted to live out their physical lives on the intended job because of obsolescence. Extra design costs for lengthening physical lives therefore have no economic advantage except perhaps to raise the salvage values at the end of the economic life.

In designing for efficiency or for a span of life we encounter the effects of both the time value of money and the law of diminishing returns. In other words, there are optimum values for life and efficiency and therefore certain situations may favor selecting long-lived equipment.

19.10 AWARENESS OF LOSSES

An awareness of economic differences is aided by an awareness of the losses which are inherent in a process. The following example attempts to illustrate this.

EXAMPLE 19.10a A printing machine is to be driven by a 15-horsepower electric motor belted to the drive shaft on the press. The economic life of the job is expected to be 8 years and, for simplicity, salvage values are to be neglected at that date. It is estimated that the press will run 4,000 hours a year, the motor efficiency is 86%, and power costs 3 cents a kilowatt-hour.

Although not obvious, power loss will occur in the belting system. Investigation reveals this may be in the neighborhood of 7% of the motor input power. What will it cost to prevent this, and is it justifiable if the cutoff rate is 20%?

A motor, belt, pulleys, and movable base for maintaining belt tension costs $600. A slower speed motor which can be coupled to the press costs $825, including the coupling. The motor efficiencies are found to be the same. The coupling has no transmission losses. Extra maintenance on the belt is $10 a year. The minimum required rate of return is 20% before taxes.

SOLUTION.

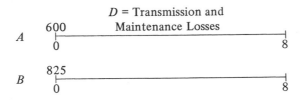

Annual cost of transmission loss:

$$\frac{(15)(0.746)(4,000)(\$0.03)(0.07)}{0.86} = \$109$$

so

$$225 \, (A/P, i, 8) = 109 + 10$$

and

$$(A/P, i, 8) = 0.529$$

whence

$$i \cong 51\%$$

which would justify the coupled motor.

Transmission losses make up a large part of man's economic losses. They include the transmission of power over electric lines, the transmission of steam and water, and the transmission through pipes of material, including gases, grain, powdered solids, and so on.

The economics of transmitting fluids, compressible or incompressible, is similar to the economics of transmitting electricity: the cost of the transmission line increases with its diameter but the losses decrease. For example, if a given flow Q in cubic feet per second (or gallons per minute) is required, the velocity decreases as the diameter of the pipe increases because

$$Q = AV$$

where A is the cross section of the pipe in square feet and V is the velocity in feet per second. Friction in the pipe varies exponentially with the velocity. For example, for all liquids having a viscosity equal to that of water,

$$\text{friction loss in feet} = k \, V^{1.85}$$

where k is a constant depending on the inside diameter of the pipe and its surface roughness.[1]

EXAMPLE 19.10b Four diameters of pipe are being considered in the construction of a long line for the transmission of fluid having a viscosity equal to water. The installation and operating costs, including the cost of friction losses, are given in Table 19.10. The lives of the pipe and pumping stations are considered to be 15 years with zero salvage. The minimum required rate of return before taxes is 20%. All costs figures are in hundreds.

SOLUTION. The analysis in Table 19.10 suggests that the 12-inch pipe is the most economical.

Computation of the economic effect of losses is easily learned, but it is more difficult (and important) to acquire an awareness of these losses so that alternatives can be conceived. With a conscious effort and with practice we believe the executive can develop this trained awareness.

It was a long while before engineers did much on a large scale about the losses existing in the transmission, transportation, and handling of materials. Many losses were permitted to exist when transport-systems were delayed (for example, by having to wait at elevators or by having to "backtrack" the material). Correction of these and similar inefficiencies leads to the larger subject of material handling. Of a similar nature are the losses and delays at highway intersections—ample reasons for economic improvements in highway designs.

The losses in manpower and productivity from industrial accidents have led to investments to eliminate or reduce these hazards. An awareness of this economic situation, which also was a long time in coming, seemed to be necessary to make safety more than just a byword.

A good approach to all of these subjects is to ask the question, "What are the losses in the present method?"

Table 19.10   ECONOMIC PIPE SIZE

Diameter (in.)	10	12	14	16
Friction loss[a]				
per 100 ft	1.01	0.415	0.196	0.102
First cost of pipeline	$5,320	6,650	8,000	9,200
Number of pumping stations	[10]	[4]	[2]	[1]
First cost of stations	2,000	800	400	200
Total first cost	$7,320	7,450	8,400	9,400
Capital recovery cost	$1,566	1,593	1,797	2,010
Annual pumping cost	540	220	105	50
Other annual disbursements	350	220	190	185
Total annual cost	$2,456	2,033	2,092	2,245

[a]Ibid.

[1]*Cameron Hydraulic Data Book*, 12th ed. (Woodcliff Lake, N.J.: Ingersoll-Rand), p. 27.

19.11 AWARENESS OF ADVANTAGES

Similar to the approach which views an operation from the standpoint of its losses is one which asks, "What are the advantages to be gained by change?" The following example will illustrate this.

EXAMPLE 19.11a Management was aware that certain advantages would accrue from a plant location in other areas of the country. As a result, a study was made, and the figures were collected and tabulated in Table 19.11a. The minimum required rate of return before income taxes is 20%. The economic life is 25 years with 20% salvage on the building and full salvage on the land.

SOLUTION. It is readily seen that Location W can be eliminated because it has both the highest first cost and operating cost. A present-worth analysis of the other two locations favors relocating the factory at C as follows:

PW, present location:

$$10,000 + 431,000 \overset{4.948}{(P/A, .20, 25)} - 60,000 \overset{0.0105}{(P/F, 25)} = \$2,232,000$$

PW, location C:

$$375,000 + 345,000 (P/A, 25) - 95,000 (P/F, 25) = \$2,081,000$$

Another illustration can be noted by examining the problems of seasonal industries. In such problems, the alternatives are between various sizes of plants to supply the same annual demand. For example, a small production unit working continuously into a large storage facility can equal the annual supply of a large production unit working seasonally with little storage capacity.

Seasonal industries generally fall into one of two classifications. The first consists of those in which the raw materials are available only a part of the year. The industries for canning vegetables, fruit, and fish are examples. In

Table 19.11a ECONOMIC PLANT LOCATION

	Present location	Location C	Location W
Land cost	$ 50,000	$ 25,000	$ 75,000
Factory cost	50,000	350,000	375,000
Total investment	$100,000	$375,000	$450,000
Property taxes	$ 25,000	$ 10,000	$ 13,000
Raw material transportation	20,000	5,000	14,000
Power	80,000	35,000	110,000
Heat	66,000	20,000	40,000
Air conditioning	5,000	100,000	35,000
Labor	225,000	160,000	230,000
Distribution cost	10,000	15,000	14,000
Annual disbursement	$431,000	$345,000	$456,000

this case the advantage of the larger plant which will handle the entire harvest or catch is the reduction in the storage cost of raw inventory and in the losses in storage. The advantage of a smaller plant is the lower first cost and investment charges.

The second class of seasonal industry arises from seasonal fluctuations in consumer demand. The advantage of the smaller plant again is the low first cost and investment charges, and the advantage of the larger plant is the reduction in finished goods inventory and storage costs and the avoidance of losses from changes in style and consumer preferences. Other merits of one or the other systems result from mass production, continuous versus intermittent production, a permanent versus a temporary labor force, and so on.

EXAMPLE 19.11b   A manufacturer of tire chains sells 240,000 sets a year to dealers but their sales occur over a relatively small portion of the year as follows:

> September 30,000
> October 50,000
> November. 80,000
> December 40,000
> January 40,000

The present plant capacity is 20,000 sets a month.

The annual cost of storage is 10 cents a set per year based on the maximum number of pairs in storage (because space must be provided for the maximum inventory). The total cost of making a chain is $9, the increment or variable cost is $5. Insurance and taxes together are 5%. The minimum required rate of return is 20% before taxes. The economic life is 10 years and salvages are essentially zero.

The present plant cost $400,000 but has a current net realizable value of $300,000. The present plant can be redesigned and enlarged to bring the capacity up to 30,000 units a month for an extra cost of $240,000. Other prospective increases in the productive capacity of the plant are listed in Table 19.11b. Observe that the increases in productive capacity do not result in increased sales but only in a reduction in average and maximum inventory. It is presumed that the increase in operating efficiency which might result from larger size will be offset by the inefficiency of intermittent operation. It is a company policy to maintain a base inventory of 5,000 pairs at all times.

SOLUTION.   The required inventory to meet sales is listed in Table 19.11b. In the case of the 30,000-pair plant, production will extend over 8 months from the first of June to the end of January. The January production will immediately go into sales along with the inventory carried over from December. The 40,000-pair plant will produce for 6 months, in which the last 3 months' production go right into sales. In the case of the 45,000-pair plant, the inventory shown is the result of producing only 25,000 in August, 35,000 in January, and 45,000 in the 4 months from September and December.

The high cost of carrying inventory favors the large intermittently operated plant of 40,000 pairs capacity. In view of this, the next logical step might

Table 19.11b ECONOMIC DESIGN OF A SEASONAL INVENTORY

Sales (pairs)	Month	Plant capacity (pairs per month)			
		20,000	30,000	40,000	45,000
		Investment			
		$300,000	$540,000	$640,000	$700,000
		End-of-Month Inventory After Sales[a]			
40,000	Jan.	0	0	0	0
0	Feb.	20,000	0	0	0
0	Mar.	40,000	0	0	0
0	Apr.	60,000	0	0	0
0	May	80,000	0	0	0
0	June	100,000	30,000	0	0
0	July	120,000	60,000	0	0
0	Aug.	140,000	90,000	40,000	25,000
30,000	Sept.	130,000	90,000	50,000	40,000
50,000	Oct.	100,000	70,000	40,000	35,000
80,000	Nov.	40,000	20,000	0	0
40,000	Dec.	20,000	10,000	0	5,000
Maximum inventory[b]		145,000	95,000	55,000	45,000
Average inventory[b]		75,800	35,800	15,800	13,750
Cost of storage (based on maximum)		$ 14,500	$ 9,500	$ 5,500	4,500
Insurance & tax (0.05) ($9) (avg. in stock)		34,110	16,110	7,110	6,190
Interest on Inventory (0.20) ($5) (avg. in stock)		75,800	35,800	15,800	13,750
Capital recovery $P(A/P, .20, 10)$		71,560	128,800	152,650	166,970
Total annual cost		$195,970	$190,210	$181,060	$191,410

[a]Above base inventory of 5,000 pairs of chains.
[b]Including base inventory of 5,000 pairs.

be the search for alternatives to utilize the unused capacity in the six months from February through July. The company might consider the manufacture of industrial chains, nautical chains, reinforcing rods for construction, and so on, from the standpoint of an income-expansion proposition.

19.12 DIFFERENCES THAT ARE HARDER TO PREDICT

There is a natural tendency to overlook differences that may be harder to predict. For this reason many personnel problems are not approached by management from the investment standpoint. However, a considerable insight into problems involving personnel turnover, absenteeism, executive or employee training, delegation of authority, safety, productivity, morale, and so on, can be obtained by sensing the economic differences between laternatives. After some thought the analyst will often find more and more ways to quantify these problems and evaluate them mathematically.

EXAMPLE 19.12 A company employing 100 salesmen does a total volume of business of $30,000,000. The net profit on sales is 5%.

It is proposed to institute a training program in engineering economy to help salesmen justify their proposals to customers by quantitative methods. The total cost of sending two trainees away for a thorough education in the subject is estimated to be $2,000. The two men will provide mutual assistance and will insure continuity of the company program which they will conduct although each will devote only one-quarter of his time to the training program. The salary of each is $10,000 a year. Each salesman will spend 20 hours in the company training program, half of which will be on company time. The incremental expense incidental to the training of each salesman for dinners, materials and special literature is $40. It is probable that some business will be lost as a result of diverting salesmen's time from selling, and it is estimated that this will be directly proportionate to the hours spent in training on company time.

It is estimated that every 3 years complete new training will be necessary. This will provide advanced and refresher instruction for everyone as well as training for new salesmen. It is also planned to prepare new trainers every 3 years.

What increase in sales would be required to justify this program if the minimum acceptable rate of return is 20% before taxes?

SOLUTION. If x is the required increase in sales, $0.05x$ is the increased profit. The loss in profit from the diversion of the salesmen's time in the first year based on 40 hours for 50 weeks and 10 hours of company time in training is

$$\left(\frac{10}{40 \times 50}\right)(30,000,000)(0.05) = \$7,500$$

The time of the trainers is chargeable only if it results in out-of-pocket expense to the company by having to hire others to do their work. This is most unlikely, but let us take the worst and assume this diversion of their time actually costs the company money:

$$(2)\left(\frac{1}{4}\right)(10,000) = \$5,000$$

It is assumed that the expense of training the salesmen will occur about a year after the education of the trainers and that the increases in profits will also be best represented as year-end sums.

Then the required annual increase in sales is:

$$(0.05x)\,\underset{2.106}{(P/A,.20,3)} = 2,000 + [7,500 + 5,000 + 40(100)]\,\underset{0.8333}{(P/F,.20,1)}$$

$$0.1053x = 2000 + 13,750$$

whence

$$x = \$149,600$$

The question of conducting a training program can now be expressed quantitatively, "Will it increase sales $149,600, one-half of one percent?" Management does not now have to predict an increase in sales but only needs an opinion of whether the most pessimistic view exceeds one-half of one percent sales increase.

19.13 RESEARCH TO ESTABLISH ECONOMIC PATTERNS

We have suggested in this chapter that one must develop an awareness of the actual or potential differences between alternatives before he can begin to suggest alternative courses of action. Often the alternatives may exist only as preliminary designs which will have certain economic characteristics. The knowledge of the difference between an existing process and one that might be built establishes the necessity which becomes the father of invention. Creativity and invention cannot be divorced from the economics of the situation.

We need more knowledge, more education, more ability in conceiving and establishing the differences between alternatives. We have the mathematics to evaluate almost any situation of any complexity, but the first problem is to find and establish the pattern of these differences. In this respect the mathematics is far ahead of our ability to determine these differences. A leading mathematician once said that Einstein was very fortunate when he conceived his ideas of relativity because the mathematicians had already developed the mathematics (without envisaging the applications). The physical model of behavior must be conceived before its mathematical model can be constructed. The mathematics is a valuable tool, but only a tool. Man is still left with the more difficult job of recognizing the economic factors and conceiving how to quantify them or else he may never discover applications for very complex mathematical procedures.

The greatest need, therefore, is for research to obtain the data needed in decision-making, and the search for this data will be guided by man's sensitivity toward the differences which exist between economic alternatives.

In a number of special cases data has become available which does require use of advanced mathematical tools.[1] Such tools include matrix algebra; numerical procedures plus random sampling the Monte Carlo method; linear, dynamic, or quadradic programming, queuing theory; game theory; iconic, analogue, and symbolic models. These uses will increase as the ability to collect data increases, and the ability to collect data will also increase as we achieve an awareness of the complex differences between alternatives which these advanced tools are prepared to handle.

---

[1]For example see C. W. Churchman, R. L. Ackoff, and E. I. Arnoff, *Introduction to Operations Research* (New York: Wiley, 1957), chapter 1.

PROBLEMS

19.1 Discuss the following topics[1] from the standpoint of economic decision-making. In your discussion identify the factors and their effects.

(a) In 1887 a 10,000-volt DC transmission line was built from Creil (France) to Paris, a distance of 32 miles. Although DC transmission lines are scientifically sound, they are not favored today. In your discussion consider also whether DC transmission is or might ever be used.

(b) When the development of Niagara was planned in 1895, cable drives and pneumatic methods were considered for transmitting power to Buffalo, 22 miles distant. These were not impossible, but they were not used. In your discussion consider also the conditions under which cable drives and pneumatic methods are, or might be, used.

(c) It is often suggested that steam plants should be located at the coal mines to save the cost of transporting coal, yet this has seldom been done.

(d) By the end of the 19th century, highly efficient filtration plants that would remove dangerous bacteria from drinking water supplies. The filtration method is not favored today.

(e) It has been said that half the cost of a bridge is buried below the surface. Another statement maintains that foundation difficulties often dictate the character of the superstructure.

19.2 Thirteen years ago a company purchased $10,000,000 worth of $2\frac{1}{2}\%$ bonds at a par value of $100. The present market price is $87 and the bonds mature at the end of 7 years. Prove whether the company should sell these bonds and replace them with bonds which pay $3\frac{7}{8}\%$ interest, presently sell at par, and also mature in 7 years?

The above-mentioned rates are for nominal annual interest; payments against the coupons will be made quarterly. Assume that brokerage fees for the transfer are negligible. The company's income tax rate is 50%.

19.3 The following is a corporation's analysis of alternative processes for producing oil-pump bodies. Sales forecasts made by the management indicated they would have to produce about 1,250,000 oil-pump bodies of the present design per year for the next 8 years. Three possible plans were available.

Plan 1: Leave things as they are. The old process has been operating for many years and is fully depreciated. To meet the production schedule, it must operate on a three-shift basis.

Plan 2: This proposed process consists of a number of highly mechanized automatic machines. It requires the least amount of labor and the highest capital investment. It meets the production schedule by working two shifts.

Plan 3: This process involves a number of relatively inexpensive, single station machines. It requires more labor, tools, etc., than Plan 2, but less than Plan 1. To meet production, it must operate on a two-shift schedule.

---

[1] Suggested by discussion in James Kip Finch, *Engineering and Western Civilization* (New York: McGraw-Hill, 1951).

The salvage value of Plans 2 and 3 is estimated to be 30% of the initial cost. The company based its conclusions on the following data and the following analysis of it.

	Plan 1	Plan 2	Plan 3
Investment Required	None	$1,071,000	$ 850,000
Sales–1,250,000 bodies			
@ 0.82 each	$1,025,000	1,025,000	1,025,000
Cost of sales			
Material	396,000	396,000	396,000
Subcontracting	none	none	none
Direct labor	187,268	53,328	79,592
Rework	1,500	495	825
Setup and tool change	7,434	3,638	5,139
Supervision	20,250	7,000	7,000
Labor fringes	43,290	12,892	18,511
Floor space	4,435	5,443	4,760
Power	3,475	6,000	5,100
Taxes	5,000	21,420	17,000
Insurance	1,791	3,750	2,975
Perishable tools	27,050	18,750	20,100
Supplies	9,200	3,720	3,820
Scrap	26,060	13,480	18,300
Tool grinding	13,320	7,750	9,630
Machine repair	15,500	5,100	3,750
Lubrication	3,550	1,250	2,500
Depreciation	none	93,713	74,375
Miscellaneous	28,090	7,999	11,938
	$ 793,213	$ 661,728	$ 681,315
Gross profit	231,787	363,270	343,685
Selling expense	66,625	66,625	66,625
Administrative expense	43,627	36,395	37,472
Interest	none	none	none
Profit before tax	121,535	260,252	239,588
Estimate for federal income			
tax	60,767	130,126	119,794
Net profit	60,768	130,126	119,794

The analysis suggests that Plan 2 is the best investment because it will earn $69,358 more than Plan 1 and $10,332 more than Plan 3, after all expenses in each case. Do you agree with this method of analysis and with this conclusion?

19.4   A prominent airline needs additional hangar facilities at an international airport located at a major city in the United States. The airline has two basic alternatives: to construct the facilities itself or to lease them from a firm that has money to invest in the construction and ownership of these facilities. In pursuit of this, three proposals were secured from firms that would build these hangars to the desired plans and specifications and lease them to the airline. The three firms bid as follows:

	1st 10 years	2nd 10 years
Company A	$32,148/yr	$13,128/yr
Company B	28,788/yr	22,464/yr
Company C	34,800/yr	12,600/yr

All bidders were required to bid on the basis of a lease to the airline for 10 years with an option of renewal for the remaining 10 years. The payment of ground rent of $1,848 a year was to be assumed by the lessor with all facilities reverting to the city at the end of 20 years.

The alternative consideration, ownership of the hangars, involved the following costs:

(a) Total construction cost,
including engineering $145,000

(b) Maintenance   600/year

(c) Ground rent   1,848/year

(d) Taxes and insurance   3,600/year

Based on a *rate-of-return analysis*, which alternative should be selected?

19.5 A commercial photographer damaged his camera, expected to last 7 years when he purchased it a year ago for $475. A dealer quoted $150 to restore the camera to first-class working order.

The dealer also said, "It will be a lot cheaper to trade it in on a new one. I'll allow you $210 on your camera, as is, and you can save the cost of repair.

"The figures will work out like this," the dealer continued. "If you keep the camera, your remaining depreciation cost (after allowing for last year's depreciation) will be $407 divided by 6, namely, $68, to which you must add the $150 repairs for a total cost next year of $218. On the other hand, if you trade in your camera, your depreciation cost will be $475 minus the allowance of $210, and, dividing by 7, we have a total net cost of only $38.

"This disregards income tax of maybe 25%, property tax of 5%, and interest of approximately 6%, but we can overlook these because it is so much more expensive to keep the camera at a cost of $218 compared to $38 for a new one."

If the photographer asked your advice on this analysis, how would you reply?

19.6 Alternative *A* costs $100 and is expected to produce net savings of $20 at the end of year 1 and $120 at the end of year 2. Alternative *B* costs $100 and is expected to produce net savings of $100 at the end of year 1 and $32 at the end of year 2. The life period of each is 2 years and there are no other costs or incomes. Use the rate-of-return method of analysis. Which would you select if the minimum required rate of return is 5%? 15%?

19.7 The following problem came up in a discussion between two analysts. They were attempting to compare two investment opportunities, as of the present instant, that did not occur at the same time. One opportunity was to invest $1,000 today to receive an income of $171 a year for the next 15 years, the salvage being zero. The other opportunity was to invest $1,000 *eight years* from now to receive $214 a year for the following 15 years, salvage also being zero. The projects are mutually exclusive (only one may be taken). What comments would you have relative to making such a comparison?

19.8 How would you compare the following two alternatives? Project X costs $100 but will return $120 after 1 year (the end of its economic life). Project Y costs $100 but will reutrn $174.90 after 4 years (the end of its economic life).

The projects are mutually exclusive (only one may be selected). (Adopted from Ezra Solomon, "The Arithmetic of Capital Budgeting Decisions," in *The Management of Corporate Capital*, University of Chicago, School of Business Administration, 1961, pp. 74–79.)

19.9 In Problem 7.9, at the end of Chapter 7, three alternative plans for combating corrosion of an automobile body from road salt were considered by an owner who could invest at 7% in other opportunities.

In Plan 1, a standard undercoating costing $30 was added to a car costing $3,500. It was estimated that this would result in a car life of 6 years with $350 salvage value.

In Plan 2, special body materials were proposed at an extra price of $350 over the $3,500 cost of the standard car. This was presumed to give a 10-year car life with $150 salvage at that date. During the last 4 years of operation, however, the annual operating disbursements were expected to be $150 greater than for a new car.

In Plan 3, a standard undercoating was proposed for a standard car as in Plan 1. However, reconstruction of the body costing $400 was proposed at the end of the sixth year which would extend the life another 4 years with $175 salvage at that date. The annual operating disbursements during the last 4 years, as in Plan 2, would be $150 greater than for a new car.

Consider Plan 3 from the standpoint of whether it is, in fact, a combination of two alternatives—not concurrent alternatives as in Section 19.6, but sequential alternatives. How would you consider these separately? Might this, a combination of alternatives, have any effect on your conclusion? If so, show how.

19.10 Problem 7.13 compared two alternatives having different lives. If we compare these alternatives over a 2-year study period, we should be able to show that Design O, the alternative with the longer life, has a theoretical salvage value L at the end of year 2. This concept of "salvage value" was developed in Section 6.12 of the text. Using the data in Problem 7.13, compute the value of L at the end of year 2 for Design O.

19.11 From your own experience, or by using your imagination, present a case for one of the following statements. Illustrate the statement by assuming numerical values for the cost and income patterns that will prove your point.

1.(a) It is more economical to overload the equipment beyond its normal, rated capacity.   (b) It is more economical to underload the equipment below its normal, rated capacity.

2.(a) It is more economical to design for imperfect than for perfect operation.   (b) It is more economical to design for perfect than for imperfect operation.

3.(a) It is more economical to use decelerated depreciation instead of accelerated, and benefit by a tax saving from the loss on disposal. (b) It is more economical to use accelerated depreciation and pay a tax on the gain on disposal if the salvage value exceeds the resulting book value.

19.12   Subject to further rules established by your instructor, perform the following project:

Visit a business of your choice and consult someone responsible for proposing expenditures (i.e., the head of the engineering, operations, or planning department) or someone responsible for approving expenditures—or passing them for approval—(i.e., a financial officer).

Obtain a proposition that has been studied and, therefore, for which data has been collected.   This proposal may have resulted in a recent purchase (or rejection), or it may be for one about to occur.   Get all the collected data as well as irreducible considerations.   If a decision has been made, find out, if possible, the basis for it and the method of analysis.   Offer to show your future analysis to the person who gives you the data.

It is likely that a visit to only one company may be sufficient to locate a project.   If a project is not available, however, do not propose that data be collected for your benefit.   In that event, a visit to another company may be necessary.

Make an analysis and prepare a report (with a copy for the person who donated the data, if he wants one).   Fashion this report after one you would expect to make to top management requesting approval of a capital expenditure or suggesting its rejection, as the case may be.

At the election of your instructor, this project may serve as a term report and should be written accordingly.

19.13   Locate in any professional journal an article that reports on the economic evaluation of some new (or established) technology.   An illustration of this type of article, and one that has appeared many times in journals, is the use of capacitors or synchronous machines for power-factor correction.   In your written report, make your own analysis; use the author's data and, in addition, give a critical review of the article.

19.14   Locate, study, and report on the technique employed by some company for the analysis and evaluation of proposed capital expenditures.   Limit yourself to companies that have published manuals outlining their techniques.   This restricts you to cases where manuals are available to you or your instructor.   When these can be obtained, consider making them the property of your school library for future reference and the use of subsequent classes.

Manuals of this type are prepared by certain manufacturing companies, electric utilities, and telephone companies for the use of their financial and operating departments in proposing and judging expenditures. Most often these will be available on request to your or your instructor, but be prepared to find that they may be considered confidential. In other cases, certain manufacturers publish sales brochures outlining a method for evaluating and proving the economic advantage of their product in proposed applications in customers' plants.

Make a written report outlining the method used and criticize, favorably or unfavorably, the techniques employed.

This report will be considered as a term paper if you are so directed by your instructor.

19.15 Select one of the Harvard Business School Cases, published by the President and Fellows of Harvard College, which requires you to use the principles and techniques for analyzing and evaluating capital expenditures. These cases may be obtained by writing the Director of Case Distribution, Intercollegiate Case Clearing House, Soldiers Field Post Office, Boston 63, Massachusetts. Free Sample cases are available to instructors, and quantities may be obtained for student use at small charge. The instructor may also obtain five bibliographies in which these cases are abstracted.

Examples of cases, one or more of which might be selected for class use, are as follows:

Continental Oil Co.	Order No. 1C12
Norwalk Screw Co. et al.	Order No. 3C11
Avella, Inc.	Order No. 4C3
Rhodes Tool Co.	Order No. 4C4
Fall River Lumber Co.	Order No. 4C23
White Eagle Oil Co. (Case D)	Order No. 4C48
White Eagle Oil Co. (Case E)	Order No. 4C49
Star Cap & Closure Co.	Order No. 5C7R
Time Magazine	Order No. 5C31
Dem-A-Lex Dynamics Corp.	Order No. 6C59
Anscott Corp.	Order No. 6C63
Chocolates & Candy Co.	Order No. 6C73
Radford Corp.	Order No. 7C3
McCarthy's Bowl Inn	Order No. 7C9
Blue Bell Biscuits, Inc.	Order No. 7C23
Monitor Textile Co. (Case A)	Order No. 7C46
Monitor Textile Co. (Case B)	Order No. 7C47
Venus Air Lines	Order No. 7C44

If not used as a term report, assignment will be made at least a week in advance. The written report should contain your conclusions adequately supported by your reasons and explanations of the error of reasoning advanced in the case. The conclusion reached in the report will also be discussed in class.

19.16 The examination for professional engineers in the State of New York requires the candidate to answer questions on "Engineering Economics and Practice." Past examinations provide a large store of questions for the practicing engineer as well as for the student who anticipates taking professional engineering examinations in New York or any other state. These questions appear in Part III, Group A, of the New York State examination.   The following is a sample of those appearing in recent examinations:

1. An engineer must select a pump for a service requiring 14,000 gpm at 11 feet total dynamic head. The specific gravity of the liquid is 1.45.

Supplier *A* offers a pump of all-iron construction with an efficiency of 70% at a price of $5,600; Supplier *B* offers a pump of all-Monel construction with an efficiency of 75% at a price of $14,700. Iron contamination of the product can be tolerated.

Installation costs and or replacement costs for either pump are $1,000. Routine maintenance costs are assumed the same in either case, and power is available at $0.01 per kw-hr. Operation will be 24 hours per day for 300 days per year.

It is expected that the Monel pump will last for 20 years, at which time the plant will be obsolete, and the Monel pump will have a salvage value of 25% of its original cost. If money is available at 6%, what minimum service life must be expected from the all-iron pump in order to justify its selection?

2. A plant can produce 100 tons per day of Product *A* plus 110 tons per day of Product *B* on a continuous basis. Product *A* sells for $60 per ton; Product *B* sells for $90 per ton. The total installed cost of the plant is $10,000,000, and it is desired to depreciate this over a 20-year period with interest at 6%. The average annual operating rate is 80% of capacity.

If the company desired to make a gross profit before taxes of 10% of its sales income, what operating cost per ton of total product (*A* and *B*) must be maintained? If the company accomplishes the above and finds that 30% of the per-ton cost is fixed overhead, what is their break-even point in terms of percent of installed capacity?

3. It is required that a $60°$ cone bottom be fabricated for a 24-foot-0-inch-diameter process vessel using $\frac{3}{8}$-inch 20% Type 316 stainless-steel-clad steel plate weighing 15.34 pounds per square foot.

Specify the plate size of sizes and the number of plates of each size which must be ordered for minimum material costs if the base price of the material is 50.25 cents per pound and the extras to be considered are as follows:

Width extras (inches)	Cents per pound
36 and under	9.50
Over 36 to 48, exclusive	8.25
48 to 96, inclusive	7.25
Over 96 to 140, inclusive	8.00
Over 140 to 160, inclusive	8.50
Over 160 to 180, inclusive	9.00
Greater widths not available.	

Length extras (inches)	Cents per pound
Under 96	1.75
96 to 240, inclusive	None
Over 240 to 288, inclusive	1.00
Over 288 to 312, inclusive	1.50
Over 312 to 336, inclusive	2.50
Over 336 to 360, inclusive	4.00
Over 360 to 380, inclusive	6.00
Greater lengths not available.	

4. A man paid $3,000 down in purchasing a $14,000 house and lot and secured a 20-year, 4% mortgage requiring equal annual payments to cover the balance. Taxes started at $275 per year and increased an average of $3\frac{1}{2}\%$ per year. Maintenance and insurance costs averaged out at $600 per year. If the market value of the property remains at $14,000 after the mortgage is paid off, what has been the average annual cost to the owner during the life of the mortgage?

19.17 Prepare a time sacle illustrating MAPI's Variant B projection pattern. How does this account for functional degradation?

Bibliography

American Telephone and Telegraph Co. 1977. *Engineering Economy*. New York: AT&T Co.

Anthony, R. N. 1970. *Management Accounting*. Rev. ed. Homewood, Ill.: Richard D. Irwin.

Barish, N. N. 1962. *Economic Analysis for Engineering and Managerial Decision-Making*. New York: McGraw-Hill.

Bierman, H., and Smidt, S. 1972. *The Capital Budgeting Decision*. New York: Macmillan.

Bowman, E. H., and Fetter, R. B. 1961. *Analysis for Production Management*. Homewood, Ill.: Richard D. Irwin.

Bullinger, C. E. 1958. *Engineering Economy*. New York: McGraw-Hill.

Canada, J. R. 1971. *Intermediate Economic Analysis for Management and Engineering*. Englewood Cliffs, N. J.: Prentice Hall.

Chernoff, H., and Moses, L. E. 1959. *Elementary Decision Theory*. New York: Wiley.

Churchman, C. W., Ackoff, R. L., and Arnoff, E. L. 1957. *Introduction to Operations Research*. New York: Wiley.

Churchman, C. W. 1961. *Prediction and Optimal Decision*. Englewood Cliffs, N.J.: Prentice-Hall.

Clarke, J. M. 1923. *Studies in the Economics of Overhead Costs*. Chicago: University of Chicago Press.

Coughlan, J. D., and Strand, W. P. 1969. *Depreciation: Accounting, Taxes, and Business*. New York: Ronald Press.

Dasgupta, A. K., and Pearce, D. W. 1972. *Cost-Benefit Analysis: Theory & Practice*. New York: Barnes and Noble.

Dean, J. 1951. *Capital Budgeting*. New York: Columbia University Press.

De Garmo, E. P., and Canada, J. R. 1973. *Engineering Economy*. 5th ed. New York: Macmillan.

The Engineering Economist, a quarterly journal published at the University of Texas at Dallas by the Engineering Economy division of the American Society for Engineering Education.

English, J. M. ed. 1972. *Economics of Engineering and Social Systems*. New York: Wiley.

482

Fabrycky, W. J., and Thuesen, G. J. 1974. *Economic Decision Analysis*. Englewood Cliffs, N. J.: Prentice Hall.

Finch, J. K. 1942. *An Introduction to the Economics of Civil Engineering*. New York: Columbia University Press.

Fish, J. C. L. 1923. *Engineering Economics*. New York: McGraw-Hill.

Fleischer, G. 1969. *Capital Allocation Theory: The Study of Investment Decisions*. New York: Appleton-Century-Crofts.

Goldman, O. B. 1920. *Financial Engineering*. New York: Wiley.

Grant, E. L., and Bell, L. F. 1964. *Basic Accounting and Cost Accounting*. 2nd ed. New York: McGraw-Hill.

Grant, E. L., Ireson, W. G., and Leavenworth, R. S. 1976. *Principles of Engineering Economy*. 6th ed. New York: Ronald Press.

Happel, J. 1968. *Chemical Process Economics*. New York: Wiley.

Harvard Business Review. See the cases listed in Prob. 19.15 at the end of Chapter 19 of this text.

Hillier, F. S. The derivation of Probabilistic information for the evaluation of risky investments. *Management Science*. April 1963.

Jelen, F. C. 1970. *Cost and Optimization Engineering*. New York: McGraw-Hill.

Jeynes, P. H. 1968. *Profitability and Economic Choice*. Ames, Iowa: Iowa State University Press.

La Londe, W. S., Jr. 1966. *Professional Engineer's Examination Questions and Answers*. 2nd ed. New York: McGraw-Hill.

Mao, J. 1969. *Quantitative Analysis in Finance*. New York: MacMillan.

Marston, A., Winfrey, R., and Hempstead, J. C. 1963. *Engineering Valuation and Depreciation*. Ames, Iowa: Iowa State University Press.

McCloskey, J. F. and Trefethen, F. N. 1955, 1956. *Operations Research for Management*. 2 vols. Baltimore: Johns Hopkins Press.

Machinery and Allied Products Institute. 1950. *MAPI Replacement Manual*. Washington, D.C.: Machinery and Allied Products Institute.

McKean R. N. 1958. *Efficiency in Government through Systems Analysis*. New York: Wiley.

Manne, A. S. 1961. Economic Analysis for Business Decisions. New York: McGraw-Hill.

Merrett, A. J., and Sykes, A. 1963. *The Finance and Analysis of Capital Projects*. New York: Wiley.

Morris, W. T. 1976. *Engineering Economy: The Analysis of Management Decisions*. Homewood, Ill.: Richard D. Irwin.

Newnan, D. G.   1977. *Engineering Economic Analysis*. San Jose, Cal.: Engineering Press.

Norton, P. T., Jr. 1934. *Economic Lot Sizes in Manufacturing*. Bulletin no. 31, Blacksburg, Va.: Virginia Polytechnic Institute.

Ostwald, P. F.   1974.   *Cost Estimating for Engineering and Management*. Englewood Cliffs, N. J.: Prentice-Hall.

Radford, K. J.   1975. *Management Decision Making*. Reston, Va.: Reston Publishing Co.

Raitta, H. 1968. *Decision Analysis, Lectures on Choices under Uncertainty*. Reading, Mass.: Addison-Wesley.

Rautenstrauch, W. and Villers, R. 1968. *Budgetary Control*. 2nd ed. New York: Funk and Wagnall's.

Reisman, A. 1971. *Managerial and Engineering Economics*. Boston: Allyn and Bacon.

Riggs, J. L. 1977. *Engineering Economics* New York: McGraw-Hill.

Rosenthal, S. A.   1964.   *Engineering Economics and Practice*. New York: MacMillan Co.

Schlaifer, R. 1959. *Probability and Statistics for Business Decisions*. New York: McGraw-Hill.

Schweyer, H. E.   1964.   *Analytical Models for Managerial and Engineering Economics*. New York: Van Nostrand Reinhold.

Smith, G. W. 1973. *Engineering Economy*. Ames: Iowa State University Press.

Solomon, E. 1963. *The Theory of Financial Management*. New York: Columbia University Press.

Solomon, E., ed. 1959. *Management of Corporate Capital*. New York: Free Press of Glencoe.

Tarquin, A. J., and Bank, L.   1976.   *Engineering Economy: A Behavioral Approach*. New York: McGraw-Hill.

Terborgh, G. 1976. *Business Investment Management*. Washington, D. C.: Machinery & Allied Products Institute.

Terborgh, G. 1958. *Business Investment Policy*. Washington, D.C.: Machinery and Allied Products Institute.

―― 1949. *Dynamic Equipment Policy*. New York: McGraw-Hill.

Thuesen, H. G., Fabrycky, W. J., and Thuesen, G. J. 1977. *Engineering Economy*. 5th ed. Englewood Cliffs, N. J.: Prentice-Hall.

Tyler, C., and Winter, C. H., Jr. 1959. *Chemical Engineering Economics*. 4th ed. New York: McGraw-Hill.

Villers, R.   1960.   *Dynamic Management in Industry*.   Englewood Cliffs, N.J.: Prentice-Hall.

Ward, H. A., and Corrigan, F. J.   1963.   *Financial Management*.   Boston: Houghton Mifflin.

Wellington, A. M.   1887.   *The Economic Theory of Railway Location*. New York: Wiley.

Weingarten, H. M. 1963. *Mathematical Programming and the Analysis of Capital Budgeting Problems*. Englewood Cliffs, N.J.: Prentice-Hall.

Winfrey, R.   1969.   *Economic Analysis for Highways*.   Scranton, Pa.: International Textbook Co.

Appendix

DEFINITION OF CERTAIN SYMBOLS

Re footnote pg 28:

The letter i, as noted, is defined as the effective rate for one period on your time scale which may be a month, a quarter, or a semiannual period of time. In most industrial problems this period is one year. Therefore, where the period is one year, i is also the effective *annual* interest. Effective annual interest may also be written as i_a where "a" designates "annual."

The letter n is the number of interest periods. For example if interest is compounded quarterly on a 10-year investment, n is 40. In most industrial problems n equals the *economic life* (in years) so the interest i, or i_a, or rate of return is for an annual period.

The letter N in this text is the number of interest periods in the *tax life* compared to the periods in the *economic life n*. In some publications N is used exclusively instead of n in which case subscripts to N might be used to discriminate between the number of interest periods in the economic life and those in the tax life. See Chapter 15, Taxes.

Re footnote pg 77:

L = realizable value at the end of the economic life. See Sections 10.15 and 11.2 re degradation vs. dispose.

S = salvage value at the end of the tax life. In some publications S is used exclusively instead of L in which case subscripts to S might be used to discriminate between the value at the end of the economic life and the salvage at the end of the tax life. See Chapter 15, Taxes.

DISCRETE RATE-OF-RETURN FACTORS

n	Single Payment Compound Amount Factor SPCAF $(1 + i)^n$ F/P	Single Payment Present Worth Factor SPPWF $\dfrac{1}{(1 + i)^n}$ P/F	Capital Recovery Factor CRF $\dfrac{i(1 + i)^n}{(1 + i)^n - 1}$ A/P	Uniform Series Present Worth Factor USPWF $\dfrac{(1 + i)^n - 1}{i(1 + i)^n}$ P/A	Sinking Fund Deposit Factor SFDF $\dfrac{i}{(1 + i)^n - 1}$ A/F	Uniform Series Compound Amount Factor USCAF $\dfrac{(1 + i)^n - 1}{i}$ F/A	Arithmetic Series Factor ASF $\dfrac{1 - n(SFDF)}{i}$ A/G	Arithmetic Series Present Worth Factor ASPWF $ASF \cdot USPWF$ P/G	n
					1%					
1	1.0100	.99010	1.0100	.99010	1.0000	1.0000	–	–	1
2	1.0201	.98030	.50751	1.9704	.49751	2.0100	.49735	.97998	2
3	1.0303	.97059	.34002	2.9410	.33002	3.0301	.99319	2.9209	3
4	1.0406	.96098	.25628	3.9020	.24628	4.0604	1.4874	5.8039	4
5	1.0510	.95147	.20604	4.8534	.19604	5.1010	1.9799	9.6095	5
6	1.0615	.94205	.17255	5.7955	.16255	6.1520	2.4708	14.320	6
7	1.0721	.93272	.14863	6.7282	.13863	7.2135	2.9601	19.916	7
8	1.0829	.92348	.13069	7.6517	.12069	8.2857	3.4476	26.380	8
9	1.0937	.91434	.11674	8.5660	.10674	9.3685	3.9335	33.695	9
10	1.1046	.90529	.10558	9.4713	.09558	10.462	4.4178	41.842	10
11	1.1157	.89632	.09045	10.368	.08645	11.567	4.9004	50.805	11
12	1.1268	.88745	.08885	11.255	.07885	12.682	5.3813	60.567	12
13	1.1381	.87866	.08242	12.134	.07242	13.809	5.8606	71.111	13
14	1.1495	.86996	.07690	13.004	.06690	14.947	6.3382	82.421	14
15	1.1610	.86135	.07212	13.865	.06212	16.097	6.8142	94.479	15
16	1.1726	.85282	.06795	14.718	.05795	17.258	7.2885	107.27	16
17	1.1843	.84438	.06426	15.562	.05426	18.430	7.7612	120.78	17
18	1.1961	.83602	.06098	16.398	.05098	19.615	8.2322	134.99	18
19	1.2081	.82774	.05805	17.226	.04805	20.811	8.7015	149.89	19
20	1.2202	.81954	.05542	18.046	.04542	22.019	9.1692	165.46	20
21	1.2324	.81143	.05303	18.857	.04303	23.239	9.6353	181.69	21
22	1.2447	.80340	.05086	19.660	.04086	24.472	10.100	198.56	22
23	1.2572	.79544	.04889	20.456	.03889	25.716	10.562	216.06	23
24	1.2697	.78757	.04707	21.243	.03707	26.973	11.024	234.18	24
25	1.2824	.77977	.04541	22.023	.03541	28.243	11.483	252.89	25
26	1.2953	.77205	.04387	22.795	.03387	29.526	11.941	272.19	26
27	1.3082	.76440	.04245	23.560	.03245	30.821	12.397	292.07	27
28	1.3213	.75684	.04112	24.316	.03112	32.129	12.851	312.50	28
29	1.3345	.74934	.03990	25.066	.02990	33.450	13.304	333.48	29
30	1.3478	.74192	.03875	25.808	.02875	34.785	13.756	355.00	30
31	1.3613	.73458	.03768	26.542	.02768	36.133	14.205	377.04	31
32	1.3749	.72730	.03667	27.270	.02667	37.494	14.653	399.58	32
33	1.3887	.72010	.03573	27.990	.02573	38.869	15.099	422.63	33
34	1.4026	.71297	.03484	28.703	.02484	40.258	15.544	446.15	34
35	1.4166	.70591	.03400	29.409	.02400	41.660	15.987	470.15	35
40	1.4889	.67165	.03046	32.835	.02046	48.886	18.177	596.85	40
45	1.5648	.63906	.02771	36.094	.01771	56.481	20.327	733.70	45
50	1.6446	.60804	.02551	39.196	.01551	64.463	22.436	879.41	50
55	1.7285	.57853	.02373	42.147	.01373	72.852	24.505	1032.8	55
60	1.8167	.55045	.02224	44.955	.01224	81.670	26.533	1192.8	60
65	1.9094	.52373	.02100	47.627	.01200	90.937	28.522	1358.4	65
70	2.0068	.49832	.01993	50.168	.00993	100.68	30.470	1528.6	70
75	2.1091	.47413	.01902	52.587	.00902	110.91	32.379	1702.7	75
80	2.2167	.45112	.01822	54.888	.00822	121.67	34.249	1879.9	80
85	2.3298	.42922	.01752	57.078	.00752	132.98	36.080	2059.4	85
90	2.4486	.40839	.01690	59.161	.00690	144.86	37.872	2240.6	90
95	2.5735	.38857	.01636	61.143	.00636	157.35	39.626	2422.9	95
100	2.7048	.36971	.01586	63.029	.00587	170.48	41.342	2605.8	100
∞	∞	0	.01000	100.00	0	∞	100.00	10000.	∞

1½%

n	SPCAF	SPPWF	CRF	USPWF	SFDF	USCAF	ASF	ASPWF	n
	F/P	P/F	A/P	P/A	A/F	F/A	A/G	P/G	
1	1.0150	.98522	1.0150	.98522	1.0000	1.0000	–	–	1
2	1.0302	.97066	.51128	1.9559	.49628	2.0150	.49628	.97066	2
3	1.0457	.95632	.34338	2.9122	.32838	3.0452	.99011	2.8834	3
4	1.0614	.94218	.25944	3.8544	.24444	4.0909	1.4814	5.7101	4
5	1.0773	.92826	.20909	4.7827	.19409	5.1523	1.9703	9.4233	5
6	1.0934	.91454	.17552	5.6972	.16052	6.2296	2.4567	13.996	6
7	1.1098	.90103	.15156	6.5982	.13656	7.3230	2.9406	19.403	7
8	1.1265	.88771	.13358	7.4860	.11858	8.4329	3.4220	25.617	8
9	1.1434	.87459	.11961	8.3605	.10461	9.5593	3.9009	32.613	9
10	1.1605	.86167	.10843	9.2222	.09343	10.703	4.3773	40.369	10
11	1.1779	.84893	.09929	10.071	.08429	11.863	4.8513	48.858	11
12	1.1956	.83639	.09168	10.908	.07668	13.041	5.3227	58.058	12
13	1.2136	.82403	.08524	11.732	.07024	14.237	5.7918	67.946	13
14	1.2318	.81185	.07972	12.543	.06472	15.450	6.2583	78.500	14
15	1.2502	.79985	.07494	13.343	.05994	16.682	6.7224	89.698	15
16	1.2690	.78803	.07077	14.131	.05577	17.932	7.1840	101.52	16
17	1.2880	.77639	.06708	14.908	.05208	19.201	7.6431	113.94	17
18	1.3073	.76491	.06381	15.673	.04881	20.489	8.0998	126.94	18
19	1.3270	.75361	.06088	16.426	.04588	21.797	8.5540	140.51	19
20	1.3469	.74247	.05825	17.169	.04325	23.124	9.0057	154.62	20
21	1.3671	.73150	.05587	17.900	.04087	24.471	9.4550	169.25	21
22	1.3876	.72069	.05370	18.621	.03870	25.838	9.9018	184.38	22
23	1.4084	.71004	.05173	19.331	.03673	27.225	10.346	200.00	23
24	1.4295	.69954	.04992	20.030	.03492	28.634	10.788	216.09	24
25	1.4509	.68921	.04826	20.720	.03326	30.063	11.228	232.63	25
26	1.4727	.67902	.04673	21.399	.03173	31.514	11.665	249.61	26
27	1.4948	.66899	.04532	22.068	.03032	32.987	12.099	267.00	27
28	1.5172	.65910	.04400	22.727	.02900	34.482	12.531	284.80	28
29	1.5400	.64936	.04278	23.376	.02778	35.999	12.961	302.98	29
30	1.5631	.63976	.04164	24.016	.02664	37.539	13.388	321.53	30
31	1.5865	.63031	.04057	24.646	.02557	39.102	13.813	340.44	31
32	1.6103	.62099	.03958	25.267	.02458	40.688	14.236	359.69	32
33	1.6345	.61182	.03864	25.879	.02364	42.299	14.656	379.27	33
34	1.6590	.60277	.03776	26.482	.02276	43.933	15.073	399.16	34
35	1.6839	.59387	.03693	27.076	.02193	45.592	15.488	419.35	35
40	1.8140	.55126	.03343	29.916	.01843	54.268	17.528	524.36	40
45	1.9542	.51171	.03072	32.552	.01572	63.614	19.507	635.01	45
50	2.1052	.47500	.02857	35.000	.01357	73.683	21.428	749.96	50
55	2.2679	.44093	.02683	37.271	.01183	84.530	23.289	868.03	55
60	2.4432	.40930	.02539	39.380	.01039	96.215	25.093	988.17	60
65	2.6320	.37993	.02419	41.338	.00919	108.80	26.839	1109.5	65
70	2.8355	.35268	.02317	43.155	.00817	122.36	28.529	1231.2	70
75	3.0546	.32738	.02230	44.842	.00730	136.97	30.163	1352.6	75
80	3.2907	.30389	.02155	46.407	.00655	152.71	31.742	1473.1	80
85	3.5450	.28209	.02089	47.861	.00589	169.67	33.268	1592.2	85
90	3.8189	.26185	.02032	49.210	.00532	187.93	34.740	1709.5	90
95	4.1141	.24307	.01982	50.462	.00482	207.61	36.160	1824.7	95
100	4.4320	.22563	.01937	51.625	.00437	228.80	37.530	1937.5	100
∞	∞	0	.01500	66.667	0	∞	66.667	4444.4	∞

2%

1	1.0200	.98039	1.0200	.98039	1.0000	1.0000	–	–	1
2	1.0404	.96117	.51505	1.9416	.49505	2.0200	.49501	.96109	2
3	1.0612	.94232	.34675	2.8839	.32675	3.0604	.98678	2.8458	3
4	1.0824	.92385	.26262	3.8077	.24262	4.1216	1.4752	5.6173	4
5	1.1041	.90573	.21216	4.7135	.19216	5.2040	1.9604	9.2402	5
6	1.1262	.88797	.17853	5.6014	.15853	6.3081	2.4422	13.680	6
7	1.1487	.87056	.15451	6.4720	.13451	7.4343	2.9208	18.903	7
8	1.1717	.85349	.13651	7.3255	.11651	8.5830	3.3961	24.878	8

2% (continued)

n	SPCAF F/P	SPPWF P/F	CRF A/P	USPWF P/A	SFDF A/F	USCAF F/A	ASF A/G	ASPWF P/G	n
9	1.1951	.83676	.12252	8.1622	.10252	9.7546	3.8680	31.572	9
10	1.2190	.82035	.11133	8.9826	.09133	10.950	4.3367	38.955	10
11	1.2434	.80426	.10218	9.7868	.08218	12.169	4.8021	46.998	11
12	1.2682	.78849	.09456	10.575	.07456	13.412	5.2642	55.671	12
13	1.2936	.77303	.08812	11.348	.06812	14.680	5.7231	64.947	13
14	1.3195	.75788	.08260	12.106	.06260	15.974	6.1786	74.800	14
15	1.3459	.74301	.07783	12.849	.05783	17.293	6.6309	85.202	15
16	1.3728	.72845	.07365	13.578	.05365	18.639	7.0799	96.129	16
17	1.4002	.71416	.06997	14.292	.04997	20.012	7.5256	107.56	17
18	1.4282	.70016	.06670	14.992	.04670	21.412	7.9681	119.46	18
19	1.4568	.68643	.06378	15.678	.04378	22.841	8.4073	131.81	19
20	1.4859	.67297	.06116	16.351	.04116	24.297	8.8433	144.60	20
21	1.5157	.65978	.05879	17.011	.03879	25.783	9.2760	157.80	21
22	1.5460	.64684	.05663	17.658	.03663	27.299	9.7054	171.38	22
23	1.5769	.63416	.05467	18.292	.03467	28.845	10.132	185.33	23
24	1.6084	.62172	.05287	18.914	.03287	30.422	10.555	199.63	24
25	1.6406	.60953	.05122	19.523	.03122	32.030	10.974	214.26	25
26	1.6734	.59758	.04970	20.121	.02970	33.671	11.391	229.20	26
27	1.7069	.58586	.04829	20.707	.02829	35.344	11.804	244.43	27
28	1.7410	.57437	.04699	21.281	.02699	37.051	12.214	259.94	28
29	1.7758	.56311	.04578	21.844	.02578	38.792	12.621	275.71	29
30	1.8114	.55207	.04465	22.396	.02465	40.568	13.025	291.72	30
31	1.8476	.54125	.04360	22.938	.02360	42.379	13.426	307.95	31
32	1.8845	.53063	.04261	23.468	.02261	44.227	13.823	324.40	32
33	1.9222	.52023	.04169	23.989	.02169	46.112	14.217	341.05	33
34	1.9607	.51003	.04082	24.499	.02082	48.034	14.608	357.88	34
35	1.9999	.50003	.04000	24.999	.02000	49.994	14.996	374.88	35
40	2.2080	.45289	.03656	27.355	.01656	60.402	16.888	461.99	40
45	2.4379	.41020	.03391	29.490	.01391	71.893	18.703	551.56	45
50	2.6916	.37153	.03182	31.424	.01182	84.579	20.442	642.36	50
55	2.9717	.33650	.03014	33.175	.01014	98.586	22.106	733.35	55
60	3.2810	.30478	.02877	34.761	.00877	114.05	23.696	823.70	60
65	3.6225	.27605	.02763	36.197	.00763	131.13	25.215	912.71	65
70	3.9996	.25003	.02667	37.499	.00667	149.98	26.663	999.83	70
75	4.4158	.22646	.02586	38.677	.00586	170.79	28.043	1084.6	75
80	4.8754	.20511	.02516	39.745	.00516	193.77	29.357	1166.8	80
85	5.3829	.18577	.02456	40.711	.00456	219.14	30.606	1246.0	85
90	5.9431	.16826	.02405	41.587	.00405	247.16	31.793	1322.2	90
95	6.5617	.15240	.02360	42.380	.00360	278.08	32.919	1395.1	95
100	7.2446	.13803	.02320	43.098	.00320	312.23	33.986	1464.8	100
∞	∞	0	.02000	50.000	0	∞	50.000	2500.0	∞

2½%

n	SPCAF F/P	SPPWF P/F	CRF A/P	USPWF P/A	SFDF A/F	USCAF F/A	ASF A/G	ASPWF P/G	n
1	1.0250	.97561	1.0250	.97561	1.0000	1.0000	–	–	1
2	1.0506	.95181	.51883	1.9274	.49383	2.0250	.49383	.95182	2
3	1.0769	.92860	.35014	2.8560	.32514	3.0756	.98353	2.8090	3
4	1.1038	.90595	.26582	3.7620	.24082	4.1525	1.4691	5.5269	4
5	1.1314	.88385	.21525	4.6458	.19025	5.2563	1.9506	9.0623	5
6	1.1597	.86230	.18155	5.5081	.15655	6.3877	2.4280	13.374	6
7	1.1887	.84127	.15750	6.3494	.13250	7.5474	2.9013	18.421	7
8	1.2184	.82075	.13947	7.1701	.11447	8.7361	3.3704	24.166	8
9	1.2489	.80073	.12546	7.9709	.10046	9.9545	3.8355	30.572	9
10	1.2801	.78120	.11426	8.7521	.08926	11.203	4.2965	37.603	10
11	1.3121	.76214	.10511	9.5142	.08011	12.483	4.7534	45.225	11
12	1.3449	.74356	.09749	10.258	.07249	13.796	5.2062	53.404	12
13	1.3785	.72542	.09105	10.983	.06605	15.140	5.6549	62.109	13
14	1.4130	.70773	.08554	11.691	.06054	16.519	6.0995	71.309	14
15	1.4483	.69047	.08077	12.381	.05577	17.932	6.5401	80.976	15
16	1.4845	.67362	.07660	13.055	.05160	19.380	6.9766	91.080	16
17	1.5216	.65720	.07293	13.712	.04793	20.865	7.4091	101.60	17
18	1.5597	.64117	.06967	14.353	.04467	22.386	7.8375	112.50	18

2½% (continued)

n	SPCAF F/P	SPPWF P/F	CRF A/P	USPWF P/A	SFDF A/F	USCAF F/A	ASF A/G	ASPWF P/G	n
19	1.5987	.62553	.06676	14.979	.04176	23.946	8.2619	123.75	19
20	1.6386	.61027	.06415	15.589	.03915	25.545	8.6823	135.35	20
21	1.6796	.59539	.06179	16.185	.03679	27.183	9.0986	147.26	21
22	1.7216	.58086	.05965	16.765	.03465	28.863	9.5110	159.46	22
23	1.7646	.56670	.05770	17.332	.03270	30.584	9.9193	171.92	23
24	1.8087	.55288	.05591	17.885	.03091	32.349	10.324	184.64	24
25	1.8539	.53939	.05428	18.424	.02928	34.158	10.724	197.58	25
26	1.9003	.52623	.05277	18.951	.02777	36.012	11.121	210.74	26
27	1.9478	.51340	.05138	19.464	.02638	37.912	11.513	224.09	27
28	1.9965	.50088	.05009	19.965	.02509	39.860	11.902	237.61	28
29	2.0464	.48866	.04889	20.454	.02389	41.856	12.286	251.30	29
30	2.0976	.47674	.04778	20.930	.02278	43.903	12.667	265.12	30
31	2.1500	.46511	.04674	21.395	.02174	46.000	13.044	279.07	31
32	2.2038	.45377	.04577	21.849	.02077	48.150	13.417	293.14	32
33	2.2589	.44270	.04486	22.292	.01986	50.354	13.786	307.31	33
34	2.3153	.43191	.04401	22.724	.Q1901	52.613	14.151	321.56	34
35	2.3732	.42137	.04321	23.145	.01821	54.928	14.512	335.89	35
40	2.6851	.37243	.03984	25.103	.01484	67.403	16.262	408.22	40
45	3.0379	.32917	.03727	26.833	.01227	81.516	17.918	480.81	45
50	3.4371	.29094	.03526	28.362	.01026	97.484	19.484	552.61	50
55	3.8888	.25715	.03365	29.714	.00865	115.55	20.961	622.83	55
60	4.3998	.22728	.03235	30.909	.00735	135.99	22.352	690.87	60
65	4.9780	.20089	.03128	31.965	.00628	159.12	23.660	756.28	65
70	5.6321	.17755	.03040	32.898	.00540	185.28	24.888	818.76	70
75	6.3722	.15693	.02965	33.723	.00465	214.89	26.039	878.12	75
80	7.2096	.13870	.02903	34.452	.00403	248.38	27.117	934.22	80
85	8.1570	.12259	.02849	35.096	.00349	286.28	28.123	987.03	85
90	9.2289	.10836	.02804	35.666	.00304	329.15	29.063	1036.5	90
95	10.442	.09577	.02765	36.169	.00265	377.66	29.938	1082.8	95
100	11.814	.08464	.02731	36.614	.00231	432.55	30.752	1126.0	100
∞	∞	0	.02500	40.000	0	∞	40.000	1600.0	∞

3%

n	SPCAF F/P	SPPWF P/F	CRF A/P	USPWF P/A	SFDF A/F	USCAF F/A	ASF A/G	ASPWF P/G	n
1	1.0300	.97087	1.0300	.97087	1.0000	1.0000	–	–	1
2	1.0609	.94260	.52261	1.9135	.49261	2.0300	.49258	.94254	2
3	1.0927	.91514	.35353	2.8286	.32353	3.0909	.98027	2.7728	3
4	1.1255	.88849	.26903	3.7171	.23903	4.1836	1.4630	5.4382	4
5	1.1593	.86261	.21835	4.5797	.18835	5.3091	1.9409	8.8887	5
6	1.1941	.83748	.18460	5.4172	.15460	6.4684	2.4138	13.076	6
7	1.2299	.81309	.16051	6.2303	.13051	7.6625	2.8818	17.955	7
8	1.2668	.78941	.14246	7.0197	.11246	8.8923	3.3449	23.480	8
9	1.3048	.76642	.12843	7.7861	.09843	10.159	3.8032	29.612	9
10	1.3439	.74409	.11723	8.5302	.08723	11.464	4.2565	36.309	10
11	1.3842	.72242	.10808	9.2526	.07808	12.808	4.7049	43.533	11
12	1.4258	.70138	.10046	9.9540	.07046	14.192	5.1485	51.248	12
13	1.4685	.68095	.09403	10.635	.06403	15.618	5.5872	59.419	13
14	1.5126	.66112	.08853	11.296	.05853	17.086	6.0210	68.014	14
15	1.5580	.64186	.08377	11.938	.05377	18.599	6.4500	77.000	15
16	1.6047	.62317	.07961	12.561	.04961	20.157	6.8742	86.347	16
17	1.6528	.60502	.07595	13.166	.04595	21.762	7.2935	96.028	17
18	1.7024	.58739	.07271	13.754	.04271	23.414	7.7081	106.01	18
19	1.7535	.57029	.06981	14.324	.03981	25.117	8.1179	116.28	19
20	1.8061	.55368	.06722	14.877	.03722	26.870	8.5228	126.80	20
21	1.8603	.53755	.06487	15.415	.03487	28.676	8.9231	137.55	21
22	1.9161	.52189	.06275	15.937	.03275	30.537	9.3186	148.51	22
23	1.9736	.50669	.06081	16.444	.03081	32.453	9.7093	159.66	23
24	2.0328	.49193	.05905	16.936	.02905	34.426	10.095	170.97	24
25	2.0938	.47761	.05743	17.413	.02743	36.459	10.477	182.43	25
26	2.1566	.46369	.05594	17.877	.02594	38.553	10.853	194.03	26
27	2.2213	.45019	.05456	18.327	.02456	40.710	11.226	205.73	27
28	2.2879	.43708	.05329	18.764	.02329	42.931	11.593	217.53	28

Discrete Rate-of-Return Factors

3% (continued)

n	SPCAF F/P	SPPWF P/F	CRF A/P	USPWF P/A	SFDF A/F	USCAF F/A	ASF A/G	ASPWF P/G	n
29	2.3566	.42435	.05212	19.188	.02212	45.219	11.956	229.41	29
30	2.4273	.41199	.05102	19.600	.02102	47.575	12.314	241.36	30
31	2.5001	.39999	.05000	20.000	.02000	50.003	12.668	253.36	31
32	2.5751	.38834	.04905	20.389	.01905	52.503	13.017	265.40	32
33	2.6523	.37703	.04816	20.766	.01816	55.078	13.362	277.46	33
34	2.7319	.36605	.04732	21.132	.01732	57.730	13.702	289.54	34
35	2.8139	.35538	.04654	21.487	.01654	60.462	14.037	301.63	35
40	3.2620	.30656	.04326	23.115	.01326	75.401	15.650	361.75	40
45	3.7816	.26444	.04079	24.519	.01079	92.720	17.156	420.63	45
50	4.3839	.22811	.03887	25.730	.00887	112.80	18.557	477.48	50
55	5.0821	.19677	.03735	26.774	.00735	136.07	19.860	531.74	55
60	5.8916	.16973	.03613	27.676	.00613	163.05	21.067	583.05	60
65	6.8300	.14641	.03515	28.453	.00515	194.33	22.184	631.20	65
70	7.9178	.12630	.03434	29.123	.00434	230.59	23.215	676.09	70
75	9.1789	.10895	.03367	29.702	.00367	272.63	24.163	717.70	75
80	10.641	.09398	.03311	30.201	.00311	321.36	25.035	756.09	80
85	12.336	.08107	.03265	30.631	.00265	377.86	25.835	791.35	85
90	14.300	.06993	.03226	31.002	.00226	443.35	26.567	823.63	90
95	16.578	.06032	.03193	31.323	.00193	519.27	27.235	853.07	95
100	19.219	.05203	.03165	31.599	.00165	607.29	27.844	879.85	100
∞	∞	0	.03000	33.333	0	∞	33.333	1111.1	∞

3½%

n	SPCAF F/P	SPPWF P/F	CRF A/P	USPWF P/A	SFDF A/F	USCAF F/A	ASF A/G	ASPWF P/G	n
1	1.0350	.96618	1.0350	.96618	1.0000	1.0000	–	–	1
2	1.0712	.93351	.52640	1.8997	.49140	2.0350	.49140	.93351	2
3	1.1087	.90194	.35693	2.8016	.32193	3.1062	.97708	2.7374	3
4	1.1475	.87144	.27225	3.6731	.23725	4.2149	1.4570	5.3517	4
5	1.1877	.84197	.22148	4.5151	.18648	5.3625	1.9312	8.7196	5
6	1.2293	.81350	.18767	5.3286	.15267	6.5502	2.3997	12.787	6
7	1.2723	.78599	.16354	6.1145	.12854	7.7794	2.8625	17.503	7
8	1.3168	.75941	.14548	6.8740	.11048	9.0517	3.3196	22.819	8
9	1.3629	.73373	.13145	7.6077	.09645	10.368	3.7710	28.689	9
10	1.4106	.70892	.12024	8.3166	.08524	11.731	4.2167	35.069	10
11	1.4600	.68495	.11109	9.0016	.07609	13.142	4.6568	41.919	11
12	1.5111	.66178	.10348	9.6633	.06848	14.602	5.0912	49.198	12
13	1.5640	.63940	.09706	10.303	.06206	16.113	5.5200	56.871	13
14	1.6187	.61778	.09157	10.921	.05657	17.677	5.9431	64.902	14
15	1.6753	.59689	.08683	11.517	.05183	19.296	6.3607	73.259	15
16	1.7340	.57671	.08268	12.094	.04768	20.971	6.7726	81.909	16
17	1.7947	.55720	.07904	12.651	.04404	22.705	7.1790	90.824	17
18	1.8575	.53836	.07582	13.190	.04082	24.500	7.5799	99.977	18
19	1.9225	.52016	.07294	13.710	.03794	26.357	7.9752	109.34	19
20	1.9898	.50257	.07036	14.212	.03536	28.280	8.3651	118.89	20
21	2.0594	.48557	.06804	14.698	.03304	30.269	8.7495	128.60	21
22	2.1315	.46915	.06593	15.167	.03093	32.329	9.1284	138.45	22
23	2.2061	.45329	.06402	15.620	.02902	34.460	9.5019	148.42	23
24	2.2833	.43796	.06227	16.058	.02727	36.667	9.8701	158.50	24
25	2.3632	.42315	.06067	16.482	.02567	38.950	10.233	168.65	25
26	2.4460	.40884	.05921	16.890	.02421	41.313	10.590	178.87	26
27	2.5316	.39501	.05785	17.285	.02285	43.759	10.942	189.14	27
28	2.6202	.38165	.05660	17.667	.02160	46.291	11.289	199.45	28
29	2.7119	.36875	.05545	18.036	.02045	48.911	11.631	209.77	29
30	2.8068	.35628	.05437	18.392	.01937	51.623	11.967	220.11	30
31	2.9050	.34423	.05337	18.736	.01837	54.429	12.299	230.43	31
32	3.0067	.33259	.05244	19.069	.01744	57.334	12.625	240.74	32
33	3.1119	.32134	.05157	19.390	.01657	60.341	12.946	251.03	33
34	3.2209	.31048	.05076	19.701	.01576	63.453	13.262	261.27	34
35	3.3336	.29998	.05000	20.001	.01500	66.674	13.573	271.47	35
40	3.9593	.25257	.04683	21.355	.01183	84.550	15.055	321.49	40
45	4.7024	.21266	.04445	22.495	.00945	105.78	16.417	369.31	45
50	5.5849	.17905	.04263	23.456	.00763	131.00	17.666	414.37	50

3½% (continued)

n	SPCAF	SPPWF	CRF	USPWF	SFDF	USCAF	ASF	ASPWF	n
	F/P	P/F	A/P	P/A	A/F	F/A	A/G	P/G	
55	6.6331	.15076	.04121	24.264	.00621	160.95	18.808	456.35	55
60	7.8781	.12693	.04009	24.945	.00509	196.52	19.848	495.10	60
65	9.3567	.10688	.03919	25.518	.00419	238.76	20.793	530.60	65
70	11.113	.08999	.03846	26.000	.00346	288.94	21.650	562.90	70
75	13.199	.07577	.03787	26.407	.00287	348.53	22.423	592.12	75
80	15.676	.06379	.03738	26.749	.00238	419.31	23.120	618.44	80
85	18.618	.05371	.03699	27.037	.00199	503.37	23.747	642.04	85
90	22.112	.04522	.03666	27.279	.00166	603.21	24.308	663.12	90
95	26.262	.03808	.03639	27.484	.00139	721.78	24.811	681.89	95
100	31.191	.03206	.03616	27.655	.00116	862.61	25.259	698.55	100
∞	∞	0	.03500	28.571	0	∞	28.571	816.33	∞

4%

n	SPCAF	SPPWF	CRF	USPWF	SFDF	USCAF	ASF	ASPWF	n
1	1.0400	.96154	1.0400	.96154	1.0000	1.0000	–	–	1
2	1.0816	.92456	.53020	1.8861	.49020	2.0400	.49018	.92452	2
3	1.1249	.88900	.36035	2.7751	.32035	3.1216	.97384	2.7025	3
4	1.1699	.85480	.27549	3.6299	.23549	4.2465	1.4510	5.2669	4
5	1.2167	.82193	.22463	4.4518	.18463	5.4163	1.9216	8.5546	5
6	1.2653	.79031	.19076	5.2421	.15076	6.6330	2.3857	12.506	6
7	1.3159	.75992	.16661	6.0021	.12661	7.8983	2.8433	17.066	7
8	1.3686	.73069	.14853	6.7327	.10853	9.2142	3.2944	22.180	8
9	1.4233	.70259	.13449	7.4353	.09449	10.583	3.7391	27.801	9
10	1.4802	.67556	.12329	8.1109	.08329	12.006	4.1772	33.881	10
11	1.5395	.64958	.11415	8.7605	.07415	13.486	4.6090	40.377	11
12	1.6010	.62460	.10655	9.3851	.06655	15.026	5.0343	47.248	12
13	1.6651	.60057	.10014	9.9856	.06014	16.627	5.4533	54.454	13
14	1.7317	.57748	.09467	10.563	.05467	18.292	5.8658	61.962	14
15	1.8009	.55526	.08994	11.118	.04994	20.024	6.2721	69.735	15
16	1.8730	.53391	.8582	11.652	.04582	21.825	6.6720	77.744	16
17	1.9479	.51337	.08220	12.166	.04220	23.697	7.0656	85.958	17
18	2.0258	.49363	.07899	12.659	.03899	25.645	7.4530	94.349	18
19	2.1068	.47464	.07614	13.134	.03614	27.671	7.8341	102.89	19
20	2.1911	.45639	.07358	13.590	.03358	29.778	8.2091	111.56	20
21	2.2788	.43883	.07128	14.029	.03128	31.969	8.5779	120.34	21
22	2.3699	.42196	.06920	14.451	.02920	34.248	8.9406	129.20	22
23	2.4647	.40573	.06731	14.857	.02731	36.618	9.2973	138.13	23
24	2.5633	.39012	.06559	15.247	.02559	39.083	9.6479	147.10	24
25	2.6658	.37512	.06401	15.622	.02401	41.646	9.9925	156.10	25
26	2.7725	.36059	.06257	15.983	.02257	44.312	10.331	165.12	26
27	2.8834	.34682	.06124	16.330	.02124	47.084	10.664	174.14	27
28	2.9987	.33348	.06001	16.663	.02001	49.968	10.991	183.14	28
29	3.1186	.32065	.05888	16.984	.01888	52.966	11.312	192.12	29
30	3.2434	.30832	.05783	17.292	.01783	56.085	11.627	201.06	30
31	3.3731	.29646	.05686	17.588	.01686	59.328	11.937	209.96	31
32	3.5081	.28506	.05595	17.874	.01595	62.701	12.241	218.79	32
33	3.6484	.27409	.05510	18.148	.01510	66.209	12.540	227.56	33
34	3.7943	.26355	.05432	18.411	.01432	69.858	12.832	236.26	34
35	3.9461	.25342	.05358	18.665	.01358	73.652	13.120	244.88	35
40	4.8010	.20829	.05052	19.793	.01052	95.025	14.476	286.53	40
45	5.8412	.17120	.04826	20.720	.00826	121.03	15.705	325.40	45
50	7.1067	.14071	.04655	21.482	.00655	152.67	16.812	361.16	50
55	8.6464	.11566	.04523	22.109	.00523	191.16	17.807	393.69	55
60	10.520	.09506	.04420	22.623	.00420	237.99	18.697	423.00	60
65	12.799	.07813	.04339	23.047	.00339	294.97	19.491	449.20	65
70	15.572	.06422	.04275	23.395	.00275	364.29	20.196	472.48	70
75	18.945	.05278	.04223	23.680	.00223	448.63	20.821	493.04	75
80	23.050	.04338	.04181	23.915	.00181	551.24	21.372	511.12	80
85	28.044	.03566	.04148	24.109	.00148	676.09	21.857	526.94	85
90	34.119	.02931	.04121	24.267	.00121	827.98	22.283	540.74	90
95	41.511	.02409	.04099	24.398	.00099	1012.8	22.655	552.73	95
100	50.505	.01980	.04081	24.505	.00081	1237.6	22.980	563.12	100
∞	∞	0	.04000	25.000	0	∞	25.000	625.00	∞

Discrete Rate-of-Return Factors

4½%

n	SPCAF F/P	SPPWF P/F	CRF A/P	USPWF P/A	SFDF A/F	USCAF F/A	ASF A/G	ASPWF P/G	n
1	1.0450	.95694	1.0450	.95694	1.0000	1.0000	–	–	1
2	1.0920	.91573	.53400	1.8727	.48900	2.0450	.48900	.91573	2
3	1.1412	.87630	.36377	2.7490	.31877	3.1370	.97066	2.6683	3
4	1.1925	.83856	.27874	3.5875	.23374	4.2782	1.4450	5.1840	4
5	1.2462	.80245	.22779	4.3900	.18279	5.4707	1.9120	8.3938	5
6	1.3023	.76790	.19388	5.1579	.14888	6.7169	2.3718	12.233	6
7	1.3609	.73483	.16970	5.8927	.12470	8.0192	2.8242	16.642	.7
8	1.4221	.70319	.15161	6.5959	.10661	9.3800	3.2694	21.565	8
9	1.4861	.67290	.13757	7.2688	.09257	10.802	3.7073	26.948	9
10	1.5530	.64393	.12638	7.9127	.08138	12.288	4.1380	32.743	10
11	1.6229	.61620	.11725	8.5289	.07225	13.841	4.5616	38.905	11
12	1.6959	.58966	.10967	9.1186	.06467	15.464	4.9779	45.391	12
13	1.7722	.56427	.10328	9.6829	.05828	17.160	5.3871	52.163	13
14	1.8519	.53997	.09782	10.223	.05282	18.932	5.7892	59.182	14
15	1.9353	.51672	.09311	10.740	.04811	20.784	6.1843	66.416	15
16	2.0224	.49447	.08902	11.234	.04402	22.719	6.5723	73.833	16
17	2.1134	.47318	.08542	11.707	.04042	24.742	6.9534	81.404	17
18	2.2085	.45280	.08224	12.160	.03724	26.855	7.3275	89.102	18
19	2.3079	.43330	.07941	12.593	.03441	29.064	7.6947	96.901	19
20	2.4117	.41464	.07688	13.008	.03188	31.371	8.0550	104.78	20
21	2.5202	.39679	.07460	13.405	.02960	33.783	8.4086	112.72	21
22	2.6337	.37970	.07255	13.784	.02755	36.303	8.7555	120.69	22
23	2.7522	.36335	.07068	14.148	.02568	38.937	9.0956	128.68	23
24	2.8760	.34770	.06899	14.495	.02399	41.689	9.4291	136.68	24
25	3.0054	.33273	.06744	14.828	.02244	44.565	9.7561	144.67	25
26	3.1407	.31840	.06602	15.147	.02102	47.571	10.077	152.63	26
27	3.2820	.30469	.06472	15.451	.01972	50.711	10.391	160.55	27
28	3.4297	.29157	.06352	15.743	.01852	53.993	10.698	168.42	28
29	3.5840	.27902	.06241	16.022	.01741	57.423	10.999	176.23	29
30	3.7453	.26700	.06139	16.289	.01639	61.007	11.295	183.98	30
31	3.9139	.25550	.06044	16.544	.01544	64.752	11.583	191.64	31
32	4.0900	.24450	.05956	16.789	.01456	68.666	11.866	199.22	32
33	4.2740	.23397	.05874	17.023	.01374	72.756	12.143	206.71	33
34	4.4664	.22390	.05798	17.247	.01298	77.030	12.414	214.10	34
35	4.6673	.21425	.05727	17.461	.01227	81.497	12.679	221.38	35
40	5.8164	.17193	.05434	18.402	.00934	107.03	13.917	256.10	40
45	7.2482	.13796	.05220	19.156	.00720	138.85	15.020	287.73	45
50	9.0326	.11071	.05060	19.762	.00560	178.50	15.998	316.14	50
55	11.256	.08884	.04939	20.248	.00439	227.92	16.860	341.37	55
60	14.027	.07129	.04845	20.638	.00345	289.50	17.617	363.57	60
65	17.481	.05721	.04773	20.951	.00273	366.24	18.278	382.95	65
70	21.784	.04590	.04717	21.202	.00217	461.87	18.854	399.75	70
75	27.147	.03684	.04672	21.404	.00172	581.04	19.354	414.24	75
80	33.830	.02956	.04637	21.565	.00137	729.56	19.785	426.68	80
85	42.158	.02372	.04609	21.695	.00109	914.63	20.157	437.31	85
90	52.537	.01903	.04587	21.799	.00087	1145.3	20.476	446.36	90
95	65.471	.01527	.04570	21.883	.00070	1432.7	20.749	454.04	95
100	81.589	.01226	.04556	21.950	.00056	1790.9	20.981	460.54	100
∞	∞	0	.04500	22.222	0	∞	22.222	493.83	∞

5%

n	SPCAF F/P	SPPWF P/F	CRF A/P	USPWF P/A	SFDF A/F	USCAF F/A	ASF A/G	ASPWF P/G	n
1	1.0500	.95238	1.0500	.95238	1.0000	1.0000	–	–	1
2	1.1025	.90703	.53780	1.8594	.48780	2.0500	.48780	.90703	2
3	1.1576	.86384	.36721	2.7232	.31721	3.1525	.96748	2.6347	3
4	1.2155	.82270	.28201	3.5460	.23201	4.3101	1.4391	5.1028	4
5	1.2763	.78353	.23097	4.3295	.18097	5.5256	1.9025	8.2369	5
6	1.3401	.74622	.19702	5.0757	.14702	6.8019	2.3579	11.968	6
7	1.4071	.71068	.17282	5.7864	.12282	8.1420	2.8052	16.232	7
8	1.4775	.67684	.15472	6.4632	.10472	9.5491	3.2445	20.970	8
9	1.5513	.64461	.14069	7.1078	.09069	11.027	3.6758	26.127	9
10	1.6289	.61391	.12950	7.7217	.07951	12.578	4.0991	31.652	10

5% (continued)

n	SPCAF F/P	SPPWF P/F	CRF A/P	USPWF P/A	SFDF A/F	USCAF F/A	ASF A/G	ASPWF P/G	n
11	1.7103	.58468	.12039	8.3064	.07039	14.207	4.5144	37.499	11
12	1.7959	.55684	.11283	8.8633	.06283	15.917	4.9219	43.624	12
13	1.8856	.53032	.10646	9.3936	.05646	17.713	5.3215	49.988	13
14	1.9799	.50507	.10102	9.8986	.05102	19.599	5.7133	56.554	14
15	2.0789	.48102	.09634	10.380	.04634	21.579	6.0973	63.288	15
16	2.1829	.45811	.09227	10.838	.04227	23.657	6.4736	70.160	16
17	2.2920	.43630	.08870	11.274	.03870	25.840	6.8423	77.140	17
18	2.4066	.41552	.08555	11.690	.03555	28.132	7.2034	84.204	18
19	2.5269	.39573	.08275	12.085	.03275	30.539	7.5569	91.327	19
20	2.6533	.37689	.08024	12.462	.03024	33.066	7.9030	98.488	20
21	2.7860	.35894	.07800	12.821	.02800	35.719	8.2416	105.67	21
22	2.9253	.34185	.07597	13.163	.02597	38.505	8.5730	112.85	22
23	3.0715	.32557	.07414	13.489	.02414	41.430	8.8971	120.01	23
24	3.2251	.31007	.07247	13.799	.02247	44.502	9.2140	127.14	24
25	3.3864	.29530	.07095	14.094	.02095	47.727	9.5238	134.23	25
26	3.5557	.28124	.06956	14.375	.01956	51.113	9.8266	141.26	26
27	3.7335	.26785	.06829	14.643	.01829	54.669	10.122	148.22	27
28	3.9201	.25509	.06712	14.898	.01712	58.403	10.411	155.11	28
29	4.1161	.24295	.06605	15.141	.01605	62.323	10.694	161.91	29
30	4.3219	.23138	.06505	15.372	.01505	66.439	10.969	168.62	30
31	4.5380	.22036	.06413	15.593	.01413	70.761	11.238	175.23	31
32	4.7649	.20987	.06328	15.803	.01328	75.299	11.501	181.74	32
33	5.0032	.19987	.06249	16.003	.01249	80.064	11.757	188.14	33
34	5.2533	.19035	.06176	16.193	.01176	85.067	12.006	194.42	34
35	5.5160	.18129	.06107	16.374	.01107	90.320	12.250	200.58	35
40	7.0400	.14205	.05828	17.159	.00828	120.80	13.377	229.55	40
45	8.9850	.11130	.05626	17.774	.00626	159.70	14.364	255.31	45
50	11.467	.08720	.05478	18.256	.00478	209.35	15.223	277.91	50
55	14.636	.06833	.05367	18.633	.00367	272.71	15.966	297.51	55
60	18.679	.05354	.05283	18.929	.00283	353.58	16.606	314.34	60
65	23.840	.04195	.05219	19.161	.00219	456.80	17.154	328.69	65
70	30.426	.03287	.05170	19.343	.00170	588.53	17.621	340.84	70
75	38.833	.02575	.05132	19.485	.00132	756.65	18.018	351.07	75
80	49.561	.02018	.05103	19.596	.00103	971.23	18.353	359.65	80
85	63.254	.01581	.05080	19.684	.00080	1245.1	18.635	366.80	85
90	80.730	.01239	.05063	19.752	.00063	1594.6	18.871	372.75	90
95	103.03	.00971	.05049	19.806	.00049	2040.7	19.069	377.68	95
100	131.50	.00760	.05038	19.848	.00038	2610.0	19.234	381.75	100
∞	∞	0	.05000	20.000	0	∞	20.000	400.00	∞

5½%

n	SPCAF F/P	SPPWF P/F	CRF A/P	USPWF P/A	SFDF A/F	USCAF F/A	ASF A/G	ASPWF P/G	n
1	1.0550	.94787	1.0550	.94787	1.0000	1.0000	–	–	1
2	1.1130	.89845	.54162	1.8463	.48662	2.0550	.48662	.89845	2
3	1.1742	.85161	.37065	2.6979	.31565	3.1680	.96433	2.6017	3
4	1.2388	.80722	.28529	3.5052	.23029	4.3423	1.4331	5.0233	4
5	1.3070	.76513	.23418	4.2703	.17918	5.5811	1.8931	8.0839	5
6	1.3788	.72525	.20018	4.9955	.14518	6.8881	2.3441	11.710	6
7	1.4547	.68744	.17596	5.6830	.12096	8.2669	2.7864	15.835	7
8	1.5347	.65160	.15786	6.3346	.10286	9.7216	3.2198	20.396	8
9	1.6191	.61763	.14384	6.9522	.08884	11.256	3.6445	25.337	9
10	1.7081	.58543	.13267	7.5376	.07767	12.875	4.0604	30.606	10
11	1.8021	.55491	.12357	8.0925	.06857	14.584	4.4677	36.155	11
12	1.9012	.52598	.11603	8.6185	.06103	16.386	4.8664	41.941	12
13	2.0058	.49856	.10968	9.1171	.05468	18.287	5.2565	47.923	13
14	2.1161	.47257	.10428	9.5896	.04928	20.293	5.6380	54.067	14
15	2.2325	.44793	.09963	10.038	.04463	22.409	6.0112	60.338	15
16	2.3553	.42458	.09558	10.462	.04058	24.641	6.3760	66.707	16
17	2.4848	.40245	.09204	10.865	.03704	26.996	6.7325	73.146	17
18	2.6215	.38147	.08892	11.246	.03392	29.481	7.0808	79.631	18
19	2.7656	.36158	.08615	11.608	.03115	32.103	7.4209	86.139	19
20	2.9178	.34273	.08368	11.950	.02868	34.868	7.7530	92.651	20

5½% (continued)

n	SPCAF F/P	SPPWF P/F	CRF A/P	USPWF P/A	SFDF A/F	USCAF F/A	ASF A/G	ASPWF P/G	n
21	3.0782	.32486	.08146	12.275	.02646	37.786	8.0771	99.148	21
22	3.2475	.30793	.07947	12.583	.02447	40.864	8.3933	105.61	22
23	3.4262	.29187	.07767	12.875	.02267	44.112	8.7018	112.04	23
24	3.6146	.27666	.07604	13.152	.02104	47.538	9.0026	118.40	24
25	3.8134	.26223	.07455	13.414	.01955	51.153	9.2958	124.69	25
26	4.0231	.24856	.07319	13.662	.01819	54.966	9.5815	130.91	26
27	4.2444	.23560	.07195	13.898	.01695	58.989	9.8598	137.03	27
28	4.4778	.22332	.07081	14.121	.01581	63.234	10.131	143.06	28
29	4.7241	.21168	.06977	14.333	.01477	67.711	10.395	148.99	29
30	4.9840	.20064	.06881	14.534	.01381	72.435	10.652	154.81	30
31	5.2581	.19018	.06792	14.724	.01292	77.419	10.902	160.51	31
32	5.5473	.18027	.06710	14.904	.01210	82.678	11.145	166.10	32
33	5.8524	.17087	.06633	15.075	.01133	88.225	11.381	171.57	33
34	6.1742	.16196	.06563	15.237	.01063	94.077	11.611	176.91	34
35	6.5138	.15352	.06497	15.391	.00997	100.25	11.834	182.13	35
40	8.5133	.11746	.06232	16.046	.00732	136.61	12.858	206.32	40
45	11.127	.08988	.06043	16.548	.00543	184.12	13.738	227.33	45
50	14.542	.06877	.05906	16.932	.00406	246.22	14.490	245.33	50
55	19.006	.05262	.05805	17.225	.00305	327.38	15.127	260.57	55
60	24.840	.04026	.05731	17.450	.00231	433.45	15.665	273.35	60
65	32.465	.03081	.05675	17.622	.00175	572.08	16.116	283.99	65
70	42.430	.02357	.0563	17.753	.00133	753.27	16.492	292.79	70
75	55.454	.01803	.05601	17.854	.00101	990.08	16.805	300.03	75
80	72.476	.01380	.05577	17.931	.00077	1299.6	17.063	305.95	80
85	94.724	.01056	.05559	17.990	.00059	1704.1	17.275	310.77	85
90	123.80	.00808	.05545	18.035	.00045	2232.7	17.449	314.69	90
95	161.80	.00619	.05534	18.069	.00034	2923.7	17.591	317.86	95
100	211.47	.00473	.05526	18.096	.00026	3826.7	17.707	320.42	100
∞	∞	0	.05500	18.182	0	∞	18.182	330.58	

6%

n	SPCAF F/P	SPPWF P/F	CRF A/P	USPWF P/A	SFDF A/F	USCAF F/A	ASF A/G	ASPWF P/G	n
1	1.0600	.94340	1.0600	.94340	1.0000	1.0000	–	–	1
2	1.1236	.89000	.54544	1.8334	.48544	2.0600	.48543	.88999	2
3	1.1910	.83962	.37411	2.6730	.31411	3.1836	.96117	2.5692	3
4	1.2625	.79209	.28859	3.4651	.22859	4.3746	1.4272	4.9455	4
5	1.3382	.74726	.23740	4.2124	.17740	5.6371	1.8836	7.9345	5
6	1.4185	.70496	.20336	4.9173	.14336	6.9753	2.3304	11.459	6
7	1.5036	.66506	.17914	5.5824	.11914	8.3938	2.7676	15.450	7
8	1.5938	.62741	.16104	6.2098	.10104	9.8975	3.1952	19.842	8
9	1.6895	.59190	.14702	6.8017	.08702	11.491	3.6133	24.577	9
10	1.7908	.55839	.13587	7.3601	.07587	13.181	4.0220	29.602	10
11	1.8983	.52679	.12679	7.8869	.06679	14.972	4.4213	34.870	11
12	2.0122	.49697	.11928	8.3838	.05928	16.870	4.8113	40.337	12
13	2.1329	.46884	.11296	8.8527	.05296	18.882	5.1920	45.963	13
14	2.2609	.44230	.10758	9.2950	.04759	21.015	5.5635	51.713	14
15	2.3966	.41727	.10296	9.7122	.04296	23.276	5.9260	57.555	15
16	2.5404	.39365	.09895	10.106	.03895	25.673	6.2794	63.459	16
17	2.6928	.37136	.09545	10.477	.03545	28.213	6.6240	69.401	17
18	2.8543	.35034	.09236	10.828	.03236	30.906	6.9597	75.357	18
19	3.0256	.33051	.08962	11.158	.02962	33.760	7.2867	81.306	19
20	3.2071	.31180	.08719	11.470	.02719	36.786	7.6051	87.230	20
21	3.3996	.29416	.08501	11.764	.02501	39.993	7.9151	93.114	21
22	3.6035	.27751	.08304	12.042	.02305	43.392	8.2166	98.941	22
23	3.8197	.26180	.08128	12.303	.02128	46.996	8.5099	104.70	23
24	4.0489	.24698	.07968	12.550	.01968	50.816	8.7951	110.38	24
25	4.2919	.23300	.07823	12.783	.01823	54.864	9.0722	115.97	25
26	4.5494	.21981	.07690	13.003	.01690	59.156	9.3414	121.47	26
27	4.8223	.20737	.07570	13.211	.01570	63.706	9.6029	126.86	27
28	5.1117	.19563	.07459	13.406	.01459	68.528	9.8568	132.14	28
29	5.4184	.18456	.07358	13.591	.01358	73.640	10.103	137.31	29
30	5.7435	.17411	.07265	13.765	.01265	79.058	10.342	142.36	30

6% (continued)

n	SPCAF	SPPWF	CRF	USPWF	SFDF	USCAF	ASF	ASPWF	n
	F/P	P/F	A/P	P/A	A/F	F/A	A/G	P/G	
31	6.0881	.16425	.07179	13.929	.01179	84.802	10.574	147.29	31
32	6.4534	.15496	.07100	14.084	.01100	90.890	10.799	152.09	32
33	6.8406	.14619	.07027	14.230	.01027	97.343	11.017	156.77	33
34	7.2510	.13791	.06960	14.368	.00960	104.18	11.228	161.32	34
35	7.6861	.13011	.06897	14.498	.00897	111.43	11.432	165.74	35
40	10.286	.09722	.06646	15.046	.00646	154.76	12.359	185.96	40
45	13.765	.07265	.06470	15.456	.00470	212.74	13.141	203.11	45
50	18.420	.05429	.06344	15.762	.00344	290.34	13.796	217.46	50
55	24.650	.04057	.06254	15.991	.00254	394.17	14.341	229.32	55
60	32.988	.03031	.06188	16.161	.00188	533.13	14.791	239.04	60
65	44.145	.02265	.06139	16.289	.00139	719.08	15.160	246.95	65
70	59.076	.01693	.06103	16.385	.00103	967.93	15.461	253.33	70
75	79.057	.01265	.06077	16.456	.00077	1300.9	15.706	258.45	75
80	105.80	.00945	.06057	16.509	.00057	1746.6	15.903	262.55	80
85	141.58	.00706	.06043	16.549	.00043	2343.0	16.062	265.81	85
90	189.46	.00528	.06032	16.579	.00032	3141.1	16.189	268.39	90
95	253.55	.00394	.06024	16.601	.00024	4209.1	16.290	270.44	95
100	339.30	.00295	.06018	16.618	.00018	5638.4	16.371	272.05	100
∞	∞	0	.06000	16.667	0	∞	16.667	277.78	∞

7%

n	F/P	P/F	A/P	P/A	A/F	F/A	A/G	P/G	n
1	1.0700	.93458	1.0700	.93458	1.0000	1.0000	. _	_	1
2	1.1449	.87344	.55309	1.8080	.48309	2.0700	.48309	.87343	2
3	1.2250	.81630	.38105	2.6243	.31105	3.2149	.95493	2.5060	3
4	1.3108	.76290	.29523	3.3872	.22523	4.4399	1.4155	4.7947	4
5	1.4026	.71299	.24389	4.1002	.17389	5.7507	1.8649	7.6467	5
6	1.5007	.66634	.20980	4.7665	.13980	7.1533	2.3032	10.978	6
7	1.6058	.62275	.18555	5.3893	.11555	8.6540	2.7304	14.715	7
8	1.7182	.58201	.16747	5.9713	.09747	10.260	3.1465	18.789	8
9	1.8385	.54393	.15349	6.5152	.08349	11.978	3.5517	23.140	9
10	1.9672	.50835	.14238	7.0236	.07238	13.816	3.9461	27.716	10
11	2.1049	.47509	.13336	7.4987	.06336	15.784	4.3296	32.466	11
12	2.2522	.44401	.12590	7.9427	.05590	17.888	4.7025	37.351	12
13	2.4098	.41496	.11965	8.3576	.04965	20.141	5.0648	42.330	13
14	2.5785	.38782	.11434	8.7455	.04435	22.550	5.4167	47.372	14
15	2.7590	.36245	.10979	9.1079	.03980	25.129	5.7583	52.446	15
16	2.9522	.33873	.10586	9.4466	.03586	27.888	6.0897	57.527	16
17	3.1588	.31657	.10243	9.7632	.03243	30.840	6.4110	62.592	17
18	3.3799	.29586	.09941	10.059	.02941	33.999	6.7225	67.622	18
19	3.6165	.27651	.09675	10.336	.02675	37.379	7.0242	72.599	19
20	3.8697	.25842	.09439	10.594	.02439	40.995	7.3163	77.509	20
21	4.1406	.24151	.09229	10.836	.02229	44.865	7.5990	82.339	21
22	4.4304	.22571	.09041	11.061	.02041	49.006	7.8725	87.079	22
23	4.7405	.21095	.08871	11.272	.01871	53.436	8.1369	91.720	23
24	5.0724	.19715	.08719	11.469	.01719	58.177	8.3923	96.254	24
25	5.4274	.18425	.08581	11.654	.01581	63.249	8.6391	100.68	25
26	5.8074	.17220	.08456	11.826	.01456	68.676	8.8773	104.98	26
27	6.2139	.16093	.08343	11.987	.01343	74.484	9.1072	109.17	27
28	6.6488	.15040	.08239	12.137	.01239	80.698	9.3289	113.23	28
29	7.1143	.14056	.08145	12.278	.01145	87.346	9.5427	117.16	29
30	7.6123	.13137	.08059	12.409	.01059	94.461	9.7487	120.97	30
31	8.1451	.12277	.07980	12.532	.00980	102.07	9.9471	124.65	31
32	8.7153	.11474	.07907	12.647	.00907	110.22	10.138	128.21	32
33	9.3253	.10723	.07841	12.754	.00841	118.93	10.322	131.64	33
34	9.9781	.10022	.07780	12.854	.00780	128.26	10.499	134.95	34
35	10.677	.09366	.07723	12.948	.00723	138.24	10.669	138.14	35
40	14.974	.06678	.07501	13.332	.00501	199.63	11.423	152.29	40
45	21.002	.04761	.07350	13.606	.00350	285.75	12.036	163.76	45
50	29.457	.03394	.07246	13.801	.00246	406.53	12.529	172.91	50
55	41.315	.02420	.07174	13.940	.00174	575.93	12.921	180.12	55
60	57.946	.01725	.07123	14.039	.00123	813.52	13.232	185.77	60

7% (continued)

n	SPCAF F/P	SPPWF P/F	CRF A/P	USPWF P/A	SFDF A/F	USCAF F/A	ASF A/G	ASPWF P/G	n
65	81.273	.01230	.07087	14.110	.00087	1146.8	13.476	190.15	65
70	113.99	.00677	.07062	14.160	.00062	1614.1	13.666	193.52	70
75	159.88	.00625	.07044	14.196	.00044	2269.7	13.814	196.10	75
80	224.23	.00446	.07031	14.222	.00031	3189.1	13.927	198.07	80
85	314.50	.00318	.07022	14.240	.00022	4478.6	14.015	199.57	85
90	441.10	.00227	.07016	14.253	.00016	6287.2	14.081	200.70	90
95	618.67	.00161	.07011	14.263	.00011	8823.8	14.132	201.56	95
100	867.72	.00115	.07008	14.269	.00008	12382.	14.170	202.20	100
∞	∞	0	.07000	14.286	0	∞	14.286	204.08	∞

8%

n	SPCAF F/P	SPPWF P/F	CRF A/P	USPWF P/A	SFDF A/F	USCAF F/A	ASF A/G	ASPWF P/G	n
1	1.0800	.92593	1.0800	.92593	1.0000	1.0000	–	–	1
2	1.1664	.85734	.56077	1.7833	.48077	2.0800	.48077	.85734	2
3	1.2597	.79383	.38803	2.5771	.30803	3.2464	.94874	2.4450	3
4	1.3605	.73503	.30192	3.3121	.22192	4.5061	1.4040	4.6501	4
5	1.4693	.68058	.25046	3.9927	.17046	5.8666	1.8465	7.3724	5
6	1.5869	.63017	.21632	4.6229	.13632	7.3359	2.2763	10.523	6
7	1.7138	.58349	.19207	5.2064	.11207	8.9228	2.6937	14.024	7
8	1.8509	.54027	.17401	5.7466	.09402	10.637	3.0985	17.806	8
9	1.9990	.50025	.16008	6.2469	.08008	12.488	3.4910	21.808	9
10	2.1589	.46319	.14903	6.7101	.06903	14.487	3.8713	25.977	10
11	2.3316	.42888	.14008	7.1390	.06008	16.645	4.2395	30.266	11
12	2.5182	.39711	.13270	7.5361	.05270	18.977	4.5957	34.634	12
13	2.7196	.36770	.12652	7.9038	.04652	21.495	4.9402	39.046	13
14	2.9372	.34046	.12130	8.2442	.04130	24.215	5.2731	43.472	14
15	3.1722	.31524	.11683	8.5595	.03683	27.152	5.5945	47.886	15
16	3.4259	.29189	.11298	8.8514	.03298	30.324	5.9046	52.264	16
17	3.7000	.27027	.10963	9.1216	.02963	33.750	6.2037	56.588	17
18	3.9960	.25025	.10670	9.3719	.02670	37.450	6.4920	60.843	18
19	4.3157	.23171	.10413	9.6036	.02413	41.446	6.7697	65.013	19
20	4.6610	.21455	.10185	9.8181	.02185	45.762	7.0369	69.090	20
21	5.0338	.19866	.09983	10.017	.01983	50.423	7.2940	73.063	21
22	5.4365	.18394	.09803	10.201	.01803	55.457	7.5412	76.926	22
23	5.8715	.17032	.09642	10.371	.01642	60.893	7.7786	80.673	23
24	6.3412	.15770	.09498	10.529	.01498	66.765	8.0066	84.300	24
25	6.8485	.14602	.09368	10.675	.01368	73.106	8.2254	87.804	25
26	7.3964	.13520	.09251	10.810	.01251	79.954	8.4352	91.184	26
27	7.9881	.12519	.09145	10.935	.01145	87.351	8.6363	94.439	27
28	8.6271	.11591	.09049	11.051	.01049	95.339	8.8289	97.569	28
29	9.3173	.10733	.08962	11.158	.00962	103.97	9.0133	100.57	29
30	10.063	.09938	.08883	11.258	.00883	113.28	9.1897	103.46	30
31	10.868	.09202	.08811	11.350	.00811	123.35	9.3584	106.22	31
32	11.737	.08520	.08745	11.435	.00745	134.21	9.5197	108.86	32
33	12.676	.07889	.08685	11.514	.00685	145.95	9.6737	111.38	33
34	13.690	.07305	.08630	11.587	.00630	158.63	9.8208	113.79	34
35	14.785	.06764	.08580	11.655	.00580	172.32	9.9611	116.09	35
40	21.725	.04603	.08386	11.925	.00386	259.06	10.570	126.04	40
45	31.920	.03133	.08259	12.108	.00259	386.51	11.045	133.73	45
50	46.902	.02132	.08174	12.233	.00174	573.77	11.411	139.59	50
55	68.914	.01451	.08118	12.319	.00118	848.92	11.690	144.01	55
60	101.26	.00988	.08080	12.377	.00080	1253.2	11.902	147.30	60
65	148.78	.00672	.08054	12.416	.00054	1847.2	12.060	149.74	65
70	218.61	.00457	.08037	12.443	.00037	2720.1	12.178	151.53	70
75	321.20	.00311	.08025	12.461	.00025	4002.6	12.266	152.84	75
80	471.95	.00212	.08017	12.474	.00017	5886.9	12.330	153.80	80
85	693.46	.00144	.08012	12.482	.00012	8655.7	12.377	154.49	85
90	1018.9	.00098	.08008	12.488	.00008	12724.	12.412	154.99	90
95	1497.1	.00067	.08005	12.492	.00005	18702.	12.437	155.35	95
100	2199.8	.00045	.08004	12.494	.00004	27484.	12.455	155.61	100
∞	∞	0	.08000	12.500	0	∞	12.500	156.25	∞

9%

n	SPCAF F/P	SPPWF P/F	CRF A/P	USPWF P/A	SFDF A/F	USCAF F/A	ASF A/G	ASPWF P/G	n
1	1.0900	.91743	1.0900	.91743	1.0000	1.0000	–	–	1
2	1.1881	.84168	.56847	1.7591	.47847	2.0900	.47847	.84168	2
3	1.2950	.77218	.39505	2.5313	.30505	3.2781	.94262	2.3860	3
4	1.4116	.70843	.30867	3.2397	.21867	4.5731	1.3925	4.5113	4
5	1.5386	.64993	.25709	3.8897	.16709	5.9847	1.8282	7.1111	5
6	1.6771	.59627	.22292	4.4859	.13292	7.5233	2.2498	10.092	6
7	1.8280	.54703	.19869	5.0330	.10869	9.2004	2.6574	13.375	7
8	1.9926	.50187	.18067	5.5348	.09067	11.028	3.0512	16.888	8
9	2.1719	.46043	.16680	5.9952	.07680	13.021	3.4312	20.571	9
10	2.3674	.42241	.15582	6.4177	.06582	15.193	3.7978	24.373	10
11	2.5804	.38753	.14695	6.8052	.05695	17.560	4.1510	28.248	11
12	2.8127	.35553	.13965	7.1607	.04965	20.141	4.4910	32.159	12
13	3.0658	.32618	.13357	7.4869	.04357	22.953	4.8182	36.073	13
14	3.3417	.29925	.12843	7.7862	.03843	26.019	5.1326	39.963	14
15	3.6425	.27454	.12406	8.0607	.03406	29.361	5.4346	43.807	15
16	3.9703	.25187	.12030	8.3126	.03030	33.003	5.7245	47.585	16
17	4.3276	.23107	.11705	8.5436	.02705	36.974	6.0024	51.282	17
18	4.7171	.21199	.11421	8.7556	.02421	41.301	6.2687	54.886	18
19	5.1417	.19449	.11173	8.9501	.02173	46.018	6.5236	58.387	19
20	5.6044	.17843	.10955	9.1285	.01955	51.160	6.7675	61.777	20
21	6.1088	.16370	.10762	9.2922	.01762	56.765	7.0006	65.051	21
22	6.6586	.15018	.10590	9.4424	.01591	62.873	7.2232	68.205	22
23	7.2579	.13778	.10438	9.5802	.01438	69.532	7.4357	71.236	23
24	7.9111	.12640	.10302	9.7066	.01302	76.790	7.6384	74.143	24
25	8.6231	.11597	.10181	9.8226	.01181	84.701	7.8316	76.926	25
26	9.3992	.10639	.10072	9.9290	.01072	93.324	8.0156	79.586	26
27	10.245	.09761	.09974	10.027	.00973	102.72	8.1906	82.124	27
28	11.167	.08955	.09885	10.116	.00885	112.97	8.3571	84.542	28
29	12.172	.08216	.09806	10.198	.00806	124.14	8.5154	86.842	29
30	13.268	.07537	.09734	10.274	.00734	136.31	8.6657	89.028	30
31	14.462	.06915	.09669	10.343	.00669	149.58	8.8083	91.102	31
32	15.763	.06344	.09610	10.406	.00610	164.04	8.9436	93.069	32
33	17.182	.05820	.09556	10.464	.00556	179.80	9.0718	94.931	33
34	18.728	.05340	.09508	10.518	.00508	196.98	9.1933	96.693	34
35	20.414	.04899	.09464	10.567	.00464	215.71	9.3083	98.359	35
40	31.409	.03184	.09296	10.757	.00296	337.88	9.7957	105.38	40
45	48.327	.02069	.09190	10.881	.00190	525.86	10.160	110.56	45
50	74.358	.01345	.09123	10.962	.00123	815.08	10.430	114.33	50
55	114.41	.00874	.09079	11.014	.00079	1260.1	10.626	117.04	55
60	176.03	.00568	.09051	11.048	.00051	1944.8	10.768	118.97	60
65	270.85	.00369	.09033	11.070	.00033	2998.3	10.870	120.33	65
70	416.73	.00240	.09022	11.084	.00022	4619.2	10.943	121.29	70
75	641.19	.00156	.09014	11.094	.00014	7113.2	10.994	121.96	75
80	986.55	.00101	.09009	11.100	.00009	10951.	11.030	122.43	80
85	1517.9	.00066	.09006	11.104	.00006	16855.	11.055	122.75	85
90	2335.5	.00043	.09004	11.106	.00004	25939.	11.073	122.98	90
95	3593.5	.00028	.09003	11.108	.00003	39917.	11.085	123.13	95
100	5529.0	.00018	.09002	11.109	.00002	61423.	11.093	123.23	100
∞	∞	0	.09000	11.111	0	∞	11.111	123.45	∞

10%

n	F/P	P/F	A/P	P/A	A/F	F/A	A/G	P/G	n
1	1.1000	.90909	1.1000	.90909	1.0000	1.0000	–	–	1
2	1.2100	.82645	.57619	1.7355	.47619	2.1000	.47619	.82645	2
3	1.3310	.75131	.40211	2.4869	.30211	3.3100	.93656	2.3291	3
4	1.4641	.68301	.31547	3.1699	.21547	4.6410	1.3812	4.3781	4
5	1.6105	.62092	.26380	3.7908	.16380	6.1051	1.8101	6.8618	5
6	1.7716	.56447	.22961	4.3553	.12961	7.7156	2.2236	9.6842	6
7	1.9487	.51316	.20541	4.8684	.10541	9.4872	2.6216	12.763	7
8	2.1436	.46651	.18744	5.3349	.08744	11.436	3.0045	16.029	8
9	2.3579	.42410	.17364	5.7590	.07364	13.579	3.3724	19.421	9
10	2.5937	.38554	.16275	6.1446	.06275	15.937	3.7255	22.891	10

10% (continued)

n	SPCAF F/P	SPPWF P/F	CRF A/P	USPWF P/A	SFDF A/F	USCAF F/A	ASF A/G	ASPWF P/G	n
11	2.8531	.35049	.15396	6.4951	.05396	18.531	4.0641	26.396	11
12	3.1384	.31863	.14676	6.8137	.04676	21.384	4.3884	29.901	12
13	3.4523	.28966	.14078	7.1034	.04078	24.523	4.6988	33.377	13
14	3.7975	.26333	.13575	7.3667	.03575	27.975	4.9955	36.801	14
15	4.1772	.23939	.13147	7.6061	.03147	31.772	5.2789	40.152	15
16	4.5950	.21763	.12782	7.8237	.02782	35.950	5.5493	43.416	16
17	5.0545	.19784	.12466	8.0216	.02466	40.545	5.8071	46.582	17
18	5.5599	.17986	.12193	8.2014	.02193	45.599	6.0526	49.640	18
19	6.1159	.16351	.11955	8.3649	.01955	51.159	6.2861	52.583	19
20	6.7275	.14864	.11746	8.5136	.01746	57.275	6.5081	55.407	20
21	7.4003	.13513	.11562	8.6487	.01562	64.003	6.7189	58.110	21
22	8.1403	.12285	.11401	8.7715	.01401	71.403	6.9189	60.689	22
23	8.9543	.11168	.11257	8.8832	.01257	79.543	7.1085	63.146	23
24	9.8497	.10153	.11130	8.9847	.01130	88.497	7.2881	65.481	24
25	10.835	.09230	.11017	9.0770	.01017	98.347	7.4580	67.696	25
26	11.918	.08391	.10916	9.1609	.00916	109.18	7.6187	69.794	26
27	13.110	.07628	.10826	9.2372	.00826	121.10	7.7704	71.777	27
28	14.421	.06934	.10745	9.3066	.00745	134.21	7.9137	73.650	28
29	15.863	.06304	.10673	9.3696	.00673	148.63	8.0489	75.415	29
30	17.449	.05731	.10608	9.4269	.00608	164.49	8.1762	77.077	30
31	19.194	.05210	.10550	9.4790	.00550	181.94	8.2962	78.640	31
32	21.114	.04736	.10497	9.5264	.00497	201.14	8.4091	80.108	32
33	23.225	.04306	.10450	9.5694	.00450	222.25	8.5152	81.486	33
34	25.548	.03914	.10407	9.6086	.00407	245.48	8.6149	82.777	34
35	28.102	.03558	.10369	9.6442	.00369	271.02	8.7086	83.987	35
40	45.259	.02210	.10226	9.7791	.00226	442.59	9.0962	88.953	40
45	72.890	.01372	.10139	9.8628	.00139	718.90	9.3740	92.454	45
50	117.39	.00852	.10086	9.9148	.00086	1163.9	9.5704	94.889	50
55	189.06	.00529	.10053	9.9471	.00053	1880.6	9.7075	96.562	55
60	304.48	.00328	.10033	9.9672	.00033	3034.8	9.8023	97.701	60
65	490.37	.00204	.10020	9.9796	.00020	4893.7	9.8672	98.471	65
70	789.75	.00127	.10013	9.9873	.00013	7887.5	9.9113	98.987	70
75	1271.9	.00079	.10008	9.9921	.00008	12709.	9.9410	99.332	75
80	2048.4	.00049	.10005	9.9951	.00005	20474.	9.9609	99.561	80
85	3299.0	.00030	.10030	9.9970	.00003	32980.	9.9742	99.712	85
90	5313.0	.00019	.10002	9.9981	.00002	53120.	9.9831	99.812	90
95	8556.7	.00012	.10001	9.9988	.00001	85557.	9.9889	99.877	95
100	13781.	.00007	.10001	9.9993	.00001		9.9927	99.920	100
∞	∞	0	.10000	10.000	0	∞	10.000	100.00	∞

12%

n	SPCAF F/P	SPPWF P/F	CRF A/P	USPWF P/A	SFDF A/F	USCAF F/A	ASF A/G	ASPWF P/G	n
1	1.1200	.89286	1.1200	.89286	1.0000	1.0000	–	–	1
2	1.2544	.79719	.59170	1.6901	.47170	2.1200	.47170	.79720	2
3	1.4049	.71178	.41635	2.4018	.29635	3.3744	.92461	2.2208	3
4	1.5735	.63552	.32923	3.0373	.20923	4.7793	1.3589	4.1273	4
5	1.7623	.56743	.27741	3.6048	.15741	6.3528	1.7746	6.3970	5
6	1.9738	.50663	.24323	4.1114	.12323	8.1152	2.1720	8.9302	6
7	2.2107	.45235	.21912	4.5638	.09912	10.089	2.5515	11.644	7
8	2.4760	.40388	.20130	4.9676	.08130	12.300	2.9131	14.471	8
9	2.7731	.36061	.18768	5.3283	.06768	14.776	3.2574	17.356	9
10	3.1058	.32197	.17698	5.6502	.05698	17.549	3.5847	20.254	10
11	3.4786	.28748	.16842	5.9377	.04842	20.655	3.8953	23.129	11
12	3.8960	.25668	.16144	6.1944	.04143	24.133	4.1897	25.952	12
13	4.3635	.22917	.15568	6.4235	.03568	28.029	4.4683	28.702	13
14	4.8871	.20462	.15087	6.6282	.03087	32.393	4.7317	31.362	14
15	5.4736	.18270	.14682	6.8109	.02682	37.280	4.9803	33.920	15
16	6.1304	.16312	.14339	6.9740	.02339	42.753	5.2147	36.367	16
17	6.8660	.14564	.14046	7.1196	.02046	48.884	5.4353	38.697	17
18	7.6900	.13004	.13794	7.2497	.01794	55.750	5.6427	40.908	18
19	8.6128	.11611	.13576	7.3658	.01576	63.440	5.8375	42.998	19
20	9.6463	.10367	.13388	7.4694	.01388	72.052	6.0202	44.968	20

12% (continued)

n	SPCAF F/P	SPPWF P/F	CRF A/P	USPWF P/A	SFDF A/F	USCAF F/A	ASF A/G	ASPWF P/G	n
21	10.804	.09256	.13224	7.5620	.01224	81.699	6.1913	46.819	21
22	12.100	.08264	.13081	7.6446	.01081	92.503	6.3514	48.554	22
23	13.552	.07379	.12956	7.7184	.00956	104.60	6.5010	50.178	23
24	15.179	.06588	.12846	7.7843	.00846	118.16	6.6406	51.693	24
25	17.000	.05882	.12750	7.8431	.00750	133.33	6.7708	53.105	25
26	19.040	.05252	.12665	7.8957	.00665	150.33	6.8921	54.418	26
27	21.325	.04689	.12590	7.9426	.00590	169.37	7.0049	55.637	27
28	23.884	.04187	.12524	7.9844	.00524	190.70	7.1098	56.767	28
29	26.750	.03738	.12466	8.0218	.00466	214.58	7.2071	57.814	29
30	29.960	.03338	.12414	8.0552	.00414	241.33	7.2974	58.782	30
31	33.555	.02980	.12369	8.0850	.00369	271.29	7.3811	59.676	31
32	37.582	.02661	.12328	8.1116	.00328	304.85	7.4586	60.501	32
33	42.092	.02376	.12292	8.1354	.00292	342.43	7.5302	61.261	33
34	47.143	.02121	.12260	8.1566	.00260	384.52	7.5965	61.961	34
35	52.800	.01894	.12232	8.1755	.00232	431.66	7.6577	62.605	35
40	93.051	.01075	.12130	8.2438	.00130	767.09	7.8988	65.116	40
45	163.99	.00610	.12074	8.2825	.00074	1358.2	8.0572	66.734	45
50	289.00	.00346	.12042	8.3045	.00045	2400.0	8.1597	67.762	50
55	509.32	.00196	.12024	8.3170	.00024	4236.0	8.2251	68.408	55
60	897.60	.00111	.12013	8.3240	.00013	7471.7	8.2664	68.810	60
65	1581.9	.00063	.12008	8.3281	.00008	13174.	8.2922	69.058	65
70	2787.8	.00036	.12004	8.3303	.00004	23223.	8.3082	69.210	70
75	4913.1	.00020	.12002	8.3316	.00002	40934.	8.3181	69.303	75
80	8658.5	.00012	.12001	8.3324	.00001	72146.	8.3241	69.359	80
85	15259.	.00007	.12001	8.3328	.00001		8.3278	69.393	85
90	26892.	.00004	.12000	8.3330	.00000		8.3300	69.414	90
95	47393.	.00002	.12000	8.3332	.00000		8.3313	69.426	95
100	83522.	.00001	.12000	8.3332	.00000		8.3321	69.434	100
∞	∞	0	.12000	8.3333	0	∞	8.3333	69.444	∞

15%

n	SPCAF F/P	SPPWF P/F	CRF A/P	USPWF P/A	SFDF A/F	USCAF F/A	ASF A/G	ASPWF P/G	n
1	1.1500	.86957	1.1500	.86957	1.0000	1.0000	–	–	1
2	1.3225	.75614	.61512	1.6257	.46512	2.1500	.46512	.75615	2
3	1.5209	.65752	.43798	2.2832	.28798	3.4725	.90713	2.0712	3
4	1.7490	.57175	.35027	2.8550	.20027	4.9934	1.3263	3.7864	4
5	2.0114	.49718	.29832	3.3522	.14832	6.7424	1.7228	5.7751	5
6	2.3131	.43233	.26424	3.7845	.11424	8.7537	2.0972	7.9368	6
7	2.6600	.37594	.24036	4.1604	.09036	11.067	2.4499	10.192	7
8	3.0590	.32690	.22285	4.4873	.07285	13.727	2.7813	12.481	8
9	3.5179	.28426	.20957	4.7716	.05957	16.786	3.0922	14.755	9
10	4.0456	.24718	.19925	5.0188	.04925	20.304	3.3832	16.979	10
11	4.6524	.21494	.19107	5.2337	.04107	24.349	3.6549	19.129	11
12	5.3503	.18691	.18448	5.4206	.03448	29.002	3.9082	21.185	12
13	6.1528	.16253	.17911	5.5831	.02911	34.352	4.1438	23.135	13
14	7.0757	.14133	.17469	5.7245	.02469	40.505	4.3624	24.973	14
15	8.1371	.12289	.17102	5.8474	.02102	47.580	4.5650	26.693	15
16	9.3576	.10686	.16795	5.9542	.01795	55.717	4.7522	28.296	16
17	10.761	.09293	.16537	6.0472	.01537	65.075	4.9251	29.783	17
18	12.375	.08081	.16319	6.1280	.01319	75.836	5.0843	31.156	18
19	14.232	.07027	.16134	6.1982	.01134	88.212	5.2307	32.421	19
20	16.367	.06110	.15976	6.2593	.00976	102.44	5.3651	33.582	20
21	18.822	.05313	.15842	6.3125	.00842	118.81	5.4883	34.645	21
22	21.645	.04620	.15727	6.3587	.00727	137.63	5.6010	35.615	22
23	24.891	.04017	.15628	6.3988	.00628	159.28	5.7040	36.499	23
24	28.625	.03493	.15543	6.4338	.00543	184.17	5.7979	37.302	24
25	32.919	.03038	.15470	6.4641	.00470	212.79	5.8834	38.031	25
26	37.857	.02642	.15407	6.4906	.00407	245.71	5.9612	38.692	26
27	43.535	.02297	.15353	6.5135	.00353	283.57	6.0319	39.289	27
28	50.066	.01997	.15306	6.5335	.00306	327.10	6.0960	39.828	28
29	57.575	.01737	.15265	6.5509	.00265	377.17	6.1541	40.315	29
30	66.212	.01510	.15230	6.5660	.00230	434.75	6.2066	40.753	30

15% (continued)

n	SPCAF F/P	SPPWF P/F	CRF A/P	USPWF P/A	SFDF A/F	USCAF F/A	ASF A/G	ASPWF P/G	n
31	76.144	.01313	.15200	6.5791	.00200	500.96	6.2541	41.147	31
32	87.565	.01142	.15173	6.5905	.00173	577.10	6.2970	41.501	32
33	100.70	.00993	.15150	6.6005	.00150	664.67	6.3357	41.818	33
34	115.80	.00864	.15131	6.6091	.00131	765.37	6.3705	42.103	34
35	133.18	.00751	.15113	6.6166	.00113	881.17	6.4019	42.359	35
40	267.86	.00373	.15056	6.6418	.00056	1779.1	6.5168	43.283	40
45	538.77	.00186	.15028	6.6543	.00028	3585.1	6.5830	43.805	45
50	1083.7	.00092	.15014	6.6605	.00014	7217.7	6.6205	44.096	50
55	2179.6	.00046	.15007	6.6636	.00007	14524.	6.6414	44.256	55
60	4384.0	.00023	.15003	6.6651	.00003	29220.	6.6530	44.343	60
65	8817.8	.00011	.15002	6.6659	.00002	58779.	6.6593	44.390	65
70	17736.	.00006	.15001	6.6663	.00001		6.6627	44.416	70
75	35673.	.00003	.15000	6.6665	.00000		6.6646	44.429	75
80	71751.	.00001	.15000	6.6666	.00000		6.6656	44.436	80
∞	∞	0	.15000	6.6667	0	∞	6.6667	44.444	∞

17%

n	SPCAF F/P	SPPWF P/F	CRF A/P	USPWF P/A	SFDF A/F	USCAF F/A	ASF A/G	ASPWF P/G	n
1	1.1700	.85470	1.1700	.85470	1.0000	1.0000	–	–	1
2	1.3689	.73051	.63083	1.5852	.46083	2.1700	.46083	.73051	2
3	1.6016	.62437	.45257	2.2096	.28257	3.5389	.89576	1.9793	3
4	1.8739	.53365	.36453	2.7432	.19453	5.1405	1.3051	3.5802	4
5	2.1924	.45611	.31256	3.1993	.14256	7.0144	1.6893	5.4046	5
6	2.5652	.38984	.27861	3.5892	.10861	9.2068	2.0489	7.3538	6
7	3.0012	.33320	.25495	3.9224	.08495	11.772	2.3845	9.3530	7
8	3.5115	.28478	.23769	4.2072	.06769	14.773	2.6969	11.346	8
9	4.1084	.24340	.22469	4.4506	.05469	18.285	2.9870	13.294	9
10	4.8068	.20804	.21466	4.6586	.04466	22.393	3.2555	15.166	10
11	5.6240	.17781	.20676	4.8364	.03677	27.200	3.5035	16.944	11
12	6.5801	.15197	.20047	4.9884	.03047	32.824	3.7318	18.616	12
13	7.6987	.12989	.19538	5.1183	.02538	39.404	3.9417	20.175	13
14	9.0075	.11102	.19123	5.2293	.02123	47.103	4.1340	21.618	14
15	10.539	.09489	.18782	5.3242	.01782	56.110	4.3098	22.946	15
16	12.330	.08110	.18500	5.4053	.01500	66.649	4.4702	24.163	16
17	14.426	.06932	.18266	5.4746	.01266	78.979	4.6162	25.272	17
18	16.879	.05925	.18071	5.5339	.01071	93.406	4.7488	26.279	18
19	19.748	.05064	.17907	5.5845	.00907	110.28	4.8689	27.190	19
20	23.106	.04328	.17769	5.6278	.00769	130.03	4.9776	28.013	20
21	27.034	.03699	.17653	5.6648	.00653	153.14	5.0757	28.753	21
22	31.629	.03162	.17555	5.6964	.00555	180.17	5.1641	29.417	22
23	37.006	.02702	.17472	5.7234	.00472	211.80	5.2436	30.011	23
24	43.297	.02310	.17402	5.7465	.00402	248.81	5.3149	30.542	24
25	50.658	.01974	.17342	5.7662	.00342	292.10	5.3789	31.016	25
26	59.270	.01687	.17292	5.7831	.00292	342.76	5.4362	31.438	26
27	69.345	.01442	.17249	5.7975	.00249	402.03	5.4873	31.813	27
28	81.134	.01233	.17212	5.8099	.00212	471.38	5.5329	32.146	28
29	94.927	.01053	.17181	5.8204	.00181	552.51	5.5736	32.441	29
30	111.06	.00900	.17154	5.8294	.00154	647.44	5.6098	32.702	30
31	129.95	.00770	.17132	5.8371	.00132	758.50	5.6419	32.932	31
32	152.04	.00658	.17113	5.8437	.00113	888.45	5.6705	33.136	32
33	177.88	.00562	.17096	5.8493	.00096	1040.5	5.6958	33.316	33
34	208.12	.00480	.17082	5.8541	.00082	1218.4	5.7182	33.475	34
35	243.50	.00411	.17070	5.8582	.00070	1426.5	5.7380	33.614	35
40	533.87	.00187	.17032	5.8713	.00032	3134.5	5.8073	34.097	40
45	1170.5	.00085	.17015	5.8773	.00015	6879.3	5.8439	34.346	45
50	2566.2	.00039	.17007	5.8801	.00007	15090.	5.8629	34.474	50
55	5626.3	.00018	.17003	5.8813	.00003	33090.	5.8726	34.538	55
60	12335.	.00008	.17001	5.8819	.00001	72555.	5.8775	34.571	60
65	27045.	.00004	.17001	5.8821	.00001		5.8799	34.587	65
70	59294.	.00002	.17000	5.8823	.00000		5.8812	34.595	70
∞	∞	0	.17000	5.8824	0	∞	5.8824	34.602	∞

20%

n	SPCAF F/P	SPPWF P/F	CRF A/P	USPWF P/A	SFDF A/F	USCAF F/A	ASF A/G	ASPWF P/G	n
1	1.2000	.83333	1.2000	.83333	1.0000	1.0000	–	–	1
2	1.4400	.69444	.65455	1.5278	.45455	2.2000	.45455	.69444	2
3	1.7280	.57870	.47473	2.1065	.27473	3.6400	.87912	1.8519	3
4	2.0736	.48225	.38629	2.5887	.18629	5.3680	1.2742	3.2986	4
5	2.4883	.40188	.33438	2.9906	.13438	7.4416	1.6405	4.9061	5
6	2.9860	.33490	.30071	3.3255	.10071	9.9299	1.9788	6.5806	6
7	3.5832	.27908	.27742	3.6046	.07742	12.916	2.2902	8.2551	7
8	4.2998	.23257	.26061	3.8372	.06061	16.499	2.5756	9.8831	8
9	5.1598	.19381	.24808	4.0310	.04808	20.799	2.8364	11.434	9
10	6.1917	.16151	.23852	4.1925	.03852	25.959	3.0739	12.887	10
11	7.4301	.13459	.23110	4.3271	.03110	32.150	3.2893	14.233	11
12	8.9161	.11216	.22526	4.4392	.02527	39.580	3.4841	15.467	12
13	10.699	.09346	.22062	4.5327	.02062	48.497	3.6597	16.588	13
14	12.839	.07789	.21689	4.6106	.01689	59.196	3.8175	17.601	14
15	15.407	.06491	.21388	4.6755	.01388	72.035	3.9588	18.509	15
16	18.488	.05409	.21144	4.7296	.01144	87.442	4.0851	19.321	16
17	22.186	.04507	.20944	4.7746	.00944	105.93	4.1976	20.042	17
18	26.623	.03756	.20781	4.8122	.00781	128.12	4.2975	20.680	18
19	31.948	.03130	.20646	4.8435	.00646	154.74	4.3861	21.244	19
20	38.338	.02608	.20536	4.8696	.00536	186.69	4.4643	21.739	20
21	46.005	.02174	.20444	4.8913	.00444	225.03	4.5334	22.174	21
22	55.206	.01811	.20369	4.9094	.00369	271.03	4.5941	22.555	22
23	66.247	.01510	.20307	4.9245	.00307	326.24	4.6475	22.887	23
24	79.497	.01258	.20255	4.9371	.00255	392.48	4.6943	23.176	24
25	95.396	.01048	.20212	4.9476	.00212	471.98	4.7352	23.428	25
26	114.48	.00874	.20176	4.9563	.00176	567.38	4.7709	23.646	26
27	137.37	.00728	.20147	4.9636	.00147	681.85	4.8020	23.835	27
28	164.84	.00607	.20122	4.9697	.00122	819.22	4.8291	23.999	28
29	197.81	.00506	.20102	4.9747	.00102	984.07	4.8527	24.141	29
30	237.38	.00421	.20085	4.9789	.00085	1181.9	4.8731	24.263	30
31	284.85	.00351	.20070	4.9824	.00070	1419.3	4.8908	24.368	31
32	341.82	.00293	.20059	4.9854	.00059	1704.1	4.9061	24.459	32
33	410.19	.00244	.20049	4.9878	.00049	2045.9	4.9194	24.537	33
34	492.22	.00203	.20041	4.9898	.00041	2456.1	4.9308	24.604	34
35	590.67	.00169	.20034	4.9915	.00034	2948.3	4.9406	24.661	35
40	1469.8	.00068	.20014	4.9966	.00014	7343.9	4.9728	24.847	40
45	3657.3	.00027	.20005	4.9986	.00005	18281.	4.9877	24.932	45
50	9100.4	.00011	.20002	4.9995	.00002	45497.	4.9945	24.970	50
55	22645.	.00004	.20001	4.9998	.00001		4.9976	24.987	55
60	56347.	.00002	.20000	4.9999	.00000		4.9989	24.994	60
∞	∞	0	.20000	5.0000	0	∞	5.0000	25.000	∞

25%

n	SPCAF F/P	SPPWF P/F	CRF A/P	USPWF P/A	SFDF A/F	USCAF F/A	ASF A/G	ASPWF P/G	n
1	1.2500	.80000	1.2500	.80000	1.0000	1.0000	–	–	1
2	1.5625	.64000	.69444	1.4400	.44444	2.2500	.44444	.64000	2
3	1.9531	.51200	.51230	1.9520	.26230	3.8125	.85246	1.6640	3
4	2.4414	.40960	.42344	2.3616	.17344	5.7656	1.2249	2.8928	4
5	3.0518	.32768	.37185	2.6893	.12185	8.2070	1.5631	4.2035	5
6	3.8147	.26214	.33882	2.9514	.08882	11.259	1.8683	5.5142	6
7	4.7684	.20972	.31634	3.1611	.06634	15.073	2.1424	6.7725	7
8	5.9605	.16777	.30040	3.3289	.05040	19.842	2.3872	7.9469	8
9	7.4506	.13422	.28876	3.4631	.03876	25.802	2.6048	9.0207	9
10	9.3132	.10737	.28007	3.5705	.03007	33.253	2.7971	9.9870	10
11	11.642	.08590	.27349	3.6564	.02349	42.566	2.9663	10.846	11
12	14.552	.06872	.26845	3.7251	.01845	54.208	3.1145	11.602	12
13	18.190	.05498	.26454	3.7801	.01454	68.760	3.2437	12.262	13
14	22.737	.04398	.26150	3.8241	.01150	86.949	3.3559	12.833	14
15	28.422	.03518	.25912	3.8593	.00912	109.69	3.4530	13.326	15
16	35.527	.02815	.25724	3.8874	.00724	138.11	3.5366	13.748	16
17	44.409	.02252	.25576	3.9099	.00576	173.64	3.6084	14.108	17
18	55.511	.01801	.25459	3.9279	.00459	218.04	3.6698	14.415	18
19	69.389	.01441	.25366	3.9424	.00366	273.56	3.7222	14.674	19
20	86.736	.01153	.25292	3.9539	.00292	342.94	3.7667	14.893	20

25% (continued)

n	SPCAF F/P	SPPWF P/F	CRF A/P	USPWF P/A	SFDF A/F	USCAF F/A	ASF A/G	ASPWF P/G	n
21	108.42	.00922	.25233	3.9631	.00233	429.68	3.8045	15.078	21
22	135.53	.00738	.25186	3.9705	.00186	538.10	3.8365	15.233	22
23	169.41	.00590	.25148	3.9764	.00148	673.63	3.8634	15.362	23
24	211.76	.00472	.25119	3.9811	.00119	843.03	3.8861	15.471	24
25	264.70	.00378	.25095	3.9849	.00095	1054.8	3.9052	15.562	25
26	330.87	.00302	.25076	3.9879	.00076	1319.5	3.9212	15.637	26
27	413.59	.00242	.25061	3.9903	.00061	1650.4	3.9346	15.700	27
28	516.99	.00193	.25048	3.9923	.00048	2064.0	3.9457	15.752	28
29	646.23	.00155	.25039	3.9938	.00039	2580.9	3.9551	15.796	29
30	807.79	.00124	.25031	3.9950	.00031	3227.2	3.9628	15.832	30
31	1009.7	.00099	.25025	3.9960	.00025	4035.0	3.9693	15.861	31
32	1262.2	.00079	.25020	3.9968	.00020	5044.7	3.9746	15.886	32
33	1577.7	.00063	.25016	3.9975	.00016	6306.9	3.9791	15.906	33
34	1972.2	.00051	.25013	3.9980	.00012	7884.6	3.9828	15.923	34
35	2465.2	.00041	.25010	3.9984	.00010	9856.8	3.9858	15.937	35
40	7523.2	.00013	.25003	3.9995	.00003	30089.	3.9947	15.977	40
45	22959.	.00004	.25001	3.9998	.00001	91831.	3.9980	15.991	45
50	70065.	.00001	.25000	3.9999	.00000		3.9993	15.997	50
∞	∞	0	.25000	4.0000	0	∞	4.0000	16.000	∞

30%

n	SPCAF F/P	SPPWF P/F	CRF A/P	USPWF P/A	SFDF A/F	USCAF F/A	ASF A/G	ASPWF P/G	n
1	1.3000	.76923	1.3000	.76923	1.0000	1.0000	–	–	1
2	1.6900	.59172	.73478	1.3609	.43478	2.3000	.43478	.59172	2
3	2.1970	.45517	.55063	1.8161	.25063	3.9900	.82707	1.5020	3
4	2.8561	.35013	.46163	2.1662	.16163	6.1870	1.1783	2.5524	4
5	3.7129	.26933	.41058	2.4356	.11058	9.0431	1.4903	3.6297	5
6	4.8268	.20718	.37839	2.6427	.07839	12.756	1.7654	4.6656	6
7	6.2748	.15937	.35687	2.8021	.05687	17.583	2.0063	5.6218	7
8	8.1573	.12259	.34192	2.9247	.04192	23.858	2.2156	6.4800	8
9	10.604	.09430	.33124	3.0190	.03124	32.015	2.3963	7.2343	9
10	13.786	.07254	.32346	3.0915	.02346	42.619	2.5512	7.8872	10
11	17.922	.05580	.31773	3.1473	.01773	56.405	2.6833	8.4452	11
12	23.298	.04292	.31345	3.1903	.01345	74.327	2.7952	8.9173	12
13	30.287	.03302	.31024	3.2233	.01024	97.625	2.8895	9.3135	13
14	39.374	.02540	.30782	3.2487	.00782	127.91	2.9685	9.6437	14
15	51.186	.01954	.30598	3.2682	.00598	167.29	3.0344	9.9172	15
16	66.542	.01503	.30458	3.2832	.00458	218.47	3.0892	10.143	16
17	86.504	.01156	.30351	3.2948	.00351	285.01	3.1345	10.328	17
18	112.46	.00889	.30269	3.3037	.00269	371.52	3.1718	10.479	18
19	146.19	.00684	.30207	3.3105	.00207	483.97	3.2025	10.602	19
20	190.05	.00526	.30159	3.3158	.00159	630.16	3.2275	10.702	20
21	247.06	.00405	.30122	3.3198	.00122	820.21	3.2480	10.783	21
22	321.18	.00311	.30094	3.3230	.00094	1067.3	3.2646	10.848	22
23	417.54	.00240	.30072	3.3254	.00072	1388.5	3.2781	10.901	23
24	542.80	.00184	.30055	3.3272	.00055	1806.0	3.2890	10.943	24
25	705.64	.00142	.30043	3.3286	.00043	2348.8	3.2979	10.977	25
26	917.33	.00109	.30033	3.3297	.00033	3054.4	3.3050	11.005	26
27	1192.5	.00084	.30025	3.3305	.00025	3971.8	3.3107	11.026	27
28	1550.3	.00065	.30019	3.3312	.00019	5164.3	3.3153	11.044	28
29	2015.4	.00050	.30015	3.3317	.00015	6714.6	3.3189	11.058	29
30	2620.0	.00038	.30011	3.3321	.00011	8730.0	3.3219	11.069	30
31	3406.0	.00029	.30009	3.3324	.00009	11350.	3.3242	11.078	31
32	4427.8	.00023	.30007	3.3326	.00007	14756.	3.3261	11.085	32
33	5756.1	.00017	.30005	3.3328	.00005	19184.	3.3276	11.090	33
34	7483.0	.00013	.30004	3.3329	.00004	24940.	3.3288	11.094	34
35	9727.8	.00010	.30003	3.3330	.00003	32423.	3.3297	11.098	35
40	36119.	.00003	.30001	3.3332	.00001		3.3322	11.107	40
∞	∞	0	.30001	3.3333	0	∞	3.3333	11.111	∞

35%

n	SPCAF F/P	SPPWF P/F	CRF A/P	USPWF P/A	SFDF A/F	USCAF F/A	ASF A/G	ASPWF P/G	n
1	1.3500	.74074	1.3500	.74074	1.0000	1.0000	–	–	1
2	1.8225	.54870	.77553	1.2894	.42553	2.3500	.42553	.54870	2
3	2.4604	.40644	.58966	1.6959	.23966	4.1725	.80288	1.3616	3
4	3.3215	.30107	.50076	1.9969	.15076	6.6329	1.1341	2.2648	4
5	4.4840	.22301	.45046	2.2200	.10046	9.9544	1.4220	3.1568	5
6	6.0534	.16520	.41926	2.3852	.06926	14.438	1.6698	3.9828	6
7	8.1721	.12237	.39880	2.5075	.04880	20.492	1.8811	4.7170	7
8	11.032	.09064	.38489	2.5982	.03489	28.664	2.0597	5.3515	8
9	14.894	.06714	.37519	2.6653	.02519	39.696	2.2094	5.8886	9
10	20.107	.04974	.36832	2.7150	.01832	54.590	2.3338	6.3363	10
11	27.144	.03684	.36339	2.7519	.01339	74.697	2.4364	6.7047	11
12	36.644	.02729	.35982	2.7792	.00982	101.84	2.5205	7.0049	12
13	49.470	.02021	.35722	2.7994	.00722	138.48	2.5889	7.2474	13
14	66.784	.01497	.35532	2.8144	.00532	187.95	2.6443	7.4421	14
15	90.158	.01109	.35393	2.8255	.00393	254.74	2.6889	7.5974	15
16	121.71	.00822	.35290	2.8337	.00290	344.90	2.7246	7.7206	16
17	164.31	.00609	.35214	2.8398	.00214	466.61	2.7530	7.8180	17
18	221.82	.00451	.35158	2.8443	.00159	630.92	2.7756	7.8946	18
19	299.46	.00334	.35117	2.8476	.00117	852.75	2.7935	7.9547	19
20	404.27	.00247	.35087	2.8501	.00087	1152.2	2.8075	8.0017	20
21	545.77	.00183	.35064	2.8519	.00064	1556.5	2.8186	8.0384	21
22	736.79	.00136	.35048	2.8533	.00048	2102.3	2.8272	8.0659	22
23	994.66	.00101	.35035	2.8543	.00035	2839.0	2.8340	8.0890	23
24	1342.8	.00074	.35026	2.8550	.00026	3833.7	2.8393	8.1061	24
25	1812.8	.00055	.35019	2.8556	.00019	5176.5	2.8433	8.1194	25
26	2447.2	.00041	.35014	2.8560	.00014	6989.3	2.8465	8.1296	26
27	3303.8	.00030	.35011	2.8563	.00011	9436.5	2.8490	8.1374	27
28	4460.1	.00022	.35008	2.8565	.00008	12740.	2.8509	8.1435	28
29	6021.1	.00017	.35006	2.8567	.00006	17200.	2.8523	8.1481	29
30	8128.5	.00012	.35004	2.8568	.00004	23222.	2.8535	8.1517	30
31	10974.	.00009	.35003	2.8569	.00003	31350.	2.8543	8.1545	31
32	14814	.00007	.35002	2.8570	.00002	42324.	2.8550	8.1565	32
33	19999.	.00005	.35002	2.8570	.00002	57138.	2.8555	8.1581	33
34	26999.	.00004	.35001	2.8570	.00001	77137.	2.8559	8.1594	34
35	36449.	.00003	.35001	2.8571	.00001		2.8562	8.1603	35
		0	.35000	2.8571	0		2.8571	8.1633	

40%

n	SPCAF F/P	SPPWF P/F	CRF A/P	USPWF P/A	SFDF A/F	USCAF F/A	ASF A/G	ASPWF P/G	n
1	1.4000	.71429	1.4000	.71429	1.0000	1.0000	–	–	1
2	1.9600	.51020	.81667	1.2245	.41667	2.4000	.41667	.51020	2
3	2.7440	.36443	.62936	1.5889	.22936	4.3600	.77982	1.2391	3
4	3.8416	.26031	.54077	1.8492	.14077	7.1040	1.0923	2.2200	4
5	5.3782	.18593	.49136	2.0352	.09136	10.946	1.3580	2.7637	5
6	7.5295	.13281	.46126	2.1680	.06126	16.324	1.5811	3.4278	6
7	10.541	.09487	.44192	2.2628	.04192	23.853	1.7664	3.9970	7
8	14.758	.06776	.42907	2.3306	.02907	34.395	1.9185	4.4713	8
9	20.661	.04840	.42034	2.3790	.02035	49.153	2.0422	4.8585	9
10	28.925	.03457	.41432	2.4136	.01432	69.814	2.1419	5.1696	10
11	40.496	.02469	.41013	2.4383	.01013	98.739	2.2215	5.4166	11
12	56.694	.01764	.40718	2.4559	.00718	139.23	2.2845	5.6106	12
13	79.371	.01260	.40510	2.4685	.00510	195.93	2.3341	5.7618	13
14	111.12	.00900	.40363	2.4775	.00363	275.30	2.3729	5.8788	14
15	155.57	.00643	.40259	2.4839	.00259	386.42	2.4030	5.9688	15
16	217.80	.00459	.40185	2.4885	.00185	541.99	2.4262	6.0376	16
17	304.91	.00328	.40132	2.4918	.00132	759.78	2.4441	6.0901	17
18	426.88	.00234	.40094	2.4941	.00094	1064.7	2.4577	6.1299	18
19	597.63	.00167	.40067	2.4958	.00067	1491.6	2.4682	6.1601	19
20	836.68	.00120	.40048	2.4970	.00048	2089.2	2.4761	6.1828	20
21	1171.4	.00085	.40034	2.4979	.00034	2925.9	2.4821	6.1998	21
22	1639.9	.00061	.40024	2.4985	.00024	4097.2	2.4866	6.2127	22
23	2295.9	.00044	.40017	2.4989	.00017	5737.1	2.4900	6.2222	23
24	3214.2	.00031	.40012	2.4992	.00012	8033.0	2.4925	6.2294	24

	40% (continued)								
n	SPCAF	SPPWF	CRF	USPWF	SFDF	USCAF	ASF	ASPWF	n
	F/P	P/F	A/P	P/A	A/F	F/A	A/G	P/G	
25	4499.9	.00022	.40009	2.4994	.00009	11247.	2.4944	6.2347	25
26	6299.8	.00016	.40006	2.4996	.00006	15747.	2.4959	6.2387	26
27	8819.8	.00011	.40005	2.4997	.00005	22047.	2.4969	6.2416	27
28	12348.	.00008	.40003	2.4998	.00003	30867.	2.4977	6.2438	28
29	17287.	.00006	.40002	2.4999	.00002	43214.	2.4983	6.2454	29
30	24201.	.00004	.40002	2.4999	.00001	60501.	2.4988	6.2466	30
31	33882.	.00003	.40001	2.4999	.00001	84702.	2.4991	6.2475	31
32	47435.	.00002	.40001	2.4999	.00001		2.4993	6.2482	32
33	66409.	.00002	.40001	2.5000	.00001		2.4995	6.2487	33
34	92972.	.00001	.40000	2.5000	.00000		2.4996	6.2490	34
∞	∞	0	.40000	2.5000	0	∞	2.5000	6.2500	∞

	45%								
1	1.4500	.68966	1.4500	.68966	1.0000	1.0000	–	–	1
2	2.1025	.47562	.85816	1.1653	.40816	2.4500	.40816	.47562	2
3	3.0486	.32802	.66966	1.4933	.21966	4.5525	.75783	1.1317	3
4	4.4205	.22622	.58156	1.7195	.13156	7.6011	1.0528	1.8103	4
5	6.4097	.15601	.53318	1.8755	.08318	12.022	1.2980	2.4344	5
6	9.2941	.10759	.50426	1.9831	.05426	18.431	1.4988	2.9723	6
7	13.476	.07420	.48607	2.0573	.03607	27.725	1.6612	3.4176	7
8	19.541	.05118	.47427	2.1085	.02427	41.202	1.7907	3.7758	8
9	28.334	.03529	.46646	2.1438	.01646	60.743	1.8930	4.0581	9
10	41.085	.02434	.46123	2.1681	.01123	89.077	1.9728	4.2772	10
11	59.573	.01679	.45768	2.1849	.00768	130.16	2.0344	4.4450	11
12	86.381	.01158	.45527	2.1965	.00527	189.73	2.0817	4.5724	12
13	125.25	.00798	.45362	2.2045	.00362	276.12	2.1176	4.6682	13
14	181.62	.00551	.45249	2.2100	.00249	401.37	2.1447	4.7398	14
15	263.34	.00380	.45172	2.2138	.00172	582.98	2.1650	4.7929	15
16	381.85	.00262	.45118	2.2164	.00118	846.32	2.1802	4.8322	16
17	553.68	.00181	.45081	2.2182	.00081	1228.2	2.1915	4.8611	17
18	802.83	.00125	.45056	2.2195	.00056	1781.8	2.1998	4.8823	18
19	1164.1	.00086	.45039	2.2203	.00039	2584.7	2.2059	4.8978	19
20	1688.0	.00059	.45027	2.2209	.00027	3748.8	2.2104	4.9090	20
21	2447.5	.00041	.45018	2.2213	.00018	5436.7	2.2136	4.9172	21
22	3548.9	.00028	.45013	2.2216	.00013	7884.3	2.2160	4.9231	22
23	5145.9	.00019	.45009	2.2218	.00009	11433.	2.2178	4.9274	23
24	7461.6	.00013	.45006	2.2219	.00006	16579.	2.2190	4.9305	24
25	10819.	.00009	.45004	2.2220	.00004	24041.	2.2199	4.9327	25
26	15688.	.00006	.45003	2.2221	.00003	34860.	2.2206	4.9343	26
27	22748.	.00004	.45002	2.2221	.00002	50548.	2.2210	4.9354	27
28	32984.	.00003	.45001	2.2222	.00001	73296.	2.2214	4.9362	28
29	47827.	.00002	.45001	2.2222	.00001		2.2216	4.9368	29
30	69349.	.00001	.45001	2.2222	.00001		2.2218	4.9372	30
∞	∞	0	.45000	2.2222	0	∞	2.2222	4.9383	∞

	50%								
1	1.5000	.66667	1.5000	.66667	1.0000	1.0000	–	–	1
2	2.2500	.44444	.90000	1.1111	.40000	2.5000	.40000	.44444	2
3	3.3750	.29630	.71053	1.4074	.21053	4.7500	.73684	1.0370	3
4	5.0625	.19753	.62308	1.6049	.12308	8.1250	1.0154	1.6296	4
5	7.5937	.13169	.57583	1.7366	.07583	13.187	1.2417	2.1564	5
6	11.391	.08779	.54812	1.8244	.04812	20.781	1.4226	2.5953	6
7	17.086	.05853	.53108	1.8829	.03108	32.172	1.5648	2.9465	7
8	25.629	.03902	.52030	1.9220	.02030	49.258	1.6752	3.2196	8
9	38.443	.02601	.51335	1.9480	.01335	74.887	1.7596	3.4277	9
10	57.665	.01734	.50882	1.9653	.00882	113.33	1.8235	3.5838	10
11	86.498	.01156	.50585	1.9769	.00585	171.00	1.8713	3.6994	11
12	129.75	.00771	.50388	1.9846	.00388	257.49	1.9068	3.7842	12
13	194.62	.00514	.50258	1.9897	.00258	387.24	1.9329	3.8459	13
14	291.93	.00343	.50172	1.9931	.00172	581.86	1.9519	3.8904	14
15	437.89	.00228	.50114	1.9954	.00114	873.79	1.9657	3.9224	15

50% (continued)

n	SPCAF F/P	SPPWF P/F	CRF A/P	USPWF P/A	SFDF A/F	USCAF F/A	ASF A/G	ASPWF P/G	n
16	656.84	.00152	.50076	1.9970	.00076	1311.7	1.9756	3.9452	16
17	985.26	.00102	.50051	1.9980	.00051	1968.5	1.9827		17
18	1477.9	.00068	.50034	1.9986	.00034	2953.8	1.9878	3.9729	18
19	2216.8	.00045	.50023	1.9991	.00023	4431.7	1.9914	3.9811	19
20	3325.3	.00030	.50015	1.9994	.00015	6648.5	1.9940	3.9868	20
21	4987.9	.00020	.50010	1.9996	.00010	9973.8	1.9958	3.9908	21
22	7481.8	.00013	.50007	1.9997	.00007	14962.	1.9971	3.9936	22
23	11223.	.00009	.50004	1.9998	.00004	22443.	1.9980	3.9955	23
24	16834.	.00006	.50003	1.9999	.00003	33666.	1.9986	3.9969	24
25	25251.	.00004	.50002	1.9999	.00002	50500.	1.9990	3.9979	25
26	37877.	.00003	.50001	1.9999	.00001	75751.	1.9993	3.9985	26
27	56815.	.00008	.50001	2.0000	.00001		1.9995	3.9990	27
28	85223.	.00001	.50001	2.0000	.00001		1.9997	3.9993	28
∞	∞	0	.50000	2.0000	0	∞	2.0000	4.0000	∞

60%

n	SPCAF F/P	SPPWF P/F	CRF A/P	USPWF P/A	SFDF A/F	USCAF F/A	ASF A/G	ASPWF P/G	n
1	1.6000	.62500	1.6000	.62500	1.0000	1.0000	–	–	1
2	2.5600	.39063	.98462	1.0156	.38462	2.6000	.38462	.39063	2
3	4.0960	.24414	.79380	1.2598	.19380	5.1600	.69767	.87891	3
4	6.5536	.15259	.70804	1.4124	.10804	9.2560	.94641	1.3367	4
5	10.486	.09537	.66325	1.5077	.06325	15.810	1.1396	1.7181	5
6	16.777	.05961	.63803	1.5673	.03803	26.295	1.2864	2.0162	6
7	26.844	.03725	.62322	1.6046	.02322	43.073	1.3958	2.2397	7
8	42.950	.02328	.61430	1.6279	.01430	69.916	1.4760	2.4027	8
9	68.719	.01455	.60886	1.6424	.00886	112.87	1.5338	2.5191	9
10	109.95	.00910	.60551	1.6515	.00551	181.59	1.5749	2.6009	10
11	175.92	.00568	.60343	1.6572	.00343	291.54	1.6038	2.6578	11
12	281.47	.00355	.60214	1.6607	.00214	467.46	1.6239	2.6969	12
13	450.36	.00222	.60134	1.6630	.00134	748.93	1.6377	2.7235	13
14	720.58	.00139	.60083	1.6644	.00083	1199.3	1.6472	2.7415	14
15	1152.9	.00087	.60052	1.6652	.00052	1919.9	1.6536	2.7537	15
16	1844.7	.00054	.60033	1.6658	.00033	3072.8	1.6580	2.7618	16
17	2951.5	.00034	.60020	1.6661	.00020	4917.5	1.6609	2.7672	17
18	4722.4	.00021	.60013	1.6663	.00013	7868.9	1.6629	2.7708	18
19	7555.8	.00013	.60008	1.6664	.00008	12591.	1.6642	2.7732	19
20	12089.	.00008	.60005	1.6665	.00005	20147.	1.6650	2.7748	20
21	19343.	.00005	.60003	1.6666	.00003	32236.	1.6656	2.7758	21
22	30948.	.00003	.60002	1.6666	.00002	51579.	1.6660	2.7765	22
23	49518.	.00002	.60001	1.6666	.00001	82528.	1.6662	2.7769	23
24	79228.	.00001	.60001	1.6666	.00001		1.6664	2.7772	24
∞	∞	0	.60000	1.6667	0	∞	1.6667	2.7778	∞

70%

n	SPCAF F/P	SPPWF P/F	CRF A/P	USPWF P/A	SFDF A/F	USCAF F/A	ASF A/G	ASPWF P/G	n
1	1.7000	.58824	1.7000	.58824	1.0000	1.0000	–	–	1
2	2.8900	.34602	1.0704	.93426	.37037	2.7000	.37037	.34602	2
3	4.9130	.20354	.87889	1.1378	.17889	5.5900	.66190	.75310	3
4	8.3521	.11973	.79521	1.2575	.09521	10.503	.88451	1.1123	4
5	14.199	.07043	.75304	1.3280	.05304	18.855	1.0497	1.3940	5
6	24.138	.04143	.73025	1.3694	.03025	33.054	1.1693	1.6012	6
7	41.034	.02437	.71749	1.3938	.01749	57.191	1.2537	1.7474	7
8	69.758	.01434	.71018	1.4081	.01018	98.225	1.3122	1.8477	8
9	118.59	.00843	.70595	1.4165	.00595	167.98	1.3520	1.9152	9
10	201.60	.00496	.70349	1.4215	.00349	286.57	1.3787	1.9598	10
11	342.72	.00292	.70205	1.4244	.00205	488.17	1.3964	1.9890	11
12	582.62	.00172	.70120	1.4261	.00120	830.89	1.4079	2.0079	12
13	990.46	.00101	.70071	1.4271	.00071	1413.5	1.4154	2.0200	13
14	1683.8	.00059	.70042	1.4277	.00042	2404.0	1.4203	2.0277	14
15	2862.4	.00035	.70024	1.4281	.00024	4087.7	1.4233	2.0326	15
16	4866.1	.00021	.70014	1.4283	.00014	6950.2	1.4253	2.0357	16
17	8272.4	.00012	.70008	1.4284	.00008	11816.	1.4265	2.0376	17
18	14063.	.00007	.70005	1.4285	.00005	20089.	1.4273	2.0388	18

70% (continued)

n	SPCAF	SPPWF	CRF	USPWF	SFDF	USCAF	ASF	ASPWF	n
	F/P	P/F	A/P	P/A	A/F	F/A	A/G	P/G	
19	23907.	.00004	.70003	1.4285	.00003	34152.	1.4278	2.0396	19
20	40642.	.00002	.70002	1.4285	.00002	58059.	1.4281	2.0401	20
21	69092.	.00001	.70001	1.4286	.00001	98701.	1.4283	2.0404	21
∞	∞	0	.70000	1.4286	0	∞	1.4286	2.0408	∞

80%

n	SPCAF	SPPWF	CRF	USPWF	SFDF	USCAF	ASF	ASPWF	n
	F/P	P/F	A/P	P/A	A/F	F/A	A/G	P/G	
1	1.8000	.55556	1.8000	.55556	1.0000	1.0000	–	–	1
2	3.2400	.30864	1.1571	.86420	.35714	2.8000	.35714	.30864	2
3	5.8320	.17147	.96556	1.0357	.16556	6.0400	.62914	.65158	3
4	10.498	.09526	.88423	1.1309	.08423	11.872	.82884	.93736	4
5	18.896	.05292	.84470	1.1838	.04470	22.370	.97060	1.1490	5
6	34.012	.02940	.82423	1.2132	.02423	41.265	1.0682	1.2961	6
7	61.222	.01633	.81328	1.2296	.01328	75.277	1.1338	1.3941	7
8	110.20	.00907	.80733	1.2387	.00733	136.50	1.1767	1.4576	8
9	198.36	.00504	.80405	1.2437	.00405	246.70	1.2044	1.4979	9
10	357.05	.00280	.80225	1.2465	.00225	445.06	1.2219	1.5231	10
11	642.68	.00156	.80125	1.2481	.00125	802.10	1.2329	1.5387	11
12	1156.8	.00086	.80069	1.2489	.00069	1444.8	1.2396	1.5482	12
13	2082.3	.00048	.80038	1.2494	.00038	2601.6	1.2438	1.5539	13
14	3748.1	.00027	.80021	1.2497	.00021	4683.9	1.2463	1.5574	14
15	6746.6	.00015	.80012	1.2498	.00012	8432.0	1.2478	1.5595	15
16	12144.	.00008	.80007	1.2499	.00007	15179.	1.2487	1.5607	16
17	21859.	.00005	.80004	1.2499	.00004	27323.	1.2492	1.5615	17
18	39346.	.00003	.80002	1.2500	.00002	49182.	1.2495	1.5619	18
19	70823.	.00001	.80001	1.2500	.00001	88528.	1.2497	1.5621	19
∞	∞	0	.80000	1.2500	0	∞	1.2500	1.5625	∞

90%

n	SPCAF	SPPWF	CRF	USPWF	SFDF	USCAF	ASF	ASPWF	n
	F/P	P/F	A/P	P/A	A/F	F/A	A/G	P/G	
1	1.9000	.52632	1.9000	.52632	1.0000	1.0000	–	–	1
2	3.6100	.27701	1.2448	.80332	.34483	2.9000	.34483	.27701	2
3	6.8590	.14579	1.0536	.94912	.15361	6.5100	.59908	.56860	3
4	13.032	.07673	.97480	1.0259	.07480	13.369	.77867	.79880	4
5	24.761	.04039	.93788	1.0662	.03788	26.401	.90068	.96034	5
6	47.046	.02126	.91955	1.0875	.01955	51.162	.98081	1.0666	6
7	89.387	.01119	.91018	1.0987	.01018	98.208	1.0319	1.1337	7
8	169.84	.00589	.90533	1.1046	.00533	187.60	1.0637	1.1750	8
9	322.69	.00310	.90280	1.1077	.00280	357.43	1.0831	1.1998	9
10	613.11	.00163	.90147	1.1093	.00147	680.12	1.0948	1.2144	10
11	1164.9	.00086	.90077	1.1102	.00077	1293.2	1.1017	1.2230	11
12	2213.3	.00045	.90041	1.1106	.00041	2458.1	1.1057	1.2280	12
13	4205.3	.00024	.90021	1.1108	.00021	4671.4	1.1080	1.2308	13
14	7990.1	.00013	.90011	1.1110	.00011	8876.7	:.1094	1.2325	14
15	15181.	.00007	.90006	1.1110	.00006	16867.	1.1101	1.2334	15
16	28844.	.00003	.90003	1.1111	.00003	32048.	1.1106	1.2339	16
17	54804.	.00002	.90002	1.1111	.00002	60892.	1.1108	1.2342	17
∞	∞	0	.90000	1.1111	0	∞	1.1111	1.2346	∞

100%

n	SPCAF	SPPWF	CRF	USPWF	SFDF	USCAF	ASF	ASPWF	n
	F/P	P/F	A/P	P/A	A/F	F/A	A/G	P/G	
1	2.0000	.50000	2.0000	.50000	1.0000	1.0000	–	–	1
2	4.0000	.25000	1.3333	.75000	.33333	3.0000	.33333	.25000	2
3	8.0000	.12500	1.1429	.87500	.14286	7.0000	.57143	.50000	3
4	16.000	.06250	1.0667	.93750	.06667	15.000	.73333	.68750	4
5	32.000	.03125	1.0323	.96875	.03226	31.000	.83871	.81250	5
6	64.000	.01563	1.0159	.98438	.01587	63.000	.90476	.89063	6
7	128.00	.00781	1.0079	.99219	.00787	127.00	.94488	.93750	7
8	256.00	.00391	1.0039	.99609	.00392	255.00	.96863	.96484	8
9	512.00	.00195	1.0020	.99805	.00196	511.00	.98239	.98047	9
10	1024.0	.00098	1.0010	.99902	.00098	1023.0	.99022	.98926	10
11	2048.0	.00049	1.0005	.99951	.00049	2047.0	.99463	.99414	11
12	4096.0	.00024	1.0002	.99976	.00024	4095.0	.99707	.99683	12

100% (continued)

n	SPCAF F/P	SPPWF P/F	CRF A/P	USPWF P/A	SFDF A/F	USCAF F/A	ASF A/G	ASPWF P/G	n
13	8192.0	.00012	1.0001	.99988	.00012	8191.0	.99841	.99829	13
14	16384.	.00006	1.0001	.99994	.00006	16383.	.99915	.99908	14
15	32768.	.00003	1.0000	.99997	.00003	32767.	.99954	.99951	15
16	65536.	.00002	1.0000	.99998	.00002	65535.	.99976	.99974	16
∞	∞	0	1.0000	1.0000	0	∞	1.0000	1.0000	∞

110%

n									n
1	2.1000	.47619	2.1000	.47619	1.0000	1.0000	–	–	1
2	4.4100	.22676	1.4226	.70295	.32258	3.1000	.32258	.22676	2
3	9.2610	.10798	1.2332	.81093	.13316	7.5100	.54594	.44272	3
4	19.448	.05142	1.1596	.86235	.05963	16.771	.69227	.59697	4
5	40.841	.02449	1.1276	.88683	.02761	36.219	.78359	.69491	5
6	85.766	.01166	1.1130	.89849	.01298	77.060	.83831	.75321	6
7	180.11	.00555	1.1061	.90404	.00614	162.83	.87001	.78653	7
8	378.23	.00264	1.1029	.90669	.00292	342.93	.88788	.80503	8
9	794.28	.00126	1.1014	.90795	.00139	721.16	.89775	.81511	9
10	1668.0	.00060	1.1007	.90855	.00066	1515.4	.90309	.82050	10
11	3502.8	.00029	1.1003	.90883	.00031	3183.4	.90595	.82336	11
12	7355.8	.00014	1.1001	.90897	.00015	6686.2	.90746	.82485	12
13	15447.	.00006	1.1001	.90903	.00007	14042.	.90825	.82563	13
14	32439.	.00003	1.1000	.90906	.00003	29489.	.90866	.82603	14
15	68122	.00001	1.1000	.90908	.00002	61928.	.90887	.82623	15
∞	∞	0	1.0000	.90909	0	∞	.90909	.82645	∞

120%

n									n
1	2.2000	.45455	2.2000	.45455	1.0000	1.0000	–	–	1
2	4.8400	.20661	1.5125	.66116	.31250	3.2000	.31250	.20661	2
3	10.648	.09391	1.3244	.75507	.12438	8.0400	.52239	.39444	3
4	23.426	.04268	1.2535	.79776	.05351	18.688	.65497	.52251	4
5	51.536	.01940	1.2237	.81716	.02375	42.114	.73439	.60012	5
6	113.38	.00882	1.2107	.82598	.01068	93.650	.77994	.64422	6
7	249.44	.00401	1.2048	.82999	.00483	207.03	.80516	.66827	7
8	548.76	.00182	1.2022	.83182	.00219	456.47	.81873	.68103	8
9	1207.3	.00083	1.2010	.83264	.00099	1005.2	.82587	.68766	9
10	2656.0	.00038	1.2005	.83302	.00045	2212.5	.82957	.69105	10
11	5843.2	.00017	1.2002	.83319	.00021	4868.5	.83145	.69276	11
12	12855.	.00008	1.2001	.83327	.00009	10712.	.83240	.69361	12
13	28281.	.00004	1.2000	.83330	.00004	23567.	.83287	.69404	13
14	62218.	.00002	1.2000	.83332	.00002	51848.	.83311	.69425	14
∞	∞	0	1.2000	.83333	0	∞	.83333	.69444	∞

130%

n									n
1	2.3000	.43478	2.3000	.43478	1.0000	1.0000	–	–	1
2	5.2900	.18904	1.6030	.62382	.30303	3.3000	.30303	.18904	2
3	12.167	.08219	1.4164	.70601	.11641	8.5900	.50058	.35342	3
4	27.984	.03574	1.3482	.74174	.04818	20.757	.62100	.46062	4
5	64.363	.01554	1.3205	.75728	.02052	48.741	.69032	.52277	5
6	148.04	.00676	1.3088	.76403	.00884	113.10	.72842	.55654	6
7	340.48	.00294	1.3038	.76697	.00383	261.14	.74861	.57416	7
8	783.11	.00128	1.3017	.76825	.00166	601.62	.75900	.58310	8
9	1801.1	.00056	1.3007	.76880	.00072	1384.7	.76423	.58754	9
10	4142.6	.00024	1.3003	.76905	.00031	3185.9	.76682	.58972	10
11	9528.1	.00010	1.3001	.76915	.00014	7328.5	.76808	.59077	11
12	21915	.00005	1.3001	.76920	.00006	16857.	.76868	.59127	12
13	50404.	.00002	1.3000	.76922	.00003	38771.	.76897	.59151	13
14		.00001	1.3000	.76922	.00001	89175.	.76911	.59162	14
∞	∞	0	1.3000	.76923	0	∞	.76923	.59172	∞

140%

n									n
1	2.4000	.41667	2.4000	.41667	1.0000	1.0000	–	–	1
2	5.7600	.17361	1.6941	.59028	.29412	3.4000	.29412	.17361	2

140% (continued)

n	SPCAF F/P	SPPWF P/F	CRF A/P	USPWF P/A	SFDF A/F	USCAF F/A	ASF A/G	ASPWF P/G	n
3	13.824	.07234	1.5092	.66262	.10917	9.1600	.48035	.31829	3
4	33.178	.03014	1.4435	.69276	.04351	22.984	.58998	.40871	4
5	79.626	.01256	1.4178	.70532	.01781	56.162	.65069	.45894	5
6	191.10	.00523	1.4074	.71055	.00736	135 79	.68272	.48511	6
7	458.65	.00218	1.4031	.71273	.00306	326.89	.69899	.49819	7
8	1100.8	.00091	1.4013	.71364	.00127	785.54	.70701	.50455	8
9	2641.8	.00038	1.4005	.71402	.00053	1886.3	.71088	.50758	9
10	6340.3	.00016	1.4002	.71417	.00022	4528.1	.71271	.50900	10
11	15217.	.00007	1.4001	.71424	.00009	10868.	.71356	.50965	11
12	36520.	.00003	1.4000	.71427	.00004	26085.	.71396	.50996	12
13	87649.	.00001	1.4000	.71428	.00002	62605.	.71414	.51009	13
∞	∞	0	1.4000	.71429	0	∞	.71429	.51020	∞

150%

n	SPCAF F/P	SPPWF P/F	CRF A/P	USPWF P/A	SFDF A/F	USCAF F/A	ASF A/G	ASPWF P/G	n
1	2.5000	.40000	2.5000	.40000	1.0000	1.0000	–	–	1
2	6.2500	.16000	1.7857	.56000	.28571	3.5000	.28571	.16000	2
3	15.625	.06400	1.6026	.62400	.10256	9.7500	.46154	.28800	3
4	39.062	.02560	1.5394	.64960	.03941	25.375	.56158	.36480	4
5	97.656	.01024	1.5155	.65984	.01552	64.437	.61494	.40576	5
6	244.14	.00410	1.5062	.66394	.00617	162.09	.64199	.42624	6
7	610.35	.00164	1.5025	.66557	.00246	406.23	.65518	.43607	7
8	1525.9	.00066	1.5010	.66623	.00098	1016.6	.66142	.44066	8
9	3814.7	.00026	1.5004	.66649	.00039	2542.5	.66431	.44276	9
10	9536.7	.00010	1.5002	66660	.00016	6357.1	.66562	.44370	10
11	23842.	.00004	1.5001	.66664	.00006	15894.	.66621	.44412	11
12	59604.	.00002	1.5000	.66666	.00003	39736.	.66647	.44430	12
13		.00001	1.5000	.66666	.00001	99340.	.66658	.44438	13
∞	∞	0	1.5000	.66667	0	∞	.66667	.44444	∞

CONTINUOUS RATE-OF-RETURN FACTORS

n	Single Payment Compound Amount Factor SPCAF	Single Payment Present Worth Factor SPPWF	Capital Recovery Factor CRF	Uniform Series Present Worth Factor USPWF	Sinking Fund Deposit Factor SFDF	Uniform Series Compound Amount Factor USCAF	Arithmetic Series Factor ASF	n
	e^{rn}	e^{-rn}	$\dfrac{re^{rn}}{e^{rn}-1}$	$\dfrac{e^{rn}-1}{re^{rn}}$	$\dfrac{r}{e^{rn}-1}$	$\dfrac{e^{rn}-1}{r}$	$\dfrac{1}{e^{r}-1}-\dfrac{n}{e^{rn}-1}$	
	F/P	P/F	$\bar{A}/P$	$P/\bar{A}$	$\bar{A}/F$	$F/\bar{A}$	A/G	

1% = 1% continuous

(NOMINAL = 0.99504%)

n								n
1	1.0100	.99010	1.0050	.99504	.99503	1.0050	–	1
2	1.0201	.98030	.50499	1.9802	.49504	2.0200	.49735	2
3	1.0303	.97059	.33833	2.9557	.32838	3.0452	.99324	3
4	1.0406	.96098	.25501	3.9214	.24506	4.0807	1.4875	4
5	1.0510	.95147	.20502	4.8777	.19507	5.1265	1.9800	5
6	1.0615	.94205	.17169	5.8244	.16174	6.1827	2.4709	6
7	1.0721	.93272	.14789	6.7618	.13794	7.2495	2.9601	7
8	1.0829	.92348	.13004	7.6899	.12009	8.3270	3.4477	8
9	1.0937	.91434	.11616	8.6088	.10621	9.4153	3.9336	9
10	1.1046	.90529	.10506	9.5186	.09511	10.514	4.4178	10
11	1.1157	.89632	.09598	10.419	.08603	11.625	4.9004	11
12	1.1268	.88745	.08841	11.311	.07846	12.746	5.3814	12
13	1.1381	.87866	.08201	12.194	.07206	13.878	5.8606	13
14	1.1495	.86996	.07652	13.069	.06657	15.022	6.3383	14
15	1.1610	.86135	.07177	13.934	.06182	16.177	6.8142	15
16	1.1726	.85282	.06761	14.791	.05766	17.344	7.2885	16
17	1.1843	.84438	.06394	15.640	.05399	18.522	7.7612	17
18	1.1961	.83602	.06068	16.480	.05073	19.713	8.2322	18
19	1.2081	.82774	.05776	17.312	.04781	20.915	8.7016	19
20	1.2202	.81954	.05514	18.136	.04519	22.129	9.1693	20
21	1.2324	.81143	.05277	18.951	.04282	23.355	9.6353	21
22	1.2447	.80340	.05061	19.759	.04066	24.594	10.100	22
23	1.2572	.79544	.04864	20.558	.03869	25.845	10.562	23
24	1.2697	.78757	.04684	21.349	.03689	27.108	11.024	24
25	1.2824	.77977	.04518	22.133	.03523	28.384	11.483	25
26	1.2953	.77205	.04365	22.909	.03370	29.673	11.941	26
27	1.3082	.76440	.04224	23.677	.03228	30.975	12.397	27
28	1.3213	.75684	.04092	24.438	.03097	32.289	12.851	28
29	1.3345	.74934	.03970	25.191	.02975	33.617	13.304	29
30	1.3478	.74192	.03856	25.937	.02861	34.959	13.756	30
31	1.3613	.73458	.03749	26.675	.02754	36.313	14.205	31
32	1.3749	.72730	.03649	27.406	.02654	37.681	14.653	32
33	1.3887	.72010	.03555	28.129	.02560	39.063	15.099	33
34	1.4026	.71297	.03467	28.846	.02472	40.459	15.544	34
35	1.4166	.70591	.03384	29.555	.02388	41.868	15.987	35
40	1.4889	.67165	.03030	82.999	.02035	49.130	18.178	40
45	1.5648	.63906	.02757	36.275	.01762	56.763	20.327	45
50	1.6446	.60804	.02539	39.392	.01544	64.785	22.436	50
55	1.7285	.57853	.02361	42.358	.01366	73.216	24.505	55
60	1.8167	.55045	.02213	45.179	.01218	82.077	26.533	60
65	1.9094	.52373	.02089	47.864	.01094	91.391	28.522	65
70	2.0068	.49832	.01983	50.419	.00988	101.18	30.470	70
75	2.1091	.47413	.01892	52.850	.00897	111.47	32.379	75
80	2.2167	.45112	.01813	55.162	.00818	122.28	34.249	80
85	2.3298	.42922	.01743	57.363	.00748	133.64	36.080	85
90	2.4486	.40839	.01682	59.456	.00687	145.59	37.872	90
95	2.5735	.38857	.01627	61.448	.00632	158.14	39.626	95
100	2.7048	.36971	.01579	63.344	.00584	171.33	41.342	100
∞	∞	0	.00995	100.50	0	∞	100.00	∞

Continuous Rate-of-Return Factors

2%

(NOMINAL 1.9803%)

n	SPCAF F/P	SPPWF P/F	$\overline{CRF}$ $\overline{A}/P$	$\overline{USPWF}$ $P/\overline{A}$	$\overline{SFDF}$ $\overline{A}/F$	$\overline{USCAF}$ $F/\overline{A}$	$\overline{ASF}$ A/G	n
1	1.0200	.98039	1.0099	.99016	.99013	1.0100	–	1
2	1.0404	.96117	.50997	1.9609	.49016	2.0401	.49505	2
3	1.0612	.94232	.34333	2.9126	.32353	3.0909	.98681	3
4	1.0824	.92385	.26003	3.8457	.24023	4.1627	1.4753	4
5	1.1041	.90573	.21006	4.7604	.19026	5.2559	1.9604	5
6	1.1262	.88797	.17676	5.6573	.15696	6.3710	2.4423	6
7	1.1487	.87056	.15299	6.5365	.13318	7.5084	2.9208	7
8	1.1717	.85349	.13516	7.3985	.11536	8.6685	3.3961	8
9	1.1951	.83676	.12131	8.2436	.10150	9.8519	3.8681	9
10	1.2190	.82035	.11023	9.0721	.09043	11.059	4.3368	10
11	1.2434	.80426	.10117	9.8844	.08137	12.290	4.8021	11
12	1.2682	.78849	.09363	10.681	.07382	13.546	5.2643	12
13	1.2936	.77303	.08725	11.461	.06745	14.827	5.7231	13
14	1.3195	.75787	.08179	12.227	.06198	16.133	6.1786	14
15	1.3459	.74301	.07706	12.977	.05726	17.466	6.6309	15
16	1.3728	.72845	.07292	13.713	.05312	18.825	7.0799	16
17	1.4002	.71416	.06928	14.434	.04948	20.212	7.5257	17
18	1.4282	.70016	.06604	15.141	.04624	21.626	7.9681	18
19	1.4568	.68643	.06315	15.835	.04335	23.068	8.4073	19
20	1.4859	.67297	.06055	16.514	.04075	24.540	8.8433	20
21	1.5157	.65978	.05821	17.181	.03840	26.040	9.2760	21
22	1.5460	.64684	.05607	17.834	.03627	27.571	9.7055	22
23	1.5769	.63416	.05413	18.475	.03433	29.132	10.132	23
24	1.6084	.62172	.05235	19.102	.03255	30.725	10.555	24
25	1.6406	.60953	.05072	19.718	.03091	32.350	10.974	25
26	1.6734	.59758	.04921	20.322	.02941	34.007	11.391	26
27	1.7069	.58586	.04782	20.913	.02801	35.697	11.804	27
28	1.7410	.57437	.04653	21.493	.02672	37.421	12.214	28
29	1.7758	.56311	.04533	22.062	.02552	39.179	12.621	29
30	1.8114	.55207	.04421	22.620	.02441	40.972	13.025	30
31	1.8476	.54125	.04317	23.166	.02336	42.802	13.426	31
32	1.8845	.53063	.04219	23.702	.02239	44.668	13.823	32
33	1.9222	.52023	.04128	24.228	.02147	46.571	14.217	33
34	1.9607	.51003	.04042	24.743	.02061	48.513	14.608	34
35	1.9999	.50003	.03961	25.248	.01981	50.493	14.996	35
40	2.2080	.45289	.03620	27.628	.01639	61.004	16.889	40
45	2.4379	.41020	.03358	29.784	.01377	72.609	18.703	45
50	2.6916	.37153	.03151	31.737	.01171	85.422	20.442	50
55	2.9717	.33650	.02985	33.505	.01004	99.569	22.106	55
60	3.2810	.30478	.02848	35.107	.00868	115.19	23.696	60
65	3.6225	.27605	.02735	36.558	.00755	132.43	25.215	65
70	3.9996	.25003	.02640	37.872	.00660	151.47	26.663	70
75	4.4158	.22646	.02560	39.063	.00580	172.49	28.043	75
80	4.8754	.20511	.02491	40.141	.00511	195.70	29.357	80
85	5.3829	.18577	.02432	41.117	.00452	221.33	30.606	85
90	5.9431	.16826	.02381	42.001	.00401	249.62	31.793	90
95	6.5617	.15240	.02336	42.802	.00356	280.86	32.919	95
100	7.2446	.13803	.02297	43.528	.00317	315.34	33.986	100
∞	∞	0	.01980	50.498	0	∞	50.000	∞

3%

(NOMINAL 2.9559%)

1	1.0300	.97087	1.0149	.98536	.98529	1.0149	–	1
2	1.0609	.94260	.51493	1.9420	.48537	2.0603	.49260	2
3	1.0927	.91514	.34833	2.8708	.31877	3.1370	.98029	3
4	1.1255	.88849	.26507	3.7726	.23551	4.2461	1.4631	4
5	1.1593	.86261	.21514	4.6481	.18558	5.3884	1.9409	5
6	1.1941	.83748	.18188	5.4980	.15232	6.5650	2.4138	6
7	1.2299	.81309	.15815	6.3233	.12859	7.7768	2.8818	7
8	1.2668	.78941	.14036	7.1245	.11080	9.0251	3.3450	8

3% (continued)

(NOMINAL 2.9559%)

n	SPCAF F/P	SPPWF P/F	$\overline{CRF}$ $\overline{A}/P$	$\overline{USPWF}$ $P/\overline{A}$	$\overline{SFDF}$ $\overline{A}/F$	$\overline{USCAF}$ $F/\overline{A}$	$\overline{ASF}$ A/G	n
9	1.3048	.76642	.12655	7.9023	.09699	10.311	3.8032	9
10	1.3439	.74409	.11551	8.6575	.08595	11.635	4.2565	10
11	1.3842	.72242	.10649	9.3907	.07693	12.999	4.7049	11
12	1.4258	.70138	.09899	10.103	.06943	14.404	5.1485	12
13	1.4685	.68095	.09265	10.794	.06309	15.851	5.5872	13
14	1.5126	.66112	.08722	11.465	.05767	17.341	6.0210	14
15	1.5580	.64186	.08254	12.116	.05298	18.877	6.4500	15
16	1.6047	.62317	.07844	12.749	.04888	20.458	6.8742	16
17	1.6528	.60502	.07484	13.363	.04528	22.086	7.2936	17
18	1.7024	.58739	.07164	13.959	.04208	23.764	7.7081	18
19	1.7535	.57029	.06879	14.538	.03923	25.492	8.1179	19
20	1.8061	.55368	.06623	15.100	.03667	27.271	8.5229	20
21	1.8603	.53755	.06392	15.645	.03436	29.105	8.9231	21
22	1.9161	.52189	.06183	16.175	.03227	30.993	9.3186	22
23	1.9736	.50669	.05992	16.689	.03036	32.937	9.7093	23
24	2.0328	.49193	.05818	17.188	.02862	34.940	10.095	24
25	2.0938	.47761	.05658	17.673	.02703	37.003	10.477	25
26	2.1566	.46369	.05512	18.144	.02556	39.128	10.853	26
27	2.2213	.45019	.05376	18.601	.02420	41.317	11.226	27
28	2.2879	.43708	.05251	19.044	.02295	43.572	11.593	28
29	2.3566	.42435	.05135	19.475	.02179	45.894	11.956	29
30	2.4273	.41199	.05027	19.893	.02071	48.286	12.314	30
31	2.5001	.39999	.04926	20.299	.01971	50.749	12.668	31
32	2.5751	.38834	.04833	20.693	.01877	53.286	13.017	32
33	2.6523	.37703	.04745	21.076	.01789	55.900	13.362	33
34	2.7319	.36604	.04663	21.447	.01707	58.592	13.702	34
35	2.8139	.35538	.04586	21.808	.01630	61.365	14.037	35
40	3.2620	.30656	.04263	23.460	.01307	76.527	15.650	40
45	3.7816	.26444	.04019	24.885	.01063	94.104	17.156	45
50	4.3839	.22811	.03829	26.114	.00874	114.48	18.558	50
55	5.0821	.19677	.03680	27.174	.00724	138.10	19.860	55
60	5.8916	.16973	.03560	28.089	.00604	165.49	21.067	60
65	6.8300	.14641	.03463	28.878	.00507	197.23	22.184	65
70	7.9178	.12630	.03383	29.558	.00427	234.04	23.215	70
75	9.1789	.10895	.03317	30.145	.00361	276.70	24.163	75
80	10.641	.09398	.03263	30.652	.00307	326.16	25.035	80
85	12.336	.08107	.03217	31.088	.00261	383.50	25.835	85
90	14.300	.06993	.03178	31.465	.00222	449.97	26.567	90
95	16.578	.06032	.03146	31.790	.00190	527.02	27.235	95
100	19.219	.05203	.03118	32.071	.00162	616.35	27.844	100
∞	∞	0	.02956	33.831	0	∞	33.333	∞

4%

(NOMINAL 3.9221%)

n	SPCAF F/P	SPPWF P/F	$\overline{CRF}$ $\overline{A}/P$	$\overline{USPWF}$ $P/\overline{A}$	$\overline{SFDF}$ $\overline{A}/F$	$\overline{USCAF}$ $F/\overline{A}$	$\overline{ASF}$ A/G	n
1	1.0400	.96154	1.0197	.98064	.98052	1.0199	–	1
2	1.0816	.92456	.51987	1.9236	.48065	2.0805	.49020	2
3	1.1249	.88900	.35333	2.8302	.31411	3.1836	.97386	3
4	1.1699	.85480	.27012	3.7020	.23090	4.3308	1.4510	4
5	1.2167	.82193	.22025	4.5403	.18103	5.5239	1.9216	5
6	1.2653	.79031	.18705	5.3463	.14782	6.7648	2.3857	6
7	1.3159	.75992	.16336	6.1213	.12414	8.0552	2.8433	7
8	1.3686	.73069	.14563	6.8665	.10641	9.3973	3.2944	8
9	1.4233	.70259	.13187	7.5831	.09265	10.793	3.7391	9
10	1.4802	.67556	.12089	8.2721	.08167	12.245	4.1773	10
11	1.5395	.64958	.11193	8.9345	.07270	13.754	4.6090	11
12	1.6010	.62460	.10448	9.5715	.06526	15.324	5.0343	12
13	1.6651	.60057	.09819	10.184	.05897	16.957	5.4533	13
14	1.7317	.57748	.09283	10.773	.05360	18.655	5.8659	14
15	1.8009	.55526	.08819	11.339	.04897	20.421	6.2721	15

4% (continued)

(NOMINAL 3.9221%)

n	SPCAF F/P	SPPWF P/F	CRF $\overline{A}/P$	USPWF $P/\overline{A}$	SFDF $\overline{A}/F$	USCAF $F/\overline{A}$	ASF A/G	n
16	1.8730	.53391	.08415	11.884	.04493	22.258	6.6720	16
17	1.9479	.51337	.08060	12.407	.04138	24.168	7.0656	17
18	2.0258	.49363	.07745	12.911	.03823	26.155	7.4530	18
19	2.1068	.47464	.07466	13.395	.03544	28.221	7.8342	19
20	2.1911	.45639	.07215	13.860	.03293	30.370	8.2091	20
21	2.2788	.43883	.06989	14.308	.03067	32.604	8.5779	21
22	2.3699	.42196	.06785	14.738	.02863	34.928	8.9407	22
23	2.4647	.40573	.06600	15.152	.02678	37.345	9.2973	23
24	2.5633	.39012	.06431	15.550	.02509	39.859	9.6479	24
25	2.6658	.37512	.06277	15.932	.02354	42.473	9.9925	25
26	2.7725	.36069	.06135	16.300	.02213	45.192	10.331	26
27	2.8834	.34682	.06005	16.654	.02083	48.020	10.664	27
28	2.9987	.33348	.05884	16.994	.01962	50.960	10.991	28
29	3.1187	.32065	.05773	17.321	.01851	54.019	11.312	29
30	3.2434	.30832	.05670	17.636	,01748	57.199	11.627	30
31	3.3731	.29646	.05575	17.938	.01653	60.507	11.937	31
32	3.5081	.28506	.05486	18.229	.01564	63.947	12.241	32
33	3.6484	.27409	.05403	18.508	.01481	67.525	12.540	33
34	3.7943	.26355	.05326	18.777	.01404	71.246	12.832	34
35	3.9461	.25342	.05253	19.035	.01331	75.116	13.120	35
40	4.8010	.20829	.04954	20.186	.01032	96.914	14.477	40
45	5.8412	.17120	.04732	21.132	.00810	123.43	15.705	45
50	7.1067	.14071	.04564	21.909	.00642	155.70	16.812	50
55	8.6464	.11566	.04435	22.548	.00513	194.96	17.807	55
60	10.520	.09506	.04334	23.073	.00412	242.72	18.697	60
65	12.799	.07813	.04255	23.505	.00332	300.83	19.491	65
70	15.572	.06422	.04191	23.859	.00269	371.53	20.196	70
75	18.945	.05278	.04141	24.151	.00219	457.55	20.821	75
80	23.050	.04338	.04100	24.391	.00178	562.20	21.372	80
85	28.044	.03566	.04067	24.588	.00145	689.52	21.857	85
90	34.119	.02931	.04041	24.749	.00118	844.43	22.283	90
95	41.511	.02409	.04019	24.883	.00097	1032.9	22.655	95
100	50.505	.01980	.04001	24.992	.00079	1262.2	22.980	100
∞	∞	0	.03922	25.497	0	∞	25.000	∞

5%

(NOMINAL 4.8790%)

n	F/P	P/F	$\overline{A}/P$	$P/\overline{A}$	$\overline{A}/F$	$F/\overline{A}$	A/G	n
1	1.0500	.95238	1.0246	.97600	.97580	1.0248	–	1
2	1.1025	.90703	.52479	1.9055	.47600	2.1008	.48781	2
3	1.1576	.86384	.35832	2.7908	.30953	3.2307	.96749	3
4	1.2155	.82270	.27519	3.6339	.22640	4.4170	1.4391	4
5	1.2763	.78353	.22539	4.4368	.17660	5.6626	1.9025	5
6	1.3401	.74622	.19225	5.2016	.14346	6.9706	2.3579	6
7	1.4071	.71068	.16864	5.9299	.11985	8.3439	2.8052	7
8	1.4775	.67684	.15098	6.6235	.10219	9.7859	3.2445	8
9	1.5513	.64461	.13729	7.2841	.08850	11.300	3.6758	9
10	1.6289	.61391	.12637	7.9132	.07758	12.890	4.0991	10
11	1.7103	.58468	.11748	8.5124	.06869	14.559	4.5144	11
12	1.7959	.55684	.11010	9.0830	.06131	16.312	4.9219	12
13	1.8856	.53032	.10388	9.6265	.05509	18.152	5.3215	13
14	1.9799	.50507	.09858	10.144	.04979	20.085	5.7133	14
15	2.0789	.48102	.09401	10.637	.04522	22.114	6.0973	15
16	2.1829	.45811	.09004	11.107	.04125	24.244	6.4736	16
17	2.2920	.43630	.08655	11.554	.03776	26.481	6.8423	17
18	2.4066	.41552	.08348	11.979	.03469	28.830	7.2034	18
19	2.5270	.39573	.08074	12.385	.03195	31.296	7.5569	19
20	2.6533	.37689	.07830	12.771	.02951	33.886	7.9030	20
21	2.7860	.35894	.07611	13.139	.02732	36.605	8.2416	21
22	2.9253	.34185	.07413	13.489	.02534	39.460	8.5730	22
23	3.0715	.32557	.07234	13.823	.02355	42.458	8.8971	23

5% (continued)
(NOMINAL 4.8790%)

n	SPCAF F/P	SPPWF P/F	$\overline{CRF}$ $\overline{A}/P$	USPWF $P/\overline{A}$	SFDF $\overline{A}/F$	$\overline{USCAF}$ $F/\overline{A}$	$\overline{ASF}$ A/G	n
24	3.2251	.31007	.07072	14.141	.02193	45.606	9.2140	24
25	3.3864	.29530	.06924	14.443	.02045	48.911	9.5238	25
26	3.5557	.28124	.06788	14.732	.01909	52.381	9.8266	26
27	3.7335	.26785	.06664	15.006	.01785	56.025	10.122	27
28	3.9201	.25509	.06550	15.268	.01671	59.851	10.411	28
29	4.1161	.24295	.06445	15.517	.01566	63.868	10.694	29
30	4.3219	.23138	.06348	15.754	.01469	68.086	10.969	30
31	4.5380	.22036	.06258	15.979	.01379	72.515	11.238	31
32	4.7649	.20987	.06175	16.195	.01296	77.166	11.501	32
33	5.0032	.19987	.06098	16.399	.01219	82.049	11.757	33
34	5.2533	.19035	.06026	16.594	.01147	87.176	12.006	34
35	5.5160	.18129	.05959	16.780	.01080	92.560	12.250	35
40	7.0400	.14205	.05687	17.585	.00808	123.80	13.377	40
45	8.9850	.11130	.05490	18.215	.00611	163.66	14.364	45
50	11.467	.08720	.05345	18.709	.00466	214.54	15.223	50
55	14.636	.06833	.05237	19.096	.00358	279.48	15.966	55
60	18.679	.05354	.05155	19.399	.00276	362.35	16.606	60
65	23.840	.04195	.05093	19.636	.00214	468.13	17.154	65
70	30.426	.03287	.05045	19.822	.00166	603.12	17.621	70
75	38.833	.02575	.05008	19.968	.00129	775.42	18.018	75
80	49.561	.02018	.04980	20.082	.00100	995.31	18.635	80
85	63.254	.01581	.04957	20.172	.00078	1276.0	18.635	85
90	80.730	.01239	.04940	20.242	.00061	1634.1	18.871	90
95	103.03	.00971	.04927	20.297	.00048	2091.3	19.069	95
100	131.50	.00760	.04916	20.340	.00037	2674.7	19.234	100
∞	∞	0	.04879	20.496	0	∞	20.000	∞

6%
(NOMINAL 5.8269%)

n	SPCAF F/P	SPPWF P/F	$\overline{CRF}$ $\overline{A}/P$	USPWF $P/\overline{A}$	SFDF $\overline{A}/F$	$\overline{USCAF}$ $F/\overline{A}$	$\overline{ASF}$ A/G	n
1	1.0600	.94340	1.0294	.97142	.97115	1.0297	–	1
2	1.1236	.89000	.52970	1.8879	.47143	2.1212	.48544	2
3	1.1910	.83962	.36332	2.7524	.30505	3.2782	.96118	3
4	1.2625	.79209	.28027	3.5680	.22200	4.5046	1.4272	4
5	1.3382	.74726	.23055	4.3375	.17228	5.8046	1.8836	5
6	1.4185	.70496	.19750	5.0634	.13923	7.1825	2.3304	6
7	1.5036	.66506	.17376	5.7482	.11570	8.6432	2.7676	7
8	1.5938	.62741	.15639	6.3943	.09812	10.192	3.1952	8
9	1.6895	.59190	.14278	7.0038	.08451	11.833	3.6133	9
10	1.7908	.55839	.13195	7.5787	.07368	13.572	4.0220	10
11	1.8983	.52679	.12313	8.1212	.06487	15.416	4.4213	11
12	2.0122	.49697	.11584	8.6329	.05757	17.371	4.8113	12
13	2.1329	.46884	.10970	9.1157	.05143	19.443	5.1920	13
14	2.2609	.44230	.10448	9.5711	.04621	21.639	5.5635	14
15	2.3966	.41727	.09999	10.001	.04172	23.967	5.9260	15
16	2.5404	.39365	.09610	10.406	.03783	26.435	6.2794	16
17	2.6928	.37136	.09269	10.789	.03442	29.051	6.6240	17
18	2.8543	.35034	.08969	11.149	.03142	31.824	6.9597	18
19	3.0256	.33051	.08704	11.490	.02877	34.763	7.2867	19
20	3.2071	.31180	.08467	11.811	.02640	37.878	7.6051	20
21	3.3996	.29416	.08255	12.114	.02428	41.181	7.9151	21
22	3.6035	.27751	.08065	12.399	.02238	44.681	8.2166	22
23	3.8197	.26180	.07893	12.669	.02067	48.392	8.5099	23
24	4.0489	.24698	.07738	12.923	.01911	52.325	8.7951	24
25	4.2919	.23300	.07597	13.163	.01770	56.494	9.0722	25
26	4.5494	.21981	.07469	13.389	.01642	60.914	9.3415	26
27	4.8223	.20737	.07351	13.603	.01524	65.598	9.6029	27
28	5.1117	.19563	.07244	13.804	.01417	70.564	9.8568	28
29	5.4184	.18456	.07146	13.994	.01319	75.828	10.103	29
30	5.7435	.17411	.07055	14.174	.01228	81.407	10.342	30
31	6.0881	.16425	.06972	14.343	.01145	87.321	10.574	31

6% (continued)

(NOMINAL 5.8269%)

n	SPCAF F/P	SPPWF P/F	$\overline{CRF}$ $\overline{A}/P$	USPWF $P/\overline{A}$	$\overline{SFDF}$ $\overline{A}/F$	USCAF $F/\overline{A}$	$\overline{ASF}$ A/G	n
32	6.4534	.15496	.06895	14.502	.01069	93.590	10.799	32
33	6.8406	.14619	.06825	14.653	.00998	100.24	11.017	33
34	7.2510	.13791	.06759	14.795	.00932	107.28	11.228	34
35	7.6861	.13011	.06698	14.929	.00871	114.75	11.432	35
40	10.286	.09722	.06454	15.493	.00628	159.36	12.359	40
45	13.765	.07265	.06283	15.915	.00456	219.06	13.141	45
50	18.420	.05429	.06161	16.230	.00334	298.96	13.796	50
55	24.650	.04057	.06073	16.466	.00246	405.88	14.341	55
60	32.988	.03031	.06009	16.642	.00182	548.97	14.791	60
65	44.145	.02265	.05962	16.773	.00135	740.45	15.160	65
70	59.076	.01693	.05927	16.871	.00100	996.69	15.461	70
75	79.057	.01265	.05902	16.945	.00075	1339.6	15.706	75
80	105.80	.00945	.05883	17.000	.00056	1798.5	15.903	80
85	141.58	.00706	.05868	17.041	.00041	2412.6	16.062	85
90	189.46	.00528	.05858	17.071	.00031	3234.4	16.189	90
95	253.55	.00394	.05850	17.094	.00023	4334.2	16.290	95
100	339.30	.00295	.05844	17.111	.00017	5805.9	16.371	100
∞	∞	0	.05827	17.162	0	∞	16.667	∞

7%

(NOMINAL 6.7659%)

n	SPCAF F/P	SPPWF P/F	$\overline{CRF}$ $\overline{A}/P$	USPWF $P/\overline{A}$	$\overline{SFDF}$ $\overline{A}/F$	USCAF $F/\overline{A}$	$\overline{ASF}$ A/G	n
1	1.0700	.93458	1.0342	.96692	.96655	1.0346	–	1
2	1.1449	.87344	.53459	1.8706	.46693	2.1416	.48309	2
3	1.2250	.81630	.36831	2.7151	.30065	3.3262	.95493	3
4	1.3108	.76290	.28535	3.5044	.21769	4.5936	1.4155	4
5	1.4026	.71299	.23573	4.2421	.16807	5.9497	1.8650	5
6	1.5007	.66634	.20278	4.9315	.13512	7.4008	2.3032	6
7	1.6058	.62275	.17935	5.5758	.11169	8.9535	2.7304	7
8	1.7182	.58201	.16187	6.1779	.09421	10.615	3.1465	8
9	1.8385	.54393	.14835	6.7407	.08069	12.392	3.5517	9
10	1.9672	.50835	.13762	7.2666	.06996	14.295	3.9461	10
11	2.1049	.47509	.12890	7.7582	.06124	16.330	4.3296	11
12	2.2522	.44401	.12169	8.2175	.05403	18.507	4.7025	12
13	2.4098	.41496	.11565	8.6469	.04799	20.838	5.0648	13
14	2.5785	.38782	.11052	9.0481	.04286	23.331	5.4167	14
15	2.7590	.36245	.10612	9.4231	.03846	25.999	5.7583	15
16	2.9522	.33873	.10232	9.7736	.03466	28.853	6.0897	16
17	3.1588	.31657	.09900	10.101	.03134	31.907	6.4110	17
18	3.3799	.29586	.09609	10.407	.02843	35.176	6.7225	18
19	3.6165	.27651	.09352	10.693	.02586	38.672	7.0242	19
20	3.8697	.25842	.09124	10.961	.02358	42.414	7.3163	20
21	4.1406	.24151	.08920	11.210	.02154	46.418	7.5990	21
22	4.4304	.22571	.08738	11.444	.01972	50.702	7.8725	22
23	4.7405	.21095	.08575	11.662	.01809	55.285	8.1369	23
24	5.0724	.19715	.08427	11.866	.01661	60.190	8.3923	24
25	5.4274	.18425	.08294	12.057	.01528	65.438	8.6391	25
26	5.8074	.17220	.08173	12.235	.01407	71.053	8.8773	26
27	6.2139	.16093	.08064	12.402	.01298	77.061	9.1072	27
28	6.6488	.15040	.07964	12.557	.01198	83.490	9.3289	28
29	7.1143	.14056	.07872	12.703	.01107	90.369	9.5427	29
30	7.6123	.13137	.07789	12.838	.01023	97.730	9.7487	30
31	8.1451	.12277	.07713	12.965	.00947	105.61	9.9471	31
32	8.7153	.11474	.07643	13.084	.00877	114.03	10.138	32
33	9.3253	.10723	.07579	13.195	.00813	123.05	10.322	33
34	9.9781	.10022	.07520	13.299	.00754	132.70	10.499	34
35	10.677	.09366	.07465	13.396	.00699	143.02	10.669	35
40	14.974	.06678	.07250	13.793	.00484	206.54	11.423	40
45	21.002	.04761	.07104	14.076	.00338	295.64	12.036	45
50	29.457	.03395	.07004	14.278	.00238	420.60	12.529	50
55	41.315	.02420	.06934	14.422	.00168	595.86	12.921	55

7% (continued)

(NOMINAL 6.7659%)

n	SPCAF F/P	SPPWF P/F	$\overline{CRF}$ $\overline{A}/P$	$\overline{USPWF}$ $P/\overline{A}$	$\overline{SFDF}$ $\overline{A}/F$	$\overline{USCAF}$ $F/\overline{A}$	$\overline{ASF}$ A/G	n
60	57.946	.01726	.06885	14.525	.00119	841.67	13.232	60
65	81.273	.01230	.06850	14.598	.00084	1186.4	13.476	65
70	113.99	.00877	.06826	14.650	.00060	1670.0	13.666	70
75	159.88	.00625	.06809	14.688	.00043	2348.2	13.814	75
80	224.23	.00446	.06796	14.714	.00030	3299.4	13.927	80
85	314.50	.00318	.06787	14.733	.00022	4633.6	14.015	85
90	441.10	.00227	.06781	14.747	.00015	6504.8	14.081	90
95	618.67	.00162	.06777	14.756	.00011	9129.2	14.132	95
100	867.72	.00115	.06774	14.763	.00008	12810.	14.170	100
∞	∞	0	.06766	14.780	0	∞	14.286	∞

8%

(NOMINAL 7.6961%)

n	SPCAF F/P	SPPWF P/F	$\overline{CRF}$ $\overline{A}/P$	$\overline{USPWF}$ $P/\overline{A}$	$\overline{SFDF}$ $\overline{A}/F$	$\overline{USCAF}$ $F/\overline{A}$	$\overline{ASF}$ A/G	n
1	1.0800	.92593	1.0390	.96249	.96201	1.0395	–	1
2	1.1664	.85734	.53947	1.8537	.46251	2.1621	.48077	2
3	1.2597	.79383	.37329	2.6789	.29633	3.3746	.94875	3
4	1.3605	.73503	.29045	3.4429	.21349	4.6840	1.4040	4
5	1.4693	.68058	.24094	4.1504	.16398	6.0983	1.8465	5
6	1.5869	.63017	.20810	4.8054	.13114	7.6256	2.2763	6
7	1.7138	.58349	.18478	5.4120	.10782	9.2751	2.6937	7
8	1.8509	.54027	.16740	5.9736	.09044	11.057	3.0985	8
9	1.9990	.50025	.15400	6.4936	.07704	12.981	3.4910	9
10	2.1589	.46319	.14337	6.9750	.06641	15.059	3.8713	10
11	2.3316	.42888	.13476	7.4209	.05779	17.303	4.2395	11
12	2.5182	.39711	.12765	7.8337	.05069	19.726	4.5957	12
13	2.7196	.36770	.12172	8.2159	.04476	22.344	4.9402	13
14	2.9372	.34046	.11669	8.5698	.03973	25.171	5.2731	14
15	3.1722	.31524	.11239	8.8975	.03543	28.224	5.5945	15
16	3.4259	.29189	.10869	9.2009	.03172	31.522	5.9046	16
17	3.7000	.27027	.10546	9.4818	.02850	35.083	6.2037	17
18	3.9960	.25025	.10265	9.7420	.02569	38.929	6.4920	18
19	4.3157	.23171	.10017	9.9828	.02321	43.083	6.7697	19
20	4.6610	.21455	.09798	10.206	.02102	47.569	7.0369	20
21	5.0338	.19866	.09604	10.412	.01908	52.414	7.2940	21
22	5.4365	.18394	.09431	10.604	.01735	57.647	7.5412	22
23	5.8715	.17032	.09276	10.781	.01580	63.298	7.7786	23
24	6.3412	.15770	.09137	10.945	.01441	69.401	8.0066	24
25	6.8485	.14602	.09012	11.096	.01316	75.993	8.2254	25
26	7.3964	.13520	.08899	11.237	.01203	83.112	8.4352	26
27	7.9881	.12519	.08797	11.367	.01101	90.800	8.6363	27
28	8.6271	.11591	.08705	11.487	.01009	99.103	8.8289	28
29	9.3173	.10733	.08621	11.599	.00925	108.07	9.0133	29
30	10.063	.09938	.08545	11.702	.00849	117.76	9.1897	30
31	10.868	.09202	.08476	11.798	.00780	128.22	9.3584	31
32	11.737	.08520	.08413	11.887	.00717	139.51	9.3197	32
33	12.676	.07889	.08355	11.969	.00659	151.71	9.6737	33
34	13.690	.07305	.08303	12.044	.00606	164.89	9.8208	34
35	14.785	.06754	.08354	12.115	.00558	179.12	9.9611	35
40	21.725	.04603	.08068	12.395	.00371	269.29	10.570	40
45	31.920	.03133	.07945	12.587	.00249	401.77	11.045	45
50	46.902	.02132	.07864	12.717	.00168	596.43	11.411	50
55	68.914	.01451	.07809	12.805	.00113	882.45	11.690	55
60	101.26	.00988	.07773	12.865	.00077	1302.7	11.902	60
65	148.78	.00672	.07748	12.906	.00052	1920.2	12.060	65
70	218.61	.00457	.07732	12.934	.00035	2827.5	12.178	70
75	321.20	.00311	.07720	12.953	.00024	4160.6	12.266	75
80	471.95	.00212	.07712	12.966	.00016	6119.4	12.330	80
85	693.46	.00144	.07707	12.975	.00011	8997.5	12.377	85
90	1018.9	.00098	.07704	12.981	.00008	13226.	12.412	90
95	1497.1	.00067	.07701	12.985	.00005	19440.	12.437	95

8% (continued)
(NOMINAL 7.6961%)

n	SPCAF	SPPWF	CRF	USPWF	SFDF	USCAF	ASF	n
	F/P	P/F	$\overline{A}/P$	$P/\overline{A}$	$\overline{A}/F$	$F/\overline{A}$	A/G	
100	2199.8	.00045	.07700	12.988	.00003	28570.	12.455	100
∞	∞	0	.07696	12.994	0	∞	12.500	∞

9%
(NOMINAL 8.6178%)

n	SPCAF	SPPWF	CRF	USPWF	SFDF	USCAF	ASF	n
1	1.0900	.91743	1.0437	.95812	.95753	1.044 ,	–	1
2	1.1881	.84168	.54433	1.8371	.45815	2.1827	.47847	2
3	1.2950	.77218	.37828	2.6436	.29210	3.4235	.94262	3
4	1.4116	.70843	.29556	3.3834	.20938	4.7760	1.3925	4
5	1.5386	.64993	.24617	4.0622	.16000	6.2502	1.8282	5
6	1.6771	.59627	.21345	4.6849	.12727	7.8570	2.2498	6
7	1.8280	.54703	.19025	5.2562	.10407	9.6085	2.6574	7
8	1.9926	.50187	.17300	5.7803	.08682	11.518	3.0512	8
9	2.1719	.46043	.15971	6.2612	.07354	13.599	3.4312	9
10	2.3674	.42241	.14920	6.7023	.06303	15.867	3.7978	10
11	2.5804	.38753	.14071	7.1070	.05453	18.339	4.1510	11
12	2.8127	.35553	.13372	7.4783	.04754	21.034	4.4910	12
13	3.0658	.32618	.12789	7.8190	.04172	23.971	4.8182	13
14	3.3417	.29925	.12298	8.1315	.03680	27.173	5.1326	14
15	3.6425	.27454	.11879	8.4182	.03261	30.663	5.4346	15
16	3.9703	.25187	.11519	8.6813	.02901	34.467	5.7245	16
17	4.3276	.23107	.11208	8.9226	.02590	38.614	6.0024	17
18	4.7171	.21199	.10936	9.1440	.02318	43.133	6.2687	18
19	5.1417	.19449	.10699	9.3471	.02081	48.060	6.5236	19
20	5.6044	.17843	.10489	9.5334	.01872	53.429	6.7675	20
21	6.1088	.16370	.10305	9.7044	.01687	59.282	7.0006	21
22	6.6586	.15018	.10141	9.8612	.01523	65.662	7.2232	22
23	7.2579	.13778	.09995	10.005	.01377	72.616	7.4357	23
24	7.9111	.12640	.09865	10.137	.01247	80.196	7.6384	24
25	8.6231	.11597	.09748	10.258	.01131	88.458	7.8316	25
26	9.3992	.10639	.09644	10.369	.01026	97.463	8.0156	26
27	10.245	.09761	.09550	10.471	.00932	107.28	8.1906	27
28	11.167	.08955	.09465	10.565	.00848	117.98	8.3571	28
29	12.172	.08216	.09389	10.651	.00771	129.64	8.5154	29
30	13.268	.07537	.09320	10.729	.00702	142.35	8.6657	30
31	14.462	.06915	.09258	10.802	.00640	156.21	8.8083	31
32	15.763	.06344	.09202	10.868	.00584	171.31	8.9436	32
33	17.182	.05820	.09150	10.929	.00533	187.78	9.0718	33
34	18.728	.05340	.09104	10.984	.00486	205.72	9.1933	34
35	20.414	.04899	.09062	11.035	.00444	225.28	9.3083	35
40	31.409	.03184	.08901	11.234	.00283	352.87	9.7957	40
45	48.327	.02069	.08800	11.364	.00182	549.18	10.160	45
50	74.358	.01345	.08735	11.448	.00117	851.24	10.430	50
55	114.41	.00874	.08694	11.503	.00076	1316.0	10.626	55
60	176.03	.00568	.08667	11.538	.00049	2031.1	10.768	60
65	270.85	.00369	.08650	11.561	.00032	3131.3	10.870	65
70	416.73	.00240	.08639	11.576	.00021	4824.1	10.943	70
75	641.19	.00156	.08631	11.586	.00013	7428.7	10.994	75
80	986.55	.00101	.08627	11.592	.00009	11436.	11.030	80
85	1517.9	.00066	.08624	11.596	.00006	17602.	11.055	85
90	2335.5	.00043	.08622	11.599	.00004	27090.	11.073	90
95	3593.5	.00028	.08620	11.601	.00002	41687.	11.085	95
100	5529.0	.00018	.08619	11.602	.00002	64147.	11.093	100
∞	∞	0	.08618	11.604	0	∞	11.111	∞

10%
(NOMINAL 9.5310%)

n	SPCAF	SPPWF	CRF	USPWF	SFDF	USCAF	ASF	n
1	1.1000	.90909	1.0484	.95382	.95310	1.0492	–	1
2	1.2100	.82645	.54917	1.8209	.45386	2.2033	.47619	2

10% (continued)
(NOMINAL 9.5310%)

n	SPCAF F/P	SPPWF P/F	$\overline{CRF}$ $\overline{A}/P$	USPWF $P/\overline{A}$	SFDF $\overline{A}/F$	USCAF $F/\overline{A}$	$\overline{ASF}$ A/G	n
3	1.3310	.75131	.38326	2.6092	.28795	3.4729	.93656	3
4	1.4641	.68301	.30068	3.3258	.20537	4.8694	1.3812	4
5	1.6105	.62092	.25143	3.9773	.15612	6.4055	1.8101	5
6	1.7716	.56447	.21884	4.5696	.12353	8.0953	2.2236	6
7	1.9487	.51316	.19577	5.1080	.10046	9.9540	2.6216	7
8	2.1436	.46651	.17865	5.5974	.08334	11.999	3.0045	8
9	2.3579	.42410	.16550	6.0424	.07019	14.248	3.3724	9
10	2.5937	.38554	.15511	6.4469	.05980	16.722	3.7255	10
11	2.8531	.35049	.14674	6.8147	.05143	19.443	4.0641	11
12	3.1384	.31863	.13988	7.1490	.04457	22.437	4.3884	12
13	3.4523	.28966	.13418	7.4529	.03887	25.729	4.6988	13
14	3.7975	.26333	.12938	7.7292	.03407	29.352	4.9955	14
15	4.1772	.23939	.12531	7.9803	.03000	33.336	5.2789	15
16	4.5950	.21763	.12182	8.2087	.02651	37.719	5.5493	16
17	5.0545	.19784	.11882	8.4163	.02351	42.540	5.8071	17
18	5.5599	.17986	.11621	8.6050	.02090	47.843	6.0526	18
19	6.1159	.16351	.11394	8.7765	.01863	53.676	6.2861	19
20	6.7275	.14864	.11195	8.9325	.01664	60.093	6.5081	20
21	7.4003	.13513	.11020	9.0743	.01489	67.152	6.7189	21
22	8.1403	.12285	.10866	9.2032	.01335	74.916	6.9189	22
23	8.9543	.11168	.10729	9.3203	.01198	83.457	7.1085	23
24	9.8497	.10153	.10608	9.4268	.01077	92.852	7.2881	24
25	10.835	.09230	.10500	9.5237	.00969	103.19	7.4580	25
26	11.918	.08391	.10404	9.6117	.00873	114.55	7.6187	26
27	13.110	.07628	.10318	9.6917	.00787	127.06	7.7704	27
28	14.421	.06934	.10241	9.7645	.00710	140.81	7.9137	28
29	15.863	.06304	.10172	9.8306	.00641	155.94	8.0489	29
30	17.449	.05731	.10110	9.8908	.00579	172.59	8.1762	30
31	19.194	.05210	.10055	9.9454	.00524	190.90	8.2962	31
32	21.114	.04736	.10005	9.9951	.00474	211.03	8.4091	32
33	23.225	.04306	.09960	10.040	.00428	233.19	8.5152	33
34	25.548	.03914	.09919	10.081	.00388	257.56	8.6149	34
35	28.102	.03558	.09883	10.119	.00352	284.36	8.7086	35
40	45.259	.02210	.09746	10.260	.00215	464.37	9.0962	40
45	72.891	.01372	.09664	10.348	.00133	754.28	9.3740	45
50	117.39	.00852	.09613	10.403	.00082	1221.2	9.5704	50
55	189.06	.00529	.09581	10.437	.00051	1973.1	9.7075	55
60	304.48	.00328	.09562	10.458	.00031	3184.1	9.8023	60
65	490.37	.00204	.09551	10.471	.00019	5134.5	9.8672	65
70	789.75	.00127	.09543	10.479	.00012	8275.6	9.9113	70
75	1271.9	.00079	.09539	10.484	.00007	13334.	9.9410	75
80	2048.4	.00049	.09536	10.487	.00005	21481.	9.9609	80
85	3299.0	.00030	.09534	10.489	.00003	34602.	9.9742	85
90	5313.0	.00019	.09533	10.490	.00002	55734.	9.9831	90
95	8556.7	.00012	.09532	10.491	.00001	89767.	9.9889	95
100	13781.	.00007	.09532	10.491	.00001		9.9927	100
∞	∞	0	.09531	10.492	0	∞	10.000	∞

15%
(NOMINAL 13.976%)

n	F/P	P/F	$\overline{A}/P$	$P/\overline{A}$	$\overline{A}/F$	$F/\overline{A}$	A/G	n
1	1.1500	.86957	1.0715	.93326	.93175	1.0733	–	1
2	1.3225	.75614	.57313	1.7448	.43337	2.3075	.46512	2
3	1.5209	.65752	.40808	2.4505	.26832	3.7269	.90713	3
4	1.7490	.57175	.32636	3.0641	.18660	5.3592	1.3263	4
5	2.0114	.49718	.27795	3.5977	.13819	7.2363	1.7228	5
6	2.3131	.43233	.24620	4.0617	.10644	9.3950	2.0972	6
7	2.6600	.37594	.22395	4.4652	.08419	11.877	2.4498	7
8	3.0590	.32690	.20764	4.8160	.06788	14.732	2.7813	8
9	3.5179	.28426	.19527	5.1211	.05551	18.015	3.0922	9
10	4.0456	.24718	.18565	5.3864	.04589	21.791	3.3832	10

15% (continued)

(NOMINAL 13.976%)

n	SPCAF F/P	SPPWF P/F	$\overline{CRF}$ $\overline{A}/P$	$\overline{USPWF}$ $P/\overline{A}$	$\overline{SFDF}$ $\overline{A}/F$	$\overline{USCAF}$ $F/\overline{A}$	$\overline{ASF}$ A/G	n
11	4.6524	.21494	.17803	5.6171	.03827	26.133	3.6549	11
12	5.3503	.18691	.17189	5.8177	.03213	31.126	3.9082	12
13	6.1528	.16253	.16689	5.9921	.02712	36.868	4.1438	13
14	7.0757	.14133	.16277	6.1438	.02300	43.472	4.3624	14
15	8.1371	.12289	.15934	6.2757	.01958	51.066	4.5650	15
16	9.3576	.10686	.15648	6.3904	.01672	59.799	4.7522	16
17	10.761	.09293	.15408	6.4901	.01432	69.842	4.9251	17
18	12.375	.08081	.15205	6.5769	.01229	81.392	5.0843	18
19	14.232	.07027	.15032	6.6523	.01056	94.674	5.2307	19
20	16.367	.06110	.14886	6.7178	.00910	109.95	5.3651	20
21	18.822	.05313	.14760	6.7749	.00784	127.51	5.4883	21
22	21.645	.04620	.14653	6.8245	.00677	147.71	5.6010	22
23	24.891	.04017	.14561	6.8676	.00585	170.94	5.7040	23
24	28.625	.03493	.14482	6.9051	.00506	197.66	5.7979	24
25	32.919	.03038	.14414	6.9377	.00438	228.38	5.8834	25
26	37.857	.02642	.14355	6.9660	.00379	263.71	5.9612	26
27	43.535	.02297	.14305	6.9907	.00329	304.34	6.0319	27
28	50.066	.01997	.14261	7.0121	.00285	351.07	6.0960	28
29	57.575	.01737	.14223	7.0308	.00247	404.80	6.1541	29
30	66.212	.01510	.14191	7.0470	.00214	466.59	6.2066	30
31	76.144	.01313	.14162	7.0611	.00186	537.65	6.2541	31
32	87.565	.01142	.14138	7.0733	.00161	619.38	6.2970	32
33	100.70	.00993	.14116	7.0840	.00140	713.35	6.3357	33
34	115.80	.00864	.14098	7.0932	.00122	821.43	6.3705	34
35	133.18	.00751	.14082	7.1013	.00106	945.72	6.4019	35
40	267.86	.00373	.14029	7.1283	.00052	1909.4	6.5168	40
45	538.77	.00186	.14002	7.1417	.00026	3847.8	6.5830	45
50	1083.7	.00092	.13989	7.1484	.00013	7746.4	6.6205	50
55	2179.6	.00046	.13983	7.1517	.00006	15588.	6.6414	55
60	4384.0	.00023	.13979	7.1534	.00003	31360.	6.6530	60
65	8817.8	.00011	.13978	7.1542	.00002	63084.	6.6593	65
70	17736.	.00006	.13977	7.1546	.00001		6.6627	70
75	35673.	.00003	.13977	7.1548	.00000		6.6646	75
80	71751.	.00001	.13976	7.1549	.00000		6.6656	80
∞	∞	0	.13976	7.1550	0	∞	6.6667	∞

20%

(NOMINAL 18.232%)

n	F/P	P/F	$\overline{A}/P$	$P/\overline{A}$	$\overline{A}/F$	$F/\overline{A}$	A/G	n
1	1.2000	.83333	1.0939	.91414	.91161	1.0970	–	1
2	1.4400	.69444	.59669	1.6759	.41437	2.4133	.45455	2
3	1.7280	.57870	.43276	2.3107	.25044	3.9929	.87912	3
4	2.0736	.48225	.35214	2.8397	.16982	5.8885	1.2742	4
5	2.4883	.40188	.30482	3.2806	.12250	8.1632	1.6405	5
6	2.9860	.33490	.27413	3.6480	.09180	10.893	1.9788	6
7	3.5832	.27908	.25290	3.9541	.07058	14.168	2.2902	7
8	4.2998	.23257	.23757	4.2092	.05525	18.099	2.5756	8
9	5.1598	.19381	.22615	4.4218	.04383	22.816	2.8364	9
10	6.1917	.16151	.21744	4.5990	.03512	28.476	3.0739	10
11	7.4301	.13459	.21068	4.7466	.02835	35.268	3.2893	11
12	8.9161	.11216	.20535	4.8697	.02303	43.418	3.4841	12
13	10.699	.09346	.20112	4.9722	.01880	53.199	3.6597	13
14	12.839	.07789	.19772	5.0576	.01540	64.936	3.8175	14
15	15.407	.06491	.19498	5.1288	.01266	79.020	3.9588	15
16	18.488	.05409	.19275	5.1882	.01043	95.921	4.0851	16
17	22.186	.04507	.19093	5.2376	.00861	116.20	4.1976	17
18	26.623	.03756	.18944	5.2788	.00712	140.54	4.2975	18
19	31.948	.03130	.18821	5.3131	.00589	169.74	4.3861	19
20	38.338	.02608	.18720	5.3417	.00488	204.79	4.4643	20
21	46.005	.02174	.18637	5.3656	.00405	246.84	4.5334	21
22	55.206	.01811	.18569	5.3855	.00336	297.31	4.5941	22

20% (continued)

(NOMINAL 18.232%)

n	SPCAF F/P	SPPWF P/F	CRF $\overline{A}/P$	USPWF $P/\overline{A}$	SFDF $\overline{A}/F$	USCAF $F/\overline{A}$	ASF A/G	n
23	66.247	.01510	.18512	5.4020	.00279	357.87	4.6475	23
24	79.497	.01258	.18464	5.4158	.00232	430.54	4.6943	24
25	95.396	.01048	.18425	5.4273	.00193	517.75	4.7352	25
26	114.48	.00874	.18393	5.4369	.00161	622.39	4.7709	26
27	137.37	.00728	.18366	5.4449	.00134	747.97	4.8020	27
28	164.84	.00607	.18343	5.4515	.00111	898.66	4.8291	28
29	197.81	.00506	.18325	5.4571	.00093	1079.5	4.8527	29
30	237.38	.00421	.18309	5.4617	.00077	1296.5	4.8731	30
31	284.85	.00351	.18296	5.4656	.00064	1556.9	4.8908	31
32	341.82	.00293	.18286	5.4688	.00053	1869.3	4.9061	32
33	410.19	.00244	.18277	5.4714	.00045	2244.3	4.9194	33
34	492.22	.00203	.18269	5.4737	.00037	2694.3	4.9308	34
35	590.67	.00169	.18263	5.4755	.00031	3234.2	4.9406	35
40	1469.8	.00068	.18245	5.4811	.00012	8055.9	4.9728	40
45	3657.3	.00027	.18237	5.4833	.00005	20054.	4.9877	45
50	9100.4	.00011	.18234	5.4842	.00002	49909.	4.9945	50
55	22645.	.00004	.18233	5.4846	.00000		4.9976	55
60	56347.	.00002	.18232	5.4847	.00000		4.9989	60
∞	∞	0	.18232	5.4848	0	∞	5.0000	∞

25%

(NOMINAL 22.314%)

n	SPCAF F/P	SPPWF P/F	CRF $\overline{A}/P$	USPWF $P/\overline{A}$	SFDF $\overline{A}/F$	USCAF $F/\overline{A}$	ASF A/G	n
1	1.2500	.80000	1.1157	.89628	.89257	1.1204	–	1
2	1.5625	.64000	.61984	1.6133	.39670	2.5208	.44444	2
3	1.9531	.51200	.45726	2.1869	.23412	4.2714	.85246	3
4	2.4414	.40960	.37795	2.6458	.15481	6.4595	1.2249	4
5	3.0518	.32768	.33190	3.0129	.10876	9.1948	1.5631	5
6	3.8147	.26214	.30242	3.3066	.07928	12.614	1.8683	6
7	4.7684	.20972	.28236	3.5416	.05922	16.888	2.1424	7
8	5.9605	.16777	.26813	3.7296	.04498	22.230	2.3872	8
9	7.4506	.13422	.25774	3.8799	.03459	28.908	2.6048	9
10	9.3132	.10737	.24999	4.0002	.02684	37.255	2.7971	10
11	11.642	.08590	.24411	4.0965	.02097	47.689	2.9663	11
12	14.552	.06872	.23961	4.1735	.01647	60.732	3.1145	12
13	18.190	.05498	.23612	4.2351	.01298	77.035	3.2437	13
14	22.737	.04398	.23341	4.2843	.01027	97.414	3.3559	14
15	28.422	.03518	.23128	4.3237	.00814	122.89	3.4530	15
16	35.527	.02815	.22961	4.3553	.00646	154.73	3.5366	16
17	44.409	.02252	.22828	4.3805	.00514	194.53	3.6084	17
18	55.511	.01801	.22724	4.4007	.00409	244.29	3.6698	18
19	69.389	.01441	.22641	4.4168	.00326	306.48	3.7222	19
20	86.736	.01153	.22575	4.4298	.00260	384.22	3.7667	20
21	108.42	.00922	.22522	4.4401	.00208	481.40	3.8045	21
22	135.53	.00738	.22480	4.4484	.00166	602.86	3.8365	22
23	169.41	.00590	.22447	4.4550	.00133	754.70	3.8634	23
24	211.76	.00472	.22420	4.4603	.00106	944.50	3.8861	24
25	264.70	.00378	.22399	4.4645	.00085	1181.7	3.9052	25
26	330.87	.00302	.22382	4.4679	.00068	1478.3	3.9212	26
27	413.59	.00242	.22368	4.4706	.00054	1849.0	3.9346	27
28	516.99	.00193	.22358	4.4728	.00043	2312.4	3.9457	28
29	646.23	.00155	.22349	4.4745	.00034	2891.6	3.9551	29
30	807.79	.00124	.22342	4.4759	.00028	3615.6	3.9628	30
31	1009.7	.00099	.22336	4.4770	.00022	4520.6	3.9693	31
32	1262.2	.00079	.22332	4.4779	.00018	5651.9	3.9746	32
33	1577.7	.00063	.22329	4.4786	.00014	7066.0	3.9791	33
34	1972.2	.00058	.22326	4.4791	.00011	8833.6	3.9828	34
35	2465.2	.00041	.22323	4.4796	.00009	11043.	3.9858	35
40	7523.2	.00013	.22317	4.4808	.00003	33710.	3.9947	40
45	22959.	.00004	.22315	4.4812	.00001		3.9980	45
50	70065.	.00001	.22315	4.4814	.00000		3.9993	50
∞	∞	0	.22314	4.4814	0	∞	4.0000	∞

30%
(NOMINAL 26.236%)

n	SPCAF F/P	SPPWF P/F	CRF $\overline{A}/P$	USPWF $P/\overline{A}$	SFDF $\overline{A}/F$	USCAF $F/\overline{A}$	ASF A/G	n
1	1.3000	.76923	1.1369	.87958	.87455	1.1434	–	1
2	1.6900	.59172	.64260	1.5562	.38024	2.6299	.43478	2
3	2.1970	.45517	.48155	2.0766	.21918	4.5624	.82707	3
4	2.0561	.35013	.40372	2.4770	.14135	7.0745	1.1783	4
5	3.7129	.26933	.35907	2.7849	.09671	10.340	1.4903	5
6	4.8268	.20718	.33092	3.0218	.06856	14.586	1.7654	6
7	6.2749	.15937	.31210	3.2041	.04974	20.105	2.0063	7
8	8.1573	.12259	.29902	3.3442	.03666	27.280	2.2156	8
9	10.604	.09430	.28968	3.4521	.02732	36.607	2.3963	9
10	13.786	.07254	.28288	3.5350	.02052	48.733	2.5512	10
11	17.922	.05580	.27787	3.5988	.01551	64.497	2.6833	11
12	23.298	.04292	.27413	3.6479	.01177	84.989	2.7952	12
13	30.288	.03302	.27132	3.6857	.00896	111.63	2.8895	13
14	39.374	.02540	.26920	3.7147	.00684	146.26	2.9685	14
15	51.186	.01954	.26759	3.7370	.00523	191.28	3.0344	15
16	66.542	.01503	.26637	3.7542	.00400	249.81	3.0892	16
17	86.504	.01156	.26543	3.7674	.00307	325.90	3.1345	17
18	112.46	.00889	.26472	3.7776	.00235	424.81	3.1718	18
19	146.19	.00684	.26417	3.7854	.00181	553.40	3.2025	19
20	190.05	.00526	.26375	3.7914	.00139	720.56	3.2275	20
21	247.06	.00405	.26343	3.7961	.00107	937.87	3.2480	21
22	321.18	.00311	.26318	3.7996	.00082	1220.4	3.2646	22
23	417.54	.00240	.26299	3.8024	.00063	1587.6	3.2781	23
24	542.80	.00184	.26285	3.8045	.00048	2065.1	3.2890	24
25	705.64	.00142	.26274	3.8061	.00037	2685.7	3.2979	25
26	917.33	.00109	.26265	3.8073	.00029	3492.6	3.3050	26
27	1192.5	.00084	.26258	3.8083	.00022	4541.5	3.3107	27
28	1550.3	.00065	.26253	3.8090	.00017	5905.1	3.3153	28
29	2015.4	.00050	.26249	3.8096	.00013	7677.8	3.3189	29
30	2620.0	.00038	.26246	3.8100	.00010	9982.3	3.3219	30
31	3406.0	.00029	.26244	3.8104	.00008	12978.	3.3242	31
32	4427.8	.00023	.26242	3.8106	.00006	16873.	3.3261	32
33	5756.1	.00017	.26241	3.8108	.00005	21936.	3.3276	33
34	7483.0	.00013	.26240	3.8110	.00004	28517.	3.3288	34
35	9727.9	.00010	.26239	3.8111	.00003	37074.	3.3297	35
40	36119.	.00003	.26237	3.8114	.00001		3.3322	40
∞	∞	0	.26236	3.8115	0	∞	3.3333	∞

35%
(NOMINAL 30.010%)

n								n
1	1.3500	.74074	1.1575	.86390	.85744	1.1663	–	1
2	1.8225	.54870	.66497	1.5038	.36487	2.7407	.42553	2
3	2.4604	.40644	.50560	1.9778	.20550	4.8662	.80288	3
4	3.3215	.30107	.42938	2.3290	.12927	7.7357	1.1341	4
5	4.4840	.22301	.38624	2.5891	.08614	11.609	1.4220	5
6	6.0534	.16520	.35949	2.7817	.05939	16.839	1.6698	6
7	8.1721	.12237	.34195	2.9244	.04184	23.899	1.8811	7
8	11.032	.09064	.33002	3.0301	.02991	33.430	2.0597	8
9	14.894	.06714	.32170	3.1084	.02160	46.296	2.2094	9
10	20.107	.04974	.31581	3.1664	.01571	63.666	2.3338	10
11	27.144	.03684	.31158	3.2094	.01148	87.116	2.4364	11
12	36.644	.02729	.30852	3.2412	.00842	118.77	2.5205	12
13	49.470	.02021	.30630	3.2648	.00619	161.51	2.5889	13
14	66.784	.01497	.30467	3.2823	.00456	219.20	2.6443	14
15	90.158	.01109	.30347	3.2952	.00337	297.09	2.6889	15
16	121.71	.00822	.30259	3.3048	.00249	402.24	2.7246	16
17	164.31	.00609	.30194	3.3119	.00184	544.19	2.7530	17
18	221.82	.00451	.30146	3.3172	.00136	735.82	2.7756	18
19	299.46	.00334	.30111	3.3210	.00101	994.53	2.7935	19
20	404.27	.00247	.30085	3.3239	.00074	1343.8	2.8075	20

35% (continued)
(NOMINAL 30.010%)

n	SPCAF F/P	SPPWF P/F	$\overline{CRF}$ $\overline{A}/P$	USPWF $P/\overline{A}$	SFDF $\overline{A}/F$	USCAF $F/\overline{A}$	$\overline{ASF}$ A/G	n
21	545.77	.00183	.30066	3.3261	.00055	1815.3	2.8186	21
22	736.79	.00136	.30051	3.3276	.00041	2451.8	2.8272	22
23	994.66	.00101	.30041	3.3288	.00030	3311.1	2.8340	23
24	1342.8	.00074	.30033	3.3297	.00022	4471.1	2.8393	24
25	1812.8	.00055	.30027	3.3303	.00017	6037.1	2.8433	25
26	2447.2	.00041	.30023	3.3308	.00012	8151.3	2.8465	26
27	3303.8	.00030	.30020	3.3312	.00009	11005.	2.8490	27
28	4460.1	.00022	.30017	3.3314	.00007	14859.	2.8509	28
29	6021.1	.00017	.30015	3.3316	.00005	20060.	2.8523	29
30	8128.5	.00012	.30014	3.3318	.00004	27082.	2.8535	30
31	10974.	.00009	.30013	3.3319	.00003	36562.	2.8543	31
32	14814.	.00007	.30012	3.3319	.00002	49360.	2.8550	32
33	19999.	.00005	.30012	3.3320	.00002	66638.	2.8555	33
34	26999.	.00004	.30012	3.3320	.00001	89962.	2.8559	34
35	36449.	.00003	.30011	3.3321	.00001		2.8562	35
∞	∞	0	.30010	3.3322	0	∞	2.8571	∞

40%
(NOMINAL 33.647%)

n	F/P	P/F	$\overline{A}/P$	$P/\overline{A}$	$\overline{A}/F$	$F/\overline{A}$	A/G	n
1	1.4000	.71429	1.1777	.84915	.84118	1.1888	–	1
2	1.9600	.51020	.68696	1.4557	.35049	2.8531	.41667	2
3	2.7440	.36443	.52940	1.8889	.19293	5.1832	.77982	3
4	3.8416	.26031	.45488	2.1984	.11841	8.4453	1.0923	4
5	5.3782	.18593	.41332	2.4194	.07685	13.012	1.3580	5
6	7.5295	.13281	.38800	2.5773	.05153	19.406	1.5811	6
7	10.541	.09487	.37174	2.6901	.03527	28.357	1.7664	7
8	14.758	.06776	.36093	2.7706	.02446	40.889	1.9185	8
9	20.661	.04840	.35359	2.8282	.01711	58.433	2.0422	9
10	28.925	.03457	.34852	2.8693	.01205	82.995	2.1419	10
11	40.496	.02469	.34499	2.8986	.00852	117.38	2.2215	11
12	56.694	.01764	.34251	2.9196	.00604	165.52	2.2845	12
13	79.371	.01260	.34077	2.9346	.00429	232.92	2.3341	13
14	111.12	.00900	.33953	2.9453	.00306	327.28	2.3729	14
15	155.57	.00643	.33865	2.9529	.00218	459.38	2.4030	15
16	217.80	.00459	.33802	2.9584	.00155	644.32	2.4262	16
17	304.91	.00328	.33758	2.9623	.00111	903.23	2.4441	17
18	426.88	.00234	.33726	2.9651	.00079	1265.7	2.4577	18
19	597.63	.00167	.33704	2.9670	.00056	1773.2	2.4682	19
20	836.68	.00120	.33687	2.9685	.00040	2483.7	2.4761	20
21	1171.4	.00085	.33676	2.9695	.00029	3478.3	2.4821	21
22	1639.9	.00061	.33668	2.9702	.00021	4870.8	2.4866	22
23	2295.9	.00044	.33662	2.9707	.00015	6820.3	2.4900	23
24	3214.2	.00031	.33658	2.9711	.00010	9549.7	2.4925	24
25	4499.9	.00022	.33655	2.9714	.00007	13371.	2.4944	25
26	6299.8	.00016	.33653	2.9715	.00005	18720.	2.4959	26
27	8819.8	.00011	.33651	2.9717	.00004	26209.	2.4969	27
28	12348.	.00008	.33650	2.9718	.00003	36694.	2.4977	28
29	17287.	.00006	.33649	2.9718	.00002	51373.	2.4983	29
30	24201.	.00004	.33649	2.9719	.00001	71924.	2.4988	30
31	33882.	.00003	.33648	2.9719	.00001		2.4991	31
32	47435.	.00002	.33648	2.9720	.00001		2.4993	32
33	66409.	.00002	.33648	2.9720	.00001		2.4995	33
34	92972.	.00001	.33648	2.9720	.00000		2.4996	34
∞	∞	0	.33647	2.9720	0	∞	2.5000	∞

45%
(NOMINAL 37.156%)

n	F/P	P/F	$\overline{A}/P$	$P/\overline{A}$	$\overline{A}/F$	$F/\overline{A}$	A/G	n
1	1.4500	.68966	1.1973	.83524	.82570	1.2111	–	1
2	2.1025	.47562	.70858	1.4113	.33702	2.9672	.40816	2

45% (continued)
(NOMINAL 37.156%)

n	SPCAF F/P	SPPWF P/F	CRF $\overline{A}/P$	USPWF $P/\overline{A}$	SFDF $\overline{A}/F$	USCAF $F/\overline{A}$	ASF A/G	n
3	3.0486	.32802	.55294	1.8085	.18137	5.5135	.75783	3
4	4.4205	.22622	.48019	2.0825	.10863	9.2057	1.0528	4
5	6.4097	.15601	.44025	2.2714	.06868	14.559	1.2980	5
6	9.2941	.10760	.41636	2.4018	.04480	22.322	1.4988	6
7	13.476	.07420	.40134	2.4916	.02978	33.578	1.6612	7
8	19.541	.05118	.39160	2.5536	.02004	49.900	1.7907	8
9	28.334	.03529	.38516	2.5963	.01359	73.566	1.8930	9
10	41.085	.02434	.38083	2.6258	.00927	107.88	1.9728	10
11	59.573	.01679	.37791	2.6462	.00634	157.64	2.0344	11
12	86.381	.01158	.37592	2.6602	.00435	229.79	2.0817	12
13	125.25	.00798	.37455	2.6698	.00299	334.40	2.1176	13
14	181.62	.00551	.37362	2.6765	.00206	486.09	2.1447	14
15	263.34	.00380	.37298	2.6811	.00142	706.05	2.1650	15
16	381.85	.00262	.37254	2.6843	.00098	1025.0	2.1802	16
17	553.68	.00181	.37224	2.6865	.00067	1487.4	2.1915	17
18	802.83	.00125	.37203	2.6880	.00046	2158.0	2.1998	18
19	1164.1	.00086	.37188	2.6890	.00032	3130.3	2.2059	19
20	1688.0	.00059	.37178	2.6897	.00022	4540.1	2.2104	20
21	2447.5	.00041	.37172	2.6902	.00015	6584.4	2.2136	21
22	3548.9	.00028	.37167	2.6906	.00010	9548.6	2.2160	22
23	5145.9	.00019	.37164	2.6908	.00007	13847.	2.2178	23
24	7461.6	.00013	.37161	2.6910	.00005	20079.	2.2190	24
25	10819.	.00009	.37160	2.6911	.00003	29116.	2.2199	25
26	15688.	.00006	.37159	2.6912	.00002	42219.	2.2206	26
27	22748.	.00004	.37158	2.6912	.00002	61219.	2.2210	27
28	32984.	.00003	.37157	2.6912	.00001	88768.	2.2214	28
29	47827.	.00002	.37157	2.6913	.00001		2.2216	29
30	69349.	.00001	.37157	2.6913	.00001		2.2218	30
∞	∞	0	.37156	2.6913	0	∞	2.2222	∞

50%
(NOMINAL 40.547%)

n	SPCAF F/P	SPPWF P/F	CRF $\overline{A}/P$	USPWF $P/\overline{A}$	SFDF $\overline{A}/F$	USCAF $F/\overline{A}$	ASF A/G	n
1	1.5000	.66667	1.2164	.82210	.81093	1.2332	–	1
2	2.2500	.44444	.72984	1.3702	.32437	3.0829	.40000	2
3	3.3750	.29630	.57619	1.7355	.17072	5.8575	.73684	3
4	5.0625	.19753	.50527	1.9791	.09981	10.019	1.0154	4
5	7.5937	.13169	.46696	2.1415	.06149	16.262	1.2417	5
6	11.391	.08779	.44449	2.2498	.03902	25.626	1.4226	6
7	17.086	.05853	.43067	2.3220	.02521	39.673	1.5648	7
8	25.629	.03902	.42193	2.3701	.01646	60.742	1.6752	8
9	38.443	.02601	.41629	2.4021	.01083	92.347	1.7595	9
10	57.665	.01734	.41262	2.4235	.00716	139.75	1.8235	10
11	86.498	.01156	.41021	2.4378	.00474	210.86	1.8713	11
12	129.75	.00771	.40861	2.4473	.00315	317.53	1.9068	12
13	194.62	.00514	.40756	2.4536	.00209	477.52	1.9329	13
14	291.93	.00343	.40686	2.4579	.00139	717.52	1.9519	14
15	437.89	.00228	.40639	2.4607	.00093	1077.5	1.9657	15
16	656.84	.00152	.40608	2.4625	.00062	1617.5	1.9756	16
17	985.26	.00102	.40588	2.4638	.00041	2427.5	1.9827	17
18	1477.9	.00068	.40574	2.4646	.00027	3642.5	1.9878	18
19	2216.8	.00045	.40565	2.4652	.00018	5464.9	1.9914	19
20	3325.3	.00030	.40559	2.4656	.00012	8198.6	1.9940	20
21	4987.9	.00020	.40555	2.4658	.00008	12299.	1.9958	21
22	7481.8	.00013	.40552	2.4660	.00005	18450.	1.9971	22
23	11223.	.00009	.40550	2.4661	.00004	27676.	1.9980	23
24	16834.	.00006	.40549	2.4662	.00002	41516.	1.9986	24
25	25251.	.00004	.40548	2.4662	.00002	62275.	1.9990	25
26	37877.	.00003	.40548	2.4662	.00001	93413.	1.9993	26
27	56815.	.00002	.40547	2.4663	.00001		1.9995	27
28	85223.	.00001	.40547	2.4663	.00000		1.9997	28
∞	∞	0	.40547	2.4663	0	∞	2.0000	∞

60%

(NOMINAL 47.000%)

n	SPCAF F/P	SPPWF P/F	CRF $\overline{A}/P$	USPWF $P/\overline{A}$	SFDF $\overline{A}/F$	USCAF $F/\overline{A}$	ASF A/G	n
1	1.6000	.62500	1.2533	.79787	.78334	1.2766	–	1
2	2.5600	.39063	.77129	1.2965	.30128	3.3191	.38462	2
3	4.0960	.24414	.62181	1.6082	.15181	6.5872	.69767	3
4	6.5536	.15259	.55463	1.8030	.08463	11.816	.94641	4
5	10.486	.09537	.51955	1.9247	.04955	20.182	1.1396	5
6	16.777	.05961	.49979	2.0008	.02979	33.568	1.2864	6
7	26.844	.03725	.48819	2.0484	.01819	54.986	1.3958	7
8	42.950	.02328	.48121	2.0781	.01120	89.254	1.4760	8
9	68.719	.01455	.47694	2.0967	.00694	144.08	1.5338	9
10	109.95	.00910	.47432	2.1083	.00431	231.81	1.5749	10
11	175.92	.00568	.47269	2.1155	.00269	372.17	1.6038	11
12	281.47	.00355	.47168	2.1201	.00168	596.75	1.6239	12
13	450.36	.00222	.47105	2.1229	.00105	956.08	1.6377	13
14	720.58	.00139	.47066	2.1247	.00065	1531.0	1.6472	14
15	1152.9	.00087	.47041	2.1258	.00041	2450.9	1.6536	15
16	1844.7	.00054	.47026	2.1265	.00025	3922.7	1.6580	16
17	2951.5	.00034	.47016	2.1269	.00016	6277.6	1.6609	17
18	4722.4	.00021	.47010	2.1272	.00010	10045.	1.6629	18
19	7555.8	.00013	.47007	2.1274	.00006	16074.	1.6642	19
20	12089.	.00008	.47004	2.1275	.00004	25719.	1.6650	20
21	19343.	.00005	.47003	2.1275	.00002	41152.	1.6656	21
22	30948.	.00003	.47002	2.1276	.00002	65845.	1.6660	22
23	49518.	.00002	.47001	2.1276	.00001		1.6662	23
24	79228.	.00001	.47001	2.1276	.00001		1.6664	24
∞	∞	0	.47000	2.1276	0	∞	1.6667	∞

70%

(NOMINAL 53.063%)

1	1.7000	.58824	1.2887	.77599	.75804	1.3192	–	1
2	2.8900	.34602	.81138	1.2325	.28076	3.5618	.37037	2
3	4.9130	.20354	.66623	1.5010	.13561	7.3743	.66190	3
4	8.3521	.11973	.60280	1.6589	.07217	13.855	.88451	4
5	14.199	.07043	.57083	1.7518	.04020	24.873	1.0497	5
6	24.138	.04143	.55356	1.8065	.02293	43.604	1.1693	6
7	41.034	.02437	.54388	1.8386	.01325	75.446	1.2537	7
8	69.758	.01434	.53835	1.8575	.00772	129.58	1.3122	8
9	118.59	.00843	.53514	1.8687	.00451	221.60	1.3520	9
10	201.60	.00496	.53327	1.8752	.00265	378.04	1.3787	10
11	342.72	.00292	.53218	1.8791	.00155	643.99	1.3964	11
12	582.62	.00172	.53154	1.8813	.00091	1096.1	1.4079	12
13	990.46	.00101	.53116	1.8827	.00054	1864.7	1.4154	13
14	1683.8	.00059	.53094	1.8834	.00032	3171.3	1.4203	14
15	2862.4	.00035	.53081	1.8839	.00019	5392.5	1.4233	15
16	4866.1	.00021	.53074	1.8842	.00011	9168.6	1.4253	16
17	8272.4	.00012	.53069	1.8843	.00006	15588.	1.4265	17
18	14063.	.00007	.53067	1.8844	.00004	26501.	1.4273	18
19	23907.	.00004	.53065	1.8845	.00002	45053.	1.4278	19
20	40642.	.00002	.53064	1.8845	.00001	76591.	1.4281	20
21	69092.	.00001	.53064	1.8845	.00001		1.4283	21
∞	∞	0	.53063	1.8846	0	∞	1.4286	∞

80%

(NOMINAL 58.779%)

1	1.8000	.55556	1.3225	.75613	.73473	1.3610	–	1
2	3.2400	.30864	.85019	1.1762	.26240	3.8109	.35714	2
3	5.8320	.17147	.70943	1.4096	.12164	8.2207	.62914	3
4	10.498	.09526	.64967	1.5392	.06189	16.158	.82884	4
5	18.896	.05292	.62063	1.6113	.03285	30.446	.97060	5
6	34.012	.02940	.60559	1.6513	.01781	56.164	1.0682	6

80% (continued)

(NOMINAL 58.779%)

n	SPCAF F/P	SPPWF P/F	CRF $\overline{A}/P$	USPWF $P/\overline{A}$	SFDF $\overline{A}/F$	USCAF $F/\overline{A}$	ASF A/G	n
7	61.222	.01633	.59755	1.6735	.00976	102.46	1.1338	7
8	110.20	.00907	.59317	1.6859	.00538	185.78	1.1767	8
9	198.36	.00504	.59076	1.6927	.00298	335.77	1.2044	9
10	357.05	.00280	.58944	1.6965	.00165	605.74	1.2219	10
11	642.68	.00156	.58870	1.6987	.00092	1091.7	1.2329	11
12	1156.8	.00086	.58830	1.6998	.00051	1966.4	1.2306	12
13	2082.3	.00048	.58807	1.7005	.00028	3540.9	1.2438	13
14	3748.1	.00027	.58794	1.7008	.00016	6375.0	1.2463	14
15	6746.6	.00015	.58787	1.7010	.00009	11476.	1.2478	15
16	12144.	.00008	.58783	1.7012	.00005	20659.	1.2487	16
17	21859.	.00005	.58781	1.7012	.00003	37187.	1.2492	17
18	39346.	.00003	.58780	1.7013	.00001	66938.	1.2495	18
19	70823.	.00001	.58779	1.7013	.00001		1.2497	19
∞	∞	0	.58779	1.7013	0	∞	1.2500	∞

90%

(NOMINAL 64.185%)

1	1.9000	.52632	1.3550	.73799	.71317	1.4022	–	1
2	3.6100	.27701	.88777	1.1264	.24592	4.0663	.34483	2
3	6.8590	.14579	.75140	1.3308	.10955	9.1282	.59908	3
4	13.032	.07673	.69520	1.4384	.05335	18.746	.77867	4
5	24.761	.04039	.66887	1.4951	.02701	37.019	.90068	5
6	47.046	.02126	.65579	1.5249	.01394	71.739	.98081	6
7	89.387	.01119	.64912	1.5406	.00726	137.71	1.0319	7
8	169.84	.00589	.64566	1.5488	.00380	263.04	1.0637	8
9	322.69	.00310	.64385	1.5532	.00200	501.18	1.0831	9
10	613.11	.00163	.64290	1.5554	.00105	953.65	1.0948	10
11	1164.9	.00086	.64241	1.5566	.00055	1813.3	1.1017	11
12	2213.3	.00045	.64214	1.5573	.00029	3446.8	1.1057	12
13	4205.3	.00024	.64201	1.5576	.00015	6550.2	1.1080	13
14	7990.1	.00013	.64193	1.5578	.00008	12447.	1.1094	14
15	15181.	.00007	.64190	1.5579	.00004	23650.	1.1101	15
16	28844.	.00003	.64188	1.5579	.00002	44937.	1.1106	16
17	54804.	.00002	.64187	1.5580	.00001	85382.	1.1108	17
∞	∞	0	.64185	1.5580	0	∞	1.1111	∞

100%

(NOMINAL 69.315%)

1	2.0000	.50000	1.3863	.72135	.69315	1.4427	–	1
2	4.0000	.25000	.92420	1.0820	.23105	4.3281	.33333	2
3	8.0000	.12500	.79217	1.2624	.09902	10.099	.57143	3
4	16.000	.06250	.73936	1.3525	.04621	21.640	.73333	4
5	32.000	.03125	.71551	1.3976	.02236	44.724	.83871	5
6	64.000	.01563	.70415	1.4202	.01100	90.890	.90476	6
7	128.00	.00781	.69860	1.4314	.00546	183.22	.94488	7
8	256.00	.00391	.69587	1.4371	.00272	367.89	.96863	8
9	512.00	.00195	.69450	1.4399	.00136	737.22	.98239	9
10	1024.0	.00098	.69382	1.4413	.00068	1475.9	.99022	10
11	2048.0	.00049	.69349	1.4420	.00034	2953.2	.99463	11
12	4096.0	.00024	.69332	1.4423	.00017	5907.8	.99707	12
13	8192.0	.00012	.69323	1.4425	.00008	11817.	.99841	13
14	16384.	.00006	.69319	1.4426	.00004	23636.	.99915	14
15	32768.	.00003	.69317	1.4427	.00002	47273.	.99954	15
16	65536.	.00002	.69316	1.4427	.00001	94547.	.99976	16
∞	∞	0	.69315	1.4427	0	∞	1.0000	∞

110%
(NOMINAL 74.194%)

n	SPCAF F/P	SPPWF P/F	CRF $\overline{A}/P$	USPWF $P/\overline{A}$	SFDF $\overline{A}/F$	USCAF $F/\overline{A}$	ASF A/G	n
1	2.1000	.47619	1.4164	.70600	.67449	1.4826	–	1
2	4.4100	.22676	.95951	1.0422	.21758	4.5961	.32258	2
3	9.2610	.10798	.83175	1.2023	.08981	11.134	.54594	3
4	19.448	.05142	.78215	1.2785	.04022	24.865	.69227	4
5	40.841	.02449	.76056	1.3148	.01862	53.699	.78359	5
6	85.766	.01166	.75069	1.3321	.00875	114.25	.83831	6
7	180.11	.00555	.74608	1.3403	.00414	241.41	.87001	7
8	378.23	.00264	.74390	1.3443	.00197	508.44	.88788	8
9	794.28	.00126	.74287	1.3461	.00094	1069.2	.89775	9
10	1668.0	.00060	.74238	1.3470	.00045	2246.8	.90309	10
11	3502.8	.00029	.74215	1.3474	.00021	4719.8	.90595	11
12	7355.8	.00014	.74204	1.3476	.00010	9913.0	.90746	12
13	15447.	.00006	.74199	1.3477	.00005	20819.	.90825	13
14	32439.	.00003	.74196	1.3478	.00002	43721.	.90866	14
15	68122.	.00001	.74195	1.3478	.00001	91815.	.90887	15
∞	∞	0	.74194	1.3478	0	∞	.90909	∞

120%
(NOMINAL 78.846%)

1	2.2000	.45455	1.4455	.69180	.65705	1.5220	–	1
2	4.8400	.20661	.99378	1.0063	.20533	4.8703	.31250	2
3	10.648	.09391	.87018	1.1492	.08172	12.237	.52239	3
4	23.426	.04269	.82362	1.2142	.03516	28.442	.65497	4
5	51.536	.01940	.80406	1.2437	.01560	64.095	.73439	5
6	113.38	.00882	.79547	1.2571	.00702	142.53	.77994	6
7	249.44	.00401	.79163	1.2632	.00317	315.09	.80516	7
8	548.76	.00182	.78990	1.2660	.00144	694.72	.81873	8
9	1207.3	.00083	.78911	1.2672	.00065	1529.9	.82587	9
10	2656.0	.00038	.78875	1.2678	.00030	3367.3	.82957	10
11	5843.2	.00017	.78859	1.2681	.00013	7409.6	.83145	11
12	12855.	.00008	.78852	1.2682	.00006	16303.	.83240	12
13	28281.	.00004	.78849	1.2683	.00003	35867.	.83287	13
14	62218.	.00002	.78847	1.2683	.00001	78910.	.83311	14
∞	∞	0	.78846	1.2683	0	∞	.83333	∞

130%
(NOMINAL 83.291%)

1	2.3000	.43478	1.4736	.67861	.64070	1.5608	–	1
2	5.2900	.18904	1.0271	.97365	.19415	5.1506	.30303	2
3	12.167	.08219	.90750	1.1019	.07459	13.407	.50058	3
4	27.984	.03574	.86378	1.1577	.03087	32.397	.62100	4
5	64.363	.01554	.84605	1.1820	.01315	76.075	.69032	5
6	148.04	.00676	.83857	1.1925	.00566	176.53	.72842	6
7	340.48	.00294	.83536	1.1971	.00245	407.59	.74861	7
8	783.11	.00128	.83397	1.1991	.00107	939.01	.75900	8
9	1801.1	.00056	.83337	1.1999	.00046	2161.3	.76423	9
10	4142.6	.00024	.83311	1.2003	.00020	4972.5	.76682	10
11	9528.1	.00010	.83300	1.2005	.00009	11438.	.76808	11
12	21915.	.00005	.83295	1.2006	.00004	26310.	.76868	12
13	50404.	.00002	.83293	1.2006	.00002	60514.	.76897	13
∞	∞	0	.83291	1.2006	0	∞	.76923	∞

140%
(NOMINAL 87.547%)

1	2.4000	.41667	1.5008	.66631	.62533	1.5991	–	1
2	5.7600	.17361	1.0594	.94394	.18392	5.4371	.29412	2
3	13.824	.07234	.94374	1.0596	.06827	14.648	.48035	3
4	33.178	.03014	.90268	1.1078	.02721	36.755	.58998	4
5	79.626	.01256	.88660	1.1279	.01114	89.810	.65069	5

140% (continued)
(NOMINAL 87.547%)

n	SPCAF F/P	SPPWF P/F	$\overline{CRF}$ $\overline{A}/P$	$\overline{USPWF}$ $P/\overline{A}$	$\overline{SFDF}$ $\overline{A}/F$	$\overline{USCAF}$ $F/\overline{A}$	$\overline{ASF}$ A/G	n
6	191.10	.00523	.88007	1.1363	.00461	217.14	.68272	6
7	458.65	.00218	.87738	1.1398	.00191	522.74	.69899	7
8	1100.8	.00091	.87626	1.1412	.00080	1256.2	.70701	8
9	2641.8	.00038	.87580	1.1418	.00033	3016.4	.71088	9
10	6340.3	.00016	.87561	1.1421	.00014	7241.1	.71271	10
11	15217.	.00007	.87553	1.1422	.00006	17380.	.71356	11
12	36520.	.00003	.87549	1.1422	.00002	41714.	.71396	12
13	87649.	.00001	.87548	1.1422	.00001		.71414	13
∞	∞	0	.87547	1.1422	0	∞	.71429	∞

150%
(NOMINAL 91.629%)

n								n
1	2.5000	.40000	1.5272	.65481	.61086	1.6370	–	1
2	6.2500	.16000	1.0908	.91674	.17453	5.7296	.28571	2
3	15.625	.06400	.97894	1.0215	.06265	15.961	.46154	3
4	39.062	.02560	.94036	1.0634	.02407	41.540	.56158	4
5	97.656	.01024	.92577	1.0802	.00948	105.49	.61494	5
6	244.14	.00410	.92006	1.0869	.00377	265.35	.64199	6
7	610.35	.00164	.91779	1.0896	.00150	665.02	.65518	7
8	1525.9	.00066	.91689	1.0906	.00060	1664.2	.66142	8
9	3814.7	.00026	.91653	1.0911	.00024	4162.1	.66431	9
10	9536.7	.00010	.91639	1.0912	.00010	10407.	.66562	10
11	23842.	.00004	.91633	1.0913	.00004	26019.	.66621	11
12	59604.	.00002	.91631	1.0913	.00002	65049.	.66647	12
13		.00000	.91630	1.0913	.00001		.66658	13
∞	∞	0	.91629	1.0914	0	∞	.66667	∞

Index

References are to sections.

531

- Sell a 40,000,000 bond issue.
  payable in 25 yrs.
- interest of 17%/yr. paid to bondholders. at end of ea. yr.
- The city establishes a sinking fund.

a.) Find A if sinking fund pays. 6% comp. quarterly.

$$A = \frac{F = 40\ \text{million}}{\left[\begin{array}{c} sfdf \\ i-4 \end{array} \right] \left[\begin{array}{c} uscAf \\ i-100 \end{array} \right]}$$

b.) Find Total amt to be raised ea. yr. to pay
interest due to the bondholders & deposit into
sinking fund.

$$\text{annual } i = 40 \times 10^6 \times 17\%$$
$$\underline{\text{sink. fund} = \quad A \qquad \oplus}$$
$$\text{sum}$$